The Yearbook of Agriculture
1964

THE UNITED STATES GOVERNMENT PRINTING OFFICE

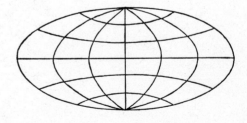

THE UNITED STATES GOVERNMENT PRINTING OFFICE

Farmer's World

The Yearbook of Agriculture

1964

THE UNITED STATES DEPARTMENT OF AGRICULTURE

FOREWORD

American and
World Agriculture

by ORVILLE L. FREEMAN
Secretary of Agriculture

AT NO TIME in three centuries has American agriculture reached so far and touched the lives of so many people as today.

At no time in thirty centuries has world agriculture faced greater problems, greater challenges, and greater opportunities.

And at no time has American agriculture been so closely connected as now with world agriculture in its gigantic task of feeding and clothing more people; husbanding and developing its various resources; expanding its trade; sharing in and contributing to the upsurge of modern science; undergirding economic growth; and, by doing all this, assuming an ever-larger role in mankind's long struggle for freedom and plenty.

This book reveals the vital stake everybody in the United States has in a healthy export trade for American agriculture, not only because farmers have so much to sell and because the livelihood of so many Americans besides farmers depends on it, but also because the world so greatly needs what we can offer.

Exports of American farm products are now at their highest level. Their total value in 1963 approximated 5 billion dollars, equivalent to one-sixth of cash receipts from all farm marketings. One acre out of every four is harvested for export. The output of about 75 million acres of our cropland is moving abroad.

These exports support at least a million jobs, both on and off the farm. They require financing, storage, and inland and ocean transportation. They would fill more than a million freight cars or more than 5 thousand cargo ships, and they are carried to more than 125 countries and territories.

Most Americans have learned that we cannot separate our agriculture from the rest of our national economy, but many have still to recognize that we cannot disconnect American agriculture from world agriculture and world business. This lesson also is contained herein.

Wheat from Kansas competes in world markets with wheat grown in Canada and Argentina. Hogs from Iowa share markets with those of Denmark and Poland. Oranges from Florida and Spain, cotton from Texas and Brazil, dairy products from Wisconsin and Denmark are increasingly part and parcel of the world market.

Just as national markets have their trading rules, so do the world markets. Trade must be orderly and subject to agreements and conventions worked out through negotiation by the organizations of which we are a part—for example, the General Agreement on Tariffs and Trade.

We hold to the belief that trade is a two-way street, and that a healthy flow of two-way traffic can be promoted by a lowering of tariffs and other trade barriers.

We pride ourselves on being good salesmen with fine products to sell. We know that we have in the Department of Agriculture men and women skilled in the arts and crafts of trade. We know that our farm and food industry is highly qualified for international competition in any liberalized trade situation.

But we know, too, that international relationships are linked closely with commerce, and vice versa. Trade involves much more than loading 5 billion dollars' worth of agricultural goods on ships bound for foreign ports. It is a matter also of supporting or competing with blocs, alinements, or groupings, whose political aims may be no less important than their economic goals.

Readers will sense this challenge in these pages.

But, above all, trade is now what it has ever been: Opportunity.

It is opportunity to share our abundance to fulfill a humanitarian obligation; opportunity to help less privileged regions develop dynamic economies of their own, thus becoming our potential customers; opportunity to raise standards of living all over the world, in the advanced nations as well as those that are emerging; opportunity to stride toward a better day for agriculture, industry, and consumers.

Trade is opportunity to enter more swiftly the age of plenty, progress, freedom, and peace that is the objective of mankind's long pursuit.

Purposes and
Ideals

by ALFRED STEFFERUD

Editor of the Yearbook

THE PURPOSE of the Yearbooks of Agriculture (including this one) since their origin many years ago has been to present unbiased, factual information of value and interest to farmers and other Americans.

Several secondary purposes may be served at the same time: To report on work in progress in the Department of Agriculture, since the Yearbooks are related to the annual reports of the Secretary of Agriculture; to summarize developments in the agricultural sciences; to discuss problems in rural affairs and to indicate in an objective fashion the ways in which they may be solved; to point out changes in knowledge, attitudes, and production and consumption; and to present one at a time over the years an integrated, encyclopedic reference series.

A book of science ("A science teaches us to know, and an art to do, and all the more perfect sciences lead to the creation of corresponding useful arts") indulges in no special pleading, however worthy the cause; is dedicated to the pursuit of truth and fact; tries to be clear and to clarify but not to be "popular" in the ways of polls and TV ratings; and takes the long view of programs, policies, and transient pressures.

Those purposes and ideals are apparent, we trust, in the present Yearbook of Agriculture, which encompasses a much broader field than any of its predecessors—a field hitherto untilled and made somewhat precarious by rapid changes in world affairs (including, for example, the names of countries), and the complexity of the subject.

Two special points about this book:

First, its intended readers.

We address ourselves, as always, primarily to American farmers, consumers, and others who have an interest in agriculture, but farmers, agricultural administrators, and policymakers anywhere should find much of value in it.

A paragraph in the notes sent to prospective contributors reads:

"The book will inform Americans about America's growing stake in world agriculture and explain how our actions, trade, and policies affect and are affected by agricultural, natural, and political developments abroad. It will inform people everywhere of the greatness of American agriculture, the problems we face, the importance of international understanding and joint effort, and the expenditures we consider necessary to achieve agricultural prosperity and security."

The fact of change also is brought out. Changes in production, consumption, trade, governments, organizations, laws, and programs posed a problem and a challenge as we labored to make a book of lasting value. Life and its components never stand still, but we believe we present a body of information that will remain valid for a number of years—as an introduction to the subject of world trade if nothing else. Periodicals and other publications are available from the Department of Agriculture to producers, dealers, exporters, and others who need current information on specific aspects of production and trade.

Second, its emphasis on the importance of farmers in this changing, striving, industrially developing world.

On farmers rests progress, whether social, political, administrative, or economic. In a world of automation, technology, conferences and international maneuvers, machines, and impersonal relationships, we must keep in mind the men—as men, as human beings—who provide the basic elements of life and whose bond with the earth is an abiding verity.

The members of the 1964 Yearbook Committee are:

Foreign Agricultural Service: W. A. Minor, CHAIRMAN; Kenneth W. Olson, SECRETARY; James O. Howard; Douglas M. Crawford; Afif I. Tannous; Ralph E. Spencer; John H. Dean; Harald C. Larsen.

Economic Research Service: Wilhelm Anderson, Kenneth L. Bachman, Nelson P. Guidry.

Agricultural Marketing Service: Omer W. Herrmann, Howard P. Davis.

Agricultural Stabilization and Conservation Service: Murray Thompson, Ernest W. Grove.

Agricultural Research Service: G. E. Hilbert, Kenneth Haines.

Forest Service: Robert K. Winters.

Soil Conservation Service: Guy D. Smith.

Federal Extension Service: Raymond C. Scott, Dana G. Dalrymple.

CONTENTS

Production

Marketing

World Trade

Our Trade

Agreements

Assistance

Needs

FARMER'S WORLD

Valley to Valley, Country to Country

by WAYNE D. RASMUSSEN

CIVILIZATION began when man planted his first seed and tamed his first animal about 10 thousand years ago. Before that, for a million years, people lived precariously on the fruits and seeds the women gathered and the small animals the men killed. In the few years since—few, as history measures time—agriculture and civilization have advanced from valley to valley, country to country, hemisphere to hemisphere as men have shared seeds, tools, skills, knowledge, and hopes.

Very likely one of mankind's greatest achievements—planting and harvesting crops—came about through a primitive woman's observation while she was gathering seeds. She may have noticed that the grain-bearing grasses grew up where seeds had been spilled or stored. Then she herself placed some seeds in the ground and saw them grow.

Animal husbandry probably developed when men succeeded in taming animals that they had wounded or driven into enclosures for slaughter, but it also is likely that women saved and tamed young animals.

Farming and animal husbandry developed together for a long period. The herding of livestock came later.

Agriculture originated first in the Middle East, perhaps in the grassy uplands where the wild grains and the wild animals first to be domesticated were found. Excavations at the site of the village of Jarmo in present-day Iraq indicate that 7 thousand years ago people there had two varieties of wheat, barley, sheep, goats, pigs, cattle, horses, and dogs. Tools were of polished or chipped flint and obsidian, a volcanic glass. The use of obsidian is evidence of early trade; its nearest known source is Lake Van in Turkey.

Agriculture spread from the Middle East to such areas as the Danubian Basin, the western and northern shores of the Black Sea, the fertile crescent bordering the desert of Arabia, and the valleys of the Indus in eastern India and the Hwang Ho in northern China. The cultural pattern was much the same, except in the Americas, where agriculture probably was discovered independently.

Our farming ancestors over the centuries accomplished feats that modern man has not yet duplicated. Drawing upon wild stock, they developed all the major food plants and domestic animals grown today.

Wheat and barley were domesticated in the first area of agricultural development, southwestern Asia. Rice and bananas were developed later in southeastern Asia, and sorghum and millets in Africa. Maize, known as corn in America, and potatoes were among several major food crops developed in the New World.

Food animals were first domesticated in Asia. The turkey was domesticated in the New World. Eventually these crops, many others, and animals migrated throughout the world.

The accomplishments are even greater when we consider the tools the first farmers invented and used. A pointed stick, the digging stick, was the last tool of the food gatherer and the first of the farmer. The stick, which had been used to grub up roots, served to dig holes for seeds. Somebody added a crossbar, so that a man could use his foot to drive the stick deeper into the soil. That was the origin of the spade. A stick that had a branch at one end and could be pulled through the ground was the first hoe. Later a blade of stone or shell on the hoe gave it greater cutting power. Similarly, a stick used to knock heads of grain loose from the stalks became a sickle when stone teeth were set along one edge.

After animals were domesticated for food, they soon began to serve as beasts of burden. The next step, one never taken by the American Indian, was to fasten a heavy hoe behind an animal and induce him to pull it through the ground.

The climate of the Middle East and northern Africa gradually became drier after man first discovered agriculture. Tribes and villages moved from poorly watered sites to sources of water as the centuries passed. At the same time, man began to irrigate his cropland wherever he had access to water. The simplest device was to dip water from a well or spring and pour it on the land. Many types of buckets, ropes, and, later, pulleys were used. A more continuous flow was provided by the swipe, or shadoof, a long pole pivoted from a beam. One end of the pole held a bucket; the other held a heavy clay weight. A man pulled the bucket down to the water, and the clay weight then lifted the filled container to a height where it could be emptied into a ditch. A shadoof could raise about 600 gallons a day.

The conduction of water through ditches from streams was practiced widely in the Middle East, where the ancient canal systems still can be seen. The periodic floods of the Nile in Egypt led to the development of systems of basins on the upper Nile to hold the waters. The basins were opened to permit the water to flow over the dyke-enclosed tracts when it was needed.

Cereals were domesticated at an early age because they kept well and could be stored for use during lean years and winter. Even in his food-gathering stage, man stored grain, seeds, and nuts. Ancient Egyptians preserved meat and fish by salting and drying them in the sun.

The discovery of metal and its uses brought the Neolithic Era to an end and gave farmers sharper, stronger blades for hoes, plow points, and sickles. The change to metal took place slowly and in some areas—the Americas, for example—not at all. Most cultures first used bronze, then iron.

WHEN AGRICULTURE appeared in written history in the time of the Egyptians, Greeks, and Romans, it was already a highly developed art, backed by years of progress based on observation and trial and error. Some early Chinese historians assigned the beginning of agriculture in China to a specific year, 2737 B.C., when a continuous record of political life was started. Farming undoubtedly had been practiced before that particular year, but giving a new ruler credit for teaching farming to the people indicates the value they placed on it.

Agriculture enabled a man to produce more than enough food for himself and his family. Some labor thus could be released for the development of other aspects of civilization, such as industry, the arts and sciences, government, and writing.

Ancient civilizations, from the invention of writing to the beginning of the Christian Era, saw the adoption of systems of land use aimed at preserving or restoring soil fertility. The first farmers had practiced natural husbandry; that is, simply sowing and reaping. They moved on to new land when yields declined.

Sometimes the increase in population that usually followed the establishment of a settled village economy made it difficult to move to new land. In several parts of the world farmers then turned to fallow. Every year, according to some plan which became fixed, part of the land was given special treatment. No seed would be planted on it. The weeds and grass would be plowed under at least once during the growing season so as to rid it of some weeds and parasites, add vegetable matter, and conserve moisture. The fallow system was used in ancient Greece and Rome, in China from perhaps as early as 2000

B.C., and in Germany and northern Europe through medieval times.

But farmers of ancient times did not rely solely on fallowing to improve the soil. Ashes, animal manure, and composts were used in the Middle East, Greece, and Rome. The Greeks and Romans added lime in various forms.

The Roman farmers could draw upon farm manuals by Cato the Censor, writing about 200 B.C., or his successors, including Varro and Columella, for advice on ways to grow olives and grapes and press the fruits for oil and juice. Bread, oil, wine, figs, and grapes were staples in the ancient Mediterranean diet.

IMPROVEMENTS spread slowly.

The methods the ancients used survived with modifications in many parts of the world for centuries.

Fallowing, for example, was the basis for England's well-known two- and three-field systems of medieval times. The medieval English manor, with its villagers and lord, was divided into garden, arable, meadow, pasture, and waste land. The arable land was divided into two or three large fields, which in turn were divided into strips of an acre or less. Each villager would farm a number of scattered strips. Under the two-field system, half the land was left fallow. The other half was planted with winter and spring grain. In the three-field system, one field was fallow, one was planted in wheat or rye, and one was planted in some spring crop, such as barley, oats, peas, or beans. The three-field system permitted as much as 50 percent greater productivity than the two-field system.

Two other developments in northern Europe during medieval times also increased productivity: A heavy plow that could turn the soil was invented. The invention of the horse collar permitted the effective use of horsepower.

Fallowing sometimes gave way to rotations. Nitrogen-fixing legumes—peas, beans, vetches, alfalfa—would be grown on a field formerly fallow. The system arose through trial and error after it was noted that small grain planted on land formerly in legumes usually yielded more. It was practiced oftenest when towns and cities arose and farmers had a ready market for all they could produce. Legume rotation succeeded fallowing in limited areas of ancient Greece and Rome, in parts of China shortly before the Christian Era, and in Germany and England in the 16th century.

As THE MEDIEVAL period passed in Europe, the beginning of the modern age was marked by a renewed interest of Europeans in other parts of the world, followed by exploration and by conquest.

Some early explorers brought foreign plants and animals back to Europe. Accounts of their explorations, writings of travelers, and archeological and historical reconstructions of the past have given us a picture of farming in the 15th century.

Soil exhaustion, erosion, war, and corruption had brought such a decline in Chinese agriculture that by the year 1510 many farmers were dying of starvation. It was a factor that led to the overthrow of the Ming dynasty by the Manchus, invaders from the north, early in the 17th century.

India, the goal of many European explorers in the 15th century, was a land of fruit and spices. Rice, peas, and millet were basic crops. Curry, ginger, cloves, cinnamon, and other spices added variety to the diet. Most farmwork was done by hand by farmers who paid rents and taxes to the rulers. Irrigation works were maintained by the government in some sections. An Englishman in India in 1616 wrote that "the plenty of all provisions" was "very great throughout the whole country," and "every one there may eat bread without scarceness."

Northern Africa was well known to the Europeans of Columbus' day. The Arabs who had swept across that area and into Spain made sugar from cane and grew many kinds of wine grapes. Their irrigation systems were good. They used fertilizer, and they adapted their crops to the land. They practiced grafting and introduced many trees and plants into northern Africa.

Much less is known of farming in central Africa 500 years ago. Ruins of large cities indicate that parts of the region had an extensive agriculture. Terraces, plainly of an agricultural nature, and long-abandoned irrigation works in present-day Ethiopia, Kenya, and Rhodesia must be examined further before we can know the whole story of civilizations that flourished as late as the 15th century and then disappeared.

IN CONTRAST, the story of American Indian agriculture at the time Columbus discovered the New World is recorded. The Spaniards conquered two Indian civilizations, the Aztecs of Mexico and the Incas of Peru.

Both civilizations were based upon settled agriculture. These, like the lesser centers, had developed independently of the rest of the world.

Among the crops originating in the New World, corn, kidney and lima beans, squashes, pumpkins, and tobacco were grown in many parts of North and South America. Corn, or maize, the most important crop of American origin, was developed in the highlands of Mexico. The potato rivaled corn in importance in South America. It originated in the Andes.

Manioc, sweetpotatoes, pineapples, and peanuts were developed as sources of food in the Amazon Valley. Only incidental crops, such as the Jerusalem artichoke, were first developed in what is now the United States.

The Indians had dogs but few other domesticated animals. In Peru, they had llamas, alpacas, and guinea pigs. Turkeys were kept in Mexico and the southwestern United States. The Aztecs and Mayas of Mexico and Central America kept bees.

Irrigation was practiced from what is now Arizona to Chile. There were about 150 miles of main irrigation ditches in the Salt River Valley. Irrigation was carried out in Peru on a scale scarcely equaled in modern days. Many Indians fertilized their crops. Along the Atlantic coast, fish were placed in cornhills during planting. Nevertheless, agriculture in the New World was limited by the lack of draft animals and the failure to discover the uses of iron. Away from a few major centers of civilization, Indian farmers practiced natural husbandry, clearing new land as yields declined.

The first European colonists in the New World, particularly in what is now the United States, found it difficult to adapt European methods to American conditions. They faced starvation and survived only because of supplies received from the mother countries and the food they bought or took from the Indians. The permanence of the Colonies was not assured until agriculture was securely established, and that came after they adopted the crops and tillage methods of the natives.

While the Indians of America contributed much to world agriculture, the Europeans who conquered and settled the New World introduced livestock, crops, and tools.

The axe and the plow, with the animals to pull the plows, were carried to America by all of the national groups entering the New World.

The Spaniards brought alfalfa, barley, flax, oats, sugarcane, wheat, and many others. They brought their grapes, oranges, peaches, pears, and other fruits and vegetables.

By 1606, the French had planted cabbage, flax, hemp, oats, rye, wheat, and other crops in Canada.

The English brought all the crops and livestock they had grown at home. Other nations introduced particular breeds and varieties of animals and plants.

The new settlers themselves made some improvements. For example, John Rolfe of Virginia obtained tobacco seed from South America in 1612 and raised a crop from it, which established American exports of tobacco to England.

The agricultural methods brought to the New World by the first European immigrants differed little from those of a thousand years earlier. Yet Europe, particularly England, was on the verge of a new era of developments that were to culminate in an agricultural revolution and were marked by the scientific rotation of crops and, in England, by the enclosure of many fields and scattered strips of land. Rotation and enclosure were a result of a growing market economy and the consequent emphasis on commercial farming.

Greater emphasis on commercial farming led to some consolidation of holdings in England under the open-field system. At the same time, some pastures and croplands were enclosed. The enclosure movement in the 16th century was undertaken mainly to furnish pasturelands for sheep—the demand for wool of the spinning and weaving industries was more effective than the demand for wheat.

The development of scientific rotations owed much to new methods and crops introduced from other European nations. Clover was introduced from Spain, turnip cultivation from Flanders, and new grasses from France. Although their value was recognized by the end of the 16th century, they were not widely grown until later.

Farm tools were crude at the beginning of the period. The large and cumbersome wooden plows usually were drawn by oxen. After the soil was broken, iron- or wooden-toothed harrows were pulled over the land. All crops were seeded by hand. Grain crops were cut with scythes or reaping hooks and threshed with flails. Hoes, mattocks, spades, and forks completed the list.

Often the ideas for machines were well known before they were adopted. Grain drills are an example. The Chinese had used a wheelbarrow drill as early as 2800 B.C. The first English patent was granted in 1623. A more practical drill was described by John Worlidge in 1669. Not until about 1700, however, when Jethro Tull made and publicized a seed drill, did these devices attract much attention. Tull also urged the adoption of the French horse hoe, or cultivator.

Many types of plows were used in Great Britain, but the first definite step toward making plows in factories came in 1730, when the Rotherham plow was introduced. It had a colter and share made of iron and may have been brought to England from Holland. It was called the Dutch plow in Scotland.

The introduction of root crops, clover, and grasses into a four-course crop rotation provided support for a larger number of livestock. The principle of selective breeding had been known for generations, but the creation of new breeds that gave general satisfaction was a long process. Improvement of the old native varieties by crossing with the newer breeds took longer.

The improvement of livestock was related to the enclosure of former openfield farms and the conversion of common and waste land into pasture. The movement began in the 16th century and was partly arrested by legislation; in the 18th century it received support from Parliament. The enclosure of pastures gave the livestock farmers control over breeding and permitted more rapid improvements in their herds.

All of these slow changes in English farming resulted in an agricultural revolution, which reached its peak in the first half of the 19th century. By then, greatly improved methods had been adopted, total output of farm products and output per man-hour had gone up, and livestock and crop husbandry seemed to be in balance with each other and the rest of the economy.

Over a period of 150 years, a number of agricultural leaders influenced British farmers and landowners to adopt improved practices. They were able to influence farming because industrialization, improved transportation, and other economic forces made the adoption of the improvements practical and profitable.

The most noted of the reformers were Jethro Tull (1674–1740), Charles Townshend (1674–1738), Robert Bake-

well (1725–1795), Arthur Young (1741–1820), Sir John Sinclair (1745–1835), and Thomas Coke (1752–1842).

Tull invented a grain drill and advocated more intensive cultivation and the use of animal power. Townshend set an example of better farming through improvements in crop rotations and in emphasizing the field cultivation of turnips and clover. Bakewell devoted himself to developing better breeds of livestock. Young and Sinclair were influential writers, whose works were studied in many parts of the world. Coke developed a model agricultural estate, working particularly with wheat and sheep. Farm leaders and statesmen from many parts of the world visited his estate.

Other European countries contributed to the agricultural revolution, but advance was most rapid in England. The physiocrats, a school of economists who emphasized the importance and virtue of agriculture, influenced agricultural thought in France in the 18th century. They appeared to yearn for earlier days when agrarian interests were dominant but were indifferent to proved methods of progressive farming. For example, fallowing persisted in most of France, with little protest from the physiocrats, long after the value of the scientific rotation of crops had been demonstrated in England.

France contributed a new method of food preservation, canning. It permitted the year-round use of many otherwise perishable foods. In 1795, when France was at war, the Government offered a prize to the citizen who could devise a method of preserving food for transport on military and naval campaigns. The prize was awarded in 1810 to Nicolas Appert, a Parisian confectioner. He had filled bottles with various foods, sealed the bottles, and cooked them in boiling water.

The Napoleonic wars also gave impetus to the sugarbeet industry. Andreas Marggraf, a German chemist, in 1747 had crystallized sucrose from beets. One of his pupils, Franz Karl Achard, built the first sugarbeet factory in Silesia in 1802. With imports cut off because of war, Napoleon encouraged the building of a number of factories in France, where the industry persisted. Efforts were made to establish factories in the United States from 1830 on; the first successful American plant opened in California in 1879.

As the European nations expanded their colonies over the world, they influenced farming everywhere. The influence was greatest in the thinly populated regions, such as the New World and Australia, and least in densely populated regions like India.

When Napoleon led his armies into Egypt in 1798, he commented on the good quality of its agricultural produce and suggested that with French help the Nile Valley could become a Garden of Eden. He established a plant introduction garden in Egypt in 1800 and asked for French fruit trees. A group of French gardeners set out for Egypt the next year, but the British captured them at sea.

Many years later, in 1882, the British began a policy of agricultural reform and assistance in Egypt, building in part upon reforms introduced by the rulers of Egypt in the preceding decades. During the first decade of British rule, many irrigation works were completed and repaired, and the first Aswan dam was begun. The acreage brought under cultivation increased.

Europe's greatest impact on world agriculture followed the discovery, conquest, and settlement of the New World and, later, the development of reforms and improvements, which encouraged changes in farming.

For more than a century, however, Americans knew little of the changes in European agriculture. Gradually, scientific societies, such as the American Philosophical Society, founded in 1743, encouraged the investigation of European ideas and experiences and agricultural experimentation. Societies devoted entirely to agriculture were not organized until the United States had declared its independence. The first of record was established in New

Jersey in 1781. The Philadelphia Society for Promoting Agriculture and the South Carolina Society for Promoting and Improving Agriculture were founded in 1785.

The early agricultural societies were groups of men of all professions who could afford to experiment and who would seek out and adapt to American conditions the progress made in other countries. None were farmers who depended solely on the produce of their farms for a living. Among them were George Washington and Thomas Jefferson. They corresponded with English agricultural reformers. Both were interested in soil conservation. Washington was first in this country to raise mules. Jefferson introduced upland rice and designed a hillside plow, a moldboard for a plow that would turn the soil, and other implements.

The changes in England during the 18th century included the development of improved breeds of livestock. The first importations of Bakewell's improved cattle were made by two gentlemen farmers of Maryland and Virginia in 1783. Large numbers of Merino sheep were imported from France and Spain a few years later. The first Hereford cattle were imported by another statesman, Henry Clay, in 1817. Nevertheless, most American livestock during the first half of the 19th century wandered about the open countryside.

Some leaders recognized the need to reach ordinary farmers. Elkanah Watson organized the Berkshire Agricultural Society at Pittsfield, Mass., in 1811. Its purpose was to hold an annual fair for the farmers of the community. The idea spread rapidly but declined when farmers did not realize their exaggerated hopes of benefits to be gained. Farm journals, first the *Agricultural Museum* in 1810 and then the *American Farmer* in 1819, also tried, but they received little support.

Production per man-hour in the United States increased only a little from 1800 to 1840 and somewhat more from 1840 to 1860.

But a technological foundation was being laid for a revolution in production. At the beginning of the period, the cotton gin, invented in 1793 by Eli Whitney, greatly changed agriculture in the South. The cheap, efficient separation of the seeds from the fiber encouraged planters to grow more cotton. The extensive commercial production of cotton dominated farming and led to the expansion of the plantation system. The South grew the one crop and neglected more diversified agriculture, while it depended on England and the North for markets and for supplies of other farm products and manufactured articles. At the same time, cotton cultivation brought about the rapid settlement of the region and returned large sums to the planters.

A cast-iron plow with interchangeable parts, patented in 1819 by Jethro Wood, was a major contribution. It would not scour in the heavy soils of the prairies, however; the soil clung to the moldboard instead of sliding by and turning over. Two Illinois blacksmiths, John Lane in 1833 and John Deere in 1837, solved the problem by using a smooth steel and polished wrought iron for the shares and moldboards of their plows.

The mechanical reaper was probably the most significant single invention introduced into American farming between 1800 and the Civil War. It replaced much human power at the crucial point in grain production when the work must be completed quickly to save a crop from ruin. The reapers patented by Obed Hussey in 1833 and Cyrus H. McCormick in 1834 marked the transition from the hand to the machine age of farming.

Many other farm machines were invented between 1830 and 1860, and the bases for other farm improvements were laid. Edmund Ruffin, sometimes called America's first soil scientist, had urged the chemical analysis of soil and the use of marl as early as 1821. His work preceded that of Justus von Liebig, the great German chemist who published *Chemistry in Its Applications*

to Agriculture and Physiology in 1840. Liebig's theories brought science to agriculture in Europe, and his influence was felt in America.

Commercial fertilizer was used in the United States, beginning with Peruvian guano in the 1840's. Mixed chemical fertilizer first appeared on the market in 1849. Modern irrigation agriculture began in the United States in 1847, when Mormon pioneers opened a ditch in Utah.

The United States Congress in 1862 passed four laws, all signed by President Abraham Lincoln, which were to help transform American agriculture. The Homestead Act encouraged western settlement. The Morrill Land-Grant College Act encouraged agricultural education. The act establishing the Department of Agriculture provided a means for assisting farmers to adopt better methods. The act chartering the Union Pacific Railroad assisted in opening western land.

Agriculture from 1850 to 1870 was a decisive element in our economic development. The coming together of various lines of technology, the emphasis on agricultural reform, and the profitability of agriculture created an agricultural revolution. The profitability of farming was due primarily to the greatly increased overseas demands for American farm products and the demand for products to support the armies in the Civil War.

The Nation's farms produced enough food and fiber to satisfy the needs of our growing population and to dominate our exports. Agricultural exports in 1865 were 82.6 percent in value of our total exports. This percentage declined slowly but did not fall below 50 percent until 1911. Both value and volume increased year to year, but less rapidly than other exports.

THE UNITED STATES was not alone in increasing its total volume of agricultural exports after 1865.

Argentina, Australia, Canada, and New Zealand became competitive with the United States in shipping grain and livestock products to Europe, although commercial agriculture began about a generation later than in America. The use of refrigeration in steamships, beginning in the 1870's, offered better opportunity to get livestock products to markets.

Refrigerated ships gave Argentina its opportunity to market fresh beef in England. Modern agriculture began in Argentina in 1856, with the arrival of 208 Swiss families. A considerable flow of European immigration followed. The immigrants established and developed the great cereal belt, and later the sugar, vineyard, cotton, and fruit belts. Herd improvement, beginning about 1860, aided sheep and cattle raising, which the Spanish settlers had established.

The manorial system, established in Canada by the first French colonists, was not abolished there until 1854. Agriculture thereafter developed more rapidly in Quebec, particularly after dairying became profitable. The Civil War in the United States hastened the transition from wheat growing to mixed farming in Ontario. At about the same time, wheat growing began in the Red River Valley and then spread slowly over the prairie provinces. The creation of a variety of wheat known as Marquis, by Sir Charles E. Saunders, and its distribution to Canadian farmers beginning in 1908, was a triumph for Canadian scientific endeavor.

Wool dominated exports from Australia throughout the 19th century. It more than quadrupled in value from 1861 to 1890. During this period, millions of acres of pasture were fenced, which led to better breeding, conservation of the soil, and greater production per man-hour.

European farming was not established in New Zealand until after 1840. The outbreak of war with the native Maoris in 1859, which led to the sending of British troops to the islands, and the discovery of gold in 1861 meant a great rise in population and a larger market for food products. Over time, wheat and wool came to be the major enterprises. Both were produced for export. The introduction of refrigeration in 1882 opened new possibilities. Meat—beef, mutton, and lamb—was shipped to England immediately. Exports of butter were large after 1900. Farming became a collection of specialized industries during the 20th century.

At about the same time New Zealand was developing as an agricultural nation, another country far to the north was opening its doors to Western civilization. Japan in 1854 granted the United States minor trading concessions, a major departure from its previous isolationism. At about the same time, the feudal system collapsed, and Japan began rapid economic growth.

Concerned with its northern frontiers, Japan determined to colonize Hokkaido, an island that seemed to offer opportunity for agricultural development. The Japanese turned to America for help because weather conditions on Hokkaido and in the Northeastern United States were similar, America led the world in the use of farm machinery, and the United States was isolated from any international controversy.

The Japanese Government hired Horace Capron, Commissioner of the newly established Department of Agriculture, to head a mission to Japan. He arrived in Japan in the fall of 1871 with his group and remained there 4 years. Despite difficulties, which at times seemed insurmountable, the mission got a new, modern agricultural development underway in Hokkaido and had much to do with paving the way for better farming in Japan.

The Capron mission was responsible for establishing the first railway in Japan and encouraging the development of waterpower. By the First World War, Japan was a modern industrial nation. An authority on the economic history of Japan has said: ". . . it was the expansion of Japan's basic economy—agriculture and small-scale industry built on traditional foundations—which accounted for most of the growth of national productivity and income during this period."

Russia, Japan's rival in the Far East during the second half of the 19th century, liberated its serfs in 1861 and gave them allotments of land, administered through a communal system.

This accelerated a process of rural transformation, even though Russia suffered a great famine in 1891–1892. The period saw the encouragement of cotton growing in Turkestan and a sizable movement of peasants from European Russia into Siberia. The Russian Government made an effort to cultivate varieties of cotton that were suited to the climate of Turkestan and produced the finest staple. It kept in close touch with the U.S. Department of Agriculture, asking for samples of American cottonseed, information regarding types of staple, and advice in general. It was also cooperative in offering the United States its experience with American cotton, as well as with wheat and other crops that were of interest to American growers.

THESE VIGNETTES indicate that the years between 1850 and the First World War were years of agricultural change and development in many parts of the world. In other areas, particularly those with large populations held in colonial status, there was little or no advance.

We should bear in mind, however, that technological improvement in any aspect of farming may draw on experience from several sources.

Several European nations, for example, made substantial contributions during the 19th century to the development of dairying.

Major breeds of dairy cattle developed in Europe included the Ayrshire in southwestern Scotland, the Guernsey and Jersey in the Channel Islands, the Holstein-Friesian and the Dutch-Belted in the Netherlands, and the Brown Swiss in Switzerland.

The modern silo for storing green forage for winter use had its beginning in Germany about 1860 and was quickly adopted in France.

A Swede, Carl de Laval, in 1878 invented the centrifugal cream separator, the most important of numerous inventions that helped dairying. An American, Stephen M. Babcock, in 1890 devised a test for measuring the quantity of fat in milk. Milking machines were patented in several countries during this period and came into wide use after the First World War. Taken together, these developments provided the technological basis for modern dairy farming.

American agriculture was approaching a balance with the rest of the economy as the 20th century began. Most farmers produced for the market. The prices they received for their products in relation to prices they paid for other products seemed fair. Horse-drawn machinery had replaced much hand labor on farms. Steam engines were used for plowing and threshing in parts of the West. Inventors were at work improving tractors with internal combustion engines. Lime and chemical fertilizer were widely used in the South and East. Draining in some areas and irrigation in others made land more productive. The agricultural colleges and the Department of Agriculture had brought science to bear on farming, even though farmers were sometimes slow to adopt their recommendations. The establishment of the cooperative extension service in 1914 meant that a college-trained county agent carried the results of research to farmers.

The First World War caused major dislocations in European agriculture for nearly 6 years. The food and fiber exporting nations found demand for their products virtually unlimited. Prices rose, and many individual farmers in commercial farming areas throughout the world expanded their operations. Demand continued for about 2 years after the end of the war in 1918. By the summer of 1920, European agriculture had made a remarkable recovery, and some European countries embarked upon a program of agricultural self-sufficiency. World prices of many farm products declined sharply as a result.

World agriculture, at least among the countries producing surpluses for export, suffered chronic depression during the twenties and early thirties. Some countries developed plans to aid their farmers by influencing foreign marketing. In a few instances, where one controlled a substantial part of the supply of a commodity, attempts were made to control exports and thus raise prices.

Several nations, during the depression years, began to make particular efforts to help their farmers by extending credit, supporting farm prices, or establishing production control schemes.

The worldwide agricultural depression saw the continued development of agricultural technology, even though most farmers had neither the capital nor the financial incentive to change their methods.

Agricultural experiment stations in all parts of the world continued to develop better yielding plants and animals and to find new means to combat diseases and insects. Industry improved the tractor and other machines.

The Second World War provided the the price incentives for farmers to increase production in every way possible, mainly by the adoption of the latest advances in agricultural technology. There was no postwar deflation like that following the first war. Continued postwar demand for food in many parts of the world and price supports of one type or another for farm products kept prices up. The result was great technological advance in much of the world.

In the United States, the revolution included widespread progress in mechanization, with gasoline tractors displacing horses and mules. The commercial production of cottonpickers after the war completed the mechanization of cotton production.

Greater use of lime and fertilizer, the widespread use of cover crops and other conservation practices and improved varieties, the adoption of hybrid corn, a better balanced feeding of livestock, the more effective control of insects and disease, and the use of chemicals for such purposes as weed-killers and defoliants were part of the technological revolution.

Artificial breeding, which drew on earlier experiences in the Soviet Union and Denmark, brought major changes to the dairy industry. Such chemicals as gibberellic acid, a plant growth regulator first discovered in Japan, were placed on the market.

Hybrid sorghums, chickens, and pigs, following the great success of hybrid corn, brought our production to new heights.

The successful development of freezing food for retail sale, beginning before the First World War, and the commercial adoption of freeze-drying in the early sixties improved food marketing. Sales of partially processed and ready-to-eat convenience foods, many of them frozen, increased markedly after the war. Attractive packaging, control of quality, and improvements in supermarkets helped give Americans a constantly improving diet.

Similar advances might be cataloged for most of western Europe and Canada, Australia, New Zealand, Japan, and other countries. Yet the agricultural potentialities of many nations are still underdeveloped.

One of the great opportunities in agriculture today is to help them take part in this technological revolution through the greater development of their own natural and human resources and greater participation in world trade.

WAYNE D. RASMUSSEN *became chief of the Agricultural History Branch, Economic Research Service in* 1961. *He edited* Readings in the History of American Agriculture *and was coauthor of* Century of Service: The First 100 Years of the United States Department of Agriculture.

Bond with

the Earth

by AFIF I. TANNOUS

THE SERFS, the peasants, the tribesmen, the farmers, they are the ones whose sweat and toil produced the food that has nourished people these thousands of years and whose tie to the good earth made the foundations for the cultures and civilizations of their own time and later times.

Peons, peasants, tribesmen, and farmers there are still. Their association with the land endures. Their sweat and work continue. But times have changed: They are called on now to produce more food and fiber for the growing world population. The mechanisms of the trade and finance their products made possible and necessary are becoming bafflingly complex. They are awakening to a new consciousness of their destiny and contributions. Their welfare is of increasing concern to national and international authorities. No longer can they be neglected. Their productive effort must be amply rewarded. Their worth as citizens needs to be recognized as other segments of society have been; the contributions of their way of life to national structures merit our appreciation.

Anyone who wants a clear view of world agriculture and America's stake in it and its directions will do well to know who farmers are and how they live and work and produce because on them depend the world's food, much trade, and many institutions.

The first thing to appreciate is the bond between the land and the man who tills it, for that is an attachment that may mean the success or failure of any project or scheme of collective farming, expropriation or land reform, encouragement or discouragement of farm production, and change in established patterns of farming.

The bond is as old as the dawn of human consciousness, when man found his existence tied to the land on which he roamed, hunted, and died. The bond became stronger as man learned to domesticate animals and plants.

As herdsman he became more tied down to a certain place than as hunter. The attachment became binding when he settled down to cultivate the soil and wait for it to produce crops. That was the beginning of true civilization. Mutual aid, extensive communication, exchange of products, family life, common worship, and other human values became more possible than before.

Throughout recorded history, agriculture was man's major occupation. As he multiplied over the surface of the globe, his settlement on the land became established as his dominant way of life. Its major forms we can see today in some countries, functioning almost as they did ages ago.

NOMADIC or semisettled tribal agriculture is one of those ancient, yet still functioning, systems. It developed as man advanced from the hunting-gathering economy toward direct dependence on domesticated animals and plants. From the beginning, it seems to have existed side by side with the permanently settled agricultural village. Its importance is evident in several countries of northern Africa, the Near East, and southeastern Asia. It is dominant in the bush and savanna life of Africa south of the Sahara.

Tribal people who live in deserts and semideserts migrate far. With their livestock, they follow the seasons, seeking pastures and water. Tribes who live on the edges of the Sahara and in the south of Arabia are almost constantly on the move because of the extreme scarcity of water and pasture. Among those who are established away from the true deserts—like the tribes on the highlands of northern Africa, the plateaus of Arabia, Iran, and Afghanistan, the semidesert plains of Jordan, Syria, and Iraq, and the savanna areas of tropical Africa—migration is more regularly seasonal.

In the thick rain forest of Africa and similar tropical areas, migration takes the form mostly of shifting agriculture—burning and clearing the forest into patches of temporary agricultural production and then moving on to new sites within the tribal territory.

On more than one occasion, I observed these tribal folk on the move. In northern Iraq I saw the Kurdish tribes, during their spring migration, moving from the lowlands up the mountain slopes with their flocks of sheep and their household effects loaded on horses and donkeys. Men, women, and children were following the way of life established by their ancestors for centuries. During the same season, traveling by car and truck across the Nejd Plateau of Saudi Arabia and over the Syrian desert, I saw the caravans of Arab Bedouins with their camels, sheep, and goats, moving to northern regions after greener pastures. We overtook them as they were marching, or when they stopped to water their animals, or when they camped for the night, pitching their black tents made of goat hair.

These people do not recognize the national boundaries that have been set up in recent times and cut across their migration trails. They feel they have belonged to the heart of the vast areas of land since time immemorial, and they wish to maintain their freedom to move according to the demands of seasonal changes and the needs of their pattern of life.

In the Mediterranean region, the tribes move in winter several hundred miles away from the hills and river valleys deep into the open spaces on the rim of the desert. When the dry season begins in spring, the movement is reversed. Similar courses are followed by the leading tribes of northern Iraq, Iran, and Afghanistan.

The Fulanis of northern Nigeria move with their cattle herds between the desert areas of the north and the rim of the thick forest in the south. The controlling factors are the availability of seasonal moisture and the tsetse fly, which permits no livestock to thrive wherever it exists. The fly spreads farther north from its forest abode into the savanna areas during the rainy season and forces tribal migration accordingly.

As one drives along or flies over these courses nowadays, one can see the patterned movement of people and livestock. More than that, one can see the historical process of transition from pure nomadism to semisettled and permanent agriculture. No rigid lines or barriers divide these ways of life. They are manifestations of a total endeavor by human beings in adjustment to the forces of their environment. Some continue on the path of pure nomadism. Others are semisettled and do part-time agriculture. Others are settled permanently in agricultural villages but retain many tribal ways.

The tribal way of life continues to make contributions to the larger national structures all over the world. The tribal folk in many places produce the bulk of the camels, sheep, goats, and cattle. By nomadic grazing, they can harvest the scanty growth of the desert, where cultivated agriculture has no chance. When semisettled, they also can raise annual crops. The products of their livestock supply the markets of villages and cities and some— wool and hair, skins and hides, dairy products—may be exported.

Tribal people are sometimes the major human resource available to their countries. Their overflow over the centuries has replenished villages and urban centers. Ruthless forces of environment have selected and seasoned their race to endure, as is readily apparent, for example, in the Massai in

Kenya, the Nejdi nomad in Saudi Arabia, and the Afghan highlander.

Among the basic contributions of the tribal system to society over the ages are family and kinship solidarity, self-reliance, and individual prowess and leadership. Where we find it today in its pure form, undamaged by outside forces, its organization is basically democratic despite its austere and autocratic ways. The chief is a member of the tribe, recognized as the leader mainly on the basis of his qualities. Social and economic equality is general among tribesmen. They are free, independent, and outspoken.

They tell the story of an Arab tribal chief who moved with his flocks and people into pasture areas near Damascus. The settled village folk complained to the Ottoman Governor of Damascus about the damage caused to their crops by the grazing flocks of the Bedouins. The Governor did his best to get the chief to move away from that area, but without success. Finally he sent a messenger offering him three alternatives: To pay a tribute for grazing rights, to move away, or to go down and talk it over in Damascus. True to the Bedouin directness and independent character, the chief sent the following message to the Governor: "Greetings. Tribute we shall not pay; from here we shall not move; and down to Damascus we will not go. Peace upon you."

But the tribal system generally has been neglected by rising national powers and has been damaged by forces beyond tribal control. In many places, where the tribes are in the process of settlement, tribal chiefs may be transformed to absentee landlords, and their tribesmen may be sinking to serfdom. In other places, where the tide of nationalism is rising, serious efforts have been aimed at detribalization. Forced or poorly conceived forms of settlement have been tried in some countries, but the result has been demoralization and loss to national economies. The situation calls for more thoughtful and rational plans, based on the realities, the social-economic values, and limitations of tribal life.

THE AGRICULTURAL village settlement began in remote times, probably in the highlands of the Near East, where man first learned to cultivate plants and raise livestock. Village life that depended on mixed farming spread into Asia, westward around the Mediterranean, and into Europe.

Excavations in Palestine, northern Iraq, Iran, and other parts of the Old World have revealed much of its earliest forms. At Byblos, on the Mediterranean in Lebanon, you can still see the remains of an ancient Phoenician settlement, much older than the Crusader castle and Roman amphitheater standing on the same site. You can see the foundations of its clustered houses, the temple where people worshiped and offered sacrifice, the water hole, and many stone implements they used. Close by in a typical Lebanese village, you can see how features of the ancient settlement have prevailed despite modern changes.

The village even today is still the dominant type of settlement among farming peoples. It is firmly established in northern Africa and the Near East; in Pakistan, India, and the rest of southeastern Asia; in western Europe; and most of Latin America. Even in China, the Soviet Union, and eastern Europe, it retains its form and much of its functions despite the modifications of collectivization. The scattered farmsteads that are typical of the United States, Canada, Australia, and parts of northern Europe and southern South America form a much smaller proportion of the world farming population.

Despite widespread existence and development and despite differences of cultures and the local peculiarities, agricultural villages have several outstanding features in common. They are the centers where farmers live close together in clustered dwellings and from which they go out to work in their fields. They gain from their village a feeling of physical and social security, as they are identified with its kinship groups, its traditions, and its common activities and ways of doing things.

Family and religious ties are strong among them. So is their attachment to their ancestral land. Their desire to own it is instinctive and atavistic, but their love for it is deep even if they work it as sharecroppers or tenants. The jobs they cannot do themselves they do through the traditional forms of mutual aid or with occasional hired village labor. The farm meets many of their needs, but they trade in the regular market of the nearest town, the larger weekly market in their neighborhood, or in a city market. The land is their existence and fulfillment. Only the most compelling of economic or political conditions drive them from it.

As I grew up in my old ancestral village on the lower slopes of the Lebanon mountains, I found myself immersed in an atmosphere of intimate association between my people and the land. It was our land, the land of my ancestors, whose names I learned to recite covering eight generations. Also, I learned the proper name given to each orchard or field of our property scattered around the village.

And as my grandfather took me around, he told me about the history and folklore associated with our land.

Each family in the village was similarly identified with its land, and no one would want to part with it except under extreme conditions of emergency or deprivation. When some of the people emigrated to seek fortunes in the Americas or Australia, they preferred to mortgage the land for travel loans rather than sell it. And the first surplus income they earned was sent back home to release the land. They wanted to keep it within the family, even though they would never return to settle on it themselves.

When I returned to Lebanon in the spring of 1963, I found the situation still about the same. The basic bond between the rural folk and the earth has endured, despite the many changes brought about by modern technology and living.

But village life has limitations and problems. It is isolated and has limited horizons, and so it tends to have conflicting groups. Also, its traditionalism and strong community consciousness discourage deviation and change toward improved methods of production and living.

Aside from the more modern rural areas of western Europe and a few other regions, the village folk—the majority of the world's farmers—have had the short end of the stick. In most villages of Latin America, the Near East, Pakistan, and India, average family income is low—the equivalent of 50 to 150 dollars a year. They usually have no credit facilities and must borrow at usurious rates. Most of them are landless sharecroppers, wage earners, or owners of holdings too small to support them.

The clustered village structure and customs dictate a wasteful fragmentation of the cultivated land. Methods of cultivation generally are primitive. The ancient hand sickle, the threshing board, and the wooden plow are common. Even animal power and the wooden plow are missing in most of tropical Africa. Crops are produced by the use of the ancient short-handle hoe and are transported on men's and women's backs. Transportation facilities are inadequate. Illiteracy may be as high as 90 percent. Sanitary facilities and health services are primitive, and the incidence of disease is high.

One of my most vivid impressions during my first trip in tropical Africa was seeing so many people using that type of hoe and transporting the produce on their backs. It was the pattern of production and transportation prevailing wherever I traveled in the countries of west-central and eastern Africa. Often I saw women carrying babies on their backs and baskets of produce on their heads, going home from the fields or to the village market to sell their products.

Yet these hard-working village folk

produce most of the world's food and fiber. They and tribal people are the major human resource—70 to 80 percent of the total population—in most countries. Furthermore, the basic values of their life—endurance, directness in their relationships, family solidarity, religious faith, sociability, and neighborly sharing—are at the foundation of cultures and development.

The impact of national emancipation and international cooperation have brought a redeeming awakening to the problems, needs, and promise of village people. National authorities, now supported by international effort, have been directing more and more attention and concern to the great rural base. The need for broad programs of agrarian reform at last is recognized seriously.

New programs touch many sides of rural development—equitable distribution of the land, fair taxation, setting up cooperatives and other institutions, extension work, education, health services, centers for agricultural mechanization, experiment stations, and others.

Even in France, where agriculture has been developed to high levels, the need for further improvements in the agrarian system has been recognized. The country is now proceeding with the application of a national policy aimed at consolidation of the fragmented holdings of the villages, expansion of credit and extension services, and improvement of marketing methods and facilities.

Mexico took the lead in Latin America, and has had successful experience in land reform.

Some beginnings in that field were made by other Latin American countries before the initiation of the Alliance for Progress in 1961. Since then, some tangible and promising steps have been taken, including tax reforms in several countries and the adoption of land reform laws in others. Also, more attention has been directed toward the development of human resources through education.

Peru, for example, has begun to move ahead with determination on a wide front of rural improvement within a comprehensive program of national development.

Nicaragua passed a new agrarian reform law in 1962 for the benefit of its farmers, and so did the Dominican Republic and Chile. Chile also has completed a comprehensive aerial survey of its agricultural land, which will provide a basis for settlement and agricultural development.

Japan achieved a thorough agrarian reform with United States support at the end of the war. A community development movement in India has begun to revitalize its villages.

The Egyptian revolution of 1962 pioneered in land reform and emancipation of the peasants in the Middle East. Promising beginnings have been made in Morocco through land distribution and the paysanats, which are centers for improved agricultural methods. Similar paysanats have been established in the Congo.

Tribal village folk in Kenya are being settled on good farmland.

National leaders of Tunisia have identified themselves with rural improvement on an intensive scale on the basis of self-help.

I cannot forget how President Bourguiba of Tunisia emphasized this principle when he received us (members of the United States Wheat Team) to discuss wheat donations by the United States. We had toured the country, estimated its emergency needs, and obtained Washington's approval for the donations. The President expressed his sincere appreciation for American help, a free gift of food for his people who needed it. But he expressed his determination that the rural people receiving the aid should work for it on productive projects for their own benefit. Later on, he did just that, and the Tunisian project of self-help, using American wheat for rural improvement, became a model copied in several other countries.

Thailand is an example of what an

old country with traditional village life and agriculture could do under a sound agrarian structure. Its farmers are mostly independent and enterprising owner-operators. Their government has been concerned with the agricultural base and alert to possibilities for increasing production and exports. A sound policy aimed at these objectives has been followed since 1950 or so. The result has been the successful transformation of the economy from a one-crop base (rice) to that of several major export crops, including rice, corn, cassava, and livestock.

The Shah of Iran has fostered a comprehensive agrarian reform that may reach every village. Similar awakenings and developments have been taking place in Greece, Italy, Turkey, the Philippines, and other countries where village life is significant.

BUT A MAJOR segment of the world's village people live under Communist regimes in the Soviet Union, China, and eastern Europe. There the village was the focus of a different activity. Communist authorities from the beginning sought to destroy the traditional village organization and to replace it with centrally controlled collective farms. It amounted to the destruction of the deep roots of hundreds of millions of people.

Collective farming has existed as a minor feature of the agrarian structure in other parts. For example, it is practiced in Israel side by side with co-operative family farming; by various tribal groups in Africa; and in some old villages of the Middle East and Far East, where land is held in common.

What has happened under communism is different and unprecedented. It has been enforced ruthlessly by dictation from above in disregard of centuries-old farming systems and ways of life. It has struck swiftly and sweepingly. It is aimed at increased production and uses all available technical means, but rigid regimentation allows little initiative.

In the Soviet Union and in other Communist-controlled countries, it began with the declaration of freedom and free land for the peasants with the division of large estates. That first stage was short lived. Soon there followed the destruction of the old agrarian structure, liquidation of the large peasant farmers, effective assertion of the ownership of the land by the state, and the setting up of the kolkhoz, or collective farm, under state control.

Most Russian farmers belong to the kolkhoz system. A general description of one unit would be a fair representation of farm life in the Soviet Union today. It is basically related to the old agricultural village structure but aims at changing and replacing it.

Its members are drawn mostly from the village folk. Its land is the same land that was previously farmed by individual village families as owners or as tenants on large estates. The church and other institutions of the village were eliminated or modified. New institutions (notably schools and recreation halls) were set up according to the Communist pattern.

The dominant institution that directs the community affairs and most of life among the farmers is the kolkhoz organization itself. It receives its patterns of operation from a hierarchy of central authorities, most of whom are far away from the facts of country life.

It operates through a president and a number of administrative and professional persons who direct the members, community activities, and field operations. The members are organized into work brigades, each under a brigade leader, and assigned to activities according to the central pattern.

The achievements and rewards of workers, men and women, are calculated on the basis of the labor-day unit. The unit is given a value according to the type of work done, so that rewards are higher for higher skills and some margin is allowed for individual initiative.

Members are paid in kind and cash, the amount depending on the total output of the kolkhoz at the end of the harvest. The state quota of the crop is met first, and part of the income is turned to the kolkhoz reserve. The portion of the crop that is divided among the members is used by them or sold. Members receive free health care and free schooling for their children.

After the agonies of its early stages under the Stalin regime, when large independent farmers were liquidated and millions of people died from famine, the collective system was forced to include some private incentives. At each kolkhoz, therefore, farm families generally are allowed to own houses, small adjoining plots, some livestock and feed for them, and farm handtools.

Into this miniature farming activity, symbolic of the free private enterprise, a family pours every bit of effort it can spare from its collective duties.

The results are revealing. The farm family has better food and has some items to spare for sale on the free market for higher prices. The total area of all private plots is estimated at 3 to 4 percent of all cropland. The value of the products from the private plots amounts to about 30 percent of the total agricultural output of the Soviet Union.

The sovkhoz, or state farm, is another form of Soviet collective farming. Its objectives are similar to those of the kolkhoz, but it is completely owned and administered by the state. It usually covers a larger area per farm and is especially important in the newly opened lands of the central Soviets and southern Siberia.

In general, it is better staffed and equipped than the kolkhoz, and its workers are paid regular wages. Its production efficiency has been improving, and it has developed better institutions and services for its people.

THE COMMUNIZING of agriculture in China is somewhat like that in the Soviet Union. The vast rural base which faced the Chinese Communists in the late forties consisted mostly of the traditional, deep-rooted village community. Family and community ties were strong. Religious and social institutions were deeply traditional. Farmers cultivated small family holdings near their villages.

Aiming at ultimate collectivization and state control, the authorities appealed to the peasant farmers through the usual inducement—confiscation of large holdings and the promise of free land to the landless and small owners. The next step was to encourage and organize the farmers to cooperate in the production of crops through the traditional channels of mutual aid. So far, the procedure was in keeping with the old ways of the people. The land was apparently theirs, and they received a good share of the produce.

Then control became more centralized, as mutual aid teams were organized into the larger but rudimentary production cooperative. A third comprehensive step was taken in a few years—the consolidation of production cooperatives into advanced cooperative organizations, geared to even more central control of agricultural production. Within a short time, some 120 million farm families found themselves members of these organizations and regimented by them. The system at this stage was similar to the Russian kolkhoz. The land went under state control, but each family was allowed to retain a small plot, some implements, and livestock.

The authorities embarked on the last and most drastic move toward complete socialization in the late fifties. They declared the well-known commune system and began to apply it rigorously. That was supposed to be the final answer to the attainment of the Communist ideal in farm life.

Each commune was intended to be a large, self-sustaining, political-economic entity, composed of an average of 30 advanced cooperatives with highly centralized authority over the people.

It regimented the lives and operations of the farmers and confiscated the family plots, livestock, and implements. Everything belonged to the commune, including the people. Men and women were organized into work teams and brigades that were assigned various tasks as the situation demanded, according to a centralized pattern of production. Family ties were disregarded. Members were assigned to different production units. Children were taken care of centrally. People ate in mess halls.

Within a year, the commune system as originally conceived proved unworkable. Human endurance under absolute regimentation reached a breaking point. Family life was heavily damaged, private initiative was destroyed, and a man's dignity was lost. Agricultural production slumped, and the people were hungry.

Finally, within 3 years, the authorities were obliged to recognize their failure and retreat from the commune approach. They swung the pendulum back, roughly to the equivalent of the previous state, the less drastic production cooperative. Central state control, still strong, claimed the lion's share of the farming endeavor, but family plots were restored, and farmers were allowed to sell excess products in the free market. Total production rose, and the people had more to eat.

The Communist wave of collective farming swelled over into the countries of eastern Europe but with varying impacts, as compared to Russia and China. Collectivization was about complete in Rumania and Hungary in 1963. Not more than 15 percent of the farmland was collectivized in Poland and 12 percent in Yugoslavia. The traditional rural life, with its emphasis on the family unit, individual initiative, and private ownership of the land, has survived to some degree.

THE SEPARATE farmstead and the rural community it fostered are rather new in world agriculture. They have never taken a real hold in most of Asia and are limited in Europe.

Even in the early stage of settlement in North America, the agricultural village and the plantation prevailed. During the later stages of expansion into the valleys and the plains in the heart of the continent and the West, the isolated farmstead took firm roots, flourished, and became dominant.

Within the past century or so, it has become widespread, important, and typical in the United States. Similar settlements and rural development have occurred in Canada, Australia, New Zealand, South Africa, and somewhat in South America.

Its fundamental feature is independent, private ownership of land. The American pioneer farmer had to struggle, work, suffer, and risk his life before he was able to secure himself on the new land, but he was rewarded, perhaps as no other farmer of the Old World has been, by becoming a free and independent owner-operator. He met the challenge, knowing that the land and its fruits were his.

The significance of the farmer's ownership of land went beyond the capacity to produce amply for his needs and for national and world markets. It lay in the heart of his steady development as an independent, self-reliant individual. This pattern of development spared the United States the trials and upheavals of countries where a chasm separated peasants and the elite. Even today, this basic issue—how to emancipate every peasant through a sound and secure system of land tenure and enable him to follow other pursuits—constitutes a threat to national structure in Latin America, the Near East, southeastern Asia, and African countries that were colonies.

Members of an American farm family form a solid, self-reliant, hardworking group. They are free to cultivate, produce, plan for the future, and develop themselves, adopt improved techniques and methods, and to seek better ways of living. Still, family ties and loyalty are not so strong as to thwart initiative in the younger generation. The heavy hand of the old kinship group and the traditional community are not there to hold youth back and keep it in place. Farm families may trade in one village, go to church in another, and attend a farmers' meeting in a third. Their horizons have widened to include urban, national, and world communities. They buy and read books, subscribe for national magazines and newspapers, attend plays and concerts, keep up with developments, and vote.

My PURPOSE in pointing this out is not to make odious comparisons but to emphasize that even in these modern times of science and technology, electronics, jet planes, and mechanized agriculture, most of the world's farming people are at the lowest levels of human development.

An example: Much of the agricultural land in Latin America is held in very large estates. They are cultivated by village peasants on the basis of sharecropping or wage labor. The peasants' share of the crop is barely enough for subsistence living. They have no economic margin to improve their lot and no channels are open to seek other ways of living. The system began in the early years of the conquest. Large grants of land were made to influential individuals; with the land went the Indian people under special concessions to provide the necessary labor. Subsequent national development confirmed this type of agricultural settlement and exploitation.

ANOTHER EXAMPLE: In the Middle East, from the Atlantic borders to Pakistan, the roots of large-scale agricultural exploitation have been associated with absentee ownership.

In the forties and fifties, a wave of independence swept over the region, and new and old national entities found themselves faced with grave agrarian issues. Their superstructures tottered on shaky agrarian foundations, where the majorities of their peoples were hopelessly bound.

Like their Latin counterparts, these peasant masses were mostly sharecroppers, tied to the land of their ancestors. They were illiterate, ignorant, and slaves of primitive methods of cultivation. The magnitude of the absentee landlord was measured mostly in terms of the number of villages he owned—land, houses, and people.

He supplied some management and credit, but not enough to put the land under efficient cultivation or to give the peasants a chance to improve their lot.

The harvested crop in Iran, for instance, was divided among the five factors of production—land, labor, water, seed, and draft power. The peasant usually could claim the share of only one or two of the factors. In Egypt, the rent per acre was so high that the fellah could have barely enough to eat.

Much of this situation existed in 1964, but with a basic difference. The responsible elite in almost all of these countries—kings, presidents and other government authorities, political leaders, and intellectuals—have become increasingly aware of the seriousness of the situation. They have launched a variety of national agrarian programs to emancipate the peasants, give them ownership of the land they cultivate, furnish more secure terms of tenancy, and support services and institutions.

ISRAEL provides an unusual example of land settlement and agricultural development. The country, ancient in origin, is young as a nation. Most of its people are immigrants from all over the world who came to live on the ancient land in the past few decades.

With the exception of the original Arab settlers (now a minority concentrated mostly in the Galilee neighborhood), the incoming people attached themselves to the land according to patterns set by responsible national authorities. The new nation was not bound to any deep-rooted system of traditional agriculture.

Also, unlike its neighbors and most of the newly developing countries, Israel has only a small minority (about 20 percent) of its 2.5 million people living in rural areas and engaged mainly in agriculture. The country consequently is not faced with the usual problems of rural overpopulation and underemployment; it also has well-developed industries.

A third feature is that Israeli farmers come from a variety of cultural origins; they carry different patterns of living. They come from eastern and western Europe, from northern Africa and the Near East, and from other regions, too. They had to go through a process of adjustment under national guidance, culminating in the establishment of integrated and productive settlements. They benefit increasingly from the services of highly developed national institutions of agricultural research, extension, and training.

As they settle on the land, which is largely state owned, they are free to choose their type of settlement. One such major type is the collective, called kibbutz. Here, private property is practically nonexistent. The people work the land and share in the harvest collectively, and their living generally is communal.

Another major kind of settlement is the cooperative village, called moshav. The land is held in common, but private ownership of the houses and private family life are maintained.

The third major form is represented by Jewish and Arab village settlements, where the land is owned and operated by individual families.

Thus, within a relatively short period, (mostly from 1948 to 1964), and with substantial aid from abroad, Israel has been able to develop a highly efficient system of agriculture in balance with industrial development. Also, its experiment with various types of settlement developed voluntarily side by side—from the purely collective to the purely private operation—generally has been successful.

Fortified with highly developed technical and scientific competence, Israel has been reaching out to other emerging countries, mostly in Africa, to share with them its experiences in various aspects of agricultural settlement and development.

A SIMILARLY promising trend has been established in southeastern Asia.

Japan has succeeded in the peaceful liquidation of the old system of large-scale absentee ownership. Its peasant millions became free—and have become more efficient producers and more effective citizens.

India is in the midst of a tremendous rural development program aimed at the same objectives.

The Philippines and other countries of the region are steadily following their own national paths toward agrarian reform and sound agricultural development.

Tropical Africa is at a crossroads. Most of its agricultural development has been achieved through the plantation system.

The Republic of the Congo is an example of a plantation enterprise, established mostly by European colonial organizations or large-scale farmers. They made tremendous investments, introduced modern technology, and supplied managerial skills. They operated at heavy risks. The system has improved agricultural development and commercial production. It has developed much of the great export products such as hardwood, palm oil, rubber, cotton, tea, coffee, peanuts, and bananas.

But at the same time, the plantation has tied down to its operation a major portion of the human resource in the form of resident or migrant labor. It has given rise to a special class of landless African peasants. Their housing, health, food, and other primary needs are taken care of to one degree or another. They depend upon the plantation for their subsistence, but have no stake in its land, nor do they participate in its management.

Newly independent African countries also have inherited, among other colonial developments, the plantation enterprise.

What will the new national regimes do with it? Will extreme nationalism squeeze out European investment and management at the risk of letting the system go to pieces? Will new formulas of cooperation be established whereby the great plantation will continue to operate on a new basis? How are they to free the human resource tied up with the system?

The issue involves millions of tribal folk, who are in various stages of agricultural settlement. Some are nomadic herders. Others practice shifting agriculture. Others cultivate permanent smallholdings. Most of them operate under traditional tribal laws of land tenure.

Will national developments provide them with sound agrarian structures based on their recognized rights in the land within the context of their tribal cultures?—or will collective or other schemes be imposed on them from above? Will they develop into landless peasants in an African system of large-scale absentee ownership?

The answers will depend largely on whether the rising African elite will permit the chasm to widen between them and the village-tribal peoples, or whether they will keep close to that solid base and on it secure national development.

I think that the world's experience indicates that the key to the great rural resource is to give the cultivator a man's position as an independent farmer or tenant.

AFIF I. TANNOUS *is Area Officer for the Near East and Africa, Foreign Agricultural Service. He taught in the American University of Beirut and worked on rural development in the Near East. After earning a doctor's degree at Cornell University, he taught at the University of Minnesota and joined the Foreign Agricultural Service in 1943. His work entails much travel in the Near East and Africa and has included several assignments on United States and United Nations field missions. From 1951 to 1954, he was Deputy Director of the United States Operations Mission in Lebanon. From 1954 to 1961, he served in Foreign Agricultural Service as Chief of the Africa and the Middle East Analysis Branch.*

Migrations and Agriculture

by PHILLIPS W. FOSTER

WE IN THE UNITED STATES know how much immigrants have contributed to American farming, economics, and the texture of life: The British in New England, Spanish in the Southwest, Negroes in the South, and Germans and Scandinavians in the Midwest, for instance.

The history of every other country in the world also has been affected by immigration. There is hardly one farmer anywhere whose farm life and farm activities are not influenced in one way or another by a migration sometime in the past.

Famine has caused several of the world's most dramatic migrations, including that of thousands of Irish during and after the Irish potato famine of 1845–1848.

People have gone to new homes in distant lands also because of a long pressure on the food supply.

People have migrated because of a promise of new or better ground to till, or because they wanted to set up a trading post somewhere far from home, or because there were prospects for a better job somewhere else.

People have migrated for non-economic reasons. They have moved because they thought the new home-land would provide them with a better place in which to practice their religion. They have moved to gain political freedom or intellectual stimulation. They have moved to get away from social ostracism. People have migrated involuntarily. Some were sold into slavery, taken captive in war, or shipped to Siberia.

GREAT MIGRATIONS, whatever their cause, always have influenced agriculture. Sometimes the migrants have brought new plants and animals with them.

Sometimes they have introduced different institutions and values into the new homeland: Novel systems of land tenure, different attitudes toward work, new food habits, new credit systems, slavery.

Sometimes migrants have introduced new technology: New agricultural machinery, new techniques of cultivation, insecticides.

Sometimes they have carried with them birds and insects and organisms that have become pests and caused disease.

MOVING from place to place was the usual way of life for primitive tribes.

The movements were not normally over great distances, and a tribe usually moved within the same territory that its ancestors had known. Occasionally, in prehistoric times, people would wander to completely new lands, never to return to the old camping grounds.

Probably the earliest of such migrations of primitive peoples that affected agriculture significantly was the migration that brought the American Indians from Asia across the Bering Straits to North America.

The first wave of this migration began perhaps 24 thousand years ago. Successive waves continued until shortly before the Christian Era. Long before their "discovery" by the European world, these people had found, cultivated, and developed such important crops as corn, potatoes, and tomatoes.

Arnold Toynbee, the English historian, describes another migration of antiquity that was due to an agricul-

tural pressure and resulted in important agricultural developments.

During the most recent glacial epoch, the storms that in warmer times watered the plains of Europe were forced southward and watered the Afrasian steppe, which extends from the Atlantic coast of north Africa eastward to India and China. Somewhat more than 10 thousand years ago, as the glacier was receding and the storms were moving northward following it, the primitive Afrasian hunters and food gatherers faced the gradual desiccation of their land.

The Paleolithic men (who left their hand axes all over the Afrasian steppe from Morocco to India) had three opportunities open to them as their food supply became less and less. First, they might move northward or southward with their prey, following the climate to which they were accustomed.

Second, they might remain on the steppes and seek out a miserable existence on such game and plants as could withstand the droughts. And third, they might invade the swamps of the river valleys.

Although the Paleolithic men tried each, the ones who invaded the valleys made the most immediate contribution to agriculture, for in the process of conquering the swamps of the Nile, the Tigris-Euphrates, the Indus, and the Yellow Rivers, these people learned to grow crops and to cope with the annual flooding of the rivers by channeling the waters into irrigation canals and replanting their annually inundated fields.

It was probably the process of conquering these valleys with primitive agriculture and primitive engineering that stimulated the development of the early river-valley civilizations—the first of the great civilizations. So, while those who chose the alternative of plunging into the swamps traveled the shortest distance of any who fled from desiccation, they influenced agriculture much more than did those who at the same time traveled much greater distances.

There have been five truly great explosive migrations since recorded history began: The Bantu expansion in Africa, then the Arab expansion after Mohammed, the European expansion after the Renaissance and Reformation, the forced migration of Negroes to the Western Hemisphere, and the recent Chinese expansion into Manchuria and southeastern Asia.

Each time the migrating peoples carried their influence into new territories in the span of a few centuries.

Each time they had an important effect on the agriculture in the new territories.

THE FIRST, that of the Bantu in Africa, began about the time of Christ. The Bantu peoples, a group of tribes from eastern Nigeria and the Cameroon highlands, began the invasion of the lands of Pygmies who lived in the tropical rain forest of the Congo River Basin. They were able to make the invasion at this time, and not before, because then the Bantu acquired a group of Indonesian crops that could be grown in the rain forest.

How the Bantu acquired the Indonesian crops is a study on how rapidly man sometimes moved crops around the world with his migrations long before the time of modern transportation.

Some time before the birth of Christ, a group of people known as the Maanyan on the southeastern coast of Borneo had developed skills in navigating their outrigger canoes through trading with the inhabitants of nearby islands.

Their territory lay along a famous trade route that connected Malaya with China through the Philippines.

The Borneo navigators mastered this trade route and then ventured farther, making contact with Ceylon and India, then Arabia, and eventually Africa.

On the coast of Africa, the Indonesians set up a trading colony in Azania. (Azania corresponded roughly to the present coast of Kenya.) The Azanians themselves had migrated to the area some 2 thousand years before

the arrival of the Indonesians and had established a terraced agriculture on the African coast, leaving the nearby steppes to the bushmen hunters.

Since the Azanians already had knowledge of agriculture, it was easy for the Indonesians to introduce into Africa the crops they brought with them: Rice, bananas, taro, yams, and the sweetpotato, which some adventurous prehistoric seamen had brought to Indonesia from South America.

The Azanians adopted all the Indonesian crops but rice. Apparently they could not get used to the Indonesians' method of cultivating rice. The Azanians passed on the four Indonesian crops to their neighbors to the north, and the cultivation of the crops then spread quickly across the grasslands south of the Sahara and north of the rain forests.

When the Bantu moved into the rain forests to the south, they found the Indonesian crops they brought with them even more suited to the wet climate they encountered than to the semiarid climate of their old home. The new crops gave them a decided advantage over the Pygmies, who previously had ruled supreme in the Congo Basin.

Within 500 years, the Bantu had conquered the entire Congo, subduing the Pygmies and setting up a symbiotic relationship with them. The area they conquered in this short time span was roughly equivalent in size to the United States east of the Mississippi.

After their conquest of the Congo Basin rain forest, the Bantu emerged into the highlands of Uganda, where they relearned the cultivation of African cereals, which they had forgotten during the previous 500 years. During the next 900 years, the Bantu conquered east Africa, learned how to keep cattle, and brought the cattle from eastern Africa south across the tsetse fly belt and then conquered south-central Africa.

The tsetse fly, which attacks both cattle and humans, exists in a belt across south-central Africa. This pest had previously prevented the introduction of cattle to southern Africa. The Bantu demonstrated the superior quality of their technology when they managed to move cattle across this belt and successfully introduce them into southern Africa.

By the year 1400, the Bantu had managed to finish their occupation of practically all Africa from the Congo basin to the east and south, except the extreme southwestern corner of the continent.

It was on this southwestern corner that the Dutch were later to land and start a migration northward as part of the third great migratory explosion.

But that is getting ahead of our story, for the second great explosive migration in history began in the Middle East many centuries before the European Renaissance.

A NEW FAITH, Islam, arose about A.D. 600 in Arabia. In less than 100 years, its followers, the Moslems, had occupied territory extending from the Atlantic Ocean at Morocco eastward to the Indian Ocean and northward to the Caspian Sea.

Although the Moslem migration is better known than the Bantu migration, which was still going on when the Moslems set out, fewer people moved in the Moslem migration. The Moslem migration, especially during its first century, was predominantly military in character.

The spread of Moslem influence continued by military conquest, colonization, and trader missionaries. By 1600, less than a thousand years after the death of its founder, Islam had been carried almost all the way to its present territorial limits.

Today most of the world's 400 million Moslems live in a band stretching from Morocco through Indonesia, widening out on the south to Zanzibar and on the north into Siberia. Islam has affected the agriculture of every region it has penetrated, for wherever Islam has become predominant, swine have virtually disappeared.

THE MOST EXTENSIVE movement of people ever to occur began just as the Islamic world was completing its territorial growth. Between 1600 and 1940, more than 70 million people emigrated from Europe. Most of them migrated between 1820 and 1930. The peak of the migration occurred around 1910. The migrant streams out of Europe went first toward Latin America. Later other migrant streams moved toward North America, then Africa, Asia, Australia, and New Zealand.

When Spain and Portugal began their conquest of Central and South America shortly after Columbus' 1492 voyage, neither country was looking for new land to colonize, for they could not spare enough men to settle it. The territory was closed at first to settlers.

In line with the customs of feudal Europe, Spain and Portugal rewarded successful conquerors and others who won favor with the crown by giving them large tracts of land in the New World. The new landowners were allowed to settle on their lands and often arrived accompanied by armed guards, carpenters, bricklayers, and other craftsmen.

Large areas of Latin America were thus organized along the lines of the latifundia, or large landed estates—a system of agriculture that was common in southern Europe during the time of Spain's greatest glory. The latifundia system, employing simple agricultural techniques and much relatively unskilled labor, enabled the owner to be an absentee landlord. The latifundia system is still prevalent in Latin America and is one of many institutions restraining economic development there today.

The early European immigration into North America was different from that into Central and South America.

Early North American immigrants were largely from the countries surrounding the North Sea. To some of them, the goal of religious and political freedom was important, but the lure of free land was the major enticement.

During the two centuries before 1800, net immigration from Europe into North America may have totaled about 2 million, but this was a mere trickle compared to the 40 million or so who arrived the next 150 years.

It was during this latter period of migration that what was once a group of colonies clustered along the Atlantic seashore became, through western migration, two nations—the United States and Canada. Without intracontinental migration, the capacity of the New World to absorb immigrants would have been exhausted long ago.

This westward movement of people in North America has been credited with many accomplishments, including the development of a composite American nationality and the encouragement of democracy.

As the westward movement of people gained force and as east coast and European markets for foodstuffs developed, the pattern of subsistence farming in the North and of plantation agriculture in the South gave way increasingly to a pattern of commercially oriented, owner-operated farms.

While the Europeans and their descendants were moving west in North America, other Europeans (mostly Russians) were moving east across the Urals into Siberia. Almost 7 million settlers crossed the Urals between 1801 and 1914.

The areas of tillable land in Asiatic Russia lie chiefly in a fairly long belt, called the Siberian wedge. The wedge is never much more than 300 miles wide. It shrinks as it runs from the Urals eastward toward the Pacific Ocean. North of the wedge, it is too cold for farming; south of the wedge, it is too dry for farming.

Some of those who settled in Siberia were forced to do so, but most of them were ordinary peasants who crossed the Urals of their own volition in search of a better life. They went to Siberia to get free land and to escape serfdom and military service. Their crossing was an expression of Russian agricultural individualism.

The Russian peasants, who did Russia the triple services of peopling Siberia with Russians, bringing eastern European culture to the shores of the Pacific, and greatly enlarging Russian agricultural productive capacity, were rewarded during the Great Depression with collectivization of their newly created smallholdings.

Individual colonization in Siberia was prohibited in 1930. The law would have been unnecessary, for with the passing of free land, the motivation to colonize was killed. The phenomenon of Russian agricultural individualism, nurtured and developed by the great Siberian migration, however, has not been so easy to kill.

During the 1821–1932 period of great European emigration, Australia and New Zealand received 3.5 million immigrants. They and their descendants developed the agriculture of Australia and New Zealand in much the same way that North America west of the Appalachians grew.

The Australian westward movement was characterized by squatters, who took over the land and began ranching operations before it was officially open to settlement. Before the end of the century, more sedentary farmers were displacing the squatter-ranchers.

Africa also received its contingent of European settlers during the period of the great European exodus. Most of them settled in Algeria and the Union of South Africa. A million Europeans were on the north African coast (mostly in Algeria) by 1932, as against 12 million non-Europeans.

The Europeans in Algeria established an efficient commercial agriculture based on large owner-occupied farms. These farms used extensive amounts of non-European labor and exported wheat and wine to the European market.

With the turmoil accompanying Algerian independence in 1962, most of these commercial farms were abandoned by their owner-managers, who fled to Europe. Most of the farms in 1963 were being operated as collectives by the people who used to work them as hired laborers.

The greatest wave of immigration to South Africa occurred after the discovery of gold. During the peak period of the immigration, around 1895, some 25 thousand immigrants, mainly Europeans, arrived annually in the Union of South Africa.

For South African agriculture, however, the smaller immigrations that began centuries before were more important. The Dutch East India Company in 1625 founded a settlement on the Cape of Good Hope for the purpose of keeping open their trade route to the Far East.

Dutch settlers took cattle onto the traditional grazing lands of the Hottentots and gradually settled more and more of South Africa in a great trek eastward and northward. By the middle of the 18th century, Dutch farmers and the advance guards of the Bantu, whom I mentioned earlier, were coming into frequent contact.

The resulting conflict between the Dutch and the Bantu, known as the Kaffir Wars, marked the beginning of violent conflict between the races in South Africa.

Long before the discovery of diamonds (1867) and gold (1885) and the resulting inrush of people from Europe, the Dutch farmer had transformed extensive reaches of South Africa into ranches and farms along the patterns other European descendants used in other countries.

The Europeans had the most profound impact on agriculture in the places where they settled as serious farmers, but their influence on agriculture was felt also in places where they did not settle extensively.

The influence of the European lawmaker was felt throughout Africa and south Asia, where European concepts of land tenure have modified in varying degrees the indigenous systems of land tenure. The British in India, for instance, changed the Zamindar from an individual who merely collected the taxes on a landholding to one who both collected taxes and had certain ownership rights to the land.

Throughout the Tropics, Europeans organized and controlled vast plantations. The plantations established a new pattern of agriculture as they began the large-scale commercial production of sugar, tea, rubber, coffee, and bananas.

The Europeans who went out to settle and farm new lands in the 16th century and who thus began the great European exodus could not have known that by their acts they were laying the groundwork for two important non-European emigrations: African and Chinese.

THE AFRICAN EMIGRATION constituted the largest involuntary movement of people in history.

The African slave trade with the Western Hemisphere began in the 16th century. Slaves were brought to the Virginia Colony early in the 17th century. By the 18th century, the slave trade reached its peak. Seven million slaves were brought to the Americas. The slave trade continued illegally until the middle of the 19th century. It is estimated that nearly 15 million slaves had been imported into the Americas by the end of the slave-trading era.

The extensive slave trade undoubtedly was instrumental in the early introduction into the Americas of native west African crops, such as sorghum and watermelon, as well as the early introduction of such Western Hemisphere crops as corn and peanuts into Africa.

Slaves were a tremendously important source of labor in Latin America and in southern North America and were therefore a strategic factor in the development of commercial agriculture in the Western Hemisphere.

Negro slaves became the major source of nonfree agricultural labor in the Western Hemisphere for several reasons. They were strong, hard working, and healthy. Negroes were generally immune to many of the diseases that plagued the workers of plantation agriculture. They were inexpensive. A master could buy an African slave for life for the same price it cost him to get a European indentured servant for 10 years. They were politically unprotected. They had no monarch to whom they could appeal against abuses, as did white men. They were easy to recognize. If they decided to run away, they could not blend in with the nearby Indian or white communities. There seemed to be an inexhaustible supply. The supply of Indian slaves was limited, and white indentured servants became increasingly difficult to obtain.

THE CHINESE expansion into the "Southern Ocean," as they call the islands and peninsulas of southeastern Asia, is the last of the truly great explosive migrations.

The Chinese have been migrating to the Southern Ocean for centuries. They apparently brought the use of bronze and iron to Indonesia about 300 B.C. They were entrenched in Malacca before the arrival of the Portuguese, in the Philippines before the arrival of the Spanish, and in Indonesia before the arrival of the Dutch and the English.

But the great flood of Chinese expansion into the Southern Ocean occurred after Europeans had invested capital in enterprises such as plantations and tin mines. While the Chinese were attracted to the Southern Ocean by the economic development that was being stimulated by the European influence, they were also driven there by famines.

Famines in China and migrations away from centers of famine on the China plains are apparently as old as Chinese history. During the past 2 thousand years, more than 1,800 famines have occurred in various parts of China. During the second half of the 19th century, a succession of severe famines caused the death of millions.

The Chinese moved outward in all directions. Several million of them entered Manchuria. Lesser numbers went to Mongolia.

Migration from southern China had already shoved large numbers off the shore and into the sea. Some had colonized nearby islands, including Taiwan. Others stayed on the water and today still live by the tens of thousands on their boats.

The severity of the famines during the late 19th century, plus the fresh fields of opportunity that had been created by European enterprise and capital in southeastern Asia, provided an exceptionally strong impetus to move to the Southern Ocean. It paid to migrate as it had never paid before. More than 12 million Chinese now live in the non-Chinese lands stretching from Burma through Indonesia to the Philippines.

The great flood of Chinese expansion into the Southern Ocean occurred soon after its conquest by the Western World. Politically and economically, the Chinese migration was as important there as was the Western arrival, for the Chinese are the eternal middlemen of southeastern Asia.

The Chinese for many years have taken care of the marketing of most of the native tobacco, corn, copra, coffee, rubber, wood, fruit, and so forth in Indonesia.

Chinese have retail stores in cities throughout the Southern Ocean. It is said that Chinese control most of the rice trade in Thailand. They control the rubber marketing system in Malaya so completely that a saying has developed that if all the Chinese in the country simply stayed home one day, not an ounce of rubber would move out of the country. In the Philippines they are moneylenders and brokers and control two-thirds of the island's largely agricultural export trade.

The Chinese for a long time have had a crucial role in the credit system of southeastern Asian peasants. They often developed a lending business in a series of communities and would call each week at the door of their customers to offer a loan or collect the installment on one previously given.

The non-Chinese of the Southern Ocean often resent the success of Chinese businessmen. Most of the countries of the area have laws directed against this minority. A law adopted in the Philippines in 1954, for example, provided, among other things, that aliens (Americans excepted) are prohibited from engaging directly or indirectly in the retail trade. Nearly 20 thousand Chinese retailers were affected. Later legislation required retail enterprises owned by Philippine citizens to employ only Philippine citizens.

THE FIVE great migrations I have reviewed are not the only significant ones in recorded history. Recent lesser migrations have changed agriculture.

During this century, for example, a steady trickle of Japanese vegetable growers has headed for Latin America. They are a minority of the immigrants into Latin America, but they have set an excellent example for the other Latin American vegetable growers.

Before and after the formation of Israel, about a million Jews from around the world settled in the ancient homeland. Israel was confronted with the problem of building an agriculture with people who were willing to farm but who knew almost nothing about farming. To compensate for this lack, they invented a new form of agricultural resource organization, which they called the kibbutz. The kibbutz was organized with an individual, or a few individuals, who knew how to farm and a large number of individuals who did not, but who were willing to contribute their labor and share in common the fruits of their joint efforts.

The partition of India in 1947 was followed by the mass transfer of about 16 million people. The distance involved was not far compared to the other migrations I have mentioned, but the transfer caused great disruption of agriculture.

THE AGE of great international migrations seems to have drawn to a close just as the age of great internal migration is getting into full swing.

The trend in movement of people now is toward cities. In the Western World, the urbanization has been a phenomenon of the past 150 years, but in much of the world it is only recently gaining force.

Most Americans lived in rural areas before 1920. The urban population since has been in the majority, and its relative size has been steadily increasing. A large part of the world's population, however, is still rural. About 55 percent of the world's labor force was engaged in agriculture in 1964.

The development of commercial agriculture to a large extent made possible the growth of the cities. At the same time, the growth of the cities has been a stimulant to the further commercialization of agriculture.

Around the world, city populations are growing faster than rural populations. By the year 2000, barring some worldwide disaster, the earth's population will be clearly urban oriented.

The need for a highly productive, commercial agriculture in underdeveloped parts of the world will become increasingly urgent as the trend toward urbanization continues. As a consequence, the role of agriculture in the technical assistance programs of the developed world will have to be increasingly stressed, as will the importance of agriculture in economic development programs.

PHILLIPS W. FOSTER *joined the staff of the University of Maryland in 1961 as an associate professor of agricultural economics. A specialist in international agriculture, his research interests center on the role of agriculture in developing areas. He has served with the Department of State as a consultant on economic development. He has degrees from Cornell University and the University of Illinois. He spent 4 years as an extension specialist in agricultural economics and public policy at Michigan State University.*

Questions To Be Answered

by MONTELL OGDON

WORLD AGRICULTURAL problems are cousins and offspring of natural, social, and economic conditions and are linked so closely that an upset in a locality may be felt on the other side of the globe.

The one that comes first to mind is the hazard of drought, flood, cold, insects, diseases, and other elements of Nature that at times have reduced the production of food to the point of famine, as in Bengal in 1943, when more than a million persons died.

In some regions, such as western Europe, our Corn Belt, and the Pampas in Argentina, soils and weather are such that with the employment of scientific methods, anything approaching a crop failure seldom occurs. In countries like Denmark and the United Kingdom, the intensified application of good practices has brought steady rises in output per unit of land. In the United States, Australia, and Canada, where much of the farming is done in areas once susceptible to crop failure, agricultural advances are helping to obtain increased yields in the years of intemperate weather that once would have reduced output sharply.

But in many underdeveloped countries where technology has made less headway, the vagaries of weather are apparent in low and in variable yields from year to year, and in some countries—in western Asia, for example— extremely variable yields continue to occur because of the adverse weather. Thus in much of the world, weather is still a major problem in farming.

Closely connected with weather and the availability of food are low standards of living, which have characterized agricultural populations through the centuries. Only within the last three centuries has the situation improved significantly—and that almost entirely in industrial countries.

One of the major problems in history arises when the population on the land becomes so dense that the average producer cannot grow enough food to provide for his family.

An equalizing factor between population density and farm output used to be the high human death rate from disease and famine. The situation has changed, however, and the population pressure on the land has increased with the developments of medical science. Relieving the situation in the more densely populated countries of Europe, especially during the 18th and 19th centuries, were movements of people off the land to industrial centers and to new opportunities in North America, South America, Australia, and New Zealand.

No such relief has been available in most parts of the world, particularly in mainland China, southern Asia, and the Middle East. Improvement of the economic position of the rural population is still one of the greatest problems of underdeveloped and the developed countries alike.

In the less-developed countries whose populations are predominantly agricultural, a billion persons, one-third of the world population, live in rural districts. The value of their per capita agricultural output averages less than 100 dollars a year. The per capita gross domestic product for the agricultural sector of the economy in the less-developed countries is one-fifth of the GDP of the nonagricultural sector. In newly developing countries that have significant nonagricultural industry, the per capita GDP for agriculture is one-fourth to one-third that of the nonagricultural sector. In the most advanced industrial countries, the average per capita GDP for agriculture is usually little more than one-half of that for the nonagricultural sector of the economy.

Governments of developing countries have undertaken the slow and costly work of raising the efficiency of peasants and helping them to have a more active place in a commercial economy.

ONE HANDICAP that becomes apparent immediately is the damage being done by natural elements and man to an essential agricultural resource—the land.

The need to eke out an existence has caused overgrazing, unwise cropping, the exhaustion of fertility, and the use of manures as fuel. The exploitation by continuous cropping of land that should be fallow, the burning over of second-growth forests, and the burning of stubble or fodder after removal of the grain have ceased entirely in only a few advanced regions.

Deforestation still proceeds in many places, and the naked land is open to the natural forces of erosion that carries away much of its soil.

The immense knowledge we have of science in agriculture can build up the land or tear it down. A man and a machine and a day's time can destroy the land's usefulness for years.

Strip mining with large earthmoving equipment, construction of one-story industrial plants on flat alluvial soil, modern highways, and the extensive bulldozing of land for construction of dwellings, as the population movement to urban centers continues pellmell in many parts of the world, denude the land.

The farmer himself has been partly to blame. He tends to overlook some of the destructive consequences resulting from what he judges to be expedient use of his new machines and chemicals. The use of custom operators, or employees, more skilled in operating machinery than agriculture, for plowing, cultivating, spraying, and harvesting on a large scale increase the danger that farmers themselves can harm the land.

Suitable soil, the right amount of moisture and sunshine, fertilizers, insecticides, and mechanical power and other equipment are only a part of the inputs into agricultural production. There are also essential skills—whether supplied by the farmer with his own hands, by other members of his family, or hired workers—plus planned and scientific management under constantly changing circumstances.

Application by the modern producer of scientific knowledge—handed down from past generations, the result of his own experience, or the result of comparing the results of his own efforts with those obtained on other farms and demonstration plots—is a most important consideration.

The inputs into a modern agricultural production unit are becoming increasingly costly in many parts of the world. Land in high-producing regions tends to become capitalized at levels that reflect efficient production.

In the most underdeveloped areas, extensive education, structural changes in farm credit and marketing, new roads, housing, and certain utilities may be necessary before efficient production is attained. The investment in machinery and in management and skilled labor, if it must be hired or trained, is expensive. Because suitable new agricultural land is becoming scarce and costly and other inputs also are becoming more and more expensive, the capital investment becomes more important in the development, maintenance, and improvement of commercial farms.

MANY PROBLEMS have arisen in connection with marketing. Some, such as adjustment to changing world demand, have worsened since the First World War.

Even before then, however, functioning of the marketing process was far from perfect. Producers in colonial countries and major independent agricultural countries claimed that their products were undergraded, underweighed, and underpriced. Railway cars and ships were not always available in peak shipping seasons. Freight rates often contained inequities. In addition to the state-defined standards for weights and measures used by traders since ancient times, there was a certain amount of market regulation. Some countries had highly protective import duties. Some had preferential duties. Some had preferential transport regulations. Some even had export duties.

To assure value received to agricultural producers, governments provided for regulation of services to farmers or registration of certain persons performing agricultural marketing services, such as public weighers, graders, auctioneers, warehousemen, and traders. They set freight rates to protect farmers and sometimes set rates for milling of farm products. They sometimes set quality standards for export commodities of great importance in a country's national economy. Some countries established state monopolies for domestic buying, milling, exporting, and importing some products.

Agricultural products, until transportation comes within easy reach of the producer, usually are sold locally for local consumption or to a buyer's agent at a price that often does not represent competitive demand in world market places.

When adequate services and relatively free competition among traders existed, a definite relationship developed between the prices of staple farm products in the export country and the price in world commodity markets until 1914.

For example, making allowance for a rising or declining trend in prices, the price paid to the American farmer for wheat and the price at Minneapolis-St. Paul bore a constant relationship to the export contract price. At the same time, the United States export price showed a definite relationship to the cost, insurance, and freight import price in London, Liverpool, Rotterdam, or Hamburg.

Though the foreign demand was generally strong for farm products during the 25 years before the First World War, definite price cycles were apparent among annual average prices for major farm products in world trade; there were wide variations between lows and highs for the same commodity; and there were sharp price changes from one year to another for the same products.

The United States export price of wheat declined from 1.03 dollars a bushel in 1892 to 80 cents in 1893; that of cottonseed oil declined from 40.8 cents a gallon in 1909 to 6.6 cents a gallon in 1910. The annual average export prices of corn ranged between 31 cents and 75 cents a bushel. Upland cotton prices ranged from 5.4 cents to 14.48 cents a pound. The average annual prices of bacon and ham ranged from 7.5 cents to nearly 14 cents a pound.

Contributing to the uncertainty of price in the world market were uncertainties as to the volume of a commodity that would be purchased in the world's leading markets or what competition would be encountered.

Contributing to the uncertainty of the situation in the world market and uncertainty of farm income were variations in domestic production. In Iowa, already the largest corn-producing State in the 1890's, farmers produced a crop of 251.8 million bushels in 1893, 81.3 million bushels in 1894, and 321.7 million in 1896.

Seasonal prices varied more than did the average annual export price for the same commodity. Average monthly prices received by Nebraska producers during 1895–1914 for wheat were 37 cents to 1.10 dollars a bushel; for corn, between 10 cents and 72 cents a bushel; for butter, between 8 and 27 cents a pound.

Many major agricultural exporting countries went through a much more grueling experience than did the United States from the 1880's to 1914.

Countries that depended on exports of farm products for the gold and foreign exchange to maintain their economies became bankrupt. Currencies were depreciated. Central banks failed. Industrial development came to a standstill. Governments were shaken. Legislation was enacted to encourage both domestic cooperative marketing and exports by cooperative pools, and experimental programs, such as redistribution of land, state ownership of railroads, and payment of bounties to agricultural producers.

The decline of prices of farm products relative to prices of other products became a worldwide phenomenon, particularly between 1920 and 1933. To offset tendencies that were causing economic stress and reduced standards of living, programs initiated before or during the First World War were reassessed and extended to protect agricultural producers.

Governments in the more economically developed countries generally took various measures that helped to raise the income level of agricultural producers. They specified minimum prices for farm products. They purchased commodities to support their prices. They made acreage payments to producers. They restricted imports of competitive products. They made payments to the producers to cover the difference between prices received by farmers and a goal price.

PROGRAMS devised as remedies to farm problems and widely enacted unilaterally to cope with the effects of adverse weather and radical price declines and to give greater economic security to agriculture and society have themselves become a major problem in the handling of many commodities.

Wheat, which vies with cotton as the most widely traded agricultural commodity in world commerce, is also one of the most widely regulated. It is regulated in exporting and deficit countries alike in order to maintain or stabilize incomes of producers. It is regulated in nutritionally deficit countries in the interest of consumers.

In major exporting countries, measures to stabilize producers' incomes have arisen out of the uncertainties respecting yields, prices, and foreign demand and the increasing costs of materials needed to produce it. The measures include government-guaranteed prices to producers for certain specified quantities of wheat or unlimited quantities, payment of insurance or ad hoc grants in case of reduced size of crop resulting from adverse weather conditions, purchase and storage of wheat to support the price, control of the imports, export quality control, and the use of bilateral government-to-government sales agreements.

Governments in exporting countries use bilateral agreements among other methods of assuring export markets. Australia, for example, has used bilateral agreements to cover much of that country's commercial wheat and flour sales abroad. They have been made with West Germany, Japan, mainland China, and the Soviet Union. A "gentlemen's agreement" between Australian wheat export authorities and groups controlling the flour industry in the United Kingdom assures a market for specified amounts of Australian wheat at the world market prices.

In the more economically advanced wheat-growing deficit countries, producers are encouraged by such incentives as a guaranteed market at high guaranteed prices, subsidization of production requisites, or other payments. Millers may be required to mix homegrown wheat into their flour for bread. The price they pay for wheat and the price they charge for bread may be controlled. Imports may be subject to high customs duties, variable levies, and price fixing.

High guaranteed prices and governmental control of imports in western Europe stimulate domestic production that tends to displace wheat that can be produced much more efficiently in oversea countries. The price for domestic wheat per bushel in 1959 (before the inception of control of agricultural prices by European Economic Community among member countries) was 2.86 dollars in Germany and 2.83 in Italy. For the same year, it was 4.10 dollars in Switzerland, 3.43 in Norway, 2.78 in Japan, and 1.81 in the United States.

In less-developed countries, subsidization of wheat production is much more limited than in the more affluent countries. Yet there may be many controls, such as governmental purchase to support the domestic market price, fixed prices, compulsory planting or subsidization of production requisites to encourage increased wheat output, specified extraction rates, and maximum retail prices.

Controls over wheat are so complete in some countries that they amount virtually to governmental monopoly. In Norway, for example, the Norwegian Grain Corporation controls imports, exports, and domestic distribution of wheat, feed grains, and other feeds. In Canada, the Canadian Wheat Board buys all homegrown wheat except that used for domestic feed and is the sole wheat importer and exporter.

The common agricultural policy of the European Economic Community requires that imports of wheat be subjected to variable import levies so that imported wheat cannot interfere with the operation of the administered price system for wheat grown in European Economic Community countries.

Most countries of the British Commonwealth and some that are no longer members give preferential tariff treatment to imports from other Commonwealth countries. The United Kingdom and a few others do not have duties on wheat imports or do not give preferential tariff treatment to each other. Some, however, do give such a preference on wheat and many give it on wheat flour. For example, wheat flour entering the United Kingdom from Commonwealth sources enters duty free; flour from Australia and Canada thus largely has the British

market, because flour from the United States or Argentina would pay an ad valorem duty of 10 percent.

An international wheat agreement among the principal wheat exporting and importing countries tends to have certain short-term stabilizing effects on the world wheat prices, without interfering with the operation of production incentives, price supports, or the other domestic wheat programs.

THE DETAILS I have given at length about wheat exemplify questions that pertain to other leading crops and products:

Should their production and prices be controlled? How? What is the effect of our policy of supporting the domestic prices of cotton, say, on the production elsewhere? Do pricing policies restrict consumption—of sugar, for example? To what degree do the international agreements interfere with the marketing of a crop, like tobacco, on a competitive commercial basis? What is the effect of import licenses, duties, and price schemes on trade in fruit and vegetables?

I could cite many more. They are considered in later chapters. They emphasize two salient points: Agricultural production and trade are tremendously and increasingly complex. We need to bring to the consideration of such questions and problems a great amount of knowledge, wisdom, fairplay, and humility to achieve the goal of a decent living for all people.

EXPANSION OF OUTPUT and adjustments of production on a scale never before achieved in most countries will be required of agriculture before the end of another decade.

The annual population growth rate of the world from the end of the Second World War to 1964 rose from 1 percent to 2 percent. Before 1975, at a growth rate of 2 percent annually, the population of the world will increase by about 650 million.

Agriculture is not alone responsible

for provisioning mankind with food and other products, but it does have a major role in providing food, fiber, and other important products. The record since 1955 points to serious shortcomings in the supply-demand equilibrating factors. Per capita production from crop year 1954–1955 to 1963–1964 showed an increase of only 3 percent in the period, and a decline of 5 percent in the 5 years 1958–1959 to 1963–1964. Moreover, the distribution of the increase was uneven by regions and by commodities.

The rate of increase in the world agricultural output from year to year will have to be increased 50 percent above that of 1958–1959 to 1963–1964 if it is to keep pace with the rate at which population is rising. The race between population growth and agricultural production is too close for complacency.

IT MAY BE presumptuous to say that famine could not cause starvation in our time. Major agricultural producing areas are frequently subject to weather conditions that sharply reduce the level of harvested crops below food requirements.

India, with more than 450 million people, and other populous countries of southeastern Asia have historically been subject to droughts and floods.

Mainland China, whose estimated population is 650 million, has had serious droughts and floods since 1959.

The Soviet Union, with 218 million people, has become more susceptible to the effects of weather since wheat growing was extended into the "new lands" area east of the Urals, which has variable and low rainfall and short growing seasons.

Countries of southern Asia would have had a series of food crises during 1955–1964 had they not drawn heavily on supplies of wheat in the United States, Canada, and Australia.

FOREMOST among problems is whether developing countries, which have had difficulties with balance of payments and are heavily populated, can improve their earning capacities to meet the rising requirements of an unprecedented growth in population.

Success requires the development of agricultural methods suitable to the natural conditions peculiar to each agricultural area; construction of fertilizer plants and other costly programs, such as land clearing or irrigation; and the application by producers of the required changes in techniques.

Success in the application of improved agricultural production technology was a major factor in the changes that occurred in the pattern of commodity output between 1950 and 1964.

While world wheat output increased by 19 percent and rice 32 percent, corn production rose 43 percent. Increases in the production of such tropical oilseed products as palm oil, coconut oil, and palm kernel were small. The production of peanuts, largely in underdeveloped countries, and olive oil somewhat outpaced the growth in population. The production of soybeans increased 50 percent, largely in the United States.

Production of cash crops for export in underdeveloped countries were generally subject to better farm management and cultural practices than crops grown in the same countries largely for domestic use. Thus, for example, the output of tea rose 47 percent; cocoa, 52 percent; coffee, 64 percent; and sisal, 66 percent.

The total increase in agricultural output has been greatest in countries that were becoming increasingly industrialized and could purchase food and other farm products in the world market to meet deficits due to increasing populations and rising industrial activity.

The increase in per capita farm output from 1954 to 1964 was 15 percent in West Germany, 17 percent in France, 18 percent in the United Kingdom, 34 percent in Austria, and 43 percent in Japan.

On the other hand, in nutritionally

deficit and underdeveloped countries, which have had serious balance-of-payment problems, the increases in per capita production were slight. In Latin America and northern Africa as a whole and in several African countries south of the Sahara, per capita output in 1963–1964 was no higher than in 1953–1954.

Per capita agricultural output in 1963–1964 was below the 1935–1939 level in Afghanistan, Burma, Cambodia, Ceylon, Indonesia, Laos, Pakistan, South Vietnam, and Taiwan, and only 3 percent above 1935–1939 in India.

Significant price changes for farm products occurred in the fifties and early sixties that affected both importing and exporting countries. Some such changes accompanied the disturbances to markets at the time of the Korean war and interruption of traffic through the Suez Canal.

Decline in the world price of farm products of all types, food, beverages, fibers, and raw materials, such as vegetable oils for nonfood purposes and natural rubber, amounted to 24 percent from 1951 to 1955 and 15 percent from 1957 to 1961.

The prices of some commodities, such as sugar, coffee, and cocoa, showed sharp year-to-year fluctuations in the fifties and often necessitated adjustment in a country's economy.

The prices of many products vitally important in the export trade of underdeveloped countries continued to show sharp declines between 1957 and 1962. The world price of cocoa declined by 46 percent, coffee by 33 percent, sugar by 25 percent.

What avenues should be taken to protect the interests of producers and consumers in production, pricing, and marketing of farm products?

Should countries declare their controls to be an essential mechanism to defend their industries against the problems of production and aggressive agricultural policies of other countries?

The result could be controls so complete that production and trade would be determined not by economic utilization of resources but by a government's administrative ability to control imports and financial ability to subsidize domestic production and exports.

The dangers inherent in the present situation are reflected by the many proposals advanced during 1954–1964 that nations ameliorate conflicting agricultural policies by joint action.

Yet countries feel strongly the urge to continue their efforts on a national basis to protect producers and consumers from such vagaries as drought, extreme price fluctuation, and ad hoc protectionist action of other countries.

The welfare of producers, traders, and consumers is involved in such international programs as regional economic integration, commodity agreements, reciprocal reduction of trade barriers, and economic assistance to underdeveloped countries and in such national programs as those for advancement of resource development and conservation, crop insurance, and farm credit.

The development of agricultural resources in line with the most economic utilization of those resources should not be forgotten in any reorientation of national or international programs.

At the same time, if we are to achieve output needed for the future world population, programs must encourage maximum utilization of private capital and individual production incentives.

Much can be done along these lines in view of the greatly improved communication techniques and the knowledge and skills being developed in production, marketing, and use of information on future demand for farm products arising from population growth, urbanization, and changes in income.

MONTELL OGDON is an international agricultural economist in the Economic Research Service. Before joining the Department of Agriculture in 1939, he was an assistant in the College of Agriculture, University of Illinois; a Carnegie fellow at the University of California; and a professor at Texas Tech University.

Nutritional Status

of the World

by ESTHER F. PHIPARD and
RILEY H. KIRBY

PEOPLE must be well fed if they are to be healthy, productive, happy, and secure. Millions of people do not have enough to eat, and so problems of food supplies and nutrition must be attacked on an international scale.

The first step in solving the problems is to define and assess them—to determine the extent and severity of malnutrition in the world.

One avenue is through estimates of the kinds and amounts of foods consumed in different countries and the extent to which the diets meet the nutritional needs of the people.

These food balances—supplies of food balanced against the populations to be fed—are developed by the Food and Agriculture Organization of the United Nations as a part of its continuing study of the state of food and agriculture. They are prepared also by the Department of Agriculture to measure the world's food resources.

Food balances are developed for each commodity on the basis of domestic production, imports, exports, and changes in stocks to get the supply available for all uses. From that total are deducted amounts used for feed, seed, and industrial purposes and estimated waste. The remainder, representing amounts for human consumption, is divided by the number of persons in the population to give per capita consumption of each type of food. Estimates of the calories, protein, and other nutrients available for consumption can then be made.

Seldom are food balances models of precision. The basic data are incomplete, unreliable, or lacking in some countries, and estimates must be based on fragmentary information. Also, population statistics for many countries are unsatisfactory. Food balances nevertheless serve reasonably well to indicate variations in dietary patterns and levels of consumption and to measure changes over time.

A comparison of food balances prepared by the Department of Agriculture for more than 80 countries reveals some sharp differences. For example, some countries rely heavily on grain products and other starchy foods. Those items are much less important in other countries, where people eat more meat and other costlier foods. The calories per person per day may range from fewer than 2 thousand to more than 3 thousand. The consumption of total protein may vary from less than 50 grams to more than 100 grams per person per day. The consumption of fat varies even more.

It is more meaningful, however, to evaluate the food available per person within one country in terms of the calories and amounts of nutrients the food provides as compared to amounts needed to maintain normal health and activity in the country.

In the Department's study, *The World Food Budget, 1962 and 1966* (Foreign Agricultural Economic Report No. 4, October 1961), nutritional reference standards were established for calories, protein, and fat as being major indicators of dietary levels.

Reference standards for calories for major regions were based on requirements as developed by the Food and Agriculture Organization in the Second World Food Survey for 36 countries. The requirements take into account environmental temperature, body weights, and the distribution by age and sex of the national populations. Reference standards used by the Department of Agriculture varied from 2,710 Calories in Canada and the Soviet Union to 2,300 in the Far East and Communist Asia.

The reference standard for total protein was set at 60 grams per person per day. Some attention also was given to the sources of protein. Nutritional needs for protein can be met by foods of vegetable origin if they are combined in rather exact proportions so that the shortages of amino acids—the components of proteins—in the staple food are made good by those in other kinds of foods. Protein needs are much more likely to be met, however, if some foods of animal origin are included in the diet. Some of the better plant sources, such as dry beans, peas, and nuts, also help to safeguard protein adequacy.

The reference standard for animal protein based on 10 to 15 percent of total protein was set at a minimum of 7 grams—the approximate amount in an ounce of cheese or one egg or one frankfurter. An additional 10 grams of protein from pulses (peas and beans) was specified also, or, if animal protein exceeded 7 grams, enough from pulses to bring the total to 17 grams.

The amount of fat required for a nutritionally adequate diet is not well defined. The reference standard we adopted was the amount of fat that would provide 15 percent of the reference calories. This level was based on judgment as to what might be a reasonable nutritional "floor."

The approximate nature of these reference standards should be emphasized. Although stated as fixed figures for purposes of calculations, knowledge of human requirements does not provide a basis for such precise averages.

SET AGAINST these standards, the food balances of many countries reveal diets that are adequate and even more than adequate on the average. Among them are the United States, Canada, Australia, and New Zealand, all of which have large land resources and a mod-

ern and mechanized agriculture and produce food in export abundance. Also included are Europe, the Soviet Union, and the southern parts of South America and Africa.

In short, the industrialized countries, which have one-third of the world's population, have the science, technology, financial resources, and managerial ability to command the food supplies needed for good nutrition.

Some 70 countries, including most of Asia, Africa, and Latin America, have food supplies that are deficient in one or more nutrients, and many lack sufficient calories. Here live 2 billion people, two-thirds of the world total. Some of the more severe deficits in consumption per person occur in Africa and Latin America.

Because of the far larger numbers of people and greater density of population, however, the Far East and Communist Asia constitute the center of the world food problem. This becomes clear when deficits in daily per capita consumption of calories, protein, and fat of each country are translated into tons of specific foodstuffs necessary to meet the deficits for the entire population for a whole year.

The essential nutrients are available in a wide variety of foodstuffs, but for convenience and ease of understanding it is useful to express the deficits in terms of a few widely known and used foods. Thus deficits in animal protein can be expressed in terms of nonfat dry milk and those in pulse protein in terms of dry beans and peas. Deficits in other protein and calories can be converted to tons of wheat, and those in fat to tons of vegetable oils.

With allowances for increases in population and likely changes in production, trade, and consumption, a world food budget for 1966 shows that additional quantities of foodstuffs would be needed in all the countries in which diets are less than adequate to meet the nutritional standards equivalent to 29 million metric tons of wheat, 3 million tons of vegetable oil, 1.6 million tons of nonfat dry milk, and

165 thousand tons of dry beans and peas.

The non-Communist Far East has two-thirds of the projected wheat shortage and nearly half of the shortages in animal and pulse proteins and fats. This region accounts for 42 percent of the population of the diet-deficit regions and has 60 percent of the overall food deficit. Communist Asia accounts for most of the rest of the animal protein and fat shortages and more than 10 percent of the wheat shortage.

The deficits as calculated are on an annual basis after an allowance for consumption of foodstuffs provided under the Food for Peace program. On an overall basis, they represent only about 2 percent of the value of world agricultural production. This appears at first glance to be an amount of modest dimensions—merely 2 percent. The world's farmers increase production this much and more (2.4 percent) from one year to the next. But (and here is the rub) the world's population increases nearly as fast as the gain in production. Farm production increased more rapidly in 1954–1964 than ever before, but so did population.

Thus gains in production per person come slowly, and the slight increase that was made over the past quarter century occurred principally in regions where diets already were adequate. No improvement is registered in the 70 countries where diets are deficient, yet it is there that gains must be made.

Seen in the light of other comparisons, to produce or to buy the additional foodstuffs that represent the nutritional deficits poses a challenge of no small proportions. Twenty-nine million tons of wheat, for example, is more than 6 percent of the production of all cereals in diet-deficit areas.

It about equals the amount of all cereals imported annually by these countries in recent years, and it is not far short of the level of carryover wheat stocks built up in the United States over a period of years.

The prospects of doubling imports of food grains are not bright because most of the countries have foreign exchange problems and lack substantial industry to produce for export. Their economies are mostly agricultural, and the agriculture is not highly productive. Their arable land is limited and population is dense. Farms are small, methods are backward, and yields and output are low.

Undernutrition, or too little food to give needed calories, exists in all countries, even in the United States. The fact that a country's food supply provides enough calories per capita to meet the nutrition reference standard means only that. Averages assume values below as well as values above, but in those countries with calorie averages below reference levels, one can expect to find widespread undernutrition as well as malnutrition.

Although nutritional needs can be met by many different combinations of foods, it is agreed generally that diets in which more than two-thirds of the calories are derived from cereals, starchy roots, and sugars are likely to be of poor nutritional quality, especially if the staple foods are largely cassava, bananas, sweetpotatoes, or highly milled corn or rice. The proportion of calories from them and from sugar in some developing countries is as high as 75 to 85 percent, whereas in well-fed countries it is more like 40 to 50 percent.

The amount and sources of protein in a country's food supply is another clue to dietary adequacy. In the World Food Budget, nearly half of the countries had food providing less than the reference standard, 60 grams of total protein per person per day. Of these, 9 countries had less than 7 grams from animal sources and 13 had less than 17 grams of protein from animal foods and pulses combined. These protein-deficient countries were in the same three areas of the world where calories were short—Latin America, Africa, and the Far East.

Diets in many countries are low in

fat or oil. The reference standard, the amount to provide at least 15 percent of the reference calories, amounted to 36 to 42 grams of fat per person per day. That equals about three tablespoons of oil. Twenty-four countries and Communist Asia had less than this amount of fat in their food supplies. In two countries of the Far East, the average quantity was only half as much as the reference standard.

The nutritional significance of such low-fat diets is not known, nor is there a scientific basis for setting an optimum level of fat in the diet. Some fat is needed to furnish essential fatty acids and to aid in the absorption of fat-soluble vitamins. From a practical viewpoint, a moderate amount of fat in diets is advantageous. Because they are so concentrated, fats contribute needed calories without much bulk. It is not surprising that many of the countries with food supplies low in fat were also low in calories.

IN THE BETTER FED countries where food supplies are ample in kind and amount to provide for nutritional needs of the population, severe undernutrition and malnutrition are the exception rather than the rule. Nevertheless, with freedom to buy foods of their choice, except when limited by low incomes, many people make poor selections and end up with diets low in essential nutrients.

In the United States, for example, many individuals have in their meals less than recommended amounts of one or more nutrients, especially calcium, ascorbic acid, and vitamin A. Others may be short in thiamine and riboflavin. Clear-cut cases of deficiency diseases, such as pellagra or scurvy, are seldom seen, but wiser food choices would mean the attainment of much higher levels of health and vitality.

A more serious problem in the better fed countries is that of overnutrition or excessive calories in relation to need. The result is overweight. Part of it may be ascribed to the relatively high consumption of fat. Fat, a concen-trated source of food energy, provides more than twice as many calories per unit of weight as protein and carbohydrate. It is estimated that about 25 percent of residents of the United States are overweight to a degree that is considered a health hazard.

There is evidence that the kind and amount of fat in the diet may be a contributing factor in cardiovascular disease, one of the most frequent causes of death in the United States, in much of Europe, and in well-to-do groups in other countries. Thus malnutrition resulting from too many calories or a poor balance of food sources of calories can be just as serious in terms of life expectancy as undernutrition.

WITH TOO LITTLE food—too few calories—for long periods, the body adapts to a lower plane of existence by conserving expenditure of energy. For adults, that means a loss of weight, lower physical activity, and consequently less output of work. Poor physical stamina coupled with low income, limited technical knowledge, and perhaps lack of water or fertile soil are basic causes of food shortages. A cycle of cause and effect operates to perpetuate the situation.

When children have too little food or the wrong kinds, growth and development are affected and general health is impaired. A greater susceptibility to disease is a natural concomitant. Malnutrition among young children is especially serious. It is largely responsible for the high mortality rate, which for children 1 to 4 years old, is said to be up to 40 times greater in some of the developing areas than in the United States or other economically well-off countries.

A shortage of protein, as well as calories, is common in the postweaning period, when the child may be given a starchy gruel low in protein.

It is especially common in places where cassava and yams are the staple foods. Sometimes a better diet may be available, but the mother continues these poor feeding practices because of tradition and from lack of knowledge.

Protein-calorie malnutrition of children is perhaps the most serious and widespread deficiency disease in the world. In its severe form, known as kwashiorkor in some areas, it exists in most of the food-deficit countries of the Far East, the Middle East, Africa, and Latin America. Characteristics of the disease include growth failure, muscular wasting, edema, skin and hair changes, mental apathy, liver damage, anemia, and sometimes associated infections. If diets are not improved, the rate of mortality may be high.

Deficiencies of other nutrients in the diet also leave their mark on the nutritional status of people, adults as well as children. This is to be expected with diets so high in cereals and starchy roots and so low in dairy products, eggs, meat and fish, fruit, pulses, and vegetables.

A MAJOR CONTRIBUTION to the measurement of nutritional status around the world is being made under the program of the Interdepartmental Committee on Nutrition for National Defense.

The committee was established in 1955 to assist countries in which the United States has a special interest to identify and assess nutritional problems of the people and to help them use their resources to best advantage in solving their problems.

When a country requests it, a survey mission of American specialists assesses the nutritional health of population groups through dietary studies, clinical examinations, and biochemical measurements. Working side by side with their counterparts in the host countries, the specialists also study the quality and availability of the food supply with a view to recommending measures for its improvement.

The committee's teams by 1963 had completed nutrition surveys in eight countries in the Far East, four in the Near East, eight in South America and Central America, two in northern Africa, and one each in the West Indies and Spain.

The surveys have underscored similarities in the nutrition problems of different countries. Besides protein-calorie malnutrition of young children, certain other deficiencies are widely prevalent.

Endemic goiter (enlargement of the thyroid gland) is common in sections of food-deficit countries and in many other countries. Its prevalence is associated with insufficient intake of iodine, which is unevenly distributed in food and water and generally is more abundant near a seacoast.

Endemic goiter occurs to some extent in the United States and Canada. It has been a serious public health problem in most of the countries in Central America, South America, and the Far East. A large goiter belt extends some 1,500 miles across the north of India, where the incidence varies from 29 percent in one district to more than 40 percent in another.

Goitrous areas also exist in Thailand, Burma, and other countries in that part of the world. In a small village in Vietnam, for example, 34 percent of the individuals examined by scientists of the committee's survey team had thyroid enlargement. The proportion exceeded 50 percent for females under 15 years and was more than 60 percent for pregnant and lactating women.

Endemic goiter can be controlled through the use of iodized salt. Many countries have adopted legislation requiring iodization of salt, but problems of production and distribution of iodized salt to needy areas remain to be solved in some countries.

Evidence of riboflavin deficiency was a common finding in the nutrition surveys conducted by the committee. Riboflavin deficiency is associated with diets low in milk, meat, green vegetables, and legumes.

In the United States, nearly half of the riboflavin in the average diet comes from milk and milk products, and one-fourth from meat, fish, and eggs. In countries where those foods are not available to most of the people, shortages of riboflavin and of other nutrients they provide are common.

Vitamin A deficiency in its most severe form, xerophthalmia, is a principal cause of preventable blindness in some countries in southern and eastern Asia. It is especially prevalent among children under 5 years and often is associated with protein malnutrition in this age group. If untreated, vitamin A deficiency may lead to blindness or death.

In Malaya, half the cases of blindness are said to be due to vitamin A deficiency. It is considered the commonest cause of preventable blindness in India. Reports from Indonesia indicate that perhaps thousands of small children die or go blind every year because of lack of vitamin A along with a generally poor diet. Among contributing causes may be the poor nutritional status of the mother during pregnancy and lactation, a diet low in vitamin A following weaning, poor absorption of vitamin A or of carotene because of limited dietary fat or intestinal disturbances, and possibly because of other dietary shortages affecting metabolism of vitamin A.

Food sources of preformed vitamin A, such as egg yolk, whole milk, and liver, usually are not available to the groups affected. Yet many excellent sources of provitamin A (carotene), such as red palm oil and leafy vegetables, are available but are not given to young children.

FOR MANY COUNTRIES at least fragmentary information is available about the nutrition problems that need attention.

Even within a country the problems may differ among specific areas or among different segments of the population. In general, the most seriously malnourished are the so-called vulnerable groups—mothers during the reproductive period and young children. Families everywhere with incomes barely adequate to sustain life show evidence of malnutrition and too little food.

Despite the similarity of nutrition problems around the world, efforts to improve diets and nutritional health must be developed separately for each country or perhaps for areas within countries.

Planning must take into account the particular characteristics of the area and the people; the general economic level, agricultural resources, and capacity to increase or modify food production and to process, preserve, and distribute needed food; and the cultural aspects of food habits, including traditional practices.

Many disciplines are involved in the complex problem of improving diets. Specialists in agriculture, economics, food technology and nutrition, public health, and education all have a part in bringing about a situation where enough of the right kinds of food is available to all groups of people.

Cooperative effort is needed from the cabinet level to the rural community, where plans to improve diets may include home production of certain kinds of foods, child feeding projects, or even the provision of adequate water supplies.

Everywhere there is need for education in agricultural methods, sanitation and public health, homemaking, and the feeding and care of young children.

Progress will be slow because of the enormity of the problem, but much has already been accomplished. Leaders in many countries are taking the initiative in attacking the problems of food and nutritional health. With the help of international agencies and other government and nongovernment groups, important developments are taking place.

Since its founding in 1945, the Food and Agriculture Organization has completed more than 2 thousand technical missions to help increase food production. The programs emphasize expansion of agriculture where feasible, better farming practices to improve crop yields, and control of animal diseases and destructive pests. The program in India includes expanded fisheries, poultry keeping, milk production, and the growing of more legumes, fruit, and other protective foods. Demonstrations of food production are given in some districts as a practical kind of education in nutrition.

Fish farming, developed in Thailand and other countries with the assistance of Food and Agriculture Organization experts, has provided a source of dietary protein of good quality for many people for whom meat, milk, and eggs are not available.

A vigorous agricultural program carried out in Mexico by the government in cooperation with the Rockefeller Foundation has brought about a substantial increase in food production, partly by obtaining much larger crop yields. The result is a more varied diet with more animal protein foods and higher calorie levels for many Mexicans.

In Taiwan, rice enrichment for the armed forces was started in 1958 at the recommendation of one group of the Interdepartmental Committee on Nutrition for National Defense. Nutrients added by enrichment include thiamine, a deficiency of which causes beriberi. In some rice-eating countries, other measures are taken by the government to prevent beriberi, such as the production of parboiled rice or control of the extent of milling to retain some of the thiamine.

A food cannery in Iran was modernized with technical assistance from the International Cooperation Administration. This plant made possible a supply of canned meat, fruit, and vegetables for the armed forces and civilians. This and many other activities contributing to improved nutrition in Iran were stimulated by the medical nutrition survey of the interdepartmental committee.

DEVELOPMENT of suitable sources of protein that will help to improve low-protein diets has challenged nutrition research workers and food technologists the world over.

A number of products have been developed and tested for biological effectiveness and human acceptability. Some are in use in special feeding programs. Although ways of solving the problem will differ, the principles are the same. For long-term planning, locally available sources of protein must be found that are nutritionally effective, low in cost, and acceptable to people. Equally important are plans for getting the foods to the people who need them most.

School feeding programs have been established in many countries. Meals at school offer a way of providing milk and other nutritious foods to a needy group and encourage the development of good food habits.

The full potential of school feeding programs will be reached only when sufficient funds, food, and equipment are available and when there are enough trained personnel to conduct the program.

In all countries there is great need for more professional workers—physicians, nurses and other health workers, nutritionists, teachers—with knowledge of foods and nutrition. Consequently, expanded opportunities for training are provided by United Nations agencies, nongovernment organizations, and other groups.

Educational programs that actually reach families are an important objective. In the last analysis, it is only through better meals eaten in the homes of the country that nutritional improvement of the population will occur. Special knowledge and skills for this kind of teaching are needed by extension workers in home economics, welfare and health workers, and the teachers.

ESTHER F. PHIPARD *is Chief of the Diet Appraisal Branch, Consumer and Food Economics Research Division, Agricultural Research Service.*

RILEY H. KIRBY *became Assistant Chief of the Far East Branch, Regional Analysis Division, Economic Research Service, in 1958.*

World Sources

of Protein

by MARTIN G. WEISS and
RUTH M. LEVERTON

PROTEINS are the scarcest and most expensive of all our foodstuffs; millions of people in the world have never had the amount or the quality of proteins they need for nutritional well-being.

Proteins are present in every animal and plant cell, and they have to be made by living cells. All proteins come directly or indirectly from plants, which combine nitrogen, hydrogen, oxygen, and carbon from soil, air, and water as they grow to make these vital substances.

People and animals cannot use such simple materials and must get protein from plants or other animals. Once eaten, the proteins are digested into smaller units and rearranged to form the many special and distinct proteins of the body tissues. These are basic substances in all the body's muscles, organs, skin, hair, and other tissues.

Proteins are made up of different combinations of 22 simpler nitrogen-containing materials, the amino acids. Eight are classed as essential or indispensable because they must be supplied to the animal body in readymade form. The other amino acids are also essential for body tissues and functions, but the body can build them from carbon, hydrogen, oxygen, and nitrogen furnished by food.

The value of any food in meeting the body's needs for protein depends on the amount and assortment of amino acids, especially the essential ones. Also important is the ability of the body to digest and metabolize the food, and what and how much protein the food supplies in relation to what and how much protein the body needs.

The amount of protein needed for health depends chiefly on the person's age, whether or not he is growing or otherwise forming new tissue, and on the adequacy of his supply of energy. Supplying energy needs takes priority over all other uses of food. When there is a shortage of energy sources, proteins are used for that purpose, and their amino acids will not be available for maintaining body tissues.

In the United States and Canada, animal products provide two-thirds of the protein in human food. The proteins in meat, poultry, fish, eggs, and dairy products are ideal for human consumption. They are palatable and are nutritionally complete, as they comprise adequate amounts of each of the eight indispensable amino acids. In fact, gelatin, which is deficient in certain amino acids, is the only protein from animals that is nutritionally incomplete with respect to amino acids.

There are about 6 billion head of livestock and poultry in the world—about two animals for every human being—but the distribution is far from uniform. The world has slightly more than three times as many people as cattle, but major livestock countries, such as Argentina and New Zealand, have about two and one-half times as many cattle as people. Densely populated countries like Pakistan, Burma, Thailand, Ceylon, and Cambodia may have four to six times as many people as cattle.

It is said often that in densely populated countries people and animals may actually compete for proteins: The supply of feed and food there is such that the conversion of plant products to nutritious animal products by animals is too expensive, and animals are too inefficient in converting feed to food.

Animal scientists, however, have made great strides in lowering the feed-to-food ratio, particularly in chickens and swine.

Under efficient management conditions, the following pounds of feed are required to produce 1 pound of animal gain or product: Milk, 1.0; broilers, 2.3; eggs, 3.1; turkeys, 3.5; swine, 3.6; beef, 8.0; and lamb, 8.7. Thus the efficient producer can expect a pound of milk from each pound of feed and a pound of live-weight broiler per 2.3 pounds of feed. He must use 8 pounds of feed to produce 1 pound of live-weight gain as beef. Since poultry dresses out much higher than cattle, the price of steak naturally is much higher than the price of dressed chicken.

Scientists have determined the protein-conversion efficiency for the same products—the amount of protein animals require in their feed to make a pound of crude or total protein in the animal product.

Thus, the pounds of protein required are: Milk, 3.9; eggs, 4.1; broilers, 4.6; turkeys, 6.2; pork, 7.1; beef, 10.0; and lamb, 12.5. That range is as great as the feed-conversion efficiency; the protein-conversion efficiency of the livestock classes falls almost in the same order.

The figures indicate that in milk, eggs, and broilers, under good management, we get 1 pound of protein for the investment of about 4 pounds of protein in the feed. For a pound of protein in beefsteak or lamb chops, however, we must invest two and one-half to three times that much protein.

These comparisons must be qualified in several respects. The crude protein of the feed is determined by analyzing for total nitrogen and multiplying by the factor 6.25, which gives a good measure of protein. But this method measures all the protein, much of which would not be digestible by people. In fact, animals can utilize only 30 to 95 percent of the total protein in feeds, the percentage depending on the digestibility of the feedstuffs used. Furthermore, we must keep in mind that the animal uses protein for maintenance as well as for growth or production of meat, eggs, and other products. The conversion ratios would be higher when management conditions are not efficient—when animals have poor rations or forage for themselves and get little supplemental feed, as they do in many feed-deficient countries.

Ruminant animals, such as cattle and sheep, can convert a combination of carbohydrates and synthetic nitrogen compounds to proteins. In fact, nearly one-third of the nitrogen requirements in the ration of fattening cattle may be supplied in the form of urea. In the ordinary feeds, however, nitrogen occurs mostly as proteins. The ability to use nonprotein nitrogen therefore is not thought to be of any great importance when a balanced ration is fed.

We must conclude that large differences in feed and protein conversion exist among animal classes and products. With even the most efficient conversion, however, approximately 4 pounds of crude protein are required to produce 1 pound of animal protein. Some of this crude protein could not otherwise be converted to human use. Finally, in most countries only animals can harvest vast rangelands, woodlands, and wastelands. Also, many plant residues occur as the by-products of the harvested crops. Even though conversion rates may be unfavorable, grazing is the only means of utilizing much of these resources.

SOCIAL, RELIGIOUS, and dietary customs of some countries may reduce the consumption of animal proteins.

India, for instance, pooling cattle and water buffaloes, is estimated to have about one-half animal per person, about the same as the cattle-human ratio in the United States. Since many of these animals are unclaimed and wander about the countryside, statistics are not accurate. Some estimates have been as high as one animal per person.

Even with the large numbers of cattle and buffaloes, animal foods make up a small part of the Indian diet. Bullocks are a major source of farm and transport power. More important is the opposition to slaughter of cattle dictated by religious doctrines. The reluctance to slaughter cattle is an outgrowth of the great famines during the rule of the Mongol emperors in the 14th century, when decimation of breeding stock was threatened. It was incorporated into the Hindu religious philosophy and persists today. Slaughter of cattle is prohibited by law in more than half of the 15 Indian States. As a consequence, India is largely a country of vegetarians, and consumption of animal products is restricted chiefly to dairy products and eggs.

FISH also are a major source of animal proteins. About three-quarters of the annual catch of 41 million metric tons is used for human consumption. On a world basis, this amounts to 22 pounds per person, in comparison with 20.5 pounds of beef and 20.3 of pork.

Fish flour, sometimes called fish protein concentrate, has received increased international interest. It consists of finely ground whole fish and is used as a food additive. It is said to be the world's cheapest, most abundant, and biologically richest source of animal protein. It contains up to 95 percent protein, and all of the essential amino acids occur in adequate quantity. With present systems of processing, however, the meal is not acceptable for human food in some countries because it includes the offal of the fish.

PLANT PROTEINS, particularly in the Western World, have long been considered poor relatives of the animal proteins.

Advances in dietary research and development of refined analytical techniques have done much to clarify the situation. First, the concentration of proteins varies greatly among plants and plant parts. Secondly, plant proteins vary greatly in nutritional quality, which is determined by the ratio or balance of the eight essential amino acids required by people.

Most of the people in the world are fed by relatively few major crop plants. These crops may be grouped into six general classes: Cereals (rice, wheat, and corn); sugar plants (sugarcane and sugarbeet); root crops (potatoes, sweet potatoes, and cassava); tree crops (banana and coconut); oilseed legumes (soybeans and peanuts); and pulses (dry beans and peas, chickpeas, and broadbeans). If high yields of cotton can be combined with the newly discovered glandless (gossypolfree) genetic characteristic, cottonseed also may become a major source of food.

Rice illustrates the importance of these crops in human nutrition. It has been estimated that at least 60 percent of the energy of half the people in the world is derived from rice. More than 30 percent of all human energy on this globe therefore comes from one crop.

Because cereals as a group are the most widely grown crops for human food, they probably contribute as much vegetable protein to the human diet as all other crops combined. But their protein concentration is not high. Rice has a protein content of 7.5 percent; wheat, 13 percent; and corn, 9.5 percent.

The man of average weight requires about 70 grams of protein a day. If he were to get it from rice, he would need to eat more than 2 pounds daily. He would need 1.75 pounds of corn or 1.25 pounds of wheat.

The sugar crops, sugarcane and sugarbeet, are processed almost entirely for sugar, which contains no protein when refined. The residues, sugarcane bagasse and sugarbeet pulp, contain protein, but they are not used for human food. Sugar that is produced by noncentrifugal means usually is consumed in an unrefined condition and is sticky and doughy. The product, known as gur in India, panela in Latin America, and jaggery in Africa, contains small amounts of proteins as impurities, but they are not of dietary significance.

Potatoes, sweetpotatoes, and cassava are largely starch crops. Cassava is grown only in tropical and subtropical countries. The processed product with which we are most familiar is tapioca. On a fresh basis, both types of potatoes contain only about 2 percent protein; cassava roots contain even less. In fact, to supply the required 70 grams of protein, a man would need to eat 8 pounds of potatoes or 25 pounds of processed tapioca.

The protein concentration in bananas is low and is similar to cassava root in this regard. Coconut, on a dry-weight basis, is similar to rice in total protein content.

We should not infer that those major crops that are low in protein are undesirable food. Most are important sources of energy-rich starches, and many contain important mineral constituents of the diet.

OILSEEDS in general are first-rate sources of protein. The protein contents of most oilseeds are much higher than in cereals. Many varieties of soybeans contain more than 40 percent protein, peanuts fall in the range of 25 to 30 percent, and cottonseed contains about 16 to 18 percent.

Extraction of oil and removal of seedcoats concentrate the protein in the remaining oilmeal and oilcake. The protein in the meal and flour produced therefrom exceeds 50 percent. Concentrates that contain 72 to 74 percent protein, which is higher than that in meat on a dry-weight basis, can be made through additional processing.

High-protein soybean concentrates have been used to supplement diets in countries where nutrition is inadequate. One cup of soybean concentrate, approximately 170 grams, will supply the daily requirements of protein, vitamins, and minerals for an average adult.

The quality of protein in the oilseed crops generally is good. All are slightly lower than ideal in methionine. The quality of protein in soybeans, however, compares favorably with that of animal products.

Dry beans and peas are a major source of food throughout the world. All of the edible beans and peas are legumes. Internationally, they are collectively referred to as pulses and sometimes as grain legumes. They include a goodly number of crops and species. In the Western Hemisphere, Europe, and Africa, dry edible beans consist mostly of beans belonging to the same botanical species as snap or wax beans. They include navy, great northern, pinto, red kidney beans, and others. In the United States, we also grow lima beans, dry peas, cowpeas, lentils, and mungbeans.

The grain legume produced to the greatest extent in the Far East is chickpeas. Pigeonpeas, mungbeans, urdbeans, and dry peas also are produced in large quantities. Others include moth beans, broadbeans, hyacinth beans, and the twinflower Dolichos.

The protein contents of pulses fall within the range 22 to 26 percent on a dry-weight basis. The quality of protein in chickpeas, pigeonpeas, lima beans, and twinflower Dolichos is exceptionally good and comparable with that of animal proteins. Proteins in most of the other pulses have excellent quantities of lysine but are slightly low in the sulfur-bearing amino acids, methionine and cystine.

The full possibilities of the pulses of the world have not been realized. Grain legumes generally have not been improved as much as many other crops, partly because emphasis has been placed on the improvement of crops that are exported extensively, such as cotton, tea, and coffee.

In tropical countries, most pulses are grown largely during the dry period, with little or no irrigation. Yields are much less than optimum. The development of improved varieties and systems of culture that would give maximum production would greatly increase the potential of this important class of protein-bearing crops.

THE PLANT COLLECTION program of the United States Department of Agriculture was intensified several years ago. Cultivated plants and the plants from natural stands in their native, uncultivated habitat have been sought in many lands. The primary objective is to find new crops to provide raw materials for industry. Principal attention is given the composition of seeds, particularly their content of proteins, special oils, gums, and waxes.

The total proteins of seeds vary among plant families. Proteins in species within families vary, but not so much as some other constituents, such as oil content. For example, the species of the legume family may have 12 to 55 percent of protein; members of the grass family may have 2 to 33 percent. Despite such variations, one would expect search among the legumes to yield more high-protein species than among the grasses.

Families of plants also reveal certain patterns in the quality of the proteins in their seed. Amaranthaceae, the family to which pigweed belongs, and Umbelliferae, the parsley family to which dill and carrots belong, are moderately low in total proteins but are high in lysine. Leguminosae in general also are good sources of lysine, but a few species, such as peanut, are low. Most legume species are low in methionine. Species of Gramineae, the grass family, tend to be very low in lysine but high in methionine. The family to which sesame belongs has similar protein quality. Combinations of corn and soybeans or sesame and soybeans therefore make a good source of balanced proteins.

In quantity and quality of protein, the four most promising families for sources of seed protein for man and nonruminant animals are Leguminosae (soybeans, alfalfa, clover, and others); Compositae, to which safflower and sunflower belong; Cruciferae, which includes rape, mustard, and cabbage; and Cucurbitaceae, of which melons, cucumbers, and gourds are members.

Man's principal sources of vegetable protein are seeds. Other parts of plants, particularly of vegetables and fruit, are eaten but do not constitute major sources the world over.

Bearing in mind the growth of the world's population, we must take a fresh look at all possible sources of protein that might be available to man. We know that huge amounts of proteins exist in certain plants that have never been used very much for human food.

PROTEINS occur abundantly in the leaves of many plants. They usually are considered to be animal feed and are used directly by people to only a limited degree.

On good land in the North Central States, an acre of soybeans may yield 700 pounds of protein. Alfalfa, however, harvested or grazed from a similar acre, may readily contain 1,200 to 1,400 pounds of protein. Most of this protein could not be digested by people.

Animals can convert leaf protein to nutritious and palatable animal protein—although man could expect to recover only one-fourth to one-twelfth of the protein eaten by animals. From the more efficient animal conversions, such as milk, we can at best expect to obtain only half as much protein from an acre of alfalfa as from an acre of soybeans used directly as human food. If we prefer our protein in the form of lamb chops, we are realizing only one-seventh as much protein as from soybeans. There is no question that we prefer milk or lamb chops to some form of plant protein. If expanding populations, however, required a change, the question must be raised as to whether we can use alfalfa protein directly as human food.

Research on the processing of protein from leaves has been conducted in Great Britain. The protein is extracted by a pulping process, which consists of breaking open the leaf cells by cutting or rubbing. The juice is pressed out, and all coarse particles eliminated with fine sieves. The starch grains and chloroplast fragments, which contain the green coloring of leaves, are removed by a high-speed centrifugation. The protein in the juice is separated from the water-soluble components of the leaf by acidification to approximately pH 4 or by heating to 70° to 80° C. About 75 percent of the protein in young, succulent leaves—but only 15 to 20 percent of the protein in leaves nearing maturity—can be extracted.

The product is dark green and does not have a desirable flavor. Flavoring, of course, can be added, and the color can be masked by encasing the protein, as in ravioli. Some experiments indicated that leaf protein has a nutritive value only slightly below that of milk protein. In feeding experiments with swine and other animals, it compared favorably with fishmeal. The economic feasibility of the process had not been demonstrated in 1964.

MANY PLANTS lower on the evolutionary scale also can combine nitrogen with compounds containing carbon, hydrogen, and oxygen and thereby synthesize the basic components of proteins. In fact, the capacity of ruminant animals to make proteins from urea and corncobs or straw is really the synthesizing of proteins by microorganisms in the digestive tract of the animal.

Lower plants that have been investigated as sources of protein include the algae, yeast and other fungi, and the bacteria.

The algae include thousands of species. Some are single-celled, microscopic plants, such as those that cause green color in water allowed to stand uncovered in sunlight for a few days. Some are the giant kelps of the ocean, which may be more than 100 feet long and have leaflike structures several feet across. They have different forms, colors, and conditions of growth. Algae flourish in ponds, lakes, streams, and oceans. Some grow on trees and in soil—even on snow.

Nearly all algae bear chlorophyll, which permits them to combine carbon dioxide and water to form sugars, a process called photosynthesis. Sunlight is the source of energy for the process. The enormous part that algae have had is shown in the estimate that algae have synthesized 90 percent of the world's organic carbon.

Many algae can grow in sea water. As only 30 percent of the world's surface is covered by land, it stands to reason that 70 percent of the solar energy that reaches the earth falls on the sea. As solar energy is necessary for photosynthesis, one could reason that the seas potentially offer greater opportunities for food production than the land.

Algae in general utilize solar energy more efficiently than higher plants do. The single-celled algae are particularly efficient. Few higher plants capture as much as 2 percent of the sun's radiation; indeed, it has been estimated that only 0.2 percent of the solar energy that falls on a cornfield is utilized.

Because single-celled algae are distributed much more uniformly throughout the medium in which they grow, they miss less sunlight. Every cell is a chlorophyll-bearing, productive unit, whereas in higher plants many cells have been differentiated into conductive and storage tissues and are no longer productive. The photosynthetic efficiency of some of the green algae such as Chlorella, at low light intensities, approaches use of 25 percent of light energy.

We are interested primarily in the few algae that have a particular food potential, the large marine algae and single-celled algae adaptable to mass culture.

Marine algae, or seaweeds, are not new in the human diet. Orientals, even during the era of Confucius, regarded seaweeds as a delicacy. Chinese, Japanese, Filipinos, and Hawaiians were particularly fond of them. Until 1800, peoples of the Western World did not use them, but since that time certain types have come into food use, particularly in Scandinavia, Scotland, and the West Indies.

Several species of brown and red algae with large forms are cultivated for food in Japan. They have large holdfast structures that superficially resemble roots. Bundles of bamboo, to which the seaweeds attach themselves, are "planted" in the mud bottom of shallow marine waters. In other countries, natural stands of more than a score of species are harvested.

In general, all marine algae used as human food have large forms and are low in protein, fats, and digestible carbohydrates. The aversion of western people to extensive eating of seaweeds is due mostly to their poor digestibility and palatability. Odd as it may seem, digestibility of seaweed seems to increase with regular eating over a period of time. It is theorized that certain microflora, which aid in the digestion, are acquired and built up in the human digestive tract.

The amount of protein composition of seaweeds approximates that of the more highly developed plants. Also, like the protein in leaf tissue, it has poor digestibility unless it is processed. It rarely exceeds 15 percent in brown algae and often drops to 5 percent in late summer. Seaweeds of the red algal group may contain 25 percent of crude protein. Marine algae differ from fresh water algae and land plants in that they contain considerable nonprotein nitrogen. Ruminant animals therefore find them more nutritious than nonruminants and people do.

Except for the abundant minerals in them, seaweeds must be regarded, because of poor digestibility, as having low food value for human beings and can be only a minor supplement to the normal diet. As animal feed, particularly for ruminants, they have moderate value.

Culture of algae under controlled conditions has the potentiality of producing large quantities of proteins in a relatively small space. Algae may be cultured in large vats in the open, in large tubes on the roofs of buildings, or, when the temperature needs to be controlled, in large jars or vats in a greenhouse. This means of food production merits particular attention in operations such as space travel.

For mass culture, single-celled species are considered more efficient than the complex forms. The most widely used genus in experiments is Chlorella.

For most efficient production, the water medium in which the algae are grown must be fertilized with plant nutrients, aerated with carbon dioxide, and agitated to prevent settling and to assure uniform lighting of all cells. Temperature control and supplementary light may be required.

Experiments with Chlorella on a pilot-plant scale were conducted for a few summer months in the United States and for several years in Japan.

In the United States experiment, conducted in one large polyethylene tube on the roof of a building at Cambridge, Mass., the cost of Chlorella production was estimated as 25 to 30 cents a pound and the yield was calculated as 8 tons of protein per acre per year. With the large production systems, potential yields up to 20 tons of protein per acre have been estimated.

In Japan, Chlorella was produced in culture ponds covering about 1 acre. Sunlight furnished the only source of energy, and production was continued the year around. Over a 2-year period, about 2,200 pounds of protein a year were produced on 1 acre. The product sold for nearly 2 dollars a pound.

The protein content of the single-celled algae suitable for mass culture varies among species and with environmental conditions. Japanese-produced Chlorella averaged 40 percent crude protein. Other experiments have shown as high as 55 percent for this species. The quality of protein also varies. Most tests show low values for the amino acids methionine, histidine, and tryptophane.

Feeding trials with rats and rabbits showed higher gains than obtained when proteins were supplied with soybean meal, particularly when the algae were supplemented with amino acids that are deficient. No digestive difficulties were encountered in humans conditioned to the diet, except when more than 100 grams a day were consumed.

Certain conclusions can be drawn. Production of algal protein in mass culture as a common food is not economically feasible at present. Digestibility of algae is difficult for people, and additional processing studies are needed. The bitter, strong, spinach-like flavor is objectionable to most westerners, and further research on palatability is required.

A number of micro-organisms besides unicellular algae have been investigated as sources of proteins. Most of them do not contain chlorophyll and therefore cannot synthesize sugars. Waste sugars, however, occur in many products, such as citrus-waste press juice, molasses from sugarbeet and sugarcane, and wood sugars. In the presence of inorganic nitrogen, many micro-organisms can synthesize proteins from such wastes.

One class of organisms, yeasts and yeastlike micro-organisms, has shown particular promise. Production of a species of food or nutritional yeast, known as *Torulopsis utilis*, which is unlike baking or brewing yeasts, is an established industry in some places.

Thousands of tons of food yeast were propagated and eaten by Germans during the Second World War, and food yeast is now being produced in the United States, British West Indies, Sweden, and Germany. The product is known as torula. Yields of proteins vary with the waste sugar material on which the yeast is grown. The range of crude protein generally is 40 to 60 percent. The protein is of good quality except for a deficiency in the sulfur-containing amino acids, particularly methionine.

A number of other yeast and yeast-like organisms are being investigated experimentally and commercially for the production of food yeast.

A technique was developed to convert whey, a waste product from the cheese industry, into food yeast. The yeast micro-organism used in the process belongs to the genus *Saccharomyces*. It grows well on whey sugar, and within 3 to 5 hours produces one-half pound of yeast for each pound of whey sugar.

Of the myriad species of fungi in the world, a goodly number can grow in a medium containing sugar and inorganic nitrogen salts. A near-theoretical conversion of inorganic to organic nitrogen is accomplished by some species within 4 days. The protein productions of 10 genera of *Fungi Imperfecti* have been reported.

Crude proteins of the products of the different genera varied from 6 to 35 percent. From the better fungi, a conversion of 1 pound of protein was obtained from 6 pounds of hexose sugar. The product was white to very light buff and usually odorless and tasteless. Mouse-feeding trials indicated that the substances were not toxic. From performance of the better fungi, it was calculated that the sugar produced by an acre of sugarcane with added nitrogen could be converted by fungi to more than 2.5 tons of protein. The economic feasibility of such conversion is questionable.

As in the case of yeasts, potential commercial production probably must be reserved for sugars occurring as industrial waste products.

STILL ANOTHER class of micro-organisms, the bacteria, is worth scrutiny.

Like the yeasts and fungi, many species of bacteria can synthesize their own proteins from sugars and inorganic nitrogen. Certain bacteria also can utilize free nitrogen from the air. One group with this capacity is the Rhizobia, which enter into a symbiotic relationship with legume plants. Another group, the Azotobacter, is free living in soil. Because of its ability to grow with only the air as a source of nitrogen, a species known as *Azotobacter venelardii* has been investigated as a protein-producing organism.

In its natural habitat, the soil, the organism grows on decaying plant materials and available minerals.

When soil nitrogen is limited, it uses nitrogen of the air to build up protein within its body. Upon death of the bacteria, this nitrogen becomes available for the nutrition of plants. Scientists in the Soviet Union have reported appreciable increases in plant yields after inoculation of new lands with Azotobacter, but studies in the United States failed to support this claim.

When grown in an aerated, liquid medium containing sugar and a few simple salts, Azotobacter multiplies rapidly. If it is harvested, killed, and dried at the time of maximum growth, the nitrogen remains locked in the bacterial proteins and becomes available for the nutrition of people or animals ingesting the bacteria.

Feeding trials with mice indicated no toxic substances. Human taste panels did not distinguish biscuits in which the flour contained 2 percent Azotobacter powder. Protein content approached 75 percent, which is extremely high for vegetable products. The amino acid balance of the protein compared favorably with that from yeast and other micro-organisms.

LET us summarize the sources of proteins for nutrition.

At the outset, we must realize that man and animals are completely dependent on plants to synthesize proteins; that is, to combine inorganic nitrogen with sugars. Plants, as used in this statement, include the highly developed plants, algae, yeasts and other fungi, and the lowly bacteria. Whether the synthesis occurs in the sunny fields, the ocean, the paunch of a cow, or in the vat of a commercial establishment, the process is similar and equally vital.

Many proteins are incorporated into plant parts that are indigestible to humans. Animals can convert a large part of these proteins to digestible proteins. Regardless of population densities, animals will continue to serve as effective converters of proteins indigestible to humans and as machines to harvest plant materials in inaccessible terrain. When animals are fed proteins that are digestible by man, the conversion efficiency is low, as only one-fourth to one-twelfth of the protein will be available to man.

High-protein plant sources must be exploited to supply the protein needs of the ever-increasing numbers of people. Among the higher plants, particular attention must be given the pulses and oilseed crops.

Direct extraction of protein from green leaves and mass culture of single-celled algae have great potential for maximum protein yield per unit area. Until digestibility and palatability of these sources of protein can be improved, they cannot be considered ideal sources of nutrition for direct human consumption.

The mass culture of yeasts and other fungi and bacteria has great potentiality in producing high yields of protein with acceptable amino acid balance.

MARTIN G. WEISS *began his research career with the Department of Agriculture in 1936 in Iowa as a breeder of new soybean varieties. Improved varieties resulting from this program, notably Hawkeye, Adams, and Blackhawk, were grown on more than half of the United States acreage at the peak of their production. Soybeans have become a major source of protein in the United States and were grown on more than 29 million acres in 1964. Dr. Weiss became leader of soybean production investigations for the Department of Agriculture at Beltsville in 1950, Chief of the Field Crops Research Branch in 1953, and Associate Director of the Crops Research Division in 1957.*

RUTH M. LEVERTON, *a nutritionist, has spent all her professional career in research and graduate teaching in agricultural experiment stations and land-grant universities before joining the Department of Agriculture in 1957. In 1961 she became Assistant Administrator, Agricultural Research Service.*

Population, Income, and Food

by ROBERT D. STEVENS

THE REV. THOMAS ROBERT MALTHUS published in 1798 an essay that tried to prove that population tends to increase faster than does the production of food and other goods. The human race, he maintained, was continually threatened with food shortages, severe malnutrition, and at times starvation because of overpopulation.

At that very time, though, by an extraordinary coincidence of history there was beginning in Europe an industrial revolution, which over the years brought tremendous economic growth and large increases in income.

We know now that the industrial revolution and the accompanying agricultural revolution banished the specter of food shortages from economically developed countries. Malthus died before it became plain that the great increases in productivity destroyed his theory for nations whose economic development has been rapid.

But we know also that in many other countries population has grown apace while productivity has remained much the same.

Population in the presently developed countries grew less than 1.5 percent a year during the period of industrialization. Today in many of the underdeveloped regions the rate of population growth is 2.5 percent a year or more, primarily because of improved health conditions.

Newly developing regions, in order to have more food and other goods for every citizen—or even to maintain present per capita incomes—therefore must increase production much faster than the presently developed countries had to in the past.

In order to estimate how much more food is needed in a country, we need to know something about its growth in population.

The United Nations estimated that the population of Africa increased 2 percent a year during the fifties. In the Western Hemisphere, the average rate of population growth was estimated at 2.1 percent. The rate in the United States was 1.7 percent and in Asia, 1.9 percent annually. In Europe, where countries are well developed, it was only 0.8. The United Nations calculation of the average growth rate of world population from 1950 to 1960 was 1.8 percent a year. There were nearly 20 percent more people in the world at the end of the decade than at the beginning. The total world population for 1962 was estimated at 3.15 billion persons.

The rate of growth of world population has increased since the industrial revolution. It is now higher than it has ever been.

Population experts in many parts of the world have been studying the figures. They have analyzed the history and development of the industrialized countries and have observed a typical pattern of population growth during economic development.

Before economic development occurs, about as many people die each year as are born. Typically, there are 4 or 5 births and about the same number of deaths per 100 persons in such countries. As a result, the total population of the country remains approximately the same or increases a little from time to time when harvests are particularly good and in long periods of peace.

When economic development begins, health and other conditions usually improve, and the number of births exceeds the number of deaths. As a nation continues to develop economically, however, birth rates drop.

Some European countries in the past few decades have had birth rates of 2.5 or less per hundred persons. These low birth rates are associated with urbanization, higher incomes, and the dissemination of knowledge of methods of family planning. The death rates in those countries are low—about 1.5 deaths per hundred persons are common. Thus, with birth rates at 2.5 per hundred and death rates at 1.5 per hundred, the population increases 1.0 percent a year.

The demographers predict increased rates of population growth during the next few decades in most of the world, except Europe, the United States, and a few other countries.

Some studies indicate an increase in world population of at least 1.7 percent a year over the next decade or so. We know therefore that world food supplies must increase at least that much if people are going to continue to eat as much as they have in the past.

In many of the newly developing countries, however, population is expected to increase by 2.5 or even 3 percent a year. Over countries that have not achieved similar increases in agricultural production, Malthus' prediction still hangs.

ALL of the developed countries have succeeded in increasing their food supplies faster than their populations have grown. They did so by boosting agricultural and industrial productivity. Income per capita went up.

As income per person increases, people spend more money on food to improve their diets, according to a generalization formulated by the German economist Ernst Engel in 1857. This generalization, known as Engel's law, specifies the relation between increased family income and expenditures for food, clothing, and housing.

In the United States in the midthirties, for example, when per capita income averaged about 810 dollars (in 1947–1949 dollars), the market value of food consumed per capita averaged about 222 dollars. In the late thirties, when income per person reached an average of 1,006 dollars, food consumed was worth 249 dollars per capita. By the midfifties, per capita income had increased to about 1,400 dollars and food consumption to 331 dollars per person. A higher value of food consumption of 336 dollars per person was observed. Economists believe this high level was due to the special conditions that followed the Second World War. Similar increases in food and incomes have been observed in many countries.

The figures pertain to increases in the cost, or value, of food consumed per person as income rises. The value of food measured thus includes packaging and the full price paid for meals served in restaurants.

If we should measure food by weight instead of measuring it by its money value, a different picture is presented. The weight of the food consumed per person generally remains about the same, although in the United States the weight of food consumed per capita has dropped from 1,616 pounds in 1909 to 1,455 pounds in 1961. The decline is explained partly by the fact that Americans now do less physical labor. Because the weight of food eaten is determined by the size of a person's stomach, the amount consumed, as measured by weight, remains about the same regardless of higher incomes.

LET US RETURN to money measures of the value or cost of food.

Engel's law suggests that increases in income cause increased food consumption. The relation between increases in income and increases in food consumption is called the income elasticity of food and is measured by an income elasticity coefficient. A positive coefficient indicates that consumption of food will increase as income rises. If the coefficient is greater than

1.0, consumption will rise faster than income. A negative coefficient indicates a decline in consumption as incomes rise.

For example, in the data I cited for the United States, the income elasticity coefficient of food consumption is approximately 0.7. This means that an increase of 10 percent in income will cause an increase of 7 percent in the value of food consumed. A coefficient of 0.7 is high for developed countries and in this instance was due to special historical circumstances—a major depression and the war period—which made a coefficient of elasticity greater than in more normal periods. Most of the estimates of the current income elasticity for the value of all food in the United States are in the range of 0.3 to 0.5.

In many newer countries, the income elasticity coefficient for food consumption appears to be considerably greater than it is in the industrialized countries. An elasticity coefficient of 0.8 or even 0.9 appears to exist in some countries. That means that for every 10 percent of increase in income, one may expect an increase of 8 or 9 percent in the value of food eaten. This high elasticity is due largely to the fact that incomes in many of the newly developing nations are so low that a high proportion of increased income is used to purchase additional food.

The proportion of income a person spends for food is another aspect of Engel's law. "The poorer a family is," he said, "the greater the proportion of the total expenditure which it must use to procure food." This relation is true for countries also. Expenditures for food in the United States averaged about 20 percent of per capita income in 1964; in many low-income countries, about 50 to 60 percent of incomes is spent for food.

RISING INCOMES also affect the national diet. A poor man must buy inexpensive foods that fill his stomach and give him enough energy for work— rice, potatoes, noodles, macaroni, bread, and other things made from cereals. He will buy more preferred foods as his income increases. In each country, the preferred foods are considered luxuries. Usually fruit, fresh vegetables, dairy products, and many meats are in this group. These foods have high income elasticity coefficients.

An example is given in United States data. The pounds of preferred foods consumed per capita, including dairy products, meat, fruit, and leafy vegetables, have increased since 1909 from 679 pounds to 783 pounds in 1962. The amounts of potatoes, flour, and cereal products declined from 512 pounds in 1909 to 252 pounds. Changes in the per capita consumption of other foods have been less striking.

In percentage terms in 1909, the preferred foods I mentioned accounted for 42 percent of the weight of food consumed per capita. In 1961, these foods had increased to 54 percent of the weight of food consumed. Potatoes, flour, and cereal products represented 32 percent of the weight of food consumed in 1909, but declined to 17 percent in 1962.

Not all the changes in diet are due to rising incomes, of course. Food tastes change over time. Also, because less physical work has been required of the average American workman, he has come to eat less energy-producing foods such as potatoes and cereals. Another factor is that the average weight of a population may change as its average age goes up. Older people tend to be more sedentary and need less food. All in all, though, higher income is the main reason for changes in national diets.

We can use a simple equation to estimate food requirements: The rate of increase in national food consumption, c, is equal to the rate of population growth, a, plus the rate of increase in income per capita, b, times the income elasticity coefficient for food, x. Thus: $c = a + bx$.

The equation requires data for the three variables, a, b, and x.

For the rate of expected population

growth, *a*, we have used the medium estimates of population growth in the different parts of the world made by the United Nations Department of Economic and Social Affairs in 1958.

As to the rate of growth in per capita income, *b*, we cannot know how fast the economies of nations will grow. In general, rapidly growing countries have achieved a per capita rate of income growth of some 2 percent a year. In the past two decades, the United States rate has been around 2 percent. At that rate, it takes 35 years, or about a generation, to double per capita income.

Many countries now have economic development plans that try to increase income faster than that, but I doubt whether many newly developing countries can sustain higher rates of growth for long periods. So I use 2 percent as the rate of increase of per capita income, recognizing that the rate of increase in food consumption will be less if this rate is not achieved.

The income elasticity coefficients to be used in the calculation are based on the best available evidence. In general, as I said, they tend to be high—0.7 or 0.8 in countries of low per capita income and low (0.3 to 0.5) in industrialized countries.

The lowest rates of growth in food consumption—about 1.6 percent a year—are expected in the United Kingdom and France. In the United States, Japan, and the Soviet Union, the expected rates are 2 to 3 percent a year; in India and the Philippines, 3 or 4 percent. The figures are higher in quite a number of countries—Taiwan, the United Arab Republic, Brazil, South-West Africa, and Mexico.

The average for the world is about 3 percent a year. To repeat: The estimates refer to the money value or cost of food eaten and not to its weight or volume.

We can see the magnitude of the task in some developing nations if we compare their expected rates of growth in food consumption and the rates in industrialized countries.

In France, for example, the expected rate of growth in food consumption is 1.7 percent a year, but Brazil has more than twice that rate, 4.2 percent a year.

The data indicate that many low-income countries are likely to have a rate twice that of the so-called advanced countries because their population is growing rapidly and their income elasticity coefficient of food is considerably higher.

I foresee little likelihood that either factor will change much in the near future. The coefficient of food in low-income countries very likely will remain high, because the first thing poor people want when they receive more money is more and better food. Some form of severe government control by such methods as rationing is about the only way to prevent increases in per capita food consumption in countries as development occurs. Rates of population growth will remain high for some time, as there is little evidence yet of declines in birth rates.

INDUSTRIALIZED and developed nations have demonstrated that they can produce or import more than enough food to meet the increased requirements for food. They also have adjusted the mix of farm products produced and imported to meet the demands for changes in diet associated with economic growth. They should have no shortage of food in the foreseeable future, barring war or other unforeseen calamities. In fact, some of them have produced too much of certain food products and have had to take measures to discourage the production of some foods.

FOR THE LOW-INCOME countries, Malthus' prediction that food supplies cannot keep pace with food needs remains a serious prospect.

As we have seen, food needs are increasing much faster in those countries than in the developed countries because of higher rates of population growth and higher income elasticities for food.

Can they attain an increase of food availability of 3 or 4 percent a year? We have evidence, on the one hand, that developed countries have achieved increases of 3 percent or more, that it is physically possible for developing regions to achieve the rates of growth in food production and imports they require, and that ample technical knowledge is available so that enough food may be produced for all.

On the other hand: Many of the low-income countries are not producing enough food or raising production fast enough. How large their food shortages will become and when they will succeed in meeting their food needs through an increased domestic production or greater commercial imports of food are serious questions.

Some countries have shortages of productive land and other restraints on increasing domestic food production rapidly. Some of them therefore may have to increase their exports so they can buy the food they need from other countries.

Major hindrances to increased production and food-generating exports are lack of the necessary social and governmental institutions, lack of education, and lack of local technical knowledge. These hindrances remain even though many countries are working hard to develop new institutions that will serve agriculture and other sectors of the economy better. Improvements in educational systems and the search for needed technical knowledge are going forward—but in many countries with too little effort and money to meet the impending food needs.

ROBERT D. STEVENS *joined the Development and Trade Analysis Division of the Economic Research Service as international agricultural economist in 1961. Previously he taught at the National College of Agriculture, Bao-Loc, Vietnam, under the sponsorship of the Council on Economic and Cultural Affairs, Inc., of New York.*

Potentials for Food Production

by CHARLES E. KELLOGG

A REASONABLY prosperous agriculture—one that produces more than the needs of the rural families—laid the foundation for industrial development and economic growth in countries that we describe as developed.

As their industries grew, machines and chemicals became available to make agriculture even more efficient and to make the fullest use of their soils. It was not accomplished in a day or a generation.

So, also, in the developing countries of South America, Africa, and southern and eastern Asia, great efforts have been made to extend farm production and economic growth. Yet measures that reduced illness and death have been so effective in many countries that improvements in agriculture, far short of the potential, are partly offset by population increases. Then, too, other needs tend to compete with agriculture for the domestic resources, scarce foreign exchange, and the small cadre of educated people.

In a developing country it can seem that everything needs doing at once. Priorities are necessary, and a degree of patience. I repeat: It cannot be done in a day. The factor of time and the principle of interactions of several practices in the use of soil are points I stress over and over in consultations with representatives of other governments who seek ways to improve their agricultures and economic progress.

The machines and chemicals we have had for years made it possible to till some soils not naturally suited to crop production. Thus, yields were improved on some of the soils already in use, and new acres could be prepared for crops. Many of the soils unresponsive to our new methods for crop production now have been put to other uses.

From the beginning, cultivators—the people who till the soil—have had to prepare their soil for crop use.

Land clearing, stone removal, manuring, tillage, and simple drainage and irrigation are old practices. Then came liming and fertilization. These and other practices can now be done more easily and designed more precisely to fit local situations.

Nearly all kinds of soil now are modified for efficient crop use. The plant nutrients are increased and balanced, especially with chemical fertilizer. Water is controlled by combinations of drainage, irrigation, and control of runoff.

Powerful machines can plow the soil deeply to break up hardpans, can shape the surface for ease of control of water, can dig ditches and lay tile, and can throw up terraces and small dams. New crop varieties have been bred for high yields on improved soils. Science has given cultivators new ways to control insects and diseases.

Some of the most productive soils of western Europe and the United States have been reconstituted by combinations of practices that have drastically altered the original characteristics of the soils. Many of these practices were unknown in earlier centuries. A few, such as deep digging and shaping land surfaces, were done before power tools and are being done now in developing regions, but with low labor returns. Science now gives us more powerful methods for creating good arable soils out of indifferent soils.

Even soils of high potential require skillful management. Different kinds of soil require different combinations of management practices. Contrasting kinds of soil are being brought to similar high levels of efficiency, but by different sets of practices.

Any one kind of soil is a unique combination of many features: Depth of rooting zone; permeability to water; slope; hazard of erosion or soil blowing; reserves of the different plant nutrients being released from mineral and organic fractions; capacity to hold and release water to roots; proportions of stones, sand, silt, and clay; degree of seasonal waterlogging; acidity; abundance of soluble salts; and others.

Under modern management, one partly changes the soil and partly selects management practices and kinds of crops to develop a system that gives the optimum harvest for efficiency in terms of output over input.

The skillful agriculturist no longer asks: "What will this soil produce with simple management?" Today he asks: "How will this soil respond to a management system to bring out its potential efficiency, considering machines, chemicals, water-control devices, crop selection, and so on?"

LET US CONSIDER some of the critical qualities of a generalized ideal soil, realizing that the ideal is not identical for all crops and that the effect of any one depends also on the others.

1. The soil must have a balanced supply of the essential plant nutrients available to the roots for the crops to be grown. These include phosphorus, nitrogen, calcium, magnesium, potassium, sulfur, iron, boron, manganese, zinc, molybdenum, and perhaps others from the soil, in addition to carbon, hydrogen, and oxygen from air and water.

For efficient use, nearly all soils require chemical fertilizers, even in addition to farmyard manure, green manures, and compost. People commonly think that fertilizers simply help increase the yields of crops that could be grown anyway. Yet without fertilizers it would be uneconomic to have pastures in our Southern States, commercial vegetables along the Atlantic coast, or sugarcane in Hawaii. Nearly all soils of the Tropics require chemical fertilizer for economic yields of crop plants.

Fertilizers are better now than a generation ago. The percentage of plant nutrients in commercial fertilizer has been increased, and so the costs of shipping the actual chemical nutrients are lower. A better understanding of symptoms of deficiencies, better soil tests and fertilizer trials, and modern ways to classify soils have made possible more precise recommendations of fertilizers to apply to specific fields.

The machines to apply fertilizers are being improved. New Zealanders have made a dramatic advance. They have special airplanes for spreading fertilizer to bring otherwise productive, well-watered, steep soils into use for high-yielding sheep pasture.

2. The ideal soil has a deep rooting zone for growth and for the storage of water, air, and nutrients. Rooting zones can be deepened by heavy tillage that breaks up lower layers or by the addition of soil material to the surface.

Rooting zones in other soils are deepened by applying lime and fertilizers deeply and by using strongly rooted crops, such as alfalfa, that add organic matter in depth and furnish food for the micro-organisms that help change a massive soil into a granular one.

3. The soil must be able to furnish both water and air to the plant roots. This means water control within the soil to have enough of it without crowding out the air that roots need. Water-control practices (terraces, irrigation, or drainage, or some combination of them) and special tillage were used to make good arable soils of a high proportion of the most productive soils in the world today. These practices and the protection of low-lying soils by seawalls and river levees have been improved greatly since the Second World War. Huge dams store water to control floods and to use for expanded irrigation.

4. The ideal arable soil is stable. It does not slip down the slope, blow away, or wash onto low ground or into streams. The hazards of erosion on many steep soils and of soil blowing on many sandy or powdery soils in dry and windy places are too great for them to be made into arable soils.

Here, too, gradual progress is being made, first to appraise the hazards before development and then to use for crops only soils on which the erosion or blowing can be controlled by proper tillage, terracing, windbreaks, crop selection, and related practices.

5. Soil and air temperature must permit growth. Temperatures too low for crop growth probably limit the use of more acres of the earth's land surface than any other single factor.

Yet the boundary between soils not potentially arable because of cold and those potentially arable is being pushed back toward the poles through breeding of short-season crops, improved fertilization for rapid growth, and combinations of tillage and water control to assist early warming of the soil. In the United States, corn is grown considerably north of where it was grown in the thirties. In Canada, the Scandinavian countries, and the Soviet Union, small grains and other crops can be grown farther north.

Two other sets of requirements are essential in the management of a good arable soil.

6. Kinds and varieties of crops, in monoculture, mixtures, or sequences, must be grown that have the genetic potential to respond to the modified soil and environment. If seeds are saved over generations from crops grown on soils of low fertility, the variety is unlikely to respond enough to improved water and fertility to make the practices economic. On many acres, all three—fertility, water control, and seeds—must be changed at the same time.

The story of hybrid corn is well known. On the best farm soils of the Middle West, farmers using the hybrids had an immediate response over the older sorts because these had lacked the growth potential to use all the moisture and nutrients in the soils. Yet hybrid corn did not show a significant advantage in the Southern States until additional fertilizer was used at planting time, supplemental nitrogen was added in early summer, and the plant population was increased. Now many of the highest corn yields are in the South.

7. The crops (and soils) must be protected from insects, diseases, and other hazards, else the other management practices may come to nothing.

Of these seven principal sets of practices, four are vital on every acre of cropland in the world: A balanced supply of nutrients, water and air when the plants need them, an adapted kind and variety of crop, and crop protection. The others are also vital on many of the acres.

Thus the total harvest from an acre and the harvest per man-hour depend on a complex of interactions among the many features of the soil and the practices of management. Each one in the system has effects on the others.

This principle of interactions in soil use is of the utmost importance and needs all possible emphasis in newly developing areas changing from traditional to modern farming. Rarely does an improvement in one practice—irrigation, fertilizers, or improved seeds—give a satisfactory result. Cultivators and their advisers always must think of the systems of management in relation to the local kind of soil they have.

So FAR we have considered some of the major factors accounting for variations in soil use. They are important in estimating the acres of soils in the world that could be used to meet the expanding needs and for suggesting measures for making progress toward that end.

Laying aside for the moment the great educational, economic, and institutional needs for a productive agriculture in the newly developing countries: Has the world enough soil resources to produce the food people need?

The answer to this question changes with time, partly because the standards for the potentially usable soils change with new knowledge and technology.

Continually we find new ways to improve natural soils for crop use and to rehabilitate old arable soils of low productivity. Before the sixties, many felt that the United States might run out of cropland to take care of our domestic needs and our commitments abroad. Now a usable surplus of some 200 million acres that could be used for crops is estimated.

Even though the total land area of the world is relatively fixed, the total area of potentially arable soils—those that could produce food, fiber, and industrial crops—is highly flexible. The total depends on the state of the agricultural arts. Getting good harvests from it depends on the arts of agriculture used in communities all over the world.

The Production Yearbook for 1961 of the Food and Agriculture Organization of the United Nations gave the following percentages for the present use of land in the world: Wasteland, some of which may have potential, 40.5; forested land, 30; permanent meadows and pastures, 19; arable land and land under permanent crops, 10.5.

A figure of about 3,500 million acres was given for soil now in use—arable land and land in permanent crops. Besides ordinary food and fiber crops, it includes permanent crops (such as vines, orchards, rubber, oil and coconut palms, tea, coffee, cacao, and nut trees), temporary meadows and pastures, kitchen gardens, and temporary fallow. The distinction between permanent and temporary pasture is indefinite, and fallow land is hard to identify, especially that associated with shifting cultivation. Much of the forested land in the humid Tropics and subtropics, especially in Africa and South America, has excellent soil for crops.

Roughly one-half of the earth's surface is unsuitable for crop production; it is neither arable nor potentially arable. Several large regions have no present prospects for crop use. They include the great areas of everlasting ice and snow, essentially all the cold tundra soils, the soils of the high and rugged mountains, and soils of deserts and semideserts that lack water for irrigation. Some of the soils of the deserts and high mountains offer limited use for grazing, and some have a forest cover.

The soils now used are not necessarily the best. The location of good harbors and the position of land easily reached from them had a lot to do with the introduction of advanced agriculture in South America and Africa.

Whereas transport in countries of western Europe evolved slowly from trails to wagon roads, waterways, paved highways, railways, and finally to airlines, the intermediate steps of railways and paved trucklines have never been fully developed in Africa and South America. The unnavigability of the Congo River from the sea probably held back the development of the Congo Basin for two centuries.

Estimates of potential new cropland I made after the Second World War (in *Food, Soil, and People*, published by the United Nations Educational, Scientific, and Cultural Organization in its Food and People Series in 1951) have turned out to be conservative. If made in light of today's agricultural technology, the figure for potential new arable land (1,300 million acres) would be much higher—perhaps two or three or five times the needs of the world population in 1964. Yet many persons thought my estimate was too high at the time.

The Food and Agriculture Organization in 1963 published *Possibilities of Increasing World Food Production*, by Walter H. Pamley. It gave no esti-

mates, but the conclusion was unaltered: "It is clear that the *world potentials* for increasing food production are very substantial indeed."

For a revised edition in 1958 of *Efficient Use of Fertilizers* (Food and Agriculture Organization Agricultural Studies No. 43), a new general soil map of the world was made in the Soil Conservation Service. It is reproduced here on page 63.

ON THE BASIS of more detailed soil maps, A. C. Orvedal, Chief, World Soil Geography Unit, Soil Conservation Service, and his staff made new estimates of the acres of potential arable land in the world for both cultivated and noncultivated food, fiber, and industrial crops. An accompanying table gives those estimates for the units shown on the general soil map.

This total of some 6,589 million acres is not quite twice the figure the Food and Agriculture Organization gave in 1961 for the arable land in use. Even if this estimate is in error by as much as 15 percent either way, the conclusions are unaltered—for a long time at least, basic soil resources need not be the factor that limits production if soil management is reasonably good.

The additional acres of potentially arable soils are not equally distributed in relation to either national boundaries or population.

My 1951 estimate included 300 million acres in northern areas, but this figure would now be conservative for the United States and Canada alone.

In addition, there is a considerable area in northern Europe and Asia that currently known practices make potentially productive. The 1 thousand million acres estimated for the Tropics is low in view of current knowledge and experience with tropical soils in Queensland and many other places where the prerequisites for modern agriculture have been available.

Many people have little knowledge of the great agricultural potentials in the humid Tropics. Some still regard these "steamy jungles" with the awe

ESTIMATED POTENTIALLY ARABLE LAND IN THE WORLD

Map Unit on Accompanying Soil Map	Potentially Arable Land in Map Unit	
	Percent	Acres (millions)
1. Prairie Soils, Degraded Chernozems	80.0	242
2. Chernozems and Reddish Chestnut	70.0	660
3. Dark Gray and Black Soils of Subtropics and Tropics	50.0	618
4. Chestnut, Brown, Reddish Brown	30.0	892
5. Sierozems, Desert	.5	34
6. Podzols and Weakly Podzolized	10.0	320
7. Gray-Brown Podzolic	65.0	972
8. Latosols, Red-Yellow Podzolics	35.0	2,780
9. Red-Yellow Mediterranean	15.0	41
10. Soils of Mountains	.5	30
11. Tundra	.0	0
Total	......	6,589

These criteria were used to define arable land:

That reasonably good management would be used including appropriate combinations of adapted crop varieties, water control methods, pest control, and methods of plant nutrient maintenance, including some chemical fertilizers.

Crops include the ordinary food, fiber, and industrial crops that are normally cultivated as well as fruits, nut crops, rubber, sisal, coffee, tea, cocoa, palms, vines, and meadow crops that may or may not be cultivated.

All regular fallow land is counted, including the natural fallow under shifting cultivation.

Irrigation of arid soils is limited by water from streams and wells. Sea water is excluded as a potential source.

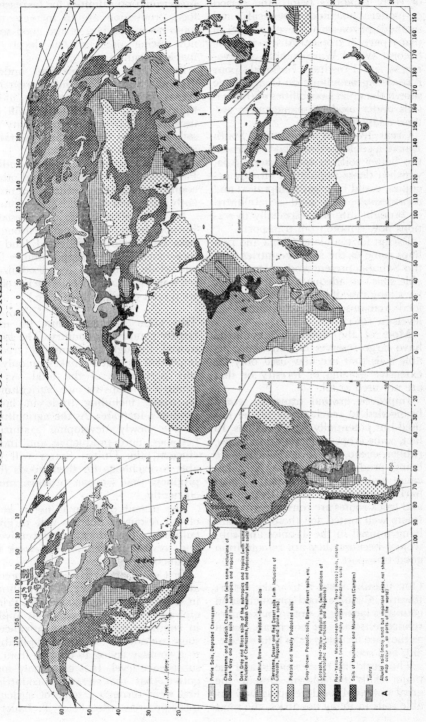

SOIL MAP OF THE WORLD

Prairie Soils, Degraded Chernozem

Chernozem and Reddish Chestnut soils (with some inclusions of Dark Grey and Black soils of the subtropics

Dark Grey and Black soils of the subtropics and tropics (with some inclusions of Chernozems, Reddish Chestnut soils and Hydromorphic soils

Chestnut, Brown, and Reddish-Brown soils

Sierozems, Desert and Red Desert soils (with inclusions of Lithosols, Regosols, and Solms soils

Podzols and Weakly Podzolized soils

Gray-Brown Podzolic soils, Brown Forest soils, etc.

Latosols, Red-Yellow Podzolic soils, (with inclusions of Hydromorphic soil, Lithosols and Regosols)

Red-Yellow Mediterranean (including Terra Rossa) soils, mostly mountainous (including many areas of Rendzina soils)

Soils of Mountains and Mountain Valleys (Complex)

Tundra

Alluvial soils (many small but important areas, not shown on map as occur in all parts of the world)

of early explorers before the period of modern machines, chemicals, and methods of research. Developments in many parts of tropical Africa since the Second World War, notably achievements of l'Institut National pour l'Etude Agronomique du Congo, have shown the great possibilities of tropical soils under modern management systems adapted to them.

Great tracts in Africa and South America could be developed. Yields on the better soils in southeastern Asia, which a dense population already occupies, could be greatly improved and considerable new land rehabilitated or brought into use, especially in sections now remote from transport.

Except for mainland China and perhaps some of the small countries near the Sahara, present and potential arable soils are adequate for food needs for a long time if international trade in food remains at approximately its levels in 1964.

Most of the developing countries have large reserves of potentially arable soils that are now used only for extensive grazing or forestry or that are not used at all.

Improved ground transport would be needed to reach many of the unused but potentially arable regions. In fact, some crops—sugarcane, bananas, rubber, cacao, and several others—are being produced where they are because soils are suitable and because harbors, navigable streams, and rail and truck routes are convenient. Large tracts well suited for those crops are lying unused in the Tropics and subtropics because they are remote from good transport.

OUR URGENT NEED is to make a start toward adequate food production in countries lacking it, not to make more refined estimates of potentials, useful as they are for analyses of future trade, aid, and such.

The world has the resources, and the major skills are known. Despite the great potential for developing new arable soils in many countries, the most promising opportunities for increasing food production are to increase the harvests on the best of the good soils now being used at low levels of management.

Better use of surface and underground water will permit a great increase in irrigation. Probably more than one-half of the increase will be used to improve the productivity of soils now used for low- or uncertain-yielding cereal crops.

Great opportunities exist in India, Pakistan, the Soviet Union, and other countries for making better use of presently cultivated soils with irrigation.

In the United States and western Europe, irrigation to reduce drought risks on presently cultivated land is increasing. (Because opportunities for wide-scale irrigation by desalinized sea water were still speculative in 1964, we do not consider them here.)

THE FOOD PROBLEM must be met largely country by country. The food moved through international trade, important as that is, makes up only a tiny percentage of the total. As a country develops its own agriculture, its trade, including trade in farm products, increases. As the agriculture of the newly developing countries becomes more productive and more efficient, the United States will be able to exchange for their goods the products that we can produce most efficiently.

The urgent problem is not a lack of soil resources but the will to give cultivators the education, incentives, and services needed for the work of producing food.

First of all, many have not appreciated the critical place of agriculture in stimulating economic growth. Principles of economic growth that apply in countries already in an advanced stage are not the ones most applicable to a country trying to emerge from a subsistence level. It is commonly forgotten that the advanced countries first went through a stage of agricultural progress. (See Peter T. Bauer's

Economic Analysis and Policy in Underdeveloped Countries.)

Agriculture needs a higher priority than many new governments have been persuaded to give it. One cannot expect a successful industry in the midst of a depressed and inefficient agriculture—unless there is some great mineral wealth or other basis for capital development. For industry in mainly agricultural countries to grow faster than it did in western Europe, agriculture must grow much faster.

Once agriculture gets a start, the industries serving it can go forward rapidly. Examples include service industries for transport, fertilizers, tools, food processing, and the like. Then further savings from agriculture and these service industries stimulate the basic industries. All highly efficient agriculture today has access to the chemicals, machines, and the other products of industry, either within the country or within a customs union with other areas.

A second factor has been the low social level of the cultivators. Many have lacked either incentive or influence. The land policy of the United States during its formative years was directed to helping men get land at reasonable terms. Farm people shared in programs for education and in political life. Some of the newly developing countries—India, for example—are making strong efforts, but lifting the social and political status of great numbers of cultivators is bound to take time. In many countries the effort is weak.

A third great handicap, closely related to low social level, is the lack of educational facilities in most rural districts of the developing countries. Few cultivators can read. Good general education is a first necessity for sustained agricultural development. Success with modern agricultural practices requires operationally literate people. Yet many cultivators are having a new awakening; they see that illiterate people have great handicaps in all economic and political activity.

They appear to realize the urgent need for schools more than many of their leaders and advisers.

Fourth, the principle of interactions is the most important technical principle to establish in the newly developing countries. The agricultural leaders and cultivators must grasp a working knowledge of it to achieve high and efficient production.

As I have pointed out, that means that several practices must be combined, fitted together, and adapted to the local kinds of soil. Each practice supports the others. Commonly, for example, an improved variety by itself gives a 10- or 20-percent increase; fertilizer by itself gives a similar increase; and proper water conservation or irrigation alone can raise yields 20 percent. With the practices properly combined on the same acre, the harvest may increase by 100 to as much as 600 percent.

Much of the effort for improved harvests in the developing regions has fallen short of hopes and potentialities. In part, the departures from this principle of interactions, or combined practices, follow from the educational handicap of the cultivators and the notion that agriculture is a simple enterprise.

Many seek a simple sloganlike program to give a dramatic, single answer to increasing production. Examples are fertilizers, improved seeds, irrigation, or pest control. In part, the failure to grasp the principle of interactions may result from the extreme narrowness of experience and education of advisers from the advanced countries. Yet successful farmers in the advanced countries understand the principle; and so do the first-class specialists who have worked with them.

Fifth, the highly efficient agriculture essential to our modern society must have many facility services from outside the farm units themselves. Besides general education, higher education and graduate schools must be available. Since countries must depend on educating most of their own scientists and engineers, the earlier universities can be well established the better.

Both field research and general research stations are essential. Many basic principles can be transferred from the advanced countries, but their application must be worked out locally. Management systems for tropical soils and crops will require new studies of many of the accepted basic principles themselves. Advisory services, organization, soil surveys, and country planning also are needed. I mentioned them in a paper, "Interactions in Agricultural Development," prepared for the United Nations Conference on the Application of Science and Technology for the Benefit of the Less Developed Areas and printed in Volume III, *Agriculture*, in 1962.

Each country needs to appraise its own soil resources. Methods vary widely even on good soils. In any scheme to improve soils or make additional arable soils, one needs to know the potentials and the most effective combination of practices to use.

Except for a few small areas, most of the newly developing areas lack soil maps for planning an efficient agriculture on either the present arable land or the potentially arable land not now being used. On the accompanying outline map of the world, the approximate availability of soil surveys basic to agricultural planning is indicated. The soil surveys give people a bridge between the whole body of agricultural knowledge and its specific application to a tract of land.

To make a soil map of any area, there must be a classification of soils, based upon the combinations of their characteristics that reflect their basic properties. In the United States, more than 70 thousand local kinds of soil are recognized, each with a unique set of characteristics. Once we have a detailed soil map of all the Tropics, we may expect many more kinds of soil there than in all the temperate countries.

With both farm and research experience related to named and described kinds of soil, the soil map is the effective tool for selecting from our knowledge the information that applies to any specific tract.

Soil maps are especially needed to avoid waste in the introduction of new systems of use. The only alternative is the direct help of a widely experienced scientist who can recognize, without soil maps, how the soils relate to others under advanced use elsewhere.

Scientists have been studying the properties, behavior, and classification of soils in the temperate areas of the earth for more than a century. Since the Second World War, much has been learned about soils of tropical and subtropical areas. Except in the places where advanced agriculture has been long established and in a few areas of concentration since the war, the data about soils in these vast areas are too scanty for the operational planning of modern systems of use.

In any country, however, a first approximation of a soil map can be had by collecting and synthesizing all the available data on soils, geology, land form, relief, vegetation, and climate. Such maps can be used to help locate the most promising broad areas for development and for suggesting the steps to take, provided the classification is scientifically consistent with basic principles.

Since soil management systems have been worked out for many of the important kinds of soil in the world, this knowledge can be transferred to areas of like soils elsewhere. If we know the kind of soil in a specific area, we have a basis for starting an appraisal. This method for transferring the results of research and experience from one area to another, even between continents, is called the method of geographic correlation.

A world map of kinds of soil, classified by uniform standards, could expedite this important method of geographic correlation.

The minimum scale for a world soil map useful in transferring agricultural knowledge and technology would be

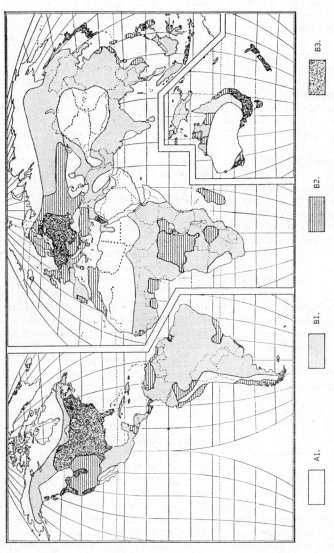

A. *Areas relatively unimportant for crops, except locally.*
  A1. *Existing soil maps of little or no usefulness for agricultural interpretations,*
      except in a few localities. Most soil maps highly schematic.
B. *Areas relatively important for crops.*
  B1. *Existing soil maps of little or no usefulness for agricultural interpretations,*
      except in a few localities; most maps small in scale and highly schematic.
  B2. *Coverage mainly by soil maps useful for broad agricultural interpretations*
      at the province level (political units about 10 million hectares—20,471,000
      acres—in size); maps of medium scale and at least partly schematic.

B3. *Coverage, with some gaps, mainly by soil maps useful for moderately*
    detailed agricultural interpretations at the county level (political units
    about 100 thousand hectares—200,471 acres—in size); high proportion
    of maps detailed or semidetailed and based largely on field investigations.
    (Boundaries are approximate and delimit dominant conditions only.
    Hence, within any areas mapped as a given category, there may be small
    areas of other categories.)

Some regions lack such coverage but have detailed or semidetailed maps
(like B3) for scattered localities.

A1. B1. B2. B3.

1:2,500,000 (about 1 inch to 40 miles). Such a map would need to indicate the kinds of soil accurately in relation to the principal railroads and highways, rivers, market towns, and other local features, so that the local users could orient themselves and read the map. From the map they need to be able to tell the kinds of soil they are dealing with locally and the other places in the world with similar soils.

In this way they can learn from what experiment stations and from what developed areas they can most likely obtain useful suggestions.

In addition to the kind of soil and its associated climate, the agricultural adviser must take account of the social facilities available and the skill of the cultivators.

It cannot be said that a complete farming system can be transferred from an area of one kind of soil in a highly advanced society to an area of the same kind of soil in a primitive society. Improvements in land tenure, such as the consolidation of fragmented holdings, usually must also be undertaken.

Yet through soil classification and its interpretation, knowledge about how the soils and crops need to be treated can be transferred and much improved local methods worked out within the framework of services, materials, and skills available in the new area.

Such transfers of knowledge and experience permit selection of promising tracts and general planning for their development. For the general planning within a country, soil maps at scales of 1:250,000 (about 1 inch to 4 miles) to 1:1,000,000 (about 1 inch to 16 miles) are needed.

As an essential first part of operational planning of a scheme, detailed soil maps of large scale, say around 1:20,000 (about 3.2 inches to the mile), give a sound basis for planning roads, water-control structures, the consolidation of fragmented holdings, and specific farming systems according to the local kinds of soil.

Substantial beginnings toward an efficient and abundant agriculture that stimulates economic growth can be made without a complete soil survey, a full set of long-time experiments, the latest in facilities for research in the basic sciences, or the highly equipped laboratories.

To appraise the fertilizer needs, for example, a start can be made by examining growing crops. The nutrient-deficiency symptoms of our most important food and industrial crops are well known. Exploratory soil maps with detailed soil surveys of sample areas can be made fairly rapidly.

Thus, through the method of geographic correlation, much information can be made available to a new area to suggest the soils most likely to respond well to management and the systems most worth testing.

Methods have been developed for field testing fertilizers, new crops, and other practices in combination rapidly. The best of the combined practices can be shown on demonstration farms.

Thus does the appraisal of resources and development proceed together. As agriculture develops and the local cultivators gain skill, the detailed soil surveys can be completed and other research facilities expanded to furnish more precise recommendations of the type highly educated farmers in the advanced countries are familiar with.

In the advanced agricultural areas, several techniques are used together to appraise soil potentials and to give advice to people growing crops. They include a properly interpreted soil survey, nutrient-deficiency symptoms on plant leaves, results of chemical tests on samples of soil, local field trials, long-time field experiments, and demonstration farms.

Actually, skilled soil scientists do not depend on any one method anywhere nor do they use all methods everywhere. To speed up the process of agricultural production in a developing area, they develop an advisory system by selecting methods that give reasonably acceptable results for the costs, the recommendations of wide acceptance and use, and maximum support to the other practices used by the cultivators.

A good approximation at once is far better for cultivators just beginning in modern agriculture than a long and expensive wait for precise results.

The more precise data give their full advantage only in a fully developed, advanced soil use system where skillful cultivators can make small differences in practices for high production that they could not at first understand.

The great need now is to make more substantial progress toward the great potential abundance in our soils by making full use of geographic correlation with the best soil maps available, and systems of simple testing methods, for individual recommendations. These can be improved with more elaborate and expensive methods as the local people have the income and the skills to benefit from them.

And, of course, additional food potentials exist in the sea and in the lakes and streams. These have not been considered here—only the soils.

Progress will require increased education and skill. Fertilizers are needed from the start on nearly all soils of the newly developing countries. They will reward the cultivator only if the fertilizer and the associated practices, including crop selection, to make it effective are fitted properly to the kind of soil he cultivates.

CHARLES E. KELLOGG *is Deputy Administrator (for Soil Survey), Soil Conservation Service. He received his doctor's degree from Michigan State University in 1929 and served on the staffs at the University of Wisconsin and North Dakota State University. He has headed the Soil Survey since July 1934. His work has taken him to many foreign countries as a representative of the United States or as a guest of foreign institutes. He was awarded the degree of doctor of science by Gembloux (Belgium), North Dakota State University, and Ghent (Belgium).*

Soil Conservation, a World Movement

by ROY D. HOCKENSMITH and PHOEBE HARRISON

MEN FROM MANY countries have come to the United States to study ways to protect the soil and augment its productivity.

Most of them were sent by their governments. Men from Kenya, the Union of South Africa, Cyprus, the Federation of Rhodesia and Nyasaland, and Basutoland came first, in the thirties. Twenty-five specialists in agriculture from Central America, South America, and Mexico arrived in 1943; they knew the agriculture of their countries but were uninformed on modern methods of conserving soil and water.

Several thousands since then have come to work for a year or more with technicians and study at universities.

When they return home, they set up training programs for professional conservationists.

Their studies embrace the management of soil; the use of soil and water in irrigation farming; the prevention and control of erosion; ways to improve soil fertility; and newly developed or redesigned conservation practices.

Examples of the last are stripcropping and grass waterway systems, which have come into use on slopes in nearly every State and in Mexico, Australia, New Zealand, Canada, Brazil, Venezuela, and elsewhere.

In Spain, where a few years ago there was no sign of the modern conservation pattern, many large tracts now have flowing, curved plantings and harvestings laid out in beautiful precision.

Other practices of ancient origin, like the bench terracing of the Phoenicians and the Incas, have been refined after research and demonstrations in California, Puerto Rico, and in the mountains of Mexico.

MANY COUNTRIES recognize that conservation of soil and water is a key to food production for growing populations and that soil must be kept productive year after year.

In the United States, per-acre increases in yields made possible in part by progress in soil and water conservation, have enabled us to grow, on fewer acres, agricultural products to meet ever-rising needs. Thus we have been able to take out of cultivation many acres that are not suited for continued cropping and to compensate for the food production lost on much good land that has been taken over by homes, industrial plants, highways, and other nonagricultural uses.

Other countries, including Mexico, Australia, New Zealand, and the Republic of South Africa, also have experienced significant per-acre increases in yields. All have excellent conservation programs, in which large numbers of technicians work directly with farmers and ranchers.

Italy and Taiwan are examples of small and heavily populated countries that have profited from conservation.

FOUR OBJECTIVES of soil conservation in the United States are:

To control soil erosion at all times and prevent soil damage in the future.

To use the better soils, wherever crops can be grown efficiently, for greater net gain per acre. The aim is to help the farmer reach a level of income and standard of living closer to that of managers in industrial enterprises.

To convert land least suitable for cultivation to pastures, forestry, recreation, and wildlife or other uses in which the soil is not disturbed.

To protect and hold in reserve soils not needed but potentially suited to cultivation until there is a demand for farm commodities from them or until they may be needed for the balancing of efficient farm units.

Good progress is being made in planned conversions in land use in our country. The acreage converted by soil conservation district cooperators to less intensive long-term uses exceeded 21.5 million acres during 1952–1961. The conversions included cropland converted to grass and woods.

The Soviet Union also has converted much land not suitable for crop production to conservation uses, such as forests and grass or water storage. In the regions of loess—highly erodible, wind-laid soil materials—thousands of gullies have been healed through conversion of cropland to grass. Soviet technicians and farmers have become adept in controlling the type of gullying peculiar to loess soils.

AN EXAMPLE of scientifically planned clearing, plowing, and cropping of new lands can be seen in Zambia, Malawi, and Southern Rhodesia. Farmers and agricultural specialists there have had the unique experience of developing an agriculture largely on virgin land.

They have used soil surveys, in terms of land capability, as the base for planning. Most other countries have had to superimpose a conservation agriculture on used lands, many of them eroded and depleted of their natural fertility.

Aside from the United States and the Soviet Union, no large country seems to have used the land conversion principle very much. Extensive, sparsely settled land does not lend itself to this particular kind of planning because there is no need for it; nor does a large, densely populated country, such as India, because the urgency for total use of the lands of all categories does not allow the money, time, and effort required.

In this period of increasing populations nearly everywhere, the four principles and objectives of soil conservation, if used persistently in planning for conservation, could help greatly in solving the problems connected with unbalanced, overbalanced, or uncertain production.

Control of erosion is a fundamental consideration because not even a good crop of grass seed, an indispensable item in any soil conservation project, can be grown on eroded land.

IN CONNECTION with problems of using water in semiarid countries, the Snowy Mountains scheme of Australia, the world's driest continent, wherein three river systems are being diverted to convert hundreds of miles of arid but fertile plains to productive land, is an interesting endeavor.

The Snowy Mountains Authority, the agency responsible for the undertaking—half completed in 1964—has adopted intensive soil conservation methods wherever the natural vegetation and soil surface have been disturbed. Drainage is controlled by use of a combination of stone and steel drains, grassed waterways, absorption and contour banks (terraces), and settling ponds. Mechanical stabilization of steep slopes is achieved by networks of woven wickerwork fences, brush matting, and bitumen sprays.

Revegetation follows mechanical stabilization. White clover has been used extensively. Trees, particularly willow and poplar, have been widely planted.

To control erosion, grazing has been eliminated on much of the high plains that comprise the watersheds of the various storage works. The deterioration of pasture cover because of harmful grazing practices, including burning the dry grass tops after the snow melted each spring, had been a serious erosion problem in Australia.

Grazing on much of the Snowy Mountains country is strictly con-trolled to prevent silting of the reservoirs and damage to slopes.

Values of the Snowy Mountains scheme, started in 1946, have become apparent. Its two main products—power for new industries and irrigation water for agriculture—and its important byproducts, recreation and an anticipated tourist industry, are in sight.

The soil conservation works, which have been largely done by the Soil Conservation Service of New South Wales and the Soil Conservation Authority of Victoria, are recognized as assurance that a valuable national asset will not depreciate through uncontrolled gullying, siltation, or destruction of the vegetation.

In the State of Israel, where water is a limiting factor in agriculture, a Soil Conservation Service has been functioning since shortly after the country was established in 1948.

Conservation plans were operating in 1964 on all land used for cultivation; a third is under irrigation. Contouring of different types is used; broad-base terraces are prominent in the landscape. Water is conserved in all possible ways, including carefully designed waterway systems, multiple-purpose ponds, and judicious watering for irrigation.

SOME PROJECTS involve a studied use of conservation techniques for opening virgin land for farming and grazing.

An example is the huge Sabi Catchment in Zambia, Malawi, and Southern Rhodesia. Soil surveys were made of the region, which had never been disturbed by man. The land was classified in detail for various uses. All clearing, opening of grassland and forest, plowing, and other operations have been done in accordance with the classification plan.

In the Republic of South Africa, district committees are advised to give special attention to the planning of watersheds, big or small, for complete conservation. Specific practices, such as construction of contour banks, receive priority. The soil conservation department of the Ministry of Agriculture is helping the districts through an intensive educational program in addition to technical assistance. Lectures and demonstrations are planned for all farmers in areas where there has been a definite decline in the number of farms planned for conservation.

Working toward conservation of a complete river basin, the Soil and Water Conservation Department of Colombia has started from scratch to make surveys and plans in the provinces of Huila, Cordoba, Magdalena, and Guabira. The surveys include all the rich alluvial lands of the Sinu River Basin.

Experiments have been undertaken to determine ways to conserve the soils of steep lands used for coffee production in Colombia. Five methods of contour planting, conforming with the same number of slope gradients, have been recommended for establishment of all coffee plantations. Other experiments involve the use of waste materials from coffee harvesting and processing to restore organic matter to soils.

The United States Department of Agriculture and ministries in other countries maintain close working relationships. Especially in research to develop new practices for tropical countries is a continuous correspondence carried on among scientists and technicians of the two Americas.

Chile in 1962 published an agrarian reform law, which made ownership of agricultural land contingent upon its proper use and improvement.

São Paulo, Minas Gerais, and Rio Grande do Sul in Brazil organized agencies that provide farmers with technical assistance in solving soil and water conservation problems.

In São Paulo, the first measures to protect the soil against erosion were taken in 1938, when the provincial department of agriculture created a terracing service. The agency was replaced in 1940 by the Division of Conservation, which became the administrative unit for a Teaching and Training Service, a Technical Assistance Service, and an Expansion (Extension) Service. Special courses in soil mapping, conservation planning, and the application of conservation practices are provided for college graduates by the Teaching and Training Service. The Technical Assistance Service supplies the technical help that farmers need to apply conservation practices to the land. The State is divided into 10 area conservancies. These are subdivided into 99 conservation units, which serve 505 townships. Equipment and an operator to do conservation work are furnished to the farmer on a rental basis.

In Rio Grande do Sul, the Soil and Forest Conservation Service was created in 1946 under the direction of the secretary of agriculture. A Renewable Resources Section was formed in 1956. It includes the Soil Conservation Service, which operates in 7 regions through 30 conservation units.

SOIL CONSERVATION in the Soviet Union is in the tradition of early Russian soil scientists, who were leaders in the basic research into the nature, genesis, and geography of soils and soil classification. Conservation needs and practices are included in all farm plans, so that there are relatively few instances of seriously misused soils. Even in the newly opened lands, care is given to protect soils subject to wind erosion.

Vegetative practices for erosion control, such as tree planting and good management of grass, are used in most parts of the country. Shelterbelts and windbreaks to protect crops against hot winds and soil blowing and sometimes to control runoff are used on collective and state farms. Legume-grass mixtures are given emphasis in acid podzolic soils and peat soils to maintain soil fertility. Essentially all farms have plans of crop rotation.

A water-conserving practice used in northern Kazakhskaya and other areas of the Soviet Union is snow ridging with tractor-drawn machines. The machines pack snow and push it into contour ridges to hold as much as possible on the field. It is said that as much as a thousand tons of additional water per hectare (2.471 acres) can be conserved as soil moisture by this method.

The Republic of the Philippines is a leader in soil conservation among Pacific regions. Despite limited financial support and other difficulties, the Philippine Soil Conservation Service has completed soil surveys of 25 million acres and erosion surveys on 10 million acres.

Nearly 100 thousand acres have been covered under cooperative soil conservation work. Numerous demonstrations and scattered areas have been treated with conservation plans and practices. A handicap to overall conservation is the predominance of small landholdings—2 to 4 acres. Conservationists have begun a concerted effort among the country's conservation agencies to correct the situation. They advocate a type of land reform that would permit formation of districts including a large number of small farms to be treated as a unit for conservation planning.

Another island country, Malagasy Republic—Madagascar—with nearly 5 million inhabitants, has a conservation program that is an interesting example of how the idea of soil conservation can be retained in the transformation of a country from colonial status to a republic.

Another interesting point is that the great island is near Kenya, the east African country where the work of conservation has been carried on for years.

In 1940, Kenya, then a colony, dispatched its newly appointed soil conservation official to the United States to learn about American methods. He returned to Kenya to encourage the conservation of Kenya's grazing lands, managed almost wholly by native tribesmen.

In 1963, soon after Kenya was pronounced a republic, the country's conservationists announced that 7 million acres had been brought under conservation use and protection. Loans from the World Bank have helped Kenya expand its program to include work to improve tenure of land and farm management.

The Agricultural Rehabilitation and Development Act was enacted in Canada in 1962. It established a nationwide soil and water conservation and development program. Work started at once on about a dozen development and research areas that covered large acreages and included a number of communities. Funds were appropriated and plans were made for an initial 3-year phase of the program to end April 1, 1965. The Provinces, all of which have carried on soil and water conservation programs for some years, benefited financially from the national program.

The Soil Conservation Service of New South Wales in Australia has a plant-hire plan, whereby heavy equipment is available to farmers for building terracing systems and dams and do other work in conservation. Officials of several South American countries have planned to use a similar scheme.

In China, an ambitious soil conservation plan, involving a vast region between the Yellow River and the Wei, with deeply eroded and gullied loess soil, was announced in 1955. It was to be carried out in connection with irrigation schemes, some of which have been completed, to reclaim urgently needed cultivable land. Nothing is known of the plan for soil conservation between the great rivers. Also unknown is the fate of the painstakingly assembled soil and water conservation experiment station and demonstrations, flourishing in 1945, at Tien-Shui in Kansu.

Across a few miles of the South China Sea, on the large island of Taiwan, Chinese have developed a soil and water conservation program. About 500 trained technicians work closely with farmers on the island.

In India, Pakistan, and the Sahara fringes, work to halt desert creep has been started in thousands of small projects. Dune-control methods that have been successful in certain places in the Great Plains, Northwest coastal areas, and dune areas of the Great Lakes region have been used.

Surveys by Pakistani and United States conservation technicians in Pakistan revealed that, aside from desert creep, flash runoff from monsoon rains, destruction of vegetation by overgrazing, up-and-down hill cultivation, and lack of vegetated contour bunds—terraces—are primary causes of extensive erosion.

Practical demonstrations of soil and water conservation methods suitable for Pakistan's different climatic and topographic areas were set up for the benefit of farm families and for training technicians, a procedure duplicating the period before formation of soil conservation districts in the United States.

A doubling of per-acre yields of food and forage crops, realized on test fields by use of practices to conserve moisture and fertilizers, gave impetus to Pakistan's plan to organize a soil conservation program for all the country.

An educational program launched in 1956 to teach conservation principles and methods to Indian villagers still farming the primitive shifting-cultivation way was bearing fruit by 1964. This was seen in many requests from village councils for technical aid in reclaiming blown soils and some tracts riddled by gullying.

A new law passed in Turkey in 1960 created a soil conservation and farm irrigation directorate and provided legal authorization for an unusually broad national program for all phases of soil and water use and conservation.

The new agency's functions extend from prevention of erosion and flood damage to encouraging land consolidation for conservation purposes. It includes reclamation of brushlands, irrigation services of all kinds, soil surveys and land capability maps,

research on soil and soil fertility, and the organization of soil conservation and irrigation districts or watershed associations.

The first activity carried out was the training of technicians at regional centers. Each training group was charged with the development of a demonstration of techniques. In this way, the initial conservation work put on the land immediately benefits a significant amount of the country's agricultural soil and water resources.

A NEW EXPERIENCE for the Soil Conservation Service—an extension of its regular functions to another country's land—began in 1962. The Republic of Tunisia requested on-the-ground technical assistance in planning and developing a pilot tract of nearly 250 thousand acres, to be used for demonstration and training.

The Tunisian Government specified that all applicable conservation and range management techniques be applied in a planned sequence; Tunisian technicians would do the work and undergo training as soil conservationists from the beginning. Funds were supplied by the Agency for International Development.

A second project was approved in 1963. A working agreement was signed with the Republic of Algeria, where the Soil Conservation Service undertook work on four large projects in conservation and land management.

The agreement designated a twofold purpose: To provide immediate employment among the rural population and to bring about better use and conservation of agricultural land. The agreement called specifically for erosion-control structures; terracing; reforestation of denuded slopes; clearing of stony lands; and construction of water-spreading systems, wells, pits, and cisterns to store irrigation water.

Long-range guides and a pattern of advisory and technical services are to be developed to become a model for the Algerian Ministry of Agriculture in carrying out a long-term soil and water conservation program. The training of Algerian technicians in procedures for conducting such a program is considered essential, as is also the devising of ways to influence the rural population in the direction of greater appreciation of its responsibilities for preservation and improvement of land, water, and forestry resources.

The stabilization of duneland, of great importance in northern Africa, has been under study and experiment in the countries north of the Sahara. Tests in Libya whereby sand is sprayed with a thin oil to stop blowing were started in 1963. Acacia and eucalyptus trees were planted in the dunes that had moisture below surface. The ground was sprayed immediately. Excellent wind erosion control and tree growth resulted on a large area that once was under natural forest.

THUS soil conservation has become a world movement. Its scientific and economic implications are beginning to be discernible, especially in countries where conservation is the people's concern, the governments having the role of technical and financial supporter. There soil conservation is understood and discussed by large numbers of people.

ROY D. HOCKENSMITH *became Director, Soil Survey Operations, Soil Conservation Service, in 1952. His worldwide experiences include service as chairman of the Commission on Soil Technology of the International Society of Soil Science, as participant at the United Nations Scientific Conference on Conservation and Utilization of Resources, and at a Food and Agriculture Organization Conference on Land and Water Utilization and Conservation.*

PHOEBE HARRISON *joined the Division of Information, Soil Conservation Service, in 1936. As a part of its regular information program, the Division handles foreign requests for information on soil and water conservation, makes studies of programs and developments in other countries, and maintains records pertaining to the world conservation movement.*

Water Has a Key Role

by ELCO L. GREENSHIELDS

TO KEEP PACE with the needs of the billion persons who have entered the world since 1940 and the needs of countless others who want to be better fed and clothed, agricultural production must rise. Agriculture can keep up, but not without greater efforts to increase efficiency and to expand into undeveloped regions.

Agricultural production can advance in two ways. One is to use more acres of potential arable land. The other is to increase the efficiency of utilization of the land now farmed. Expanding irrigation may be an absolute necessity to extend crop acreage; it may be the most productive of all possible improvements on present cropland.

Water is the key. It makes possible the full use of technology in farming— the proper application of fertilizers, suitable crop rotations, the best of adapted varieties, and so forth.

Too little attention is being given to irrigation in districts that already have a high rate of output. Too much attention is given to the glamorous projects that will make the deserts bloom. We might better concentrate our limited capital to extending irrigation into the existing farmlands rather than developing new areas.

Nevertheless, the prospects that fire the imaginations of engineers and planners are the zones where agriculture has made little progress.

One is the arid zone, which occupies more than one-third of the landmass of the globe. Most of it is in the Tropics. Deserts cover 37 percent of Africa but only 10 percent of South America. The arid zones are rich in solar energy. Their soils generally are rich in nutrients, but they lack water.

Another zone is the subpolar belt. There the challenge is to select early maturing crops for the short growing season and to discover economically feasible ways to control the effects of the untimely frosts, chilling winds, and occasional droughts.

Tropical rain forests have a great potential. The forested, humid Tropics occupy 41 percent of the total area of Africa and 43 percent of South America. They produce an enormous mass of vegetable substance, although the land itself generally is not fertile. The big question is whether to try to produce conventional food crops or by research to try to find a way to convert the canopy of the forests to usable protein extracts. It could well be that the tropical belt can be made to yield a vast supply of food from the leaves.

Irrigation was used on 370 million acres in the production of crops in the early sixties. This estimate is based on my appraisal of available reports from 95 countries and territories. (By irrigation we mean that water is artificially applied to the land or rainfall is artificially held on the land, as in paddies.)

Thus at that time 13 percent of the world's arable land was under irrigation. The major regions of the world had the following percentages of the total irrigation: Europe, 5.9; the Soviet Union, 8.3; Asia, 64.8; Africa, 3.8; Oceania, 0.6; South America, 3.2; and North America, 13.4. The United States had 10 percent.

The hydroelectric capacity of Africa is estimated at two-fifths of the world's capacity, but it has no comparable potential for irrigation. Roughly 4 million acres are under irrigation in Africa south of the Sahara and 8 million acres in northern and northwestern Africa. The whole continent has a potential of about 36 million acres—about the same as the irrigated acreage in the United States in 1964.

This estimate assumes that the total area under irrigation will reach 12 million to 14 million acres in trans-Sahara Africa; 14 million to 16 million acres in Morocco, Algeria, Tunisia, and the United Arab Republic; and possibly 10 million acres of swamplands that could be drained and given supplemental irrigation.

The perennial and seasonal swamps, a striking feature of Africa, cover about 125 thousand square miles. The more important are the Niger Delta, Lake Chad, the fresh water swamps of Nigeria, the Congo Basin, and the Kafue flats in Zambia. Their immensity suggests the possibility of draining and pumping schemes, but whether it is feasible and economically attainable is a question.

A 10-year program of the Government of Tunisia to bring its irrigated area up to 151 thousand acres includes dams for water storage to irrigate 43 thousand acres; drilled wells to irrigate 14 thousand acres; and dug wells and other small water developments to provide water for 19 thousand acres. Irrigation works had been developed in 1962 for 74 thousand acres. Estimates are that the full development of all water resources in Tunisia could provide enough water to irrigate 740 thousand acres.

Morocco has made prodigious efforts to advance irrigation agriculture—to make the country the California of Africa. The National Office of Irrigation, whose staff numbered 8 thousand in 1964, is regarded as of unusual competence. Each year between 1955 and 1964, an average of 34 thousand acres were added to the irrigated area.

MEXICO had about 10.6 million acres under irrigation in 1964. Of that, about 6.9 million acres had been developed by the government and 3.7 million by private enterprise.

There, as elsewhere in the world, rehabilitation of the oldest irrigation areas has become necessary because of salinization. The rehabilitation of seven irrigation districts has been undertaken through two loans from the International Bank for Reconstruction and Development. The Ministry of Agriculture embarked on a program to finance the improvement of new irrigated areas (some 173 thousand acres a year) and the rehabilitation of about 494 thousand acres a year. The total area proposed for irrigation in new projects is nearly 3 million acres.

A large part of the irrigation in Central America has been developed by private enterprise, but nearly all the governments of these small countries started irrigation projects in the sixties.

Information from United Nations sources included these figures on the irrigated acreages and the percentages of arable land under irrigation: Guatemala, 99 thousand, 2.7 percent; Honduras, 82 thousand, 3.3; El Salvador, 49 thousand, 2.6; Nicaragua, 30 thousand, 0.4; Costa Rica, 37 thousand, 5.3; Panama, 35 thousand, 3.1. Of a total of about 18 million acres of arable land in the six countries, 332 thousand acres—1.9 percent—were irrigated in the early sixties.

NEARLY ALL the island countries of the Caribbean have been pursuing active irrigation programs.

A survey by the Food and Agriculture Organization in 1953 indicated the countries had started projects that would put 100 thousand acres under irrigation and had scheduled projects that would irrigate another 60 thousand acres.

The Dominican Republic has made plans to increase its irrigated acreage by more than 250 thousand acres.

In Haiti, projects under construction in 1964 were designed to bring into irrigation 175 thousand acres.

Puerto Rico has a multipurpose project to irrigate 26 thousand acres.

The United Nations reported the following irrigated acreages and percentages of arable land:

The Dominican Republic, 334 thousand, 19.9 percent; Haiti, 161 thousand, 6.1; Cuba, 148 thousand, 3.0; Puerto Rico, 96 thousand, 12.4; Jamaica, 54 thousand, 9.5.

The five countries thus had about 793 thousand acres (of a total of 10.6 million acres of tillable land) under irrigation.

SOUTH AMERICA has comparatively abundant water resources, whose full potential has hardly been touched.

Most of the continent has enough rainfall for farming, but roughly a million square miles are deficient in total annual rainfall, and other districts are subject to major seasonal droughts.

The main arid zones are in Argentina, Chile, Peru, Bolivia, and Venezuela. Colombia and Ecuador have smaller ones. In what is known as the drought polygon in northeastern Brazil, rainfall is highly irregular.

Three-fourths of the irrigation in South America is in Argentina, Chile, and Peru. The irrigated land used for crops and the percentages of arable land in 1963 were:

Argentina, 2,772 thousand acres, 3.7 percent; Bolivia, 160 thousand, 2.1; Brazil, 865 thousand, 1.8; British Guiana, 148 thousand, 4.3; Chile, 3,370 thousand, 24.7; Colombia, 544 thousand, 4.3; Ecuador, 425 thousand, 8.3; Paraguay, 30 thousand, 2.3; Peru, 2,995 thousand, 62.0; Surinam, 35 thousand, 40.7; Uruguay, 64 thousand, 1.0; Venezuela, 642 thousand, 5.0.

The 12 countries thus had a total of about 189 million acres of arable land, of which 12 million acres—6.4 percent—were irrigated.

The development of irrigation relative to need and relative to the rest of the world has been gradual. Many countries in South America have failed to provide regular and continuous financing for the construction and maintenance of the larger number of irrigation projects on which construction has been reported.

Available records for 1960 show little increase over records for 1950, but projects started or planned since 1954 are a sign of considerable momentum. A study by the United Nations Economic Commission for Latin America in 1963 estimated that 32 million acres, or more than 15 percent of the cultivated land, needed irrigation.

Chile has good resources of land and water for the further development of irrigation on about 5 million acres. The Ministry of Public Works inaugurated an irrigation program to put 1.2 million acres under irrigation. Studies have been started on projects that could bring in 1.6 million acres.

Peru, too, has good water resources and also can expand its irrigation by several million acres. New projects in Peru would provide water to about 1.8 million acres. The irrigation of 1.4 million acres more may be possible.

In Brazil, where irrigation has been of minor importance, five separate projects under construction and planned in 1964 could add 270 thousand acres.

In Bolivia, two projects involve 40 thousand acres; projects under investigation could add 500 thousand acres.

Argentina began several projects and has many others under study that could more than double its irrigation. Argentina has received United Nations Special Fund technical assistance in the study of the Viedma Valley in the lower Rio Negro River Basin.

THE 1959 census reported that slightly more than 33 million acres in the United States were irrigated, an increase of 7.3 million acres in 10 years. Over several decades, irrigation has progressed steadily at the rate of about 750 thousand acres a year.

I estimate that about 37 million acres were irrigated in 1963. Farmers are equipped to irrigate at least 40 million acres if water supplies are available in the West and if there is a need in the humid East.

The United States can still advance its irrigation. A modest rate of increase can be expected over the long run. In any one year, the amount of irrigation could decline where water supplies in the West are low, economic conditions are unfavorable, or rainfall is adequate in the East.

The upper limit of irrigation in the United States is estimated to be about 70 million to 75 million acres—about 50 million acres in this century.

CANADA has vast water resources and has undertaken great waterworks for navigation and power.

Little development of water supplies for irrigation has been undertaken because natural water supplies generally are adequate for the best adapted type of agriculture.

Canada has developed 20 million kilowatts of hydroelectric capacity out of a total estimated feasible capacity of some 53 million.

Of the 3 million acres of potentially irrigable land in major projects in the western Provinces, 1.5 million acres have been or are in the process of being developed.

The major irrigation districts in Alberta actually irrigated 545 thousand acres out of a classified irrigable area of 900 thousand acres in 1960.

In British Columbia, the major irrigation districts, with an irrigable area of 400 thousand acres, irrigated a total of 218 thousand acres in 1962.

In Saskatchewan, 54 Provincial irrigation projects in 1961 covered some 440 thousand acres.

Under construction in 1964 were the St. Mary project in Alberta, to add 214 thousand acres of new irrigation to the 510 thousand acres already in the project; the Bow River project west of Medicine Hat in Alberta, whose potential is 240 thousand acres; and the South Saskatchewan River Development project for 500 thousand acres in central Saskatchewan.

THE AMOUNT of irrigation in southern Europe is relatively small—about 10 percent of the cultivated land—in relation to arable lands that could benefit by irrigation. Studies of irrigable land and available water development potential indicate that 24 percent of the farmlands could be brought under irrigation.

In southern Europe, irrigation makes possible a wide choice of crops and rotations and contributes to the diversification and intensification of farming.

In the Mediterranean countries, the influence of irrigation is small for winter crops and great for spring crops.

Irrigation is not so vital in France and Yugoslavia, where irrigation is a matter of supplementing the nearly adequate natural precipitation.

Adjusted data for seven countries in 1960 included, respectively, the acres of irrigated land and the percentages of cultivated land that were then and potentially could be irrigated: Cyprus, 195 thousand acres, 18.2 percent, 23.3 percent; France, 6,178 thousand acres, 11.6 percent, 20.4 percent; Greece, 899 thousand acres, 10.3 percent, 32.3 percent; Israel, 334 thousand acres, 31.1 percent, 54 percent; Italy, 6,864 thousand acres, 17.5 percent, 23.8 percent; Spain, 4,524 thousand acres, 8.6 percent, 21.2 percent; Yugoslavia, 297 thousand acres, 1.4 percent, 35.9 percent.

THE EXTENT of irrigation in northern Europe varies because of differences in rainfall, soil conditions, and the type of agriculture. Further expansion of irrigation will not be so great as in southern Europe, mainly because the need is less great.

Irrigation in the northern regions is a safeguard against crop damage during occasional dry periods. In places that have high winds and heavy evaporation, sprinkler irrigation is valuable. Some crops, particularly vegetables, have requirements beyond the normally heavy rainfall. Extra water is required also in places of highly pervious soils. Vineyards in Germany (195 thousand acres in 1962) are irrigated for frost control.

Irrigation in northern Europe increases grain yields by 20 to 50 percent. Yields of sugarbeets have been increased 70 to 80 percent and potato yields, 60 to 100 percent.

Much of the irrigation in Europe is by sprinklers. Flood irrigation is used principally in valleys and mostly for meadows and pastures. Flush irrigation, used in mountainous areas, can be carried out by simple means but is wasteful of water and requires that a field be cut up by numerous ditches.

ARTIFICIAL regulation of the water table, which is possible only in fairly permeable soils, is used mainly in the Netherlands. The level of ground water must be regulated precisely for the production of flower bulbs.

The European Commission on Agriculture in 1961 reported these figures as to the acres and percentages of cultivated land that are irrigated: Austria, 67 thousand acres, 1.5 percent; Belgium, 117 thousand acres, 5 percent; Denmark, 74 thousand acres, 1.1 percent; the Federal Republic of Germany, 642 thousand acres, 3.1 percent; the Netherlands, 2,065 thousand acres, 80.4 percent; Norway, 15 thousand acres, 0.7 percent; Poland, 514 thousand acres, 1.3 percent; Sweden, 62 thousand acres, 0.7 percent; Switzerland, 52 thousand acres, 4.8 percent.

Figures as to potential irrigation, as percentages of all cultivated land, were: Austria, 9.7; Belgium, 16.8; Denmark, 1.1; Federal Republic of Germany, 9.4; the Netherlands, 96.3; Norway, 0.7; Poland, 14.5; Sweden, 0.7; Switzerland, 9.3.

THE SOVIET UNION has a landmass of 8.65 million square miles, three times the size of the 48 contiguous United States, but has only 470 million acres in farms, or about 9 percent of its area.

Most of the Soviet agriculture is in the fertile triangle, which extends from the Baltic and Black Seas eastward to south-central Siberia as far as the upper valley of the Yenisei River. Six of the Soviet Union's largest rivers, the Dnepr, Don, Volga, Yana, Irtysh, and Ob, flow through the region.

Most of the territory south of 50° north latitude has an average rainfall of 4 to 16 inches a year. Its major rivers are the Dnepr, which flows into the Black Sea; the Don, which empties into the Sea of Azov; the Volga and Ural Rivers, which enter the Caspian Sea; and the two Darya Rivers, which flow into the Aral Sea.

The eastern part has a great number of channels formerly occupied by streams—an indication that the region has become dry through the centuries.

The Soviets have announced extraordinary plans to develop the water resources of this south-central region.

Soviet 5-year plans always have listed huge targets for increased irrigation. Since the severe winter of 1962–1963 and the drought of the summer of 1963 caused Russia to make large purchases of grain abroad, the Soviets can be expected to accelerate their reclamation programs. In order to obtain a guaranteed crop of 30 million tons a year, they have announced plans of investing the equivalent of 15 billion dollars in new irrigation projects and new irrigated farms.

In irrigated acreage, the Soviet Union ranks with China, India, and the United States. Before the revolution in 1917, Russia had fewer than 6 million irrigated acres. More than 13 million acres had been irrigated by 1932. The first 5-year plan added nearly 3 million acres. The irrigated area reported in 1949 was 23.7 million acres and 30.7 million acres in 1958.

A scheme launched in 1955 was to use the water of the Syr Darya River to reclaim some 741 thousand acres of the "hungry steppe" of central Asia. Its main feature is a canal with an irrigation network designed to provide water to 390 thousand acres. Two smaller canals were designed to irrigate 119 thousand and 151 thousand acres.

On the Amu Darya River, the Kara Kum Canal diverts water from the Amu Darya to the water-deficient Murgab and Tedjen Rivers. Its first stage is some 248 miles long and can irrigate 250 thousand acres. Ultimately

the main canal will extend some 560 miles and will irrigate more than a million acres.

Dams on the Dnepr are being built with a view to irrigating some 3.7 million acres in southern Ukraine and northern Crimea. Its main canal, 263 miles long, is designed to supply water to 900 thousand acres.

Plans for dams on the Volga would provide water for 2 million acres in the Caspian-trans-Volga regions. The Volga region has fertile soils, but its rainfall is irregular, and occasional droughts are severe.

Plans call for transforming the Volga into seven reservoirs along its entire course, with dams to regulate the river discharge and provide hydroelectric generation of a yearly output of 10 billion kilowatt-hours of energy. The Volga is to be linked to the Ural River by the 370-mile Stalingrad Canal, which is designed to bring about 1.5 million acres under irrigation. It is to be linked to the Don River by the 63-mile Volga-Don Canal.

The development of the Don River calls for a system of main and lateral canals to irrigate 1.87 million acres. One large reservoir will have a capacity of 10 million acre-feet. Smaller reservoirs will be built on the tributaries. The main canal will be 118 miles long and the total length of the laterals will be 353 miles. A special feature will be a system of 140 pumping stations.

It has been said that the Soviet Union can put about 102 million acres under irrigation, about half of it in central Asia, Kazakhskaya, and Trans-Caucasia. That would mean a twofold to threefold increase in irrigation in droughty areas. Russia in 1962 reported advanced planning and construction on projects to irrigate 16 million acres.

A plan advanced by the Soviet engineers (as reported in Scientific American in September 1963) would dam off the Great Ob and Yenisei Rivers, which flow north to the Arctic, connect the reservoirs thus formed by a canal, and then use canals, rivers, and lakes to transport the water south to the Aral Sea and the Caspian. The achievement of that project and others would mean that Russia may be the first nation to make any sizable reclamation of the great deserts of the world.

IRRIGATION is important in all Asia, but I give some details of only a few countries in which irrigation is most extensive.

Pakistan had 27.4 million acres under irrigation in 1963. West Pakistan is dry, and much of the farming depends on irrigation. East Pakistan has abundant rainfall during the monsoon season of 4 or 5 months. In East Pakistan's tropical climate, irrigation could bring about the production of one or two additional crops during the 7 or 8 months of dry weather.

East Pakistan, with its Brahmaputra-Ganges-Meghna River complex, has been a dreamland of planners of water resource developments. Their plans fill volumes but overlook some basic facts and ignore the fundamental human and social environment. For example, the Brahmaputra-Ganges multipurpose development of seven major schemes would supposedly convert East Bengal in 30 years into a land of plenty for its burgeoning population of 50 million.

A start was made on one part, the Ganges-Kobadak, which would provide for flood protection and irrigation of 2.2 million acres. Plans were made in 1952. Work started in 1954 as part of East Pakistan's first 5-year plan. Targets were to irrigate 150 thousand acres by 1958 and another 50 thousand acres by 1960. A large amount of scarce investment funds was spent, and much precious land was taken from thousands of cultivators for a huge network of canals that were used only in part for the first time in 1963. The first phase of the first unit was opened with ceremonies in 1962, but effective operation of the scheme failed

to be achieved. Many major problems of civil engineering remained unsolved in 1964.

IRRIGATION has been practiced in India since ancient times.

Nearly 58 million acres were irrigated in 1959—35 percent by government projects. The acreage in 1959 is a gain of 6.3 million over that in 1951.

India in 1963 irrigated nearly 20 percent of her cultivated area, yet the utilization of the water resources of her major rivers is far from complete. Only a little more than 5 percent of the annual flow of the nine most important rivers is withdrawn for irrigation. The target of the third 5-year plan of India is 90 million acres of irrigated land—nearly 30 percent of the average planted acreage in India. The long-term objective of Indian planners is to bring about 175 million acres under irrigation.

All reports I have seen indicate that China has more farmland under irrigation than any nation. The Production Yearbook of the Food and Agriculture Organization shows an unofficial report of 183 million acres irrigated in 1960—more than twice the acreage reported for 1957.

A news report in 1960 quoted Chinese authorities that mainland China had irrigated 70 percent of her 266 million cultivated acres—a total of 186 million acres irrigated. The report may be untrue, for it came at a time when China was exaggerating details of its agricultural production for political reasons.

China had 16 percent (42.5 million acres) of her cultivated land under irrigation in 1949. It is unlikely that China increased her irrigation by 120 million acres in 10 years. China claimed in 1958 to have half of her farmland—167 million acres—under irrigation and announced the launching of a program to bring 80 percent of the farmland under irrigation.

In making comparisons of irrigated land, we should remember that much of the irrigation in the Far East is so-called "rainfed" irrigation, mostly paddy. The system involves little, if any, artificial control over water. The paddies are basins that hold the rain. Water may be lifted into the basins during an occasional dry period.

The figure that is considered most accurate, the one published by the International Commission on Irrigation and Drainage in 1955, is 77.3 million irrigated acres in mainland China.

Mountainous Japan has 100 million acres of land, only about 15 percent of which is tillable. Seven million acres were under irrigation in 1950 and 8.5 million acres in 1960.

Japan has undertaken several large projects. The first was the Aichi Irrigation project, for which World Bank financing was obtained. It benefits 75 thousand acres, of which 41 thousand acres of existing paddy fields are supplied additional water, 28 thousand acres of upland fields are irrigated, and 6 thousand acres are newly reclaimed paddy fields.

A project on the Tedori River to be completed in 1966 will distribute muddy irrigation water in order to build up the existing thin layer of soil over 25 thousand acres. Its major works include soil-hauling equipment, mud-water mixing equipment, special conveying pipes, and pressure pumps.

Other projects include the Nabeta project to reclaim land from river estuaries and provide water to 1,580 acres; the Nobi project, with 57 thousand acres; the Toyokawe Irrigation project, 54 thousand acres; and the Iwate Sanroku Reclamation project, 30 thousand acres.

MEN since ancient times have had to get, use, and manage water.

The aqueducts of the Roman Empire were marvels of engineering; a conduit the Romans built 2 thousand years ago to provide a water supply to Tunis is still in use.

One modern counterpart—maybe greater, even, than the aqueducts—is the dredging, draining, and reclaiming of the Netherlands. Holland has been described as a sand and mud dump left over from the ice age. Starting about 400 B.C. with the building of dwelling mounds by the Frisians on the higher spots in the sea marshes, the Dutch have fought continuously against the sea and have made most of their productive land. Of the total of arable land, 2,538,000 acres, 1,843,000 acres have been reclaimed from the sea, river marshes, and moors.

Beginning with the early mound building, which involved moving by hand a cubic yardage of earth equal to that required in the original construction of the Suez Canal, the work moved into a second stage of building seawalls and dikes. By 1860, the Dutch had built 1,750 miles of dikes by hand. A third stage was the digging of ditches and canals, which drained and separated the fields and were canals for shipping. The ditches and canals meant moving a billion cubic yards of earth.

A fourth great task was the digging of peat, which had the double purpose of providing fuel and creating lakes, which, when drained, gave more fertile land than the original moors. Ten billion cubic yards were involved in the digging of moors. In these four stages, the Dutch had dug by hand the equivalent of a ship canal 40 feet deep, 200 feet wide, and 5 thousand miles long by 1860.

The great contemporary work is the closing of the Zuider Zee (1926–1932), diking and pumping the polders dry, and building a thriving agricultural economy. The reclamation of the Zuider Zee is one of the greatest works ever carried out by man. Its object was to create 550 thousand acres of new fertile land and provide a fresh-water reservoir in the heart of the country.

The Dutch had a setback in their fight against the sea in a flood in 1953, which took 400 thousand acres of the best tillable land in the southwest. The reconquering and remaking of that area have spurred those tireless people to make bolder plans for the future.

The next great undertaking will be the Delta scheme, the closing of the great estuaries of the Maas and Rhine Rivers. They expect to complete it by 1980. In the more distant future is the Wadden reclamation, the closing of the coast in northwestern Holland beyond the enclosure dike of the Zuider Zee.

THE RECLAMATION PROGRAM of the United States Bureau of Reclamation in 60 years has made an outstanding contribution to the economic development of the West.

Its continuing work is vital to the growth of western irrigation agriculture, for private expansion of irrigation has nearly reached its limit, easily achieved irrigation projects are a thing of the past, and further expansion becomes more difficult, more expensive.

The Bureau in 1964 had before it 134 proposals for projects and additional units that would provide full water to nearly 3 million acres and provide supplemental water to 1.6 million acres.

Reclamation projects from 1906 through 1962 produced a gross farm value of all crops amounting to 18.9 billion dollars. That is five times the cost of all reclamation projects, including both irrigation and nonirrigation features, such as hydropower, flood control, and recreation and municipal water supply. The 106 reclamation projects and major units of projects can provide water for 8.6 million acres of irrigable land. Reclamation projects in 1962 provided a full water supply for the irrigation of 3.5 million acres, a supplemental water service for 3.5 million acres, and a temporary water service to 188 thousand acres.

The Bureau of Reclamation has built many record-breaking dams. The 726-feet-high Hoover Dam, whose storage capacity is 31 million acre-feet, was completed in 1936. It kindled the imagination of engineers around the world and led to many larger works.

Bureau of Reclamation projects in operation in 1963 included 216 storage reservoirs, 136 diversion dams, 7,771

miles of main canals, 21,486 miles of laterals, and nearly 11 thousand miles of drains. Under construction were 23 storage dams and 2 diversion dams. The water surface of Bureau reservoirs covers 1.35 million acres. The hydroelectric powerplants connected with Bureau projects in operation and under construction in 1963 have a planned power capacity of more than 9 million kilowatts.

Among the mightiest projects of the Bureau of Reclamation are the Columbia Basin project, whose key feature is the Grand Coulee Dam, which serves about 1 million acres; the Central Valley project, the Bureau's most complex multipurpose project, involving three river systems in the 500-mile-long Central Valley of California; the Colorado-Big Thompson project, which involves more than 100 separate major engineering features that divert water across the Continental Divide through a 13-mile tunnel to provide supplemental water to 720 thousand acres; the Colorado River Storage project, which extends into 5 States and whose 4 huge dams will store 35 million acre-feet; and the Missouri River Basin project, which will cover 10 States and ultimately provide irrigation water for 3 million acres and supplemental water to nearly 700 thousand acres of irrigated land.

ONE OF THE MOST extensive flood control and river stabilization projects in the world is being undertaken in the alluvial valley of the lower Mississippi River. The complex system of levees, floodways, controlled outlets, and channel improvement, including cutoffs, required to control Mississippi floodwaters is the work of more than 150 years. The cost of works since 1927 approaches 2 billion dollars.

The Mississippi system drains 1,246,605 square miles in 31 States and 2 Provinces of Canada—41 percent of the 48 mainland States. A flood in 1927 covered 26 thousand square miles of land when levees broke. Several great flows since then have been passed to the Gulf of Mexico through the improved flood-control works.

Today there are 1,599 miles of levees along the Mississippi below Cairo, Ill. In addition, there are 1,507 miles of levees on tributary streams and 448 miles of levees in the Atchafalaya Basin, one of the major outlets for Mississippi floodwaters.

The levees are the best known feature of the lower Mississippi flood control plan, but the modern program for flood control and river improvement involves several features.

Among them are reservoirs on the tributary streams, within and outside the alluvial valley, to hold back flood-flow as much as practicable; levees on the tributaries and on the Mississippi to confine the flow to a carefully designed channel and backwater area; cutoffs on the river to speed flow down the river and lower the flood stages at key points in the system; revetment, which is placed to protect flood-control structures and to aid in stabilizing the channel; and overbank floodways, which divert flow from the river.

The plan also makes use of dikes, pumping plants, siphons, floodgates, and floodwalls.

The major remaining problem is to stabilize the caving banks of this meandering river. Work toward this end has been underway for several generations. The Mississippi is one of the outstanding examples of a large river on which extensive bank protection is being carried out. Many types of works have been used on the Mississippi and its tributaries.

Stabilizing a meandering stream the size of the Mississippi is a stupendous task. More than 375 million dollars have been spent on this phase of development since 1928. Considerable sums were spent before 1928 by the Government and by local levee districts. Additional revetment, which may cost 400 million dollars, will be needed to halt river movement.

The tremendous energy of the river is exerted constantly to continue its natural meanders. The levee system confines the flow to a channel about 3 miles wide. The width of the flood plain averages 45 miles. The complex phenomena that lead to bank undercutting and recession are not all eliminated by the works that now confine and regulate the flow. Engineers are apprehensive that the absence of any great overflow since 1927 has led to complacency about the task still ahead.

AROUND THE WORLD, the Tennessee Valley Authority is the best known and most talked-about river basin development. Its application of a unified approach to the development of water resources for multiple purposes has caught the attention of water resource planners everywhere.

Countries—especially the newer countries—want to pattern the development of their own rivers after TVA. To study TVA, 1,700 representatives came from 86 countries in 1961, 2 thousand from 70 countries in 1962, and 2,600 from 88 countries in 1963.

This is good, and America can be proud of TVA's accomplishments, but it is not all good, for two reasons.

One is that TVA has given most emphasis to large-scale hydroelectric, flood-control, and navigation work. Only minor attention has been given to agricultural development, and that only in recent years. The TVA pattern for an overall rich agricultural Nation like ours may be satisfactory, but agricultural purposes must be given high priority in most underdeveloped countries.

Furthermore, TVA works provide for nearly complete regulation and control of all the flow of the Tennessee River—an objective that is proper only for the most developed nations. Few underdeveloped countries can afford or should undertake that, no matter how generous the foreign aid given them. Countries with extremely scarce capital would be well advised to set a more limited objective for river basin development until such time as their agriculture, industry, and commerce can make use of it effectively.

The Tennessee River system drains 41 thousand square miles and is the fifth largest in the United States. It is the most completely developed large river in the world. Its entire flow can be turned off, so to speak, at the Kentucky Dam at a time when floods threaten the lower Ohio and Mississippi Rivers.

TVA was created in 1933 to develop the Tennessee River Basin so as to provide navigation on the main stem, control floods, and generate maximum power consistent with the objectives of flood control and navigation.

The TVA power system in 1963 had 32 major dams and 8 steamplants with a generating capacity of nearly 12.7 million kilowatts, and facilities for an additional generating capacity of 2.6 million kilowatts were being built.

At the beginning of the flood season each year, the reservoir system is operated so as to provide 12 million acre-feet of storage space for floodwater. TVA produces about 8 percent of all the electricity in the United States. The generation in 1963 was 68.5 billion kilowatt-hours.

The TVA navigation channel extends 650 miles from Knoxville to Paducah, Ky., where the Tennessee empties into the Ohio. TVA ties into the Inter-Connected Inland Waterway System of the Ohio, Missouri, and Mississippi Rivers and the Gulf Inter-Coastal System. The entire system comprises 7,265 miles of 9-foot channel and 1,895 miles of 6- to 9-foot channel. The freight traffic on the Tennessee River reached a total of 2.3 billion ton-miles in 1960. Thirteen million tons of commercial traffic were carried in 1962.

When TVA took stock of itself in 1961, it found gratifying progress in output of electric power and the associated rate of industrial development in the basin, river navigation and improved commerce, prevention of floods in urban areas in the basin, and the contribution of the system to the control of floods on the lower Ohio and Mississippi. The poorest showing was in agriculture. Improvement in agricultural incomes nowhere near matched the progress in industrialization and commercialization.

TVA therefore began intensive programs in tributary areas. The first such effort was in the 2,250-square-mile watershed of the Elk River in southern Tennessee and northern Alabama. TVA is working with local groups and State agencies to bring about economic advancement through both improvement of the physical state of the land and water resources and through improved methods of farming.

At the close of 1963, tributary area development programs were underway in 12 watersheds. Typical of these programs is the Beach River tributary in western Tennessee, which includes 14 upstream dams and 80 miles of channel improvement. The water control system will provide for flood control, recreation, and municipal, industrial, and agricultural water supply.

The intensified efforts in agriculture are encouraging but long overdue. Agriculture in the beginning paid a big price for TVA development. The full reservoirs inundated 606 thousand acres, much of it good valley farmland, to give flood protection to only 110 thousand acres of basin land.

In speaking of watershed programs, we would be remiss not to mention the outstanding achievements of the Soil Conservation Service in a relatively short span of years.

Its small watershed program started with a pilot undertaking on 62 watersheds in 1953. On January 1, 1964, operations were authorized on 528 small watersheds comprising 30 million acres. On that date, most of the pilot projects had been completed in addition to regular program projects in 60 watersheds. A total of 933 watershed projects comprising 63 million acres had been authorized for planning assistance on January 1, 1964.

These watershed projects include many purposes: Flood protection, agricultural management of water, municipal and industrial water supplies, and recreation and fish and wildlife development.

The program of work involves a combination of soil and water conservation measures on farm and ranch lands and many types of watershed improvement works—floodwater retarding dams, levees, channel improvements.

The United States small watershed program is unique in the world's experience. Few countries have water and land resource development and conservation programs on small watersheds that are anywhere near comparable to that of the Soil Conservation Service.

ISRAEL is one of the few countries whose effective utilization of the last drop of available water approaches 100 percent.

Of its 5 million acres, about 75 thousand acres were under irrigation when the State of Israel was established. Within 12 years, 340 thousand acres were irrigated. By the use of all known sources of water, a total of about 650 thousand acres can be irrigated after meeting higher priority demand; that would be one-half of all irrigable land—1.3 million acres.

The rain, which comes only in winter, averages 40 inches in the north, 8 in the midsection, and 1.25 in the far south. The north, from the country's narrowest point north of Tel Aviv, has 85 percent of the available water. Galilee and the Sea of Galilee (Lake Kinneret or Lake Tiberias) make up most of the north, which is roughly one-third of the country.

The uneven distribution of available water brought into being Israel's famous water grid, which is not unlike the electric grids of the United States, whose main purpose is to balance sources of supply with demand. The electric grid makes it possible to use hydroelectric power that otherwise would be wasted in distant areas to meet peak demands. The water grid functions in much the same way, ex-

cept that it has an added dimension of storage. The water grid not only carries water from surplus to deficit areas but in winter carries water to reservoirs in the south for later use during the crop season.

The water grid in Israel has a number of regional segments that can be connected.

The first large segment to be completed was the Yarkon River-Negev project, which diverts water of the Yarkon from its source east of Tel Aviv and carries it initially by a 66-inch conduit to the northern Negev.

A second 70-inch conduit (western Yarkon line) provides extra capacity, carries reclaimed sewage water from Tel Aviv, and is designed to carry water from the Jordan when that undertaking is completed.

Other regional segments are the western Galilee-Kishon project, which collects water from springs and wells in western Galilee and transports it by conduit to the fertile Jezreel Valley, and the Kinneret-Beit-Shean Valley project, which will carry water from the Jordan and Yarmuk to the Beit-Shean Valleys.

The biggest part of the national grid, the Kinneret-Negev project, consists of a 108-inch conduit running 150 miles from Lake Kinneret to tie in to the Yarkon-Negev conduits. At Lake Kinneret, the major water source and reservoir for the project, large pumping installations are required for lifting the water, because the lake is some 665 feet below sea level.

The Jordan-Negev project, the backbone of the national grid, is planned to link Israel's only large surface water source, the Jordan, and other rivers, spring sources, intermittent flows, and the underground aquifers of central and southern Israel. On its way from north to south, this large conduit connects regional systems and thus makes possible the central coordination of distribution. It will permit unbroken countrywide storage from the winter rainy season for use in summer and very likely in years of drought.

The water plan will do more than transport water through a national network of conduits. It will include standby pumping capacity to transfer water to underground storage and a network of wells with a peak pumping capacity above the safe yield of the aquifers. Overdraft of the aquifers during dry periods means that they can serve as storage reservoirs during wet periods.

Coastal collectors, a system of shallow wells near the coast, will control the outflow of fresh water to the sea. They will reduce the average outflow of 20 to 25 percent of annual natural recharge to as little as 6 percent.

Upon the completion of the Jordan conduit system, major construction works have been planned to reclaim sewage and industrial waste water and to recover the intermittent runoff of coastal streams. Water obtained in this way is quite expensive, and the economics of doing such work would be questionable in most other places. In Israel, necessity overrides the usual considerations of economics. That is not to say, however, that Israel has glossed over economics in its water development plans. Economics has been most carefully scrutinized in the planning of scale and the scheduling of works to receive priority.

For example, with the assistance of the United Nations Special Fund, Israel has undertaken an exhaustive examination of the economics of the flood runoff collector, the Zikim Dam. The dam is less than a mile from the seacoast and collects runoff from the Nahal Shikma watershed in the northern part of the Negev. The dam was completed in 1959 and collected the first runoff in the 1959–1960 rainy season. Water stored is immediately pumped into water-spreading ditches in the sand dunes near the coast. The water recharges a Pleistocene aquifer that had been heavily overpumped.

The study includes a thorough analysis of the cost of water retrieved by the Zikim Dam and associated works, the cost of water from possible alternative sources, and the costs by feasible methods of development, such as the collection by small dams and utilization in the upper watershed area and the costs of providing water through the national grid at places where local water resources can be developed.

Israeli engineers believe that the limit to additional water supplies for agriculture—estimated at about 900 thousand acre-feet annually—will be reached by 1970. Municipal use will be given priority. Since industrial use per unit of volume of water makes about 25 times as much contribution to the national product as agricultural use, allocation of water to industry also will have priority.

To prevent the lack of water from acting as a brake on the growth of the economy, Israel has been exploring and evaluating all possible ways and means of increasing supplies and raising efficiency—ways to use low-quality water, watershed management for water conservation, reduction of evaporation from open water, desalinization of sea water, weather modification, and water-saving irrigation.

We shall surely find new horizons in water development in this small Biblical land. Its explorations of underground water movement by isotope tracing and use of advanced methods will be the pattern for others.

It was in the center of the Negev, centuries before Christ, that the Nabatians applied techniques of desert agriculture. They conserved rainfall by diverting it from large areas into cisterns. They stacked flintstones in a way that permitted night winds to pass around them and cool them so they collected moisture. The water from the stones dripped to the ground and supported perhaps a grapevine. (At least that is the theory I accept for those strange piles of flintstones one can still see on the hillsides.) They cut channels around barren hills to divert and concentrate runoff into small areas of deep soil that retained enough moisture to grow a crop.

The reconstruction of the remains of one of these ancient collecting systems has been undertaken at Avdat. One of the so-called new techniques advocated by water planners today is called "water harvesting"—a concept no different from the methods that were practiced before the time of the Roman Empire in the Negev.

Israel's water problems typify those faced by many countries that face an unprecedented rate of increase in water needs for agriculture, domestic use, and industry.

An additional problem is that Israel's main source of water, the Jordan River, has been involved in an international dispute.

The Israelis have had to enforce strict allocation and control on water uses and devise ingenious water-charge schemes so as to encourage conservative use and prevent excessive uses.

UNUSUAL PLANS also are going forward elsewhere.

In Sudan Gezira, as the angle between the Blue Nile and the White Nile is called, an irrigation scheme has been under development for many years. It had its beginning in 1907, when British public works officials first proposed it. Up to 1963, 2 million acres had been put under irrigation. A proposed fifth stage would bring an additional 200 thousand acres under irrigation.

The economy of the Republic of the Sudan rests to a large extent on the scheme. The government's income from the Gezira has reached as high as 15 percent of its total revenue. Cotton is the main income-producing crop. The sale of cotton abroad earns about 60 percent of Sudan's foreign exchange.

In the lower basin of the Ganges-Brahmaputra in East Pakistan, the pressure of population on resources is intense, the need for water is urgent, and many difficulties must be overcome to bring about large-scale development. Many plans have been advanced. One is known as the Old Brahmaputra Multipurpose project, a three-phase proposal to divert water from the Brahmaputra River into its old channel. The project would command a gross area of 2 million acres. The first phase would irrigate 650 thousand acres and would cost more than 150 million dollars.

The first dam across the Nile at Aswan in the United Arab Republic to divert water for irrigation was built in 1891–1902. It has been raised twice since. Work began in 1960 on what is referred to as the Aswan High Dam. It will store the entire flow of the Nile in a low-flow year. Its reservoir will have a total capacity of 127 million acre-feet and a usable capacity of 68 million acre-feet a year.

The Nile drains 1.1 million square miles. Its flow at highest flood stage exceeds 1 million acre-feet a day. At Aswan Dam its low flow is about 365 thousand acre-feet, and the average flow is 650 thousand acre-feet a day.

The dam is to be 364 feet high and 11,480 feet long. Its cost has been set at 1.2 billion dollars. Construction, to take 10 years, has been planned in two stages—the erection of the subsidiary frontal and rear dams and seven diversion tunnels and the completion of the construction, including hydroelectric installations. Full use is due in 1974.

The project will extend by about 30 percent the acreage irrigated by Nile waters—up to a total of 2 million acres. Enough water will be available to put 700 thousand acres on perennial irrigation, instead of the present basin irrigation basis. In the basin method, an ancient one, floodwater is held in basins to provide only one irrigation a season.

Egypt expects the project to make possible the cultivation of 700 thousand acres of rice each year. Upon full implementation, the project is expected to increase the total national agricultural income by 35 percent. The dam will provide protection against high floods.

The Indus River Basin is one of the richest natural resource regions of the world. The headwaters of the Indus and its tributaries are in the Himalayas, and the flow is from India into Pakistan. The basin contains the world's largest single stretch of irrigated land. The canal system commands about 33 million acres, and 23 million acres are irrigated each year. The average total flow of the river is 170 million acre-feet—68 million acre-feet on an average flows to the sea during the monsoon season. All irrigation has been accomplished without mainstem storage works.

According to a resource survey made by the Canadian Colombo Plan in 1953–1954, a third of the land under command of these canals is poorly drained or waterlogged, about 5 million acres are severely saline, and saline areas exist throughout another 11 million acres. Irrigation has been practiced there for 5 thousand years, but severe waterlogging and salinity are of comparatively recent origin and have arisen with the increase of irrigation.

A reclamation and development program on the Indus, said to be the biggest of its kind ever undertaken anywhere, has been started under the Indus Water Treaty of 1960 between India and Pakistan. The two countries, with the assistance of seven other countries, including the United States, and the World Bank have set out on a program that was initially estimated to cost 1.1 billion dollars. More than that may be needed, however, to develop the Indus fully, divide the water equitably between the two countries, overcome drainage and salinity problems, avoid water shortages, and improve methods of farming.

This tremendous program includes two large dams in Pakistan to provide for a combined live storage of 9 million acre-feet and one dam in India to store 5.5 million acre-feet, hundreds of miles of canals, barrages, diversion works, power stations, and drainage works, and thousands of wells to overcome waterlogging and salinity. The works are in addition to the large Bhakra Reservoir on the Sutlej River in India.

RIVERS are the lifeblood of agricultural irrigation the world over.

The world's great river systems drain about one-half of the land and carry about 15 billion acre-feet of water to the sea each year. The other half is drained by thousands of small coastal rivers or is desertland with virtually no runoff.

The principal river of northeastern Africa and the longest—about 4,130 miles—in the world is the Nile. Its drainage basin covers about 1.2 million square miles. The basin contains Lake Victoria, the largest fresh-water lake in the Eastern Hemisphere. Each year from July to October the Nile floods its plain of variable width and gives the life sustenance to the agriculture of Egypt. It has an average annual discharge at its mouth of about 72 million acre-feet.

Most of the rivers of northwestern Africa are short, rise in the mountains in the Atlas, Grand Atlas, and Anti-Atlas ranges, and have a torrential course to the coastal plain. A large number dry up in the summer. In western Africa is the great basin of the Niger, which has its headwaters near the Atlantic coast. It heads eastward and northward into the Sahara and finally empties into the Gulf of Guinea.

The Congo River Basin takes up most of equatorial Africa. The largest of the African basins, it includes 1.4 million square miles with by far the largest discharge—2.8 million acre-feet a day.

The Zambezi in southeastern Africa, the fourth largest of the African rivers, has a drainage basin of about 463 thousand square miles. The great Kariba hydroelectric dam, which cost 220 million dollars, built downstream from Livingstone, forms the largest manmade lake in the world. Of the three main tributaries of the Zambezi, the Kafue Basin takes up most of the southwestern part of Zambia. Below the Zambezi in southeastern Africa is the Limpopo Basin of some 77 thousand square miles.

The more important rivers in southern Africa are the Great Berg and the Orange. The lower course of the Orange has no tributaries in 559 miles.

Ranging in size along with the largest, the basin of the Chad is a closed drainage basin. Lake Chad loses all the water it receives through evaporation and is gradually shrinking. Its area is approximately 896 thousand square miles.

THE RIVERS of Europe are known more as items in history and literature and trade than as sources of water for industry and agriculture.

The Danube, for one, which in songs is beautiful and blue, is a grand river. It is 1,760 miles long and drains 347 thousand square miles. Unlike other European rivers that flow north or west, the Danube flows east. Along its banks live Germans, Austrians, Czechs, Hungarians, Yugoslavs, Bulgarians, Rumanians, and Russians.

Because of its fairly regular high-volume flow, the Danube has long been a great thoroughfare for trade. Its future service to man, though, will be more and more as a source of water for towns and cities and farms.

Austria, for example, has begun work on a plan to divert water from it into a large irrigation project. The Marchfeld undertaking is designed to irrigate 450 thousand acres. The tributary and mainstem flows will be used more and more for the generation of hydroelectric power by means of dams, 14 of which have been planned in Austria.

The busy, castled Rhine, whose headwaters embrace much of Switzerland and has a delta channel that empties into the Zuider Zee, is 800 miles long and has a drainage area of 86 thousand square miles. It is navigable from the sea for a distance of about 550 miles. Its history has been written in tears and blood. Today much of its natural beauty is marred by the smoke and pollution of industries. Its waters have not been greatly developed for irrigation or power.

The Rhone, which begins at Lake Geneva and flows through the French Alps and empties into the Mediterranean, has been highly developed for hydropower. Only a small amount of its water has been developed for irrigation, but several projects have been started. One, the Durance Basin development on a major tributary, is expected to provide water for supplemental irrigation on 148 thousand acres. The Durance, which flows out of the French Alps, has a steep grade, ideal for hydroelectric development. Plans call for 24 hydroplants capable of an annual power production exceeding 6 billion kilowatt-hours and facilities that supply domestic and industrial water to 68 communities.

The Soviet Union has an unsurpassed potential for water development. It has more than 20 thousand rivers that have a total length of 1.9 million miles. More than 50 rivers have catchment basins in excess of 38 thousand square miles. The annual runoff of all her rivers is about 3.2 billion acre-feet—13 percent of all the rivers of the world, according to Soviet engineers.

Five of the world's 19 rivers that drain more than 380 thousand square miles are in Russia—the Volga, Ob, Yenisei, Lena, and Amur. Other large rivers are the Dnepr, Don, Neva, Pechora, Ural, Khatanga, Yana, Indigirka, Kolyma, and Anadyr. The last four have permafrost basins.

The Lena, Ob, and Yenisei rise in the central Asian highlands and flow into the Arctic.

The slow-flowing Lena empties into the Arctic through an ice-choked delta that is exceeded in size only by the Ganges and Niger. The Lena River Basin has almost inexhaustible forest resources and great mineral wealth.

The Ob is kept open for traffic by icebreakers. The Ob Basin is reported to be an area of vast economic development. Its great waters may someday be diverted to irrigate lands far to the south, where climate and soils are favorable for agriculture.

The Yenisei, an ancient water route

through a trackless wilderness, may also become an important resource in the future development of Asia's great landmass.

THREE FAMOUS rivers in western Asia are the Tigris-Euphrates, which empties into the Persian Gulf; the Oxus; and the Jaxartes, which flows out of the Kunlun Mountains and across the Turkistan desert to the Aral Sea.

India and Pakistan have the Indus, which flows out of the Karakorum Mountains across the Punjab Desert to the Arabian Sea, and the Ganges-Brahmaputra system, which empties into the Bay of Bengal through a network of deltas.

Three great rivers flow southward through narrow valleys in India and China—the Irrawaddy, the Salween, and the Mekong, an international river that has been studied intensively by agencies of the United Nations.

Twenty percent of the drainage area of the Mekong is in China. It is the largest river in southern Asia. Its headwaters are the tablelands of Tibet. About 3 percent of its basin is in Burma, the rest in Laos, Vietnam, Thailand, and Cambodia. Its abundant water has not been developed significantly for the benefit of the nearly 20 million people living in its lower basin. The main river is used for navigation. Its water is used to irrigate about 500 thousand acres. Parts of the river, particularly in Laos, have a high waterpower potential.

The two great rivers of China are the Yangtze and the Hwang Ho, or Yellow. The Yangtze heads in the Tibetan Mountains and cuts China in half. It is called China's lifeline. It is a great river of commerce and also supplies water for irrigation.

The Yellow River is called China's sorrow because it has changed course many times through its vast alluvial plains at flood and caused untold damage and loss of life. It carries a record volume of silt. It is used for irrigation. Perhaps someday it will be tamed for greater usefulness.

NONE OF THE rivers of Central America and Mexico is among the world's greatest, but they are important assets in their own countries. Considerable development has taken place, but the job has only begun.

In Mexico, the greatest river, the Rio Grande, is mostly a United States river. The parts of its tributaries in Mexico drain about 100 thousand square miles. The next largest river of Mexico, the Lerma-Santiago, drains 50 thousand square miles and has a mean flow of 10 thousand cubic feet a second.

In Central America, 12 principal rivers enter the Atlantic and 15 enter the Pacific. One of the largest, the Segovia, is 50 miles long. A main river that flows into the Pacific is the Tempa in El Salvador. It is about 190 miles long. The San Juan, flowing to the Atlantic along the frontiers between Nicaragua and Costa Rica, has been considered as a second possible route for an interoceanic canal.

The Canto and Sagua La Grande are important in Cuba. In Haiti and the Dominican Republic, the Yaque del Norte and Yaque del Sur have promising development possibilities. The Dominican Republic has been approaching bilateral and multilateral aid groups for assistance in surveying the Yaque del Sur.

The river systems of South America have a tremendous potential for development. One visionary plan is to connect the Orinoco in Venezuela by means of the 220-mile-long natural Casiquiare Canal to the Rio Negro of the Amazon and to connect the Amazon with the Parana-Paraguay Rivers. Much has been done, and many projects are moving into the construction stage, but the countries of South America have hardly begun to achieve full use of their rivers.

The rivers of South America that flow west are relatively short, and their basins are small because the Andes Mountains are so close to the Pacific. They have great potential for hydroelectric power, irrigation, and water supply development. The rivers flowing east and north into the Atlantic and Caribbean are long and drain broad basins. They have a low average gradient in their lower reaches and are generally suitable for navigation. In their numerous highland tributaries there is a huge hydroelectric development potential.

Studies by the United Nations Economic Commission for Latin America indicated a total hydropotential of something like 156 million kilowatts for all Latin America. Only about 7 million kilowatts, or 4.5 percent, had been developed in 1964.

The Amazon has a greater drainage area and flow than any other river. Its length is exceeded only by the Nile. The Amazon drainage area is equal to nine-tenths of the 48 mainland States. About half of its 4 thousand miles is navigable. Through its 200-mile-wide mouth, 3.6 billion acre-feet of fresh water flow annually to the sea, according to the United States Geological Survey.

The main north-flowing rivers of South America are the Magdalena and the Orinoco. About 600 miles of the Magdalena and its tributaries are navigable. Hydroelectric installation completed, under construction, and being considered would have a capacity in excess of 4 million kilowatts. In the Cauca Basin, a main tributary of the Magdalena, a large irrigation and power scheme has been launched. The Orinoco River Basin contains 340 thousand square miles. The Orinoco is navigable for about a thousand miles and has a large hydroelectric potential that has been explored only partly.

The Plate River system includes the Parana, Paraguay, and Uruguay and ranks among the world's mightiest rivers. This system drains nearly 2 million square miles and has a discharge equal to about 25 percent of the Amazon. In Argentina the river is navigable by vessels of 10 thousand tons. Its land and water resources have led some persons to call South America the continent of the future.

FERDINAND C. LANE, in his book, *Earth's Grandest Rivers*, speaks of the Mississippi-Missouri as the father of waters; associates the St. Lawrence with the Empire of the Great Lakes; calls the Rio Grande a turbulent border stream; describes the Columbia as the gateway to the Northwest; mentions the Yukon as an open door toward Russia; and refers to the Churchill as a relic of the ice age, and the Nelson and Saskatchewan as shades of the Hudson's Bay Company.

The work of the United States Geological Survey, Corps of Engineers, Bureau of Reclamation, the Tennessee Valley Authority, and the Department of Agriculture have given us incomparable information on our rivers. Water-resource planning staffs of many States have outlined in detail the developments and potentials of our rivers. Even so, the projected program of feasible river development projects grows continually larger as new vistas are opened to keep pace with needs.

The leading North American rivers and their drainage areas (in thousands of square miles) and average annual flow (in thousands of acre-feet) are: Mississippi, 1,244 and 442,360; Mackenzie, 697 and 202,720; St. Lawrence, 498 and 361,900; Nelson-Saskatchewan, 414 and 57,900; Yukon, 360 and 130,320; Columbia, 258 and 185,340; Colorado, 244 and 59,530; Rio Grande, 232 and 13,235; Frazer (Canada), 92 and 81,810; Mobile, 42 and 42,350; Susquehanna, 28 and 27,650.

Australia has one important river system, the Murray-Darling. Its 2,345 miles drain 414 thousand square miles. Its average annual discharge is 13 thousand cubic feet a second. The Murray has a relatively small flow because of the low rainfall and because it traverses so much semidesert area. The river has been developed with numerous dams and irrigation projects.

A POSTWAR DRIVE through bilateral and multilateral aid to advance the economies of less-developed areas led to the initiation of a large number of projects to develop water resources.

Through the years, as new agencies and new programs have emerged, the emphasis on water has increased. A brief examination of the major programs gives an indication of the relative effort devoted to water projects.

The International Bank for Reconstruction and Development, popularly known as the World Bank, is a bank of governments. It was conceived at the Bretton Woods economic conference in 1944 to reconstruct war-torn countries and to develop backward ones. The Bank began operations in 1946 and made its first loan in 1947 for European postwar reconstruction.

Its primary function is to lend money for development, but it also provides many technical services to its members.

Its first source of funds is the capital subscribed by member governments. The total capital subscriptions to June 30, 1963, were 20.7 billion dollars. Ten percent of the capital subscriptions have been paid in; the rest is subject to call only if required to meet the Bank's obligations. The Bank has supplemented its funds by the sale of bonds and notes to investors in some 40 countries.

In its first 18 years of operation, the Bank made loans with an original principal amount of 7.12 billion dollars. The total number of loans made by the Bank was 349. The total lent was 6.98 billion dollars, net of cancellations and refundings. Sixty-four countries and territories had borrowed from the Bank. The effective loans held by the Bank as of January 1, 1964, amounted to 4.82 billion dollars.

The total net lendings as of June 30, 1963, were used for reconstruction in Europe, 7.1 percent; electric power, 33.4 percent; transportation, 32.4 percent; communications, 0.4 percent; agricultural and forests, 7.6 percent; industry, 16.2 percent; general development, 2.9 percent.

More than three-fifths of the agricultural loans have been for irrigation and flood control. In all, 26 separate loans for irrigation and flood-control purposes were made with a total principal amount of 330.6 million dollars.

Bank loans by no means cover all the cost for the full development for irrigation or flood protection projects. In some instances, the loans are for rehabilitation of projects where major investments had been made. In other instances, the loans are a mere start on the total investment that will ultimately be required to bring about full development. In all cases, the governments are putting in a large share of the total costs, and additional financing has been from other sources.

Two Bank loans to Pakistan in connection with the Indus River Basin development are only a small part of the more than 1 billion dollars that will be required. The Governments of Australia, Canada, Germany, India, New Zealand, the United Kingdom, and the United States have planned contributions in grants and loans of more than 800 million dollars.

Of some projects, like the Dez project in Iran, the Litani in Lebanon, the Yanhee in Thailand, and the Seyhan in Turkey, irrigation is a minor part. Irrigation loans make up only a small fraction of river basin development financing by the Bank. Loans for hydroelectric dams and generator installations have accounted for more than one-fourth of all its loans.

A loan of 47 million dollars was made to Ghana for the Volta River power project, which will cost 196 million dollars. The United States is providing 37 million dollars, the United Kingdom, 14 million dollars, and Ghana, 98 million dollars.

A loan of 100 million dollars was made to Australia for its 900-million-dollar Snowy Mountains hydroelectric scheme.

Two loans of 34 million and 21 million dollars, respectively, were made to the Philippines for two separate hydroelectric projects. A loan of 30 million dollars was made to Yugoslavia for its Baina Basta project on the Drina.

Colombia received a loan of 22 million dollars for its Guadalupe River hydroelectric project, 17.6 million dollars for its Bogota River hydroelectric plant, and 37 million dollars for its Cauca Valley project. The Federal Power Board of Rhodesia and Nyasaland was given a Bank loan of 80 million dollars for part of the financing of the Great Kariba Dam and power installation on the Zambezi River.

THE INTERNATIONAL DEVELOPMENT ASSOCIATION, an affiliate of the World Bank, which completed its third year of operation on June 30, 1963, had on that date committed 495 million dollars in development credits.

Its aims are to promote economic development, increase productivity, and raise levels of living in the less-developed regions.

It provides capital on much more liberal terms of repayment than the World Bank. The loans are repayable in foreign exchange over 50 years, free of interest. Credits thus far have provided a 10-year period of grace before repayments.

Development credits in the first 3 years went to 18 countries for transport, power, communications, irrigation, and flood control. Transport has been the principal purpose, but development of water resources and irrigation has increased in importance in the operations. Of a total of 39 development credits extended by the Association, 15 credits were for water.

They were for two projects in the Republic of China, six projects in India, three projects in Pakistan, and one project each in Jordan, Nicaragua, Sudan, and Turkey.

The governments themselves, and in some cases the World Bank and bilateral aid, contribute a large part of the cost of the projects.

The total credits for water projects are about 126 million dollars, or one-fourth of all the Association's credits. The credits for the 10 irrigation projects will help complete water supply works for the eventual irrigation of 3.4 million acres. The China ground-water project involves 765 deep wells for the irrigation of 208 thousand acres.

The India Uttar Pradesh tubewell project will help finance the drilling and equipping of 800 tubewells for irrigation of 320 thousand acres. Other India projects will bring about or improve irrigation acreage as follows: Shetranji, 86 thousand; Salandi, 113 thousand; Sone, 1 million; and Purna, 152 thousand acres. The Sone River is a tributary of the Ganges, and parts of this project have been under irrigation for 80 years.

The Roseires Dam project on the Blue Nile was the first joint IDA-World Bank project. Germany also is participating in this project to make a total of 51 million dollars in financing to Sudan for this important extension of their irrigation. The project will bring in nearly 900 thousand acres of new irrigation and will benefit other areas where water supplies are inadequate.

The Brahmaputra flood-control project will protect about 400 thousand acres of cultivated land. The two IDA irrigation projects in Pakistan will benefit 320 thousand acres. The Khairpur project will restore production on 300 thousand acres of irrigated land in the Indus River Basin by pumping and drainage and salinity control.

The Seyhan River-IDA project will finance the first stage of a project in the Adana Plain and will benefit 135 thousand acres. It is a part of a long-range, multiple-purpose project involving hydroelectric power and flood control in addition to irrigation. The Government of Turkey has estimated that this first stage may cost the equivalent of 50 million dollars.

THE UNITED NATIONS Water Resources Development Center at the United Nations headquarters sets forth proposals for priority action in the activities of the United Nations to develop and utilize water resources. The Center works in cooperation with several United Nations specialized agencies, most of whose fieldwork is financed and directed by the United Nations

Special Fund. The main aim of the Special Fund is to make preinvestment surveys and studies of feasibility of proposed projects.

In its 11 sessions between May 1959 and January 1964, the Governing Council of the United Nations Special Fund had authorized 375 projects in 79 countries and territories, as well as 15 regional projects involving 50 additional countries, territories, and islands. The projects will cost an equivalent of 837 million dollars, of which 502 million dollars are being provided by the recipient governments and 335 million dollars come from the resources of the Special Fund.

About two-fifths of all Special Fund projects are investigations and studies of water and land resources, mineral wealth, and agricultural and industrial potential.

BILATERAL AID for water development has come from several countries.

France, in relation to its gross national product, has contributed heavily to help the developing regions of the world. The bulk of French aid has gone to industry and social programs in northern and western Africa. From 1946 through 1961, the total oversea aid of France amounted to 7 billion dollars. In 1960 and 1961, payment credits for soil and forest restoration amounted to 13.2 million dollars, and for agricultural equipment, 50.2 million dollars. Aid for water supply amounted to 57.3 million dollars, but this was for water supply systems in urban areas, and not for irrigation.

British engineers have laid the foundations of modern irrigation works and have been responsible for such developments in the Middle East, India, and Pakistan. On the Nile, the British have been responsible for the Delta barrages and the basin irrigation system of Upper Egypt, the existing Aswan Dam, and its associated barrages that provide perennial irrigation for Middle Egypt.

In the Sudan, the Sennar Dam built by British engineers on the Blue Nile made possible the Gezira scheme that now produces cotton and food crops on nearly a million acres.

The foundation of modern work on the Tigris and Euphrates Rivers was laid by the British. British engineers have constructed the 1,625-foot-long Kut barrage on the Tigris to provide irrigation for some 900 thousand acres. They were engaged for many years in a work to divert the Tigris floodwaters from a point near Samarra into the Wadi Tharthar depression in order to prevent the disastrous floods of the past and to store the water for irrigation. This project was inaugurated in April 1956. Also completed then was a barrage on the Euphrates at Ramadi.

Modern irrigation work in India began early in the 19th century, when engineers of the British East India Company restored and improved the ancient system of canals in the Punjab and the Madras Presidency. Later they constructed the Ganges Canal, which provided irrigation for the area between the Jumna and Ganges Rivers that is now the granary of Upper India and a series of irrigation works in the Punjab, which turned 3 million acres of waste into rich agricultural land. When British rule in India came to an end in 1947, the work of generations of British and Indian engineers had provided more than 70 million acres of irrigated land.

The amount of United States aid to help countries develop their water resources for agriculture exceeds that extended by any other source. Even so, assistance in water development has represented only a minor part of all United States aid given. During the period up to June 30, 1962, the United States had given about 100 billion dollars; 1.3 billion dollars of that amount had gone for irrigation, flood control, and power projects.

The United States had given aid through 1962 for irrigation purposes in 43 countries in connection with some 105 projects. The funds obligated on them amounted to 375 million dollars.

BECAUSE OF the huge capital amounts needed for water resources development, developing countries cannot afford to accept low returns on projects.

They cannot afford to put the prestige of a grandiose project ahead of better returns from smaller projects more in keeping with their capability.

At best, the flow of investment capital and aid from industrialized nations will fall short of the needs of developing countries. Our responsibility to succeeding generations is to make all possible effort to make the best use of available resources.

While I have emphasized here that water is the key to expanding agricultural production, it is by no means the only thing. We need increased efficiency in the application of all factors of agricultural production. As Eugene R. Black, former president of the World Bank, said, "It is Utopian to expect every country to be cultivated as efficiently as Denmark and thereby assume that the World can easily feed twice its present population."

A modern irrigation project in an undeveloped country will not give as good results as one in the western United States. It is relatively easy to transport competent engineers and construction materials and equipment to build an irrigation project. It is not easy to transform cultivators of such a country into competent farmers with managerial ability and initiative and to provide the continuing incentives so they will apply themselves energetically year after year to make effective use of the water.

ELCO L. GREENSHIELDS *joined the Agriculture Division of the Technical Operations Department, International Bank for Reconstruction and Development, as an agricultural economist on July 1, 1963. In the Bank his work consists mainly of appraisals of irrigation projects on which member countries have made application for financial assistance. Before joining the Bank, he served as Assistant to the Director, Resources Development Economics Division, Economic Research Service.*

Engineering in Agriculture

by E. G. McKIBBEN and
W. M. CARLETON

AMERICAN farmers owned 4.5 million tractors in 1964. Tractors have displaced 22 million work animals and 76 million acres that would have been needed to grow feed for them.

Tractors are an index of the evolution of engineering in agriculture— mechanization, automation, structures, and facilities for processing and storing crops and raising livestock.

Mechanization in the United States followed a logical course, beginning with the operations—mainly plowing, cultivating, and harvesting—that require the most physical effort or impose extreme time limits to harvest the product.

Let us review some aspects of the mechanical evolution to see if they can be applied in countries that apparently need more machines and obviously need more food and other agricultural products.

Multiple-horse hitches and, later, steam traction power during the latter part of the 19th century meant that tillage ceased to be the limiting factor in crop production. The reaper helped reduce the time and labor needed for harvesting grain. Developments like tractors with internal-combustion engines and combined harvester threshers virtually assured a firm supply of basic commodities.

Farmstead mechanization was accelerated greatly by the high price and shortage of farm labor after the Second World War. In some feedyards, six men feed as many as 25 thousand head of cattle by the proper use of feed-preparation units and self-unloading trailers and trucks. Many farmers have installed automatic, pushbutton, electric feeding and grinding systems.

The mechanization of the harvesting of fruit and vegetables—difficult because of the varied characteristics of different plants and because most fruit and vegetables are delicate and perishable—is well started in the United States, although little is being done elsewhere in the world.

The electrification of the American farms is an outstanding development. The percentage of farms with electricity rose from 11 in 1934 to about 98 in 1960. The use of electricity per farm has increased about eightfold between 1940 and 1964. In about 500 ways, farmers use electricity to do work they once did by hand. Among the uses they appreciate most are the automatic pressure water system and equipment for handling livestock water and feed and mixing and feeding animal rations.

As important as the adoption of the farm tractor during the period of the First World War were the almost universal adoption of the combined harvester thresher and the cornpicker, greater use of the field forage harvester and pickup baler, and acceptance of the cottonpicker after the beginning of the second war.

This evolution in the application of engineering in American agriculture has placed farming on a par with other occupations and industries. Farmers no longer need to labor from dawn to dark. A worker's output has increased greatly. A smaller and smaller proportion of the total labor force has been needed to achieve an ever-increasing production.

Less than one-tenth of the work force is on farms. In many well-developed countries, more than a third are so engaged; in other countries, farm-workers may total 80 to 90 percent.

Take rice, the major food for 60 percent of the population of the world. In the most highly mechanized rice producing section in the United States, 7.5 man-hours are required per acre; in many parts of the world, more than 700 to 900 man-hours are used.

Some of this higher productivity must be credited to improvements in other phases of agricultural technology, such as better varieties, more effective use of fertilizer, and improved cultural practices. A major factor, however, has been the increased utilization of nonhuman energy and more effective machines and implements.

WHY DID this evolution attain so high a rate in the United States?

No one can give a positive answer, but it appears that American progress is the result of several favorable circumstances, a combination unique in history and one that probably will not appear again.

Some of the elements of this combination are:

A stable government over a large area.

A government that favored individual initiative without internal trade barriers.

A publicly supported system of general education.

A psychology of increased production, developed by people who had settled in a new land to conquer it, develop it, and make it their home.

The psychology of change, which became intensified as the more adventurous of each generation moved west to pioneer a new frontier.

A rapidly expanding agriculture on new lands allowed the introduction of new machines and new methods without the need to discard the old.

A surplus of clear, level land, well suited to mechanization.

The absence of a peasant or serf class in much of the area.

A shortage of agricultural labor or an infrequent surplus of labor. Under such conditions great emphasis was placed on production per man.

Three wars, which produced severe labor shortages. The Civil War established the reaper and related machines. The First World War established the tractor and combine harvester. The Second World War established the cottonpicker and other harvesters.

A rapidly expanding and effective industrial development, which absorbed the labor released by farm mechanization and supplied many of the elements needed to perfect and produce new farm machines and implements as they evolved.

A remarkable development of transportation—railroads and high-quality hard-surfaced highways with trucks, buses, and automobiles and the airplane.

Outstanding advances in the biological sciences of agriculture. Plant breeders have greatly aided mechanization by producing varieties better suited to mechanical harvesting—grain sorghums of uniform growth, shatterproof small grains, hybrid corn, and stormproof cotton are examples.

A progressive agricultural chemical industry, which has supplied effective chemicals for fertilizing, controlling diseases, insects, and weeds and for controlling growth, such as defoliation for cotton harvest or fruit retention for a better apple harvest.

Improved processing plants that can handle mechanically harvested products. Sugar mills and cotton gins are examples.

OUR EXPERIENCE indicates that more than basic engineering technology and agricultural science is necessary for an effectively engineered agriculture.

Specialization and exchange have special significance in our system. An extensive adoption of specialization of production and a general participation in the exchange of the products is the only basis on which society can benefit from advancing agricultural technology.

Thus leadership in farm engineering is not an isolated development.

It cannot be exported and installed successfully without the related developments that made it possible in America.

These essential related developments involve almost the entire structure of society and include general literacy; stable, equitable government; minimum trade restrictions; sound money; an effective, equitable credit system; agricultural science; an agricultural chemical industry; an economic source of fuel; efficient transportation; adequate processing industries; reliable and equitable marketing and distribution systems; consumer goods industries; and service industries.

We do not list these requirements necessarily in the order of importance. In fact, we cannot assign a relative importance, because each is essential if a system of agriculture like ours is to succeed. Even the operator of farm machines must be able to read. As the system develops in any country, all participants will have an increasing need for knowledge.

The exchange phases of engineered agriculture cannot be developed without a stable, equitable government that favors few or no internal trade restrictions, sound money, and a good credit system.

If mechanical power is to be substituted for animal and human power, a source of fuel must be available at a competitive price.

Without an effectively applied agricultural technology and fertilizers, pesticides, and other products of an agricultural chemical industry, there will be little agriculture for the engineer to mechanize.

Unless transportation is efficient and extensive, processing industries are adequate and the marketing and distribution system is effective, an engineered agriculture cannot serve consumers or reward farmers.

If consumer goods and service industries are not sufficiently developed, there will be no employment for the workers released by machines, and there will be no customers for the products of an engineered agriculture.

THE FIRST TASK of research in agricultural engineering as a service to developing countries is therefore to modify and adapt our machines, facilities, and methods to the general farming situation in the particular country or to develop new methods and means if they are needed.

This adaptation and development may not be easy. Many will want to move slowly through all the steps taken here in America during the more than a century of development. Others will insist on the immediate adoption of our most advanced technology.

Both views are basically wrong. The objective should be to proceed with mechanization as rapidly as it can be assimilated and integrated with overall benefit. That will vary from country to country.

A second service to developing countries is to help bring new or abandoned land into productive use. Such lands are unused because they are difficult or impossible to farm with hand labor or even with animal power. They are forested, covered with brush or very heavy grasses, or semiarid. They require rather advanced engineering to clear, drain, or irrigate. The problems of financing such reclamation activities by public or private agencies often are formidable. Their economic feasibility often is controlled by the social, industrial, and financial factors we listed.

In fact, the limits on this type of development usually are sociological and not technological. Technically, the bringing of new land into production and the returning of abandoned land to production have great possibilities. We estimate that nearly 10 billion additional acres might be brought into use, compared to 4 billion acres that were used for agriculture in all the world in 1964.

Whether this can be done will depend on how badly society wants to do it.

Technology has reached the point where almost any physical program can be carried out if the human relationships involved can be managed successfully. For example, the United States and the Soviet Union have been spending about 100 billion dollars annually on their military establishments. That is enough each year to provide for 250 dollars an acre for 400 million acres, an additional area equal to more than 10 percent of the land now being used in world agriculture.

Or, with 100 billion dollars, probably enough plants could be built to desalt enough sea water to irrigate 15 million additional acres.

MORE THAN 90 percent of the power on the farms of the world is still being generated by human beings and by animals.

Most developing countries are not ready for mechanization as we think of it in the United States or at most are only partly ready.

Too often the outside expert, lacking experience of local conditions, assumes that the people do not wish to mechanize, when in fact it is illiteracy and lack of capital that hold them back. When they are shown a new instrument, or crop, or cultural practice that in reality fits their needs and is compatible to the local situation, they not only will accept it but they will make great efforts to find a way to pay for it.

Although the chief function of machinery is to make it possible for each man to do more work, and not to grow more food per acre, improvements in equipment can and do make contributions to raising total crop yields by performing some operations that are not practicable by hand, by enabling many operations to be performed better, and by making possible both more timely operations and the farming of some land that could not be farmed with primitive tools.

Population and mechanization are closely interrelated. In countries such as India, whose population is high and available land is scarce, a farmer working with improved indigenous implements powered by oxen may get as high yields as with tractors and their implements; yet the farmer with his oxen can handle more land than is available.

If the maximum number of years of existence without consideration to the quality of life is the controlling philosophy, long-time survival of the race depends on maximum production per acre and not upon the maximum production per hour of work.

We have estimates, for example, that 16 million persons may be added to the labor force in India during the sixties; of them, 10.5 million may go into nonagricultural work. Of the remaining, about 3.5 million may be employed in agriculture, thus raising, rather than lowering, the pressure on the land. Under such circumstances, there does not seem to be any possibility of mechanizing agriculture or even of solving the problem of food. Social changes involving population control are a necessary foundation for the technology required to raise the general level of life for all segments of a population.

Even with progress toward population control, mechanization in the developing countries is difficult because the populations are increasing most rapidly where resources are already most limited.

To a considerable degree, man can improve his lot only according to the energy he has at his command. Greater production of food in many regions depends on man's ability to harness other than manual power to better tools and equipment. But that is not possible unless he is trained to carry out new and better farming techniques to handle better and more advanced equipment.

A great deal of training will be required at all levels—research workers, extension workers, and farmers—as soon as practicable. The education and training of engineers, technicians, and fieldworkers therefore must go along at the same time as advances in mechanization. Most of this training should be carried out in the countries where it is to be used; in the end, it must be done there.

FROM THE EXPERIENCES of agricultural engineers, a pattern of needs characteristic of developing countries is emerging.

One engineer, writing from Liberia, a country that has been independent more than a century, describes an area that has great agricultural potential of land, water, and sunshine but must import food. What are the most important needs? First and foremost is a need for answers to problems.

Nigeria gained her independence in 1960 but has problems like those of Liberia. With a population of about 40 million and an area of 357 thousand square miles, Nigeria is the largest and most heavily populated country in Africa. The soils are low in fertility. A shifting cultivation practice is used. Here—as in similar countries—the twin problems of initiating elementary education and improved agricultural technology must go on concurrently. Illiteracy is high among farmers, who have few mechanical skills.

TWO PIECES of foundation work need be done before large-scale development schemes will be successful.

One is applied research to determine what agricultural practices are best suited to the local conditions.

The other is the training of the people in primary education and in agricultural practices.

While literacy is being raised, suitable varieties of plants must be developed, proper planting and fertilizing practices established, and methods of controlling plant diseases and insects worked out. All of them must go on while heavy machines are used to clear and prepare the available additional land for cultivation. General farm mechanization of the current American type can await the foundation developments.

Tractors, modern implements, and new machines are of little value to farmers in some countries. Hand labor is abundant and cheap in many regions, and it is not usually economic to supplant these men with machines.

Unless the machines will do the job better, unless they will increase overall production, and unless the work is too heavy for muscle labor, it is better to improve the indigenous tools and equipment until such time as the social and economic conditions compatible with an engineered agriculture can be developed. Otherwise mechanization may handicap development and add to unemployment.

Poor roads, inadequate storage facilities, and lack of capital and credit restrict agricultural production. The potentialities of agricultural engineering in Nigeria and similar countries are unlimited if the essential social and economic developments we listed earlier can take place.

Large acreages in many arid and semiarid countries could be brought into production if presently wasted river and floodwaters were controlled. Surveys of water potential, applied research in water usage, cultural practices with irrigation, and proper terracing policies are important and require additional equipment. The same is true for land drainage.

How to make agriculture develop fast enough in the less-developed countries is one of the most stubborn of all questions.

How to increase production to the amount needed to support the present world population and at the same time to increase it still further to catch up with the increasing population—these are research problems that will require the coordinated efforts of agricultural engineers and scientists in all the other agricultural disciplines. Topography, climate, rainfall, seasons, transportation, crop storages, irrigation, credit, and education—the problems are many and great.

So are our ways to solve them.

E. G. McKibben *and* W. M. Carleton *are the Director and Associate Director, respectively, of the Agricultural Engineering Research Division, Agricultural Research Service.*

The Need for Fertilizers

by W. L. HILL

Fertilization and appropriate liming are the only ways to maintain or increase the productivity of soil under the intense stress it is put to in making every arable acre count for the most.

A hundred-bushel corn crop removes from the soil 78 pounds of nitrogen, 36 pounds of phosphoric oxide, and 26 pounds of potassium oxide in the corn. Additional amounts of these nutrients are removed in the stover—52, 18, and 94 pounds, respectively, in a yield of 3.3 tons to the acre. To maintain the existing fertility level, fertilization must compensate for the withdrawals of nutrients in the harvested crop.

Fertilization and liming also make for efficient use of soil moisture. Fertilizers alter little, if at all, the total water supply, but their judicious use does increase the yield obtainable with the available supply, be it rainfall or irrigation. In an experiment of 12 trials with wheat, fertilization raised the average yield from 13 to 18 bushels an acre without altering the residual soil moisture at harvest. Viewed from the other side, provision of adequate moisture by irrigation increases the crop demand for nutrients, which in many instances can be met only by using suitable fertilizers.

The use of fertilizer is an avenue to increased yields of crop varieties generally. The fruits of fertilizer use are gathered immediately without a necessary waiting period of 10 to 15 years, or longer, while the plant breeder is developing high-yielding strains better adapted to the soil and climate.

Fertilization stimulates vegetative growth. The resultant robust plants sometimes are said to be less susceptible to disease and attack by pests—a generalization that is broader than the facts warrant. Actually, the healthy, rapidly growing plant is less susceptible to diseases of the roots, but lush growth favors diseases of the tops. At the same time, the vigorous plant can stand more punishment than the stunted one, and therefore rapid growth can compensate to a degree for damage by disease and pests.

So, because the use of fertilizers is a key to productivity, efficient use of moisture, varietal performance, and resistance to disease, the distribution of the world's fertilizer resources and production facilities are important factors in its agricultural economy.

NITROGEN, for which Nature's primary store is the atmosphere, is available to all countries that have a facility for winning it in useful chemical compounds. On the other hand, phosphorus and potassium reserves are piled up in a few places.

Phosphorus is stored in Nature mainly in three broad classes of mineral combinations—aluminum (iron) phosphates, calcium-aluminum (iron) phosphates, and calcium phosphates. The last is the dominant class in commerce, of which the commercial forms are phosphate rock and apatite. Members of the first two classes of phosphate are not tractable in established processing factories. Their utilization must await the development of economic methods for recovery of the phosphorus in forms suitable for fertilizers.

Known reserves of calcium phosphates amount to 47.3 billion metric tons, according to a report in 1962 of the United States Bureau of Mines. This figure does not include large deposits known to be in North Carolina

and in Peru, for which reliable tonnage estimates are not available.

Of this amount, Morocco, the United States, and the Soviet Union hold 90 percent—45, 29, and 16 percent, respectively. If the 7 percent held by Algeria, Tunisia, and the United Arab Republic be added to the Morocco share, northern Africa, the United States, and the Soviet Union have 97 percent of the known phosphate deposits. The rest occurs in 30-odd lands.

The mine production of marketable grades of phosphate rock and apatite was 46.8 million metric tons in 1962. The United States, northern Africa, and the Soviet Union produced 85 percent of it—42, 24, and 19 percent, respectively. Asia (mainly China, Christmas Island in the Indian Ocean, the Hashemite Kingdom of Jordan, and North Vietnam) contributed 5.5 percent; Oceania (mainly Makatea, Nauru, and Ocean Islands), 5 percent; Senegal, South Africa, and Togo, 2.5 percent; Brazil, 2 percent; and all others, 1 percent.

The depletion of phosphate deposits at disproportionate rates is evidenced by alinement of figures for production with those for reserves. Countries that hold 97 percent of the known reserves are contributing only 85 percent of the production; viewed the other way, 3 percent of the reserves are contributing 15 percent of the production.

Obviously, the scattered small deposits are being mined at high rates in response to the demand in the nearby trade community. When they are exhausted, material will have to be shipped into the community from distant large stores at higher costs to the users, unless future exploration uncovers new reserves nearby.

POTASSIUM occurs in more than two dozen forms, both water soluble and water insoluble, in rocks and minerals and in water solutions (brines). The dominant sources of this element for fertilizer use are brines and soluble saline deposits of the chloride or the sulfate locked in a few chemical combinations with the chloride or sulfate of magnesium, calcium, sodium, or aluminum.

World reserves of soluble potassic materials are large. Except the potassium associated with a deposit of nitrate in Chile, they appear to lie wholly in the Northern Hemisphere.

Known reserves are estimated to amount to at least 63 billion tons of ore, divided (in percentages) thus: Canada, 25; the United States, 0.6; Germany (East and West), 34; the Soviet Union, 27; France and Spain, each 0.4; Israel and Jordan (Dead Sea), 3; and others, 9. Germany, the Soviet Union, and Canada thus hold 86 percent of the known reserves.

World production of marketable potassic materials in 1962 was estimated to be 9.7 million metric tons of potassium oxide. The percentage shares of the producing countries are: Canada, 1; the United States, 23; Germany, 38; the Soviet Union, 15; France and Spain, 20; Israel, 1; and other countries, 2.

World production of potassic materials, like that of phosphate rock, is not shared proportionally by the known reserves. The trio of countries having 86 percent of the reserves furnished only 54 percent of the production. In contrast, the United States, France, and Spain, with only 1.4 percent of the reserves, produced 43 percent of the supply. The United States alone accounted for 23 percent.

These comparisons show that the small deposits, strategically located with respect to market areas, are being depleted at disproportionate rates. This observation does not necessarily mean that exhaustion is close at hand. Known domestic reserves are sufficient for about five generations at the rate of production in 1963.

Exploration in search of additional deposits of phosphate rock and potassic minerals in places distant from the few very large stores is therefore necessary if there is to be a continuing supply of these agricultural essentials at minimum cost. It is an important item that

is all too easily overlooked while supply keeps pace with demand. The search should precede the need by at least a generation, in order to provide adequate time for adaptation of mining practices to the new conditions and for appropriate modification of methods for extraction of the valuables from the mined ore.

Domestic production of phosphate rock and potassic materials accounted for 42 and 23 percent of world production in 1962. The United States that year exported 21 percent of its production of phosphate rock, valued at 27.6 million dollars, and 21 percent of its production of potassic materials, valued at 31 million dollars. Imports of these two commodities during the same period were valued at 3.6 and 22 million dollars, respectively.

Consumption of phosphate rock is divided between agricultural and industrial uses. Fertilizers and other agricultural commodities took about 70 percent of the rock sold or used by domestic producers (inclusive of imports). Fertilizers accounted for 93 percent of the domestic consumption of potassic materials.

Potassic materials are produced at the mines in ready-for-farm-use forms, although a considerable part of the sulfate is produced from the chloride at other locations. A substantial portion of the potassic materials actually reaches the farm in mixed fertilizers. Nearly 90 percent of the world production was potassium chloride (muriate) in 1960–1961. The remainder was the sulfate and smaller quantities of other materials.

Phosphate rock, on the other hand, is shipped from the mines to distant plants for processing into superphosphate, phosphoric acid, and multinutrient fertilizers of sundry sorts.

Rock, being subject to the lower freight rate, can be transported considerable distances at less cost per unit of nutrient than many of the processed phosphates. Just under seven-eighths of the phosphorus consumed by world agriculture as commercial fertilizers in 1960–1961 was derived from phosphate rock.

The world consumption was divided among materials as follows: Normal superphosphate for direct application to soil and mixed (inclusive of compound) fertilizers, each one-third plus; basic slag and concentrated phosphate (triple superphosphate, ammonium phosphates, and other things), each one-eighth; and rock for direct application, somewhat less than one-tenth. Accordingly, about four-fifths of the phosphorus used was in processed forms prepared from phosphate rock.

THE NITROGEN SUPPLY initially is won mainly in the form of ammonia by fixation of atmospheric nitrogen and by recovery as a byproduct of the coke industry. Chilean nitrate production accounted for about 45 thousand metric tons of nitrogen in 1959–1960. Ammonia is used in the manufacture of a wide variety of fertilizer materials for farm use.

The division of world nitrogen consumption among these materials is: Ammonium nitrate, including the limed product, nearly one-third; ammonium sulfate and mixed (including compound) fertilizers, each one-fifth plus; anhydrous ammonia for direct application and urea, one-eighth; and calcium nitrate, calcium cyanamide, ammonium phosphates, and sodium nitrate (with smaller quantities of other materials), one-seventh.

World production of nitrogen was about 13.6 million metric tons. Europe, North America (including Central America), and Asia contributed nearly 98 percent of it—52, 33, and 13 percent, respectively.

Four-fifths of the European production was in seven countries—Germany, France, Italy, the Netherlands, the United Kingdom, Poland, and the Soviet Union.

In North America, the United States and Canada accounted for 99 percent of the production.

The production figures for individual countries in Asia are rough estimates in many instances. Firm figures are available for seven of the countries, which share in the estimated total for Asia, as follows: Japan, 58 percent; India, 7; Taiwan, 4; South Korea and Israel, about 2 each; Pakistan and the Philippines, 0.7 and 0.4, respectively.

World production of phosphorus in 1960–1961 amounted to about 10.4 million metric tons of available phosphoric oxide (P_2O_5). Although phosphorous factories are scattered more widely than nitrogen plants, Europe, North America, and Asia provided the major part of the production—55, 27, and 7 percent, respectively, or a total share of 89 percent. Australia and New Zealand contributed Oceania's share of 7 percent, which makes a total of 96 percent of the world production accounted for.

Seven countries provided nearly three-fourths of the European production, namely: Germany, the Soviet Union, France, Italy, the United Kingdom, Belgium, and Spain.

In North America and Central America, more than 99 percent was in the United States and Canada. The United States' share was about 93 percent. Japan, India, and Taiwan provided three-fourths of the production in Asia.

In summary: The production figures show that in 1961 the manufacturing facilities for nitrogen and phosphorous materials were concentrated in 16 countries—9 in Europe, 2 in North America, 3 in eastern Asia, and 2 in Oceania. These countries produced 85 percent of the world supply of nitrogen materials and nearly 87 percent of the supply of available phosphorus.

The consumption of fertilizers parallels the production of nutrient materials rather closely. Heavy producing countries are also avid consumers.

The 16 countries accounted for 74 percent of the nitrogen and 79 percent of the available phosphorus consumed in fertilizers. As a rule, to which Norway is an exception, nations have thus far manufactured fertilizers primarily for their own use and secondarily for exportation.

According to traditional patterns of production, a country that wishes to insure adequate fertilizer for growing its food and fiber will seek to establish domestic facilities for processing nutrient materials.

The provision of factories is not enough, however. Other basic essentials are power and certain critical raw materials. Besides an economic source of power, fixation of nitrogen depends on the manufacture of hydrogen from coal, oil, natural gas, other carbonaceous fuel, or water. The production of soluble phosphates requires an economic supply of mineral acid or electric power. A country that cannot qualify on these counts will need to rely on the importation of fertilizer from countries that possess production resources.

Intercontinental movements of nitrogen and phosphorous materials in 1960–1961 carried 1.4 million metric tons of nitrogen and 15.4 million tons of phosphoric oxide, of which 0.6 million tons was in the form of processed phosphates and the rest was in the form of phosphate rock.

Movements of potassium materials amounted to 3.7 million tons of potassium oxide (inclusive of intercountry traffic in Europe).

The patterns of international trade are complicated by the circumstance that many countries are both exporters and importers of materials carrying the same nutrient.

The situation is illustrated by the traffic in nitrogen. The origin and percentage of nitrogen exports in 1960–1961 were: Europe, 78; South America, 10; North America, 8; Asia, 3; and Oceania, 0.3.

Destinations and percentages were: Asia, 45; North America, 20; Africa, 14; South America, 7; Europe, 4; Oceania, 1; undesignated, 9. European exports went to all continents. Asia took one-half, whereas Africa and North America took one-sixth each. Asian exports also went to all conti-

nents in quantities ranging from 4 thousand to 15 thousand metric tons of nitrogen. Oceania exported only to Asia. North America exported mainly to Asia (one-half), South America, Europe, and Africa. South American exports went to all continents—more than one-half to North America and one-third to Europe.

The critical need for fertilizers in nonindustrialized lands, which either do not possess resources of fertilizer or have not developed adequate manufacturing facilities, has lately gained worldwide recognition. Industrialized countries are developing a sense of responsibility for supplying the need through exportation or in other ways. In any event, manufacturers in many quarters are looking to expansion in the international market by shipment from without or by manufacture within the country with potential market demand.

Developments stemming from these commercial activities within this decade no doubt will alter markedly the world distribution of fertilizer manufacturing facilities and therewith the pattern of intercontinental trade in fertilizers.

FERTILIZER is the key to profitable crop production in many parts of the world.

Economic crop production requires fertile soil, adequate moisture, good seed of an adapted variety, and protection against pests, weeds, and disease. Failure to provide for any one of these requirements will, in general, limit yields and thus reduce the effectiveness of the effort devoted to supplying the other three.

The use of fertilizer increases the effectiveness of all four requirements.

W. L. HILL, *research chemist, became Director, the United States Fertilizer Laboratory, Soil and Water Conservation Research Division, Agricultural Research Service, in 1959. He has been engaged in research on fertilizers in the Department since 1928.*

Chemicals in Crop Production

by W. B. ENNIS, JR., and
W. D. McCLELLAN

BLIGHTS, PLAGUES, weeds, and insects always have dogged man's attempts to produce food, feed, and fiber. Sometimes he has been able to control the pests. When he has not been able to do so, his society has suffered or perished.

An example is the late blight in Ireland in 1845 and 1846 that all but destroyed the potato crops on which the Irish were almost wholly dependent as a major source of food. As a consequence, a million people died from starvation or from disease.

Before 1870, Ceylon was preeminent in coffee production. The coffee rust fungus, a serious parasite on wild coffee trees, then invaded the plantations, and yields became so low that coffee was abandoned as a crop and was replaced by tea. South America, particularly Brazil, then became the coffee empire of the world.

In the Philippines, cadang-cadang has become the most serious disease in coconuts, and if control measures are not developed, the livelihood of one-third of the population is hurt.

In the Tropics and other regions of high rainfall, crop plantings are lost year after year because of heavy weed competition despite adequate hand labor. Some crops can no longer be grown in places that have become infested with such perennial weeds as nutsedge, quackgrass, and field bind-weed. Aquatic weeds, such as Salvinia, threaten production of rice in Ceylon, and transportation on the Nile River is restricted because of the clogging of the river by water-hyacinth.

Plant parasitic nematodes undoubtedly cause crop damage throughout the world, but the extent of their damage is not known. The Incas in Peru had a custom that forbade the planting of potatoes year after year in the same fields. We know now that the golden nematode of potatoes has long been present in Peru, and it is assumed that the presence of nematodes accounted for the long rotations between crops.

History is full of other examples of the ravages of pests. Necessity has forced farmers to adopt chemicals for controlling their plant diseases, nematodes, and weeds, because chemicals generally are more effective and economical than other methods.

Native vegetation in its natural environment will not support large numbers of livestock or people. As they increase, it becomes necessary to replace native vegetation in many places with more productive plants. When native vegetation is disturbed or cultivated fields are abandoned, weeds take over.

To produce crop plants, farmers must utilize all available technology to stabilize the vegetation at a high productive level and prevent it from returning to a less productive level. The control of weeds is a basic, essential, and important aspect of this fundamental ecological process. The costs of weed control, together with reduced crop yields and quality caused by weed competition, constitute some of the highest costs in the production of crops. The control of weeds is one of the most important practices in modern farm management.

For a long time farmers had to rely on crude tools and handweeding.

Rotation of crops was recognized more than a half century ago as a valuable supplement to tillage methods of controlling weeds. It still is important.

The use of chemicals to control weeds also has a long history. Common salt was used a century ago. Between 1895 and 1909 investigators in the United States and Europe studied copper sulfate, salt, iron sulfate, sulfuric acid, and carbolic acid as chemicals for controlling weeds.

The discovery of the selective herbicidal properties of certain dinitro dye compounds by workers in France in the thirties was an important step.

No marked acceptance of chemical control methods occurred until about 1948, but early discoveries of selective chemicals, such as the dinitro compounds, demonstrated the feasibility of chemical control of weeds and stimulated continued search for chemicals that would kill some plants and not others—crop plants, that is. We call it selective action.

The discovery of the selective herbicidal action of the phenoxyacetic acids, typified by 2,4-dichlorophenoxyacetic acid (2,4-D), in 1944 had far-reaching effects in weed control. Within 5 years after its discovery, 2,4-D was being used to control weeds on more than 18 million acres of small grains and 4.5 million acres of corn in the United States.

Chemical industries in the United States and elsewhere began then to synthesize and evaluate the weed-killing properties of hundreds of chemicals. As a result, instead of three or four herbicides of commercial significance in the midforties, 181 million pounds of herbicides, representing 6 thousand formulations of more than 100 organic chemicals, were shipped for use in the United States in 1962.

In 1962–1963, herbicides comprised 20 percent of the total organic pesticide production in the United States. In 3 years from 1959 to 1962, the value of exports of 2,4-D, 2,4,5-T, and other herbicides from the United States increased from 6.7 million dollars to 22.4 million dollars.

In 1962, of the United States herbicide exports totaling more than 22 million pounds, more than 8 million

pounds of herbicides were exported to Canada; 1.7 million pounds to the Netherlands; 1.3 million pounds to Colombia; 1.1 million pounds to the Republic of South Africa; 0.9 million pounds to Venezuela; 0.6 million to Japan, Mexico, and West Germany; and more than 225 thousand pounds each to Costa Rica, Pakistan, Sweden, Spain, the United Kingdom, and Australia.

The use of herbicides in the United States more than doubled between 1959 and 1963. Herbicides were applied on an estimated 85 million acres, or about 20 percent of the Nation's cropland, in 1962. Most of the grain crops in the United Kingdom are treated with herbicides. More than 70 percent of the summer cereals of West Germany are chemically treated for weed control.

The chemical control of weeds (and other pests) hinges on the property some substances have of affecting only certain species. Selective toxicity—the basis for synthesis and formulation of effective herbicides that kill weeds and leave the crop unharmed—often is achieved through techniques of application that bring the herbicides in closer contact with weeds than with crop plants.

Sometimes the selectivity operates through differential behavior and biochemical reactivity of weeds and specific crop species to particular herbicides. Scientists in England, the Netherlands, and West Germany, as well as those in the United States, have contributed to a better understanding of the bases for selective action of herbicides.

An example of a selective herbicide is propanil (3,4-dichloropropionanilide), which is effective against barnyard grass (*Echinochloa crusgalli*) and other annual weed grasses and sedges in ricefields. Rice, a nontilled crop, is not injured by propanil at any stage of growth, but propanil is most effective on the weeds soon after they emerge. Increases in yield after treatment with propanil range from 325 to 5,300 pounds of rough rice an acre. Average gains reported in five States were 1 thousand to 2 thousand pounds.

Chemical control also lowers costs of production, reduces the amount of hand labor, and increases mechanized production. Chemical control of weeds in strawberries has reduced costs from 200 dollars an acre for handweeding to less than 30 dollars. The use of herbicides in cotton reduces cost of weed control from 24 dollars an acre to about 8 dollars and reduces man-hours from 35 to 12.

We have estimates that chemical weed control in such nontilled crops as wheat, oats, and barley and on grazing lands has raised their productivity 10 to 20 percent.

Labor for hoeing and pulling weeds in many tilled crops, such as corn, soybeans, sugarbeets, sugarcane, cotton, and vegetables, is no longer available at costs the farmers can afford.

Chemical weed control also has facilitated mechanized production. When poisonous weeds and brush are killed, productivity of pastures and rangelands is greater and leads to improved management of livestock and better milk and meat.

Herbicides also can control weeds that clog irrigation and drainage canals and interfere with the use of ponds, lakes, and streams.

All this is not an American monopoly. Other countries use agricultural chemicals and have done much to improve them. For some countries, chemical weedkillers are or can be a way to increase production and make more efficient use of labor.

In the heavy rainfall areas of tropical zones in Central and South America, chemical weed control has increased productivity of rice, maize, and other food crops. Herbicides are being used increasingly in African nations to control brush on rangeland and to clear waterways of water-hyacinth. New Zealand and Australia make extensive use of herbicides to control weeds and brush on grazing lands.

We believe herbicides will be used more extensively throughout the world to help improve farming efficiency and productivity of crops.

BLIGHTS, SMUTS, scabs, wilts, mildews, rusts, mosaics, and other diseases are caused by fungi, bacteria, and viruses. Every crop plant is affected by one or more of the diseases.

They affect seeds, seedlings, stalks, roots, leaves, tubers, fruits, and flowers. They kill many plants outright and may reduce crop production to zero. The quantity and quality of the crop may be severely curtailed by fungal, bacterial, and viral attacks in the field and after harvest.

Many virus diseases are systemic in the plant. Many may be carried by insects. Some viruses must spend a part of their cycle in the insect host before the insect is capable of transmitting them to another plant. Others are transmitted merely by mechanical contact. Bacteria can be disseminated by splashing rain, insects, and man through contact. Fungi are disseminated in many ways—most of them as spores, which are windborne or carried in drops of splashing water. Others migrate through the soil through normal growth or may be disseminated by rain and irrigation water. Some organisms attack a particular host; other parasitic organisms have a wide range of host plants.

Plant diseases are controlled by the use of resistant varieties, proper crop management, and the use of chemicals. Plant pathologists and plant breeders are constantly developing resistant varieties. Frequently the organisms themselves mutate and form new and more virulent races, and plant breeders must then develop varieties which will be resistant to these new races.

The biological control of plant diseases may moderate their destructive effects, but the use of artificial biological control methods has not been entirely successful. Losses caused by some of the insectborne virus diseases, such as the curlytop disease, which is spread by the beet leafhopper, have been reduced by spraying the overwintering sites with an insecticide before it migrates into beetfields in the spring.

Chemical control and development of resistance are the chief measures to control plant diseases. We have no effective way to control bacterial plant diseases, although the antibiotic streptomycin has been used with success against fireblight of apples and pears. A search has been underway for some time for an effective viricide.

The value of bordeaux mixture was discovered in France about 1882. It became a mainstay in plant disease control for many years. Copper sulfate, mainly bordeaux mixture, was used on potatoes to the extent of 20 million pounds a year by the time of the Second World War and almost that much was applied to apples to prevent bitterrot and blackrot. Two major companies that supply the American market with bananas have spent an estimated 18 million dollars a year for bordeaux mixture to control the Sigatoka disease of bananas in the Tropics. The disease is so severe that banana plantations must be sprayed 15 to 17 times a year.

There has been a shift away from the use of copper for controlling Sigatoka to the use of oil sprays. This has resulted in a tremendous reduction in our export of copper sulfate. In 1957, for example, 56.6 million pounds of copper sulfate were shipped from the United States to the four banana-producing countries, Guatemala, Honduras, Costa Rica, and Panama, whereas in 1962 only Honduras imported as much as 70 thousand pounds, a drop from the 20,272,000 pounds Honduras imported in 1957.

Now there is a shift back to bordeaux mixture or to the organic fungicides, since continued use of the oil sprays appears to result in smaller bunches of bananas in many areas.

The organic mercury compounds were introduced into the United States from Germany as seed treatments in 1913. Previously most cereal seed and potato seed diseases were treated with formalin. Much of the early research and development on the use of organic mercuries as seed-treating materials was done in Germany. It has been estimated that 15 million pounds of organic mercurials have been used annually in the United States for treating seed and that more than 60 million acres were planted with treated seed. Farmers used to rely on copper, sulfur, and mercury compounds, but greatly improved organic fungicides have been developed since 1945.

Some of them evolved from compounds used in making automobile tires. A patent was issued in 1934 for an alkyl dithiocarbamate as a fungicide, but it was almost 10 years before dithiocarbamate fungicides became available to the public. During this period, the fungitoxicity of chloranil (tetrachloro-p-benzoquinone) was demonstrated, but it was considered too expensive at first. Later, however, it was shown that from an investment of 70 cents an acre required to treat pea seeds, a return of as much as 21.25 dollars could be realized at 1951 prices.

Nearly all seed peas in the United States are treated.

The nitropyrazoles, the amino triazoles, the s-triazines, the quinolines, and the phenols also have been widely studied as fungicides, but only a few have come into widespread commercial use. Most fungicides have been developed as protective chemicals. Applied to the plants before spores of the causal fungus are deposited, they can prevent the development of disease if good coverage by the fungicide is obtained.

Fungicides are used to control plant diseases in many countries. They are applied to the seed to prevent rotting or to foliage as sprays or dusts to protect the plant by destroying the spores of the fungi before they penetrate the foliage and cause infection.

The dollar value of exports of fungicides from the United States has been climbing rapidly. The value of fungicides exported was 8 million dollars in 1959 and 26 million dollars in 1962.

In western Africa, especially in Nigeria, the black pod disease of cocoa (caused by *Phytophthora palmivora*) is a serious pest. This disease is practically universal wherever cocoa is grown commercially. Spraying with copper compounds of various kinds, including bordeaux mixture, is the principal control measure employed. Extensive control programs for this disease are underway in Nigeria and spray applications often are made every month.

Most fungicides now in use are inefficient, and large amounts are needed to insure protection. A constant search is being made in a number of countries for more efficient and effective fungicides. There are no effective materials for controlling most root-rotting fungi or fungi that invade the conductive tissues of plants and cause them to wilt.

Therapeutant-type chemicals, which readily move through the plant from one part to another, are easily applied, and are low in cost, are needed. They should prevent the entry of the organisms into the plants or kill them after they enter or (in the case of wilt diseases) offset their wilt effects.

Also needed are fungicides that can be applied to seeds and be absorbed by them and become systemic.

Many of the newest organic fungicides have proved satisfactory for the control of plant diseases in the Tropics. There the potential demand is great, but their widespread use is limited by the relatively low purchasing power of many farmers. Discovery and introduction of more effective and economical chemicals for use against plant diseases will contribute greatly to meeting world problems of food production by insuring a consistent production of healthy crops.

PLANT PARASITIC NEMATODES attack practically all kinds of plants and limit crop production in all parts of the United States. Field and forage crops, vegetables, fruit and nut plants, ornamentals in nurseries and around homes, and turf and grasses on lawns and golf courses are affected.

Nematodes also carry several viruses that cause plant diseases. They also incite some fungal and bacterial diseases and cause them to be more severe.

Damage caused by heavy nematode infestation often may reduce yields as much as 75 or 100 percent. Crop losses due to nematodes may amount to 1 billion dollars a year in America.

For many years root knot nematodes and the cyst-forming nematodes were thought to be the worst nematode groups, but nematologists in the Southeastern States demonstrated the severity of damage that can be caused by ectoparasitic nematodes such as the root lesion nematode.

Evidence that species of the root lesion nematode, Pratylenchus, are causing substantial crop losses in many parts of the world is accumulating rapidly. For example, the tea industry is of vital importance to Ceylon—providing 60–70 percent of its exports—and research has demonstrated that losses due to this nematode are large.

To grow many crops successfully under present conditions, some type of nematode control is necessary.

Control by nonchemical means, such as crop rotations, fallowing, and growing resistant varieties, undoubtedly has been practiced widely by growers for a long time and still is an important method of control.

Control by chemicals, or nematocides, has become of increased importance in the production of crops. An estimated 100 million pounds of nematocides were used in the United States in 1961, principally on tobacco, pineapple, and vegetable fields.

Although we have known of the damage done by nematodes, high costs and difficulties formerly restricted the use of the available materials and methods, and soil treatment was confined to high-value crops in the greenhouse and nursery. Steam, carbon bisulfide, chloropicrin (tear gas), and methyl bromide were the methods and materials available. Treatments cost 300 to 500 dollars an acre and entailed hazards and inconveniences. Nematode control consequently was achieved through the development of a few resistant varieties and crop rotation.

A significant development was the discovery in the forties of the value of a mixture of 1,2-dichloropropane and 1,3-dichloropropene (D-D mixture) for controlling nematodes in pineapple plantings. D-D mixture, a byproduct of the petroleum industry, is relatively cheap, and land can be treated for one-tenth of the cost of older materials.

Ethylene dibromide, another relatively inexpensive material, later was shown to be an effective nematocide. Because these two nematocides could be used effectively and practically on a field scale, farmers rapidly adopted them. Both are widely used in the United States, but low temperatures in Europe apparently restrict treatment to summer.

The treatment of all pineapple plantations in Hawaii with a nematocide before planting has become a standard practice. The major uses for nematocides elsewhere in the United States are for treating land to be planted to tobacco, cotton, and vegetables.

In Rhodesia root knot is widely prevalent even in the veld areas not previously cropped. Tobacco growers there practice nematode control through a combination of crop rotations and the use of nematocides. Yield increases of 400 to 500 pounds an acre are obtained when nematocides are used. Of the 224 thousand acres of tobacco in Rhodesia, 105 thousand were fumigated in 1962.

NEMATOCIDES have been used on only a fraction of the farming sections where they could be applied profitably. Better, more efficient nematocides are needed for general use.

A nematocide generally useful for controlling nematodes in planting stock is needed by nurserymen and by plant quarantine authorities responsible for preventing the introduction of plant pests. Attention should be given to the development of chemicals and methods for treating nematodes on roots several feet below the soil surface and also for controlling nematodes at the surface.

Possibilities include low-phytotoxic chemicals that can be applied to the plant leaves, where they are translocated to the roots so that they can kill or repel nematodes in the root zone. Also, the synthesis and use of possible attractant or chemisterilant chemicals in the soil might interrupt nematode feeding and reproduction activities either in the absence of host plants or in their presence and thus result indirectly in their control.

F. W. WENT's discovery in 1928 of naturally occurring auxin in plants and P. W. Zimmerman's discovery in the thirties that certain synthetic chemicals can change the growth of plants in many ways stimulated interest in discovering and developing chemicals to regulate plant growth. These chemical regulators are unlike the fertilizer chemicals, which provide nutrients for plant growth. Instead, they regulate the many physiological processes that take place during growth, fruiting, and maturation.

Now we know of chemicals that stimulate or retard the growth of plants; induce or retard sprouting, rooting, and flowering; increase resistance to cold, heat, and drought; increase or decrease the set of fruit; hasten defoliation; and cause other responses in plants.

Growth-regulating chemicals are applied in minute amounts to control the growth and behavior of crop plants. Naphthaleneacetic acid is used to treat apple trees in the fall to prevent fruit drop and thereby improve the quality. Only one teaspoonful is used on 1 acre of orchard, which produces approximately 200 thousand apples. If this chemical were not used, the grower could lose 50 percent or more of the crop.

Potatoes store best at relatively low temperatures, but the ideal storage is costly and not always possible to maintain. Potatoes sprout profusely and shrivel and deteriorate when they are stored at higher temperatures. Sprouting is prevented safely through the use of regulating chemicals.

Growth regulators are widely used to induce rooting of the vegetatively propagated plants, with no danger of poisoning animals and people.

Some chemicals are used by nurserymen and florists to produce a dwarfing effect. Others can stimulate growth and elongation.

One growth-regulating chemical, gibberellic acid, is used to increase the size and quality of grapes. It has an extremely low animal-toxicity level.

Chemicals that cause leaves to fall also are used to prepare cottonfields for mechanical harvesting. Leaf fall normally is associated with physiological aging, but it may be induced also by water stress, certain disease organisms, insect attacks, nutrient deficiencies, light frosts, and other factors, such as mechanical injuries, which injure but do not kill the leaf blades. Chemicals now provide a means of producing defoliation timed to the producers' needs.

Three general types of chemicals fall within this category—defoliants, which induce leaf fall (abscission) but do not kill the plant; desiccants, which cause severe leaf kill, with little or no leaf fall but fast drying of attached leaves; and regrowth inhibitors, which retard or prevent new leaf growth immediately after defoliation or desiccation.

Harvest-aid chemicals are used on several million acres of cotton harvested by machine in the United States, but improvements in their reliability and use are being sought.

Further knowledge of the physiological factors within the plant that control abscission and growth is being developed through research that deals with biochemical mechanisms involved in the abscission process; studies of chemical penetration and translocation in the plant and of the distribution and fate of the chemical after it is absorbed; and investigations on cultural and environmental control methods to make chemicals more dependable in action. Desiccants are also widely used before mechanical harvesting of a number of seed crops.

Numerous problems, such as tolerance of crops to frost, drought, and high salt content in the soil, may be solved through the use of chemicals.

Tremendous crop losses occur each year as a result of low-temperature injury to economic crop plants. Compounds on the horizon appear capable of increasing the tolerance of plants to low temperatures, particularly in the production of fruit and vegetables. These chemicals may delay flowering until frost hazard is over or may actually increase cold hardiness.

It may be possible that regulating chemicals can be used to lower the water requirements of plants in places of critical water supply and thus conserve water. Regulating chemicals which will increase the tolerance of crops to salt injury and thereby permit their growth in soils with high salt content probably can be developed.

Regulating chemicals are being developed that will control the size and shape of plants so as to facilitate the use of machines for harvesting them.

Retardant-type chemicals are in prospect to regulate the size of trees and shrubs along roads and streets that obstruct the visibility of automobile drivers and interfere with electric and telephone wires. Maleic hydrazide is used commercially to stunt grass along highways and thus reduce the number of mowings required for maintenance.

Many crop plants must be harvested during relatively short periods to obtain a high-quality product. There are possibilities of developing chemical methods of extending the time during which these crops can be harvested, thus facilitating harvest, reducing production costs, and improving the quality of the product for the consumer.

W. B. ENNIS, JR., *is Chief and* W. D. MCCLELLAN *is Assistant Chief of the Crops Protection Research Branch, Crops Research Division, Agricultural Research Service.*

The Place of Insecticides

by STANLEY A. HALL

No COUNTRY can have an efficient agriculture without the use of insecticides and other pestkillers.

Insecticides have made it possible to enhance the quality and amount of agricultural products and to protect the health of people.

A dramatic example is the use of insecticides, chiefly DDT, in a campaign against malaria by the World Health Organization. The program has included all but 300 million of the 1,400 million persons who live in malarious regions (other than China, North Korea, and South Vietnam). Insecticides also have scored successes in beating down other insectborne diseases, like typhus and yellow fever.

Without insecticides we would have wormy—and smaller amounts of—vegetables, fruit, grain, and stored products that insects may infest. We also would have to put up with outbreaks of grasshoppers and infestations of the Mediterranean fruit fly, cattle grubs, ticks, lice, and many more.

Problems attend their use, and therefore the types of insecticides and the methods of applying them are being changed and improved on the basis of observations, experiments, and evaluations by scientists the world over. This work has been going on a long time.

Critics and opponents of the use of chemical pestkillers stress their harmful effects on the wildlife of forest and stream and hazards to human health because of the ways they are applied and the residues that may remain in food.

Such doubts cannot be ignored, and people everywhere must be made aware of the penalties of carelessness and ignorance—as well as the benefits of the proper use of insecticides.

Rachel Carson, one of the critics, in her book, *Silent Spring*, laid much of her criticism at the door of the chlorinated hydrocarbon insecticides, of which DDT is an example.

It is true that DDT, which has been widely used, can be detected by sensitive analytical methods in tiny amounts in a number of foods and in man and animals over widely scattered parts of the earth.

This would be a worrisome situation if there were any evidence that DDT in trace amounts had any adverse effect on the health of people and animals, whether wild or domestic. But we have no evidence of any adverse effects whatsoever. Such evidence has been searched for in many carefully planned studies. The search will continue and will be intensified.

In the meantime, a worldwide shift away from DDT is being made, chiefly because of the growing resistance that some species have developed to it.

Some who oppose the use of insecticides say they would not try to eliminate them entirely but would rely on limited applications of certain insecticides, mainly on insect-killing substances in some plants. This approach would not even begin to answer the problems we have in the control of injurious insects.

I do believe, however, that every branch of science can derive benefit from questioning, doubts, and criticism, regardless of the premises on which they are based. We must weigh and measure arguments, observations, and pertinent phenomena in order to arrive at a true and balanced viewpoint. That is every scientist's goal.

The wide use of insecticides has come about in comparatively recent times as man found ways to protect crops from the insect pests that the very act of cultivation provided with ideal conditions in which to multiply.

An instance: The Colorado potato beetle in 1850 was an unknown insect feeding on wild potatoes and similar plants in the Rocky Mountain region. The settler who brought with him and planted and cultivated the potato innocently supplied the beetle with an abundance of food and the means to multiply enormously. Beetles slowly spread. By 1874 they had reached the east coast. Against potato beetles and other pests, chemicals are more effective than any other methods yet developed and available.

As to the traces of insecticides that remain on plants and elsewhere for a time after they have been applied: Here we have a mixture of real and fancied problems.

The whole matter of residues, not a new one, has become bigger, somewhat alarming, and perhaps confusing to many. These residues are exceedingly small and are measured in parts per million or even in parts per billion.

The Department of Agriculture has a responsibility to consumers, who cannot see or measure residues or even be aware of their presence and must take for granted that milk, good-looking vegetables, fruit, meat, and other foods are safe and wholesome. Without surveillance and careful control, some of the pesticides that persist conceivably could endanger the public health.

Those in the Federal and the State Governments who are charged with their regulation have adopted the basic principle that certain pesticide residues in selected foodstuffs may be allowed in amounts demonstrated to be no higher than those resulting from good agricultural practice, provided that the final amount of residue in the food is not greater than that accepted as safe for long-term consumption by man.

In establishing legal tolerances of residues, the Food and Drug Admin-istration uses at least a hundredfold factor of safety. Canada and many European countries have a similar policy.

We must make a distinction between residues of, say, DDT—which has been studied by toxicologists and pharmacologists, especially in public health laboratories, since about 1942 and about which much is known—and residues of other chlorinated hydrocarbons, such as endrin, for example, which is far more toxic and for which no legal tolerance is permitted in any food or feed.

We cannot simply lump together the chlorinated hydrocarbons and think of them as behaving all alike. Each is a different organic compound with markedly different biological properties and must be separately evaluated.

As for organophosphorous insecticides (malathion, for example)—they generally present few residue problems because they disappear rather quickly and do not accumulate, as do chlorinated insecticides in fatty or other tissues of laboratory animals when fed daily dosages higher than are ever actually encountered in practice as residues.

Problems of residues generally will be solved by changing the ways in which insecticides are used and shifting from those that tend to persist and accumulate to those that do not.

People sometimes confuse residue problems and misuse in the application of insecticides and consequent illnesses or deaths from gross exposures.

Accidental poisonings, which are more likely to occur with some of the more acutely toxic organophosphorous insecticides, can be prevented by reading and following the directions on containers and taking the prescribed precautions.

The effects of insecticides on wildlife sometimes have been adverse and surely should not be belittled or ignored. Sometimes large-scale spraying operations have harmed wildlife. Bees and other beneficial insects have been killed. These matters, of utmost concern, are being corrected by shifting to more precise applications of safer insecticides, as was done in a program to eradicate the fire ant in the Southern States.

We lack evidence that detrimental effects on wildlife are widespread generally in its various environments.

A special problem involves a series of organisms in a food chain, particularly among wildlife. One widely quoted account concerns some elm trees in the Midwest that were sprayed heavily to control the bark beetle vector of Dutch elm disease. Earthworms, which can tolerate fairly large dosages of DDT, picked up the insecticide from the soil and stored it in their body tissues. Robins arriving in the spring ate the earthworms and died.

Another illustration is the use of a larvicide in Clear Lake in California to control an exceedingly pestiferous gnat. A low dosage of TDE (a close relative of DDT) of only 1 part in 60 million parts of water controlled the gnat. But the insecticide was concentrated slowly and to an amazing degree by a chain of different organisms in the lake and finally accumulated in the fish. The fish were then eaten by birds, especially western grebes, which died.

Our growing knowledge will help us foresee and avoid such unfortunate happenings. The problem at Clear Lake has been solved by shifting to a non-residue-forming organophosphorous insecticide, which is applied precisely to accomplish the task.

It appears that the immediate solution to many residue problems will lie in shifting away wherever feasible from the insecticides that tend to build up and accumulate to those that do not. Newer insecticides on which scientists were working in 1964 were mostly the latter kind.

RESISTANCE of insects to insecticides is a mounting problem throughout the world.

Dr. A. W. A. Brown, of the University of Western Ontario, an authority on insect resistance, pointed out that a warning appeared as long ago as 1908 that the selective action of insecticides (mostly simple inorganic compounds in those days) could lead to insect families that would consist of resistant strains. The first evidence of it was in strains of the San José scale insect that developed resistance to lime-sulfur.

Later, three species of scale insects in California became resistant to hydrogen cyanide. The codling moth, peach twig borer, and two species of cattle ticks developed resistance to arsenicals. Other species developed resistance to tartar emetic, cryolite, selenium, and rotenone.

Between 1908 and 1945, however, only 13 species of insects or ticks had developed resistance.

Now the situation is different. The total number of resistant strains has risen to what Dr. Brown calls the "appalling figure" of 137 species.

In this later period, houseflies have become resistant to DDT, BHC, chlordane, and dieldrin. Resistance of insects of importance in public health involves 72 species—58 to dieldrin, 36 to DDT, and 9 to organophosphorous insecticides.

Among agricultural insects, 65 species of plant-feeding arthropods have developed resistant strains—19 to DDT, 16 to dieldrin, and 20 to organophosphorous chemicals.

This problem calls for the utmost resourcefulness and good planning of research if we are to keep ahead of it. It has no single answer.

We can meet some parts of it by shifting to other types of insecticides. A shift from a chlorinated hydrocarbon to an organophosphorous- or carbamate-type insecticide may solve some residue problems. But that is not enough.

Cross-resistance between insecticides is more the rule than the exception. The problem is severe in agriculture. The boll weevil, for example, showed a pronounced resistance to chlorinated hydrocarbons; 80 percent of the total cotton acreage and more than 95 percent of all cotton producers in the United States were affected.

And not only the grower. Also affected is the pesticide chemical industry. Because it may cost 500 thousand to 3 million dollars to develop a pesticide, the chemical industries may well question the desirability of perfecting a new chemical that may not be sold very long because insects may become immune to it.

Therefore other ways to control insects must be explored to the utmost. Some success has attended this work. While we know little about the causes of resistance, we are learning something about it and someday we may learn how to combat it.

ANOTHER APPROACH is to try to eradicate the injurious species before the resistant strains are selected out and become dominant. It is not easy generally to eradicate them with insecticides, but it can be done in certain instances.

In the Mediterranean fruit fly invasion of Florida in 1956, entomologists used an insecticide to kill the fruit flies and a specific insect attractant to tell the operators of spray equipment where and when and how much to spray to stamp out the infestation.

Another insect eradication program was achieved without the use of an insecticide. I mean the highly successful sterile-male campaign against the screw-worm, a serious pest of livestock, in the Southeastern States, Texas, and the Southwest. We are eradicating a species without killing it at all.

We rear insects in laboratories at the rate of 125 million screw-worm flies a week. They are sterilized by a measured dosage of gamma irradiation from a cobalt 60 source and then released according to plan from airplanes.

The sterilized males compete with the native males for the females in the natural population. This is a bold and imaginative scheme of turning the sex drive and enormous reproductive capacity of a destructive insect against itself.

Here are no problems of killing wildlife or beneficial insects or of residues or of selecting out resistant strains. The females lay their eggs normally, but the eggs never hatch. Without killing a single insect, the population of the pest is pushed down and down until it finally disappears.

I am sure this method will get more attention in future years for other insect species and pests that reproduce sexually.

Another possibility is to control and eradicate pests with chemosterilants.

A chemosterilant—the name is a coined one—is a chemical that causes sexual sterility in an insect. The chemical may perform a task that would not be feasible by the irradiation and release method. As examples, neither the boll weevil nor the Mexican fruit fly can take 5 thousand or 10 thousand roentgens of gamma irradiation and come out feeling fit and eager to mate. A chemosterilant is not rough on the insect and can perform its task simply and cheaply.

Chemosterilants were in the research stage in 1964. They do function. We have tested their potentialities with suitable baits.

Experiments designed to test the feasibility of eradication of houseflies with chemosterilants were carried out on three islands in the Caribbean. A similar field experiment in an isolated mango grove in Mexico revealed the power of the method in controlling the destructive Mexican fruit fly with a chemosterilant.

Results are promising, but we have much to learn about developing safe procedures before practical recommendations for their use can be developed.

Investigations of the possibilities of chemosterilants in eradicating the tsetse fly from Africa were begun under a joint research program of the Department of Agriculture and the Agricultural Research Council of Central Africa.

Emphasis has been placed on the discovery and use of materials that attract insects. A number have been found by mass screening hundreds of chemicals to find any attractant, even a weak one. Related compounds are then synthesized to obtain a more potent attractant. An attractant found in this way was used in the eradication of the Mediterranean fruit fly in 1956. Thousands of traps containing the attractant were maintained at strategic locations in Florida during the campaign.

When the medfly invader turned up again early in 1962, the infestation was quickly stamped out with a minimum use of insecticide at an estimated saving of 9 million dollars over the previous campaign, which did not have the benefit of the early warning system of attractants.

Powerful attractants are available for the melon fly and for the oriental fruit fly.

Scientists have given much attention to sex attractants ever since the structure of the gypsy moth sex attractant was determined and synthesized. A synthetic homolog of this attractant, called gyplure, is available in quantity, and its possible use for control or eradication has been investigated.

Many insects, especially among the Lepidoptera, possess sex lures, which enable the male to find the female for mating and reproduction. A sex attractant has been found in the pink bollworm, southern armyworm, tobacco hornworm, and the European corn borer.

When the pure compound is isolated, the chemical structure is determined, and synthesis has been accomplished, we then seek the best way to use this powerful material that Nature provided for reproduction—to turn this extraordinary force against the insect. This goal may be achieved by male annihilation of the harmful species or by coupling a chemosterilant with a sex attractant.

THE DEVELOPMENT of insect-resistant crop varieties has sometimes been used,

but this is necessarily a long and tedious process.

An instance is the wheat stem sawfly. The development of wheats that resist the sawfly permits the profitable growing of wheat on some 2 million acres in Canada and on more than 600 thousand acres in the North Central States.

Varieties of wheat bred for resistance to the hessian fly have been grown on 4.5 million acres in 26 States.

Breeding field crops for disease resistance has had many successes, but these triumphs are not widely heralded. While the examples in which parasites and predators have been used to achieve pest control are numerous, it is evident that not enough support has been given the work in the past, and it seems certain that it will receive far more exploration in the future.

Other biological control methods, such as the use of specific pathogens for insects and other pests, are being developed.

So, to sum up, we are planning and testing new approaches to insect control and eradication keyed to basic findings in biology and chemistry. If we were not on the move, our progress would surely be canceled out by the dynamic forces of Nature.

STANLEY A. HALL *became Chief, Pesticide Chemicals Research Branch, the Department of Agriculture, in 1956. He is a graduate of Columbia University and Polytechnic Institute of Brooklyn. He joined the Naval Stores Research Division of the former Bureau of Agricultural and Industrial Chemistry in 1939. In 1943 he transferred to Bureau of Entomology and Plant Quarantine to pursue research on insecticides, including work on an analytical method for DDT, identification of isomers, and synthesis of analogs. Later he took charge of a synthesis program primarily to find better insect repellants for the Armed Forces. That effort culminated in the discovery of the repellent deet, now widely used. He has specialized in organic phosphorus chemistry and later the synthesis of insect attractants.*

Grain, a Basic Food

by KENNETH L. MURRAY

SEVENTY PERCENT of the harvested acreage of the whole world—1.6 billion acres—is used to grow grain. That is more than one-half acre and one-third of a ton of grain for each person in the world.

Grain is a basic food and always has been. Grain provides directly roughly half the calories of the world's 3 billion people. A large portion of the other 50 percent comes indirectly from grain—the grain that has been converted into meat, milk, eggs, and other animal products.

Many countries have been expanding their production, which averaged approximately 650 million tons in 1949–1953 and more than 900 million tons in recent years. The greatest increases are in corn, rice, and wheat. Barley and sorghum are of lesser importance, but their production also has increased rapidly.

Oats and rye are declining in importance—oats because there are fewer horses and rye because less of it is used for bread in Europe.

The giants in grain production are the United States, the Soviet Union, and China, which together grow more than two-fifths of the grain.

The United States produces about 170 million tons of grain each year—almost 1 ton for each inhabitant. Our production far surpasses our domestic needs. A large share, about 1 ton of every 5 tons produced, is exported. Our abundant grain supplies have become important in our trade relations with other countries. They are a source of foreign exchange earnings and one of our "foods for peace."

MAN'S USE of grain as a food dates from the earliest civilizations. The grains are believed to have been among the first crops cultivated. Historians generally cite Asia as the area where the primitive wheats, barley, rye, and rice originated. Corn may have originated in Mexico or Central America and sorghum in tropical Africa. Oats have been traced to a European origin.

Wheat and barley may have been grown in the Mediterranean region as long ago as the late Bronze Age. Barley was being used then as an animal feed. People at first ate grain hulls and all. Later they began to remove the hulls.

The first food from wheat was in the form of boiled porridge. Later, wheat was used to make an unleavened flatbread, for which the kernels are ground or cracked, water is added, and the dough is baked on an open fire or fried. Flatbread is still popular in parts of Asia, Africa, and Europe. Corn, barley, and sometimes wheat and other grains generally are used to make flatbread. Unlike wheat and rye, barley and corn cannot be used for dough that is to be leavened, or raised.

The first raised-bread loaves may have been made by the Egyptians as early as 2600 B.C. Yeast generally is used as the agent to raise bread. Gases produced by the yeast and retained in the dough cause the loaf to raise. Only wheat and rye flours have the ability to retain these gases, but rye is inferior in leavening properties.

The book, *Breads, White and Brown*, by R. A. McCance and E. M. Widdowson, points out that "the Greeks and the Romans seemed to have recognized, as we do today, a hard wheat and a soft wheat with different baking properties and to have sown wheat in both autumn and spring."

All the grains we grow in the United States, except corn, were brought here by the early settlers. Corn was grown by the Indians, who taught the settlers how to cultivate it. At the time of the first census in 1839, corn production was almost 10 million tons. It has always been our leading grain.

Wheat was first grown in the United States in 1602 in Massachusetts on Elizabeth Island. Slightly more than 2 million tons of wheat were produced in the United States in 1839. The leading wheat States then were Ohio, Pennsylvania, and New York.

While wheat, barley, rye, corn, and other grains were developing in the Western Hemisphere, the Far Eastern civilizations were cultivating mainly rice and growing less of the other grains. Rice was grown in China 5 thousand years or so ago, but we do not know in which country rice was first grown. Rice has been a basic food in most of Asia for centuries.

In the United States, rice was successfully planted the first time about 1685 in the Carolinas. For some 100 years after that date, rice production in the United States was confined to the swampy regions of the Carolinas and Georgia. During the 19th century, other States began planting rice, and by 1889 Louisiana became the Nation's leading rice producer. Farmers in Texas, Arkansas, California, and Mississippi began to grow rice.

Production of rice requires relatively high temperatures during the growing season, an abundant supply of water (which can be supplied through irrigation), level and well-drained land, and soil that can hold water. Those conditions exist in the rice-bowl region of Asia, which includes Thailand, Indochina, and Burma. Irrigation is needed for rice in the United States.

MANKIND HAS DEVELOPED and improved many types of grains and has put them to numerous uses. With this evolutionary process has come a general classification of grains according to their greatest usefulness.

We can make three broad groupings: Grain for direct consumption (in flour or in whole-kernel form); grain for livestock and poultry feed; and grain for industrial uses, such as the production of starch and alcohol. Wheat and rice are mostly in the first group.

Corn, barley, oats, sorghum, and millet are used mainly for feed. Of the relatively small amount of grain utilized in industrial processes, barley and corn are used most commonly.

THOUSANDS of varieties of wheat are grown throughout the world, but they all fall into one of two classifications—hard or soft.

Soft wheats usually are grown in places of relatively abundant rainfall.

Both soft red and soft white wheats are grown in the United States. Most of the soft red wheat is produced in Illinois, Indiana, Ohio, Missouri, and Pennsylvania, where rainfall averages about 40 inches a year.

The soft white wheat produced in the United States is grown mainly in Washington, Oregon, and Idaho.

Precipitation in those States averages below that in the soft red Wheat Belt, but the rainfall is more evenly distributed. The bulk of the wheat produced in western Europe and in Australia consists of soft varieties.

The soft wheats are used for bread, cookies, crackers, pastries, rolls, cake mixes, and other items. Soft-wheat flour, however, is not well suited to the manufacture of packaged bread as we know it in the United States, because bread made of soft wheat has a short shelf life—it would be stale before it could be delivered to the supermarket or doorstep. Places that grow soft wheat, such as western Europe, therefore import hard wheat to blend with domestic soft wheats for flour to be used to make bread that will keep.

French bread, which many people like, is made almost solely from the domestic soft wheat, but it must be eaten soon after it is made. Paris has countless breadshops, and French families buy bread for each meal—not for a week.

In the countries that comprise the European Economic Community, a sizable amount of soft wheat, about 20 percent of production, is fed to livestock and poultry; the proportion is highest when the harvest season is wet and too much moisture causes wheat to sprout.

Hard wheat makes up the bulk of the wheat production in the United States, Canada, Argentina, and parts of western Asia and northern Africa. Wheat produced in the Soviet Union is generally considered hard.

Our main producers of hard wheat are Kansas, North Dakota, Montana, Nebraska, Washington, South Dakota, Minnesota, and Oklahoma, whose rainfall is considerably below that in the soft wheat States.

Hard wheat is used primarily for making bread. An exception is durum wheat, a variety of hard wheat used for making macaroni, spaghetti, and noodles. Durum wheat is grown in the United States, Canada, Spain, northern Africa and the Middle East, the Soviet Union, and Italy. A small amount is grown in France. The production of durum wheat in the United States is concentrated in North Dakota and South Dakota.

RICE VARIETIES number in the thousands. All fit into one of three groups—long-grain, medium-grain, and short-grain rice.

Long-grain rice, which has a kernel length about four or five times the width, is preferred by many consumers. It is clear and translucent; short-grain rice has a chalky look. Long-grain kernels tend to stick together much less than the short-grain varieties. Long-grain rice requires the longest growing season, needs more irrigation, and generally yields less than the others.

Milling long-grain rice is more expensive, and more grains break. It sells for more therefore than the short- and medium-grain sorts.

Medium-grain rice is somewhat less

desirable to most consumers, but it generally is preferred over short-grain rice and it costs less to produce and market than the long-grain varieties and therefore is the principal type grown in the United States.

Short-grain rice is the chalkiest variety and has the poorest separating qualities during cooking.

Because long-grain rice requires a lengthy growing season, it must be grown in semitropical and tropical climates. Production in southeastern Asia is principally long grain. Aromatic long-grain rice is grown in India and Pakistan; nonaromatic rice is grown in the United States. Short-grain rice is grown in Japan and other parts of northern Asia.

Rice milling differs from the milling of other grains in that a flour is not produced. The inedible hulls are merely removed. The rice remains in whole kernels; the kernels are not pulverized, as they are when wheat is milled.

There are different degrees of milling. If just the inedible hulls are removed, brown rice results—the kernel plus all the edible layers of bran. Rice in this form is most nutritious. Removal of the bran and polishing are further steps. Polished rice is preferred in many markets, including the United States.

THE COARSE GRAINS—all cereals except wheat and rice—are used mainly for animal feed and industrial purposes. Direct human consumption of coarse grains is relatively small. Rye is still a major food grain in central Europe, especially Germany and Poland, but its use for bread is declining. Corn is used for food extensively in Latin America, Africa, and eastern Europe.

Corn, the primary coarse grain, has three principal types: Dent, flint, and flour corn.

Dent corn, both yellow and white in color, forms the bulk of American and Mexican production. It mainly is used for feed, but some dent corn is used to make starch, alcohol, and other industrial products. Byproducts from the manufacture of starch from corn include corn sirup and corn oil. White dent corn is preferred for the production of starch. Some corn is milled in the United States to be eaten as meal, hominy, and grits.

Flint corn is grown principally in Latin America, Europe, and Asia. A small amount is grown in northern parts of the United States. Flint corn grown in Argentina has a higher content of carotene than the yellow dent corn grown in the United States. It produces a yellow fat in poultry and beef, and therefore enjoys a preference in some markets.

Flour corn is grown mainly in Latin America and in South Africa. Small amounts of flour corn are produced in drier sections of the United States. White, blue, and variegated are the most common colors in flour corn. Its kernel is relatively soft and well suited to the manufacture of starch.

Two less common groups of corn are popcorn and sweet corn. Both are grown mainly in the United States and are little known elsewhere. Few Europeans share (or know about) our liking for corn-on-the-cob.

Barley is predominantly a feed grain, but a relatively large share goes into industrial uses. Barley is important in making malt, which is used principally in brewing beer and making alcohol and sirups. A small amount of barley is milled for food; this type is called pot or pearl barley.

Most of the oats harvested in the world is fed to livestock, especially horses and poultry. Some is used for food. Rolled oats, or oatmeal, is made generally by passing the oats between rollers.

Grain sorghums are a feed grain in the United States, but they are important as food in Africa and parts of India.

As TO overall trends in grain consumption in the world, some factors are easily identified.

In countries with relatively high and

rising personal incomes, people eat less and less grain and more and more meat. In countries whose per capita incomes are low, diets tend to be made up mostly of cereal foods.

Feed grain is fed mainly to hogs and poultry. Beef and dairy cattle in the United States are commonly fed grain, but not in most other countries. In western Europe, for instance, cattle are mostly dual purpose (meat and milk) and are sustained on grazing rather than grain.

WHEAT, rice, and corn rank as the world's chief grains, measured in terms of production. Wheat has the largest acreage, but its yields are relatively low. Wheat and rice output has been approximately equal during the past few years; together they account for about half the world's production of grain. Corn is third; it accounts for about 20 percent. Barley, millet and sorghum, oats, and rye follow and form roughly 30 percent of world total.

THE WORLD PRODUCTION of wheat has averaged about 225 million tons. Wheat is grown in almost all countries, but in only 10 countries does average production exceed 5 million tons a year. They are the Soviet Union, the United States, China, Canada, France, India, Italy, Turkey, Australia, and Argentina.

Methods of production vary greatly. Planting, cultivation, and harvesting in mainland China, for example, still is principally handwork, as it was centuries ago. In the United States, Canada, Australia, and Argentina, those processes are highly mechanized.

The Soviet Union, the leading producer, has averaged about 50 million tons in recent years, although yields there are lower than in any of the other nine countries. The average in Russia is 12 bushels an acre. Production in the Soviet Union increased 54 percent between 1950–1954 and 1955–1959, but has stabilized since then, primarily because fewer acres have been planted to wheat. The new lands in

Siberia seem to have reached a peak in harvested grain acreage.

The total wheat production in the United States averaged about 33 million tons a year in the early sixties—a 10-percent increase over 1950–1954. The acreage needed to produce this grain has declined as a result of Government acreage allotments, but the yields have increased more than enough to offset the reduction in acreage. Wheat yields in the United States averaged 25 bushels an acre in the sixties, compared to 22 bushels in the early fifties.

Production in Canada has been relatively stable since 1950, but in 1961 a crop failure lowered production to 7.7 million tons, about half the average. Yields in Canada have not shown a tendency to increase, but seem to have stabilized at about 21 bushels an acre.

Production in France, the fifth largest grower, has risen sharply without any increase in acreage. A record crop of 14 million tons in 1962 was harvested in France; the average yield was 45 bushels an acre. Yields in some parts of northern France reached 90 bushels an acre; operations there are largely mechanized, and fertilizer is applied heavily. Also, optimum conditions prevailed during planting, growing, and harvesting.

India, Italy, and Turkey grow much wheat but generally not enough to meet their own needs. The Soviet Union, the United States, Canada, and France generally export large quantities of wheat. The Soviet Union has been a wheat exporter, but untoward weather conditions necessitated large imports in 1963–1964.

Australia and Argentina, where the wheat crop averages 7 million tons and 5 million tons, respectively, also produce more than enough for domestic needs and generally export some.

The highest wheat yields in the world are obtained in Europe. Average yields in the Netherlands reached 60 bushels an acre in 1960–1963. They were about 55 bushels in the United Kingdom. Belgium, Germany, and in

Ireland have had an average close to 50 bushels.

In western Europe as a whole, the average yields have been as high as 34 bushels an acre—compared to 24 bushels in eastern Europe, 14 in Asia, 11 in Africa, 16 in South America, and 18 in Oceania.

Among the factors that lead to variations in yields from country to country are the intensity of production and growing conditions. In countries in western Europe, wheat is grown intensively, fertilizer application is high, and farms are relatively small. In the United States and Canada, fertilizer generally is used more sparingly, and wheatfields seem endless. Growing conditions dictate the types grown and strongly influence yields. Soft winter wheats, for example, are adaptable to sections of relatively high moisture and rather mild winters.

Hard spring wheats cannot be grown in high-moisture areas and do not have the benefit of a start in the fall.

THE MAIN COARSE grains are corn, barley, oats, sorghum, and rye. World production of corn averages 190 million tons; barley, 80 million tons; oats, 50; and rye, 33.

The United States grows about half of the world's corn. Production was 70 million tons in 1950–1954 and 95 million tons in 1960–1962. This large rise in output has come although the acreage in corn was reduced. The average yield in the United States in 1950–1954 was 39 bushels an acre and 60 bushels in later years—the highest in the world. The use of hybrid corn seed has been a prime factor behind this large increase in yields.

Average yields in other major corn-producing countries have been: Brazil, 22 bushels an acre; Mexico, 14; Republic of South Africa, 21; Yugoslavia, 34; Argentina, 30; Rumania, 25; India, 15; Italy, 46; Hungary, 37. Average yields worldwide are about 30 bushels an acre.

The Soviet Union has ranked as the world's second largest producer of corn. Production there has increased from about 5 million tons in the early fifties to almost 11 million tons.

The output of Brazil, the third corn producer, equals about 10 percent of the United States production, but has gone up from about 6 million tons in the early fifties to about 10 million tons in the sixties.

Mexico, the Republic of South Africa, Yugoslavia, Argentina, and Rumania harvest about 5 million tons a year each. All of them usually export corn.

Of the leading corn producers, only the United States planted hybrid seed almost exclusively in 1964.

BARLEY is second in importance among the coarse grains. The Soviet Union leads in production, and the United States is second.

Barley commonly is planted in the spring. The effect of a severe winter on fall-sown crops sometimes determines how many acres are planted to barley. In France in 1956–1957, for example, much of the winter wheat crop was winterkilled, and the fields were resown to barley in the spring.

The Soviet Union in 1962 harvested 15 million tons of barley—double the average in the early fifties. The increase was due primarily to an extension of barley acreage. Yields rose only slightly.

France, West Germany, and Denmark also increased their production of barley. A reduction in the planted acreage in the United States has been offset by higher yields.

Yields in Denmark have surpassed an average of 70 bushels an acre. The American average has been about 32 bushels; the Soviet Union's, about 18 bushels. The world average is about 25 bushels.

OATS is the only major grain whose production has dropped in recent years. The United States' volume, about 15 million tons, has fallen off by almost 5 million tons since the early fifties. In Canada it has fluctuated but reached a high level of more than 7 million tons in 1962. Production in the Soviet Union declined from 12 million tons in the early fifties to 6 million tons in 1962.

Average yields of oats approximate 43 bushels an acre in the United States, 40 in Canada, 22 in the Soviet Union, and 37 worldwide.

Acreage under rye has been reduced, but yields have increased enough to offset the reduction. Europe produces about half of the world's rye crop. Poland, the largest producer, averages 8 million tons a year—one-fourth of the world total.

Grain sorghums, although still junior to corn and barley, have had a great upsurge among growers in the United States, which has become the world's largest producer. American production has tripled since the early fifties and has averaged about 13 million tons in later years. India is a large producer—about 10 million to 12 million tons. Grain sorghums are popular also in Argentina and the Sudan.

RICE is to the Asian countries what wheat is to the Western World. It is a staple in the diet from Pakistan to Japan.

China and India, the most populous countries, are leading producers of rice. The Food and Agriculture Organization estimated that China produces about 80 million tons a year. Production in India has averaged slightly more than 50 million tons. China and India thus grow more than half the world's rice, which is set at 200 million tons a year. India and China, however, export little or no rice; in fact, India imports about 500 thousand tons annually.

Rice is grown in China and India much as it has been for hundreds of years. Labor is cheap, and planting, cultivating, and harvesting are done by hand.

Japan, Pakistan, and Indonesia each produces 14 million to 16 million tons of rice a year. Each, however, has had to import rice to meet domestic needs.

The rice bowl of the world includes Burma, Thailand, and South Vietnam, an area well suited to growing rice. Production in each has been 5 million to 8 million tons, but that meets domestic needs and leaves some for export. The average family farm in the rice bowl grows rice on 15 acres and markets about two-thirds of its output.

Brazil, the United States, and the United Arab Republic also grow rice. Production in Brazil is partly mechanized, but hand labor is used for harvesting and some cultivating. The United States is relatively unimportant in the total world production but has led in introducing new technology. We have developed laborsaving machines, higher yielding varieties, more profitable methods of fertilization, more effective irrigation practices, and advanced marketing techniques. Production in the United States is relatively stable at about 2.5 million tons, about 1 percent of the world total.

Grain is the most important farm commodity in world commerce. Global exports of grain have approximated one-sixth of the total value of world agricultural exports.

Total world grain exports have ranged between 60 million and 80 million tons. Of that, wheat has accounted for almost 60 percent; barley, about 10 percent; corn, 17 percent; and rice, 9.

Grain is a good deal less perishable than most other food commodities in international trade. The less-developed countries whose food distribution systems are not fully efficient have found it less difficult to handle imports of grain than goods harder to store.

The United States is the leading grain exporter. American exports of wheat and flour have been about 40 percent of the world's total exports of those commodities. Our share in the international trade of corn is even higher—slightly more than 50 percent of the total world exports. We account for more than 75 percent of the world total sorghum exports and 30 percent of the world's barley exports. In total, the United States exports 30 million to 35 million tons of grain annually—the production of one in every five acres.

About 70 percent of United States wheat exports (about 14 million tons) are delivered to countries under Government programs. The main receivers of this wheat have been India, Pakistan, Brazil, Turkey, and the United Arab Republic. The remaining 30 percent of our wheat exports not under Government programs are commercially sold, mainly to countries of the European Economic Community, the United Kingdom, and Japan.

United States exports of feed grains are mainly for commercial markets. The major outlets are the United Kingdom, the European Economic Community, and Japan. Canada is an important market for corn, the major feed grain we export.

Canada is the second largest grain exporter; her shipments have averaged 9 million tons of wheat and more than 1 million tons of barley.

Canadian exports of wheat are in direct competition with United States exports, especially in the important western European markets, which require hard wheat for blending with domestic soft wheats. Exports of wheat to China and the Soviet Union have become important to the Canadians.

Canadian exports of barley have been about 18 percent of the world total. The major markets for Canadian barley are in western Europe. Canada also exports grain under a Government program, but the volume is small.

Australian exports of wheat have averaged more than 5 million tons since 1960. The main markets have been China, India, Japan, the United Kingdom, other western European countries, and the Soviet Union.

Australian wheat is called filler wheat and (unlike the hard wheats exported by Canada and the United States) is not suited for blending with soft wheat to improve quality of flour. Australia also exports about 1 million tons of coarse grains.

Argentina follows Australia in volume of grain exports. Both corn and wheat shipments average somewhat more than 2 million tons a year. Argentina's principal wheat markets are Brazil and western Europe. Argentine corn goes mainly to Europe, especially Italy. The Italian market shows a preference for the high carotene content of the Argentine flint corn. Argentina also exports relatively small amounts of sorghums and oats.

The Soviet Union, which has been a regular wheat exporter, had to import large amounts of wheat from Canada, Australia, and the United States in 1963–1964 because of small crops in 1963. Major markets for Soviet wheat have been Poland, Czechoslovakia, East Germany, and some western European countries.

France has become an important exporter of wheat, barley, and corn. French markets include its European Economic Community partners, northern Africa, eastern Europe, the United Kingdom, and China.

The Republic of South Africa has become a leading corn exporter, notably to the European Economic Community, the United Kingdom, and Japan. South African corn exports are principally white flint, which enjoys a preference in starch manufacture.

Burma and Thailand are the world's leading rice exporters. World rice exports have averaged about 6.5 million tons a year, or less than one-fifth of wheat exports. Burmese rice exports have been consistently above 1.5 million tons. Thailand's exports have ranged between 1.1 and 1.6 million tons.

The United States is third in rice exports, averaging about 900 thousand tons. Other regular rice exporters are Cambodia, the United Arab Republic, and Italy. The major importers of rice are in the Far East and western Europe.

KENNETH L. MURRAY *joined the Department of Agriculture in 1958. He is an agricultural economist in the Grain and Feed Division, Foreign Agricultural Service.*

Fruit of the Earth

by STANLEY MEHR

MOST OF OUR many kinds of fruit originated in China and southwestern Asia—not far from where the Garden of Eden is supposed to have been. The original stocks have changed considerably over the centuries and have traveled far from their birthplace.

Fruit is grown nearly everywhere now, but commercial production has developed the most in Europe, North America, and below the Tropic of Capricorn.

Nearly all fruit once was grown in backyards, farmyards, and in small orchards or vineyards or berry patches and eaten locally. Less and less of our fruit now comes from home or farm gardens and general farms.

To grow and pack acceptable fruit nowadays that will satisfy the consumer requires specialization.

Insects and diseases have to be combated. Pollination, fertilization, cultivation, irrigation, frost protection, pruning, thinning, selection and grafting of varieties, grading, storage, and marketing must be carried on properly. Machines, special buildings, and money are needed. If the fruitgrower is to make out financially, his enterprise must be large enough to employ modern techniques efficiently.

Plant scientists strive to perfect varieties that have excellent flavor, but shipping and keeping quality is vital when so many of us are far from the place where the fruit was grown: We expect to have fruit long after the harvest season. We like to have lemons all year and apples in May, even if they were harvested in September.

A shifting of acreage to regions best suited to fruit has been pronounced, particularly for deciduous fruit, like apples, pears, peaches, apricots, and prunes.

In the United States, the world's largest producer of apples, this trend is an old story. Apple production even before the Second World War was concentrated on the west coast, particularly in Washington, and in New York, New England, the Appalachian region, and Michigan. The concentration of pear growing on the west coast has been even more striking.

The same thing has been happening all over the world. In France, as an example, heavy plantings of pears have been made in the Rhone Valley. The Bolzano-Merano, Emilia-Romagna, and Po Valley sections of Italy have become important suppliers of apples and pears. In Australia, the States of Victoria, New South Wales, and South Australia (particularly in apricots) more and more dominate in the production of clingstone peaches, pears, and apricots, as Tasmania does in apple orchards.

In the Republic of South Africa, the southwestern districts of Cape Province account for an overwhelming percentage of the country's deciduous fruit, including grapes. The Argentine apple and pear crops come mainly from the big Rio Negro Valley and Mendoza Province. In apricot production in the United States, the world's leading producing country, California is dominant, as it is for clingstone peaches, grapes, plums, and prunes, among others.

As to citrus, however, crops such as oranges found their most suitable locations many years ago and have shifted little from their original sites. California has yielded first place to Florida as producer of oranges; groves in California have been subdivided for housing, and Florida has benefited from the development of frozen concentrated juice.

Ecuador, once a minor producer of bananas, has become the leader.

Production has risen sharply in Costa Rica, Guatemala, Honduras, and Panama, but has declined sharply in Mexico and Nicaragua. Trends are divergent in the Caribbean Islands—up in the Dominican Republic, Guadeloupe, Martinique, and the Windward Islands but down in Jamaica.

The acreage in pineapples has shifted little, although fairly sizable new plantings have developed in Africa—particularly in the Republic of South Africa—and Australia.

JUST AS remarkable as the shifting of acreage the world over has been the almost universal increase in production of nearly every kind of fruit that is of commercial significance because of expanded plantings and improved yields. In fact, the increase in production has been larger than consumption in places, and marketing difficulties have been cropping up.

A factor that may encourage greater consumption is the move toward better grades and standards.

Relatively few shippers before the war consistently packed fruit for export that met any reasonably high standards of quality. A few governments insisted on uniform grades and minimum standards for fruit going into export, although the United States enacted an Apple and Pear Export Act in 1933 that provided for mandatory minimum export standards.

Now many foreign exporters use improved grade standards and pack their produce in efficient, attractive containers.

A number of countries require that their exports meet minimum standards and be graded according to government specifications. Importers and consumers thus are assured of the quality and grade.

The European Common Market has shown interest in having only fruit graded as to quality and condition sold in the six countries—Belgium, France, Italy, Luxembourg, the Netherlands, and West Germany. Beginning in August 1962, only fruit of so-called Quality II or better could move from one member country to another or could come in from an outside country. The regulation applied to apples, pears, apricots, peaches, plums, sweet oranges, tangerines (mandarins and clementines), lemons, table grapes, cherries, and strawberries in 1964.

FRUIT bulks large in world trade.

West Germany, the leading importer, bought fruit and fruit products valued at 598 million dollars in 1962.

The United Kingdom ranked second with imports valued at 546 million dollars; France was third (299 million); and the United States was fourth (203 million).

Italy had exports valued at 346 million dollars and the United States 302 million dollars. Spain exported 211 million dollars of fruit and fruit products. The Republic of South Africa exported fruit worth 97 million dollars; Australia, 68 million; Greece, 52 million; and Ecuador, 41 million.

Canada imported fruit worth 174 million dollars; exports amounted to 19 million dollars.

As large as international fruit trade is, it would be still larger were it not for restrictions against imports imposed by a number of countries.

The restrictions are imposed mainly for two reasons—shortage of foreign exchange or protection of the marketings of domestic producers or of the producers in associated oversea territories from import competition.

The restrictions may take various forms, such as outright embargo of imports, imposition of quotas, admittance only during certain seasons, minimum price requirements, grade or packaging standards, or limiting entry to selected varieties.

APPLES are grown in the temperate-climate countries. They can withstand cold weather and hot summers but are not productive in places where winters are warm.

According to Dr. John R. Magness, of the Agricultural Research Service, an authority on the origin of plants, the species of apple from which our present varieties originated probably started in southeastern Asia, somewhere between the Caspian Sea and the Black Sea.

The largest producer, the United States, averages 2.81 million short tons of dessert and cooking apples annually of a world total of 12.9 million. (The production statistics I cite do not include the Soviet Union and some countries where production is negligible.)

When cider apples—the varieties suitable only for cider—are taken into account, France is the world's largest producer of apples, with 3.0 million tons. French production of cider apples, 2.5 million tons, dwarfs that of any other country. The famed cider apple trees of Normandy are being removed, however, and dessert varieties are being planted in other parts of France. For dessert and cooking apples alone, Italy is second to United States with 1.6 million tons.

West Germany is third with 1.5 million tons.

Other major producers are Japan (0.9 million), United Kingdom (0.6 million), France (0.5 million), Argentina (0.4 million), and Canada (0.3 million).

The world's largest exporter is Italy, with an annual average of 0.5 million tons. World exports in the same period (1956–1959) averaged 1.3 million tons. Italy's exports, therefore, accounted for three-eighths of all table apples in international trade.

Other principal exporters, and their exports in short tons, are Argentina (0.1 million), Australia (0.1 million), mainland China (0.08 million), the Netherlands (0.08 million), the United States (0.07 million), Canada (0.05 million), and Hungary (0.04 million).

Australia depends on exports as an outlet for nearly 40 percent of its apple crop. Italy, Argentina, the Netherlands, and China export about 25 to 30 percent of their crops. Hungary exports more than 20 percent of its crop; Canada, about 15 percent. The United States exports less than 3 percent of its crop.

West Germany leads the world as a market for the exporting countries— it imports an average of 400 thousand tons annually. The United Kingdom is second with 200 thousand tons a year; the Soviet Union is third with 100 thousand tons. Other important importers are France (50 thousand), Switzerland (50 thousand), Sweden (40 thousand), East Germany (30 thousand), and Brazil (30 thousand).

The varieties are legion. The main variety in the Western Hemisphere is the Delicious and its red forms in the United States, Argentina, and Chile. The McIntosh is first in Canada and next most important in United States. The Winesap, Jonathan, Rome Beauty, Golden Delicious, York Imperial, and Northern Spy also are leaders in the Western Hemisphere.

Sturmer Pippin, Jonathan, Granny Smith, and Delicious predominate in Australia. Others include Democrat and Cox's Orange Pippin. In New Zealand, too, these are generally the main varieties. In South Africa, Red Delicious of various types, Golden Delicious, Winter Pearmain, and the Dunn's Seedling are the leaders.

Cox's Orange Pippin is the leading dessert apple and Bramley's Seedling is the main cooking apple in the United Kingdom.

Cox's Orange Pippin, Ingrid Marie, Jonathan, Belle de Boscoop, and Gravenstein lead in Scandinavia.

Belle de Boscoop, Jonathan, Golden Delicious, and Cox's Orange Pippin are favorites in the Netherlands. Plantings of Golden Delicious have been made in Scandinavia and on the Continent, notably in France. Golden Delicious has been growing greatly in popularity in western Europe. Other major varieties on the Continent include Abbondanza (number one in

Italy), Reinette du Canada, Reinette de France, Reine des Reinette, Delicious, Rosa del Calfora, Transparent, James Grieve, and Finkenwerder.

ORANGES grow under widely varying conditions as long as there is not too much frost. A temperature of 25° F. causes some injury; temperatures below 20° injure or kill the trees.

The United States produces 4.5 million short tons of a world total of 12.6 million. Spain is second with 1.2 million; Japan is third, 1.0 million; and Italy is fourth, 0.8 million. Tangerines are included in those figures.

Other major producers are Brazil, Mexico, Argentina, Israel, Morocco, Algeria, and the Republic of South Africa. The United Arab Republic, Greece, Turkey, Cyprus, Lebanon, and the West Indies also produce a good deal. India and China grow many oranges but are not included in the above world total because usable statistics were unobtainable.

In international trade there are just two seasons of the year for oranges—summer and winter. Summer means May to November. In many Northern Hemisphere countries during these "summer" months, Valencia oranges from California are sold in competition with Washington Navels and Valencias from South Africa and the Bahianinha (little navel orange) and Pera from Brazil. All of these are the nonblood oranges; that is, oranges that do not have red coloring of the flesh. While the Southern Hemisphere oranges are new-season fruit, the California Valencias have been "tree stored" for summer marketing.

The characteristics of summer oranges from different origins are not necessarily similar. Brazil's oranges are of tropical quality, rather similar to Florida's, but South African fruit is of rich color similar to that of oranges of California or the Mediterranean.

Since the Washington Navel and Valencia varieties are so important in the world's orange production, some description of them is in order.

The former is a seedless or nearly seedless orange of medium to large size and a slightly oval shape. The peel is usually thick, with a very smooth external texture. The fruit is particularly good for eating out of hand, since the segments can be separated from each other intact. Under favorable conditions the navel is of excellent quality and sells as a fancy fruit. The "navel"—on one end of the fruit—is not always conspicuous.

The Valencia is a thin-peeled variety, late maturing, of medium to large size. It has few seeds. The flesh has a fine, tender texture, and the variety is well known for its abundant juice of excellent flavor.

In western Europe, the leading import market for oranges, summer oranges account for 15 percent of the year's imports and winter oranges for 85 percent.

The "winter" season runs from November to July. This overlaps a little with the summer season because South Africa or California may have begun to ship summer oranges while the Mediterranean is finishing the winter season with some June shipments. Winter oranges dominate European imports, and they also represent the larger part of consumption in the United States, although not necessarily in the form of fresh fruit; 90 percent of the year's orange juice is produced during the winter.

All United States oranges are nonbloods. The most important varieties are the Washington Navel and Valencia in California. In Florida the most important are the early Hamlin and Parson Brown, the midseason Pineapple, and the Valencia—the main variety for both fresh fruit and juice. The Hamlin is rather small and slightly oval. It has a smooth, fine-textured skin. It is usually seedless, although one to five seeds may occur in occasional fruits. The Pineapple is usually round and thick-skinned and possesses a few seeds, usually 8 to 15. Its juice is abundant and of rich flavor.

Many varieties not known commer-

cially in the United States are produced during the winter season in
other countries.

Washington Navels account for 25
percent and seedless nonbloods 13 percent of the Spanish harvest. The latter
include the Salustiana, which is earlier
than the Navel and the Cadenera.
Both are fine fruits. Late-season Spanish oranges, harvested March to June,
round out the nonbloods and account
for 12 percent of the Spanish crop.
The Verna is the most important late
orange. Some Valencias are also
grown. Blood oranges as a group comprise 39 percent of Spanish production
and are mostly Doble Fina, a fine,
oval-shaped variety.

North Africa produces highly colored
table oranges similar to Spain's. Navels
are important in Morocco and Algeria.
Also important in Algeria are an oval
nonblood called Maltese and an oval
semiblood called Portuguese. A considerable acreage of Valencias is in
Morocco.

Nearly all of the oranges grown in
Italy are the blood type. Moro, Ta-
rocco, and Sanguinello are outstanding. The peel is highly colored, and the
juice has a dark pigment. A glass of
orange juice in Italy may be as red as
wine. Some Italian varieties have characteristics of navels.

Israel, an important source of winter oranges, produces mostly a large,
nearly seedless table orange, the Shamouti. The well-known Jaffa is a trade
name for the Shamouti. Israel also
produces Valencias for late-season sale.

Oranges cannot be classified seasonally the world over, for somewhere in
the world the early navel and the late
Valencia are harvested every month of
the year.

The international trade in oranges
averages more than 2.6 million tons
annually.

Spain, the leading exporter, ships
nearly 700 thousand tons a year on the
average. United States and Israel are
in second place with 300 thousand
tons, followed by Morocco, Italy, Algeria, South Africa, and Brazil. The
main importing countries are France
and Germany, 500 thousand tons; the
United Kingdom, 400 thousand; Canada, 200 thousand; and the Netherlands, 150 thousand. The Soviet Union
imported 90 thousand tons each year
in 1956–1959.

PEARS follow apples among the tree
fruits in importance.

Approximately 4.4 million tons of
table pears and 0.6 million tons of
cider pears are produced annually.
France accounts for most of the world's
cider pears.

The United States and mainland
China (with more than 0.7 million tons
each) are the leaders in growing pears.
Italy is third, with more than 0.5 million tons, followed by West Germany
(0.4 million), Japan (0.2 million), and
France (0.2 million). These figures are
averages. Actually, Italian, French,
and German production has been expanding, and the most recent harvests
are much larger than those averages.
The Netherlands, Argentina, Turkey,
Australia, South Africa, and other European countries also grow substantial
quantities.

About 300 thousand tons of table
pears move every year in export
channels, although only a few countries
export pears. Italy dominates the
export trade in pears as well as in
apples. Other exporters are Argentina,
the Netherlands, the United States,
the Republic of South Africa, Australia, Belgium, and Japan.

Many pears move in international
trade in cans. From the 1961 crop, the
equivalent of about 88 thousand tons
of fresh pears were exported, of a world
production of canned pears equivalent
to more than 375 thousand tons of the
fresh fruit.

The leading varieties of pears are
Bartlett (known as Williams or Bon
Chretien abroad), Passe Crassane,
Kaiser, Dr. Jules Guyot, and Confer-
ence in Europe; Bartlett and Pack-
ham's Triumph in Australia, South
Africa, and Argentina; Kieffer, Bart-
lett, and D'Anjou in Canada; and

Bartlett, D'Anjou, Bosc, Comice, and Nelis in the United States.

BANANAS grow everywhere in the Tropics—in front yards, jungles, small commercial plots, plantations.

Plantains, also known as cooking bananas and as *Musa paradisiaca* and *Musa fehi*, are a first cousin of the banana that we are all familiar with, *Musa sapientum*. Plantains, though, remain starchy when ripe and are not palatable except when cooked. They are of great importance in tropical America and Africa and are considered an excellent food.

Because many countries do not distinguish between bananas and plantains in their statistics, it is difficult to say how many bananas are produced. A guess is 35 million tons (inclusive of some plantains), which is greater than the combined production of apples and pears (exclusive of cider fruits), plums, peaches, cherries, and apricots.

Bananas grow best in hot, humid regions, where temperatures do not fall below 55° and seldom rise above 105° and rainfall is abundant throughout the year. Irrigation is necessary where rainfall is light during certain periods of the year.

The banana, a nonwoody plant, is related to the canna lily and the orchid. The "trunk" of the banana plant consists of overlapping leaf sheaths. Pulling the plant apart is much like taking apart a stalk of celery. It is easily blown over by heavy winds, especially when mature and bearing fruit, as it is topheavy at that time. In Central America, millions of the plants are blown down during "blowdowns," with great loss of fruit. Bananas take a short time to come into bearing. The first fruit from new plantings is ready to harvest 10 to 13 months after planting.

The chief variety in world trade is the Gros Michel, although numerous varieties are cultivated. The fruit is large and ships well. Cultivation of Cavendish-type varieties has been ex-

panding because they resist fusarium wilt (Panama disease). The susceptibility of the Cavendish to bruising in transit is less of a problem now that more and more bananas are packed in boxes at the plantation and move from plantation to retailer in them.

Seven Latin-American countries—Ecuador, Honduras, Costa Rica, Panama, Brazil, Colombia, and Guatemala—and the Canary Islands export nearly three-fourths of the bananas that move in world trade.

Ecuador alone accounts for one-fourth of the world's exports. Before the war, Ecuador's exports amounted to 2 percent of the total. Several factors have contributed to the great increase. The coastal lowlands of Ecuador have a hot, humid climate, fertile soil, and an abundant rainfall during 4 or 5 months of the year. High winds are rare, and the risk of blowdowns is less. Sigatoka disease was little known before 1956–1957, and Panama disease is less serious than in older producing countries.

GRAPEFRUIT is the second most important citrus fruit in terms of quantity. The quantity, however, is much smaller than that of oranges, and grapefruit are a less popular item in international trade than oranges or lemons. Thus, while about one-fifth of the oranges and lemons enter international trade, less than 10 percent of the world's grapefruit are exported.

Actually, grapefruit can be considered an American specialty; the United States produces nearly nine-tenths of the world's crop, consumes about five-sixths of the world's crop, and accounts for nearly half of the world's exports.

The grapefruit may have originated from the pummelo or shaddock, which probably was native to the Malay Archipelago and the East Indies. The pummelo fruit has the color and general appearance of a large, coarse-skinned grapefruit. Its membranes are extremely tough. It very likely reached Europe by the middle of the

12th century and was grown, mainly as a garden curiosity, under the name "Adam's apple." Seed of the pummelo are said to have been left in Barbados by a Captain Shaddock, master of an East Indian ship. The grapefruit probably developed in the West Indies as a mutation from the pummelo.

The grapefruit as such was first described in 1750 growing in Barbados.

The name "grapefruit" may have arisen from a belief that its flavor was like that of a grape or from the fact that the fruit is frequently borne in clusters.

Most grapefruit is harvested November to June, but some is harvested during the summer in California, South Africa, and Argentina.

Marsh Seedless is the leading variety. Red Blush is grown in Texas. Some red and pink grapefruit are also raised in Florida. The seeded Duncan variety is used in Florida for canned grapefruit sections, but other countries use the Marsh variety for canning.

The United States ships more than 80 thousand tons annually. Israel ships about 50 thousand tons. The Caribbean area, South Africa, north Africa, and Cyprus also export some grapefruit. Exports of canned grapefruit are minor.

LEMONS, in terms of volume production, are the third most important citrus crop, although they are more widely grown and are much more important in international trade than grapefruit. For the world as a whole, about 1 box of lemons is produced for every 10 of oranges.

The lemon (*Citrus limon*) and lime (*Citrus aurantifolia*) are related. Their native home may have been the warm, humid district east of the Himalayas, in northern Burma, and in eastern India. The Arabs established the lemon and lime in the Middle East, whence they probably were brought to Europe by the Crusaders. Columbus brought lemons and limes, as well as oranges, to the New World.

The lemon that most of us are familiar with is the "acid" lemon. The lemon grown in the warmer, more humid regions is "acidless" and relatively bland and is of no significance in international trade. Actually, the lime is the "acid" citrus of humid regions, such as Central America and the Caribbean, but it is produced in smaller volume than the lemon.

The United States raises more lemons than any other country and is the second largest exporter. Italy is second in production and the leading exporter. Other producing countries are Argentina, Spain, Greece, Turkey, the United Arab Republic, Chile, Lebanon, Israel, and Cyprus.

California and Sicily grow most of the United States and Italian lemons. A Mediterranean or California-type climate is best suited to growing acid lemons. The Eureka is the main variety in California.

In Sicily the Femminello, Monachello, and Interdanato are the chief varieties. Italians, though, seldom speak of varieties, but rather in terms of blooms. Thus, the usual expressions "Primofiore," "Limoni," and "Verdelli" refer not to varieties but to time of bloom and the season of harvest. Primofiore means "first flower" and the crop is harvested from September to the end of November. Limoni, harvested from December to June, are the main crop and are also known as winter lemons. The Verdelli, meaning green, are summer lemons, an important crop, and are usually green.

Spain is the third most important source of export lemons, and also grows, near Murcia, a lemon known as Primofiori—in this case, the name of an early variety rather than a bloom. The major variety in Spain is the Verna or Berna. This is the same name as for the Spanish late orange. It is a large, thick-skinned fruit that is tree stored for summer harvest and has a preferred market in Germany.

Western Europe and the United States use about the same quantity of lemons, and between them consume most of the world's lemons.

Germany is the leading importer, followed by France, the United Kingdom, and the Soviet Union. Most lemons are used as fresh fruit. They are also a source of essential oil (from the peel) for flavoring. They may be processed for their juice.

PEACHES, *Prunus persica*, may have originated in China.

International trade in peaches has soared, as production and exports have soared in Italy and France.

Italian and French shippers believe that consumption of peaches will expand a great deal in Germany, the United Kingdom, and northern Europe when the prices are lower and supplies are available over a longer season.

There were 36.7 million peach trees in Italy in 1961 and 18 million in 1950; production in 1961, 1962, and 1963 averaged more than 1.1 million tons; the average 10 years earlier was 400 thousand tons.

French growers foresee crops of more than 500 thousand tons; the average has been less than 200 thousand. In 1962, Italy produced about twice as many peaches as all the other European countries together.

Large as the Italian production is, it is overshadowed by that of the United States, which raised 60 percent more peaches than Italy in 1962. United States exports of fresh peaches, however, are small compared with Italy's, but the United States exports a large amount of peaches in cans.

The Freestone varieties of peaches are those that we eat fresh; some are canned; a few are dried. Clingstone peaches are admirably suited for canning; hardly any are eaten fresh. About 65 percent of United States production is Freestone, and 35 percent is Clingstone.

European peaches are almost entirely Freestone, aside from a few in Spain. Australia, the Republic of South Africa, Japan, and Argentina, producers and exporters of canned peaches, too—though of much smaller volume than the United States—also grow Clingstones and Freestones.

The world trade in fresh peaches amounted to 331 thousand tons in 1961. Of this, Italy shipped 260 thousand tons—nearly 80 percent. Greece was second with 29 thousand tons, and the United States was third with 17 thousand tons. West Germany was the main import market, taking 206 thousand tons. Switzerland, the United Kingdom, and Canada each imported about 20 thousand tons.

At the same time, world trade in canned peaches was equivalent to 225 thousand short tons of fresh fruit, of which the United States supplied the fresh fruit equivalent of 123 thousand tons. South Africa shipped out canned peaches equivalent to 39 thousand tons, fresh. The United Kingdom is the world's largest importer of canned peaches, and West Germany is next.

PLUMS, APRICOTS, AND CHERRIES are of much less importance in world commerce than the tree fruits I have mentioned. The fresh-fruit trade in the three combined is about half of that of peaches or pears.

World production of plums, cherries, and apricots has averaged 3.5 million, 1.3 million, and 0.9 million short tons, respectively.

The leading producing areas of plums (including prunes) are eastern and central Europe and the United States. Yugoslavia, Rumania, Germany, and the United States are the world's largest plum producers. Czechoslovakia, France, the United Kingdom, Italy, and Hungary are also important producers. Many others grow plums.

A good many of the prune-type plums are dehydrated or sun dried and are possibly the best known form of the prune, the dried prune.

Of a world production of 3.5 million tons of fresh plums (and prunes), 650 thousand tons have been used to make dried prunes; well over one-third of these, the equivalent of 250 thousand tons of fresh fruit, or 80 thousand tons of dried prunes were exported.

The United States is the giant in the production and exportation of dried prunes—entirely a California product, except for a minor tonnage from Oregon. Yugoslavia is the next largest producer and exporter. French production of dried prunes has been rising rapidly because of new plantings in the Garonne Valley. Plum jam is a popular product. In central and southeastern Europe, large quantities of prunes are used to make brandy.

Cherries are grown in volume in many countries, but not many fresh cherries are exported. The perishability of the fruit and the difficulty of packing it for long-distance transportation limit the foreign trade in cherries.

The United States generally has the largest cherry crop, but if we were to relate cherry production to size of the country, a number of European countries would rank higher than United States as cherry producers. West Germany, Italy, France, Yugoslavia, and Switzerland, among others, would be ahead of the United States on that basis. Japan, famed for the flowering cherry, ranks far below most European countries in the fruiting cherry.

There is some exportation—mainly from the United States—of canned cherries, but it is a relatively minor item. There is also some international trade in jam, glacé cherries, and cherries in brine. France and Italy are the main producers, respectively, of the last two items. Brined cherries are made into maraschino or glacé cherries. West Germany is the leading importer of fresh cherries.

The name "apricot" stems from a Latin word that means "early ripe." Because it blooms early in the spring, apricot blossoms usually are killed by frosts in the Eastern States.

The fruit tends to crack badly and decay in warm rainy weather and so is difficult to grow in tropical regions. As a result, the raising of apricots in the United States is confined to the Far West, mainly California, and in Europe mainly to places with Mediterranean climates.

Favorable locations are also in northern Africa, Asia Minor, China, the Republic of South Africa, Australia, and Argentina. As a result, the production of apricots is smaller than of any of the fruits I have discussed and averages somewhat less than 900 thousand tons for the whole world.

Spain, France, Italy, and Yugoslavia, in that order, are the chief European producers. The United States, though, is the world's largest producer. Canada, Hungary, Czechoslovakia, Austria, and Switzerland also produce some apricots.

International trade is limited. The production (because of weather) and trade fluctuate sharply from year to year, but on the average about 50 thousand tons a year of the fresh fruit enter international trade. Spain, Hungary, and Italy do most of the exporting. West Germany, Switzerland, and France do most of the importing.

An even greater tonnage, equivalent to more than 50 thousand tons of fresh fruit, is exported as canned fruit. About 15 thousand tons of dried apricots, made from approximately 100 thousand tons of fresh fruit, also move annually in international trade.

Iran dominates in the production and exportation of dried apricots. Sharply declining United States production of dried apricots has not been offset by rising foreign output.

WORLD PRODUCTION of grapes, according to some estimates, has been averaging about 41 million short tons annually. Grape production exceeds that of all the deciduous tree fruits.

Most of the grapes are for wine—usually 70 to 80 percent of the world's crop. About 8 percent of the crop consists of table grapes; that is, varieties grown for fresh consumption, but some of these are also made into wine. Some grapes that are classified as wine or raisin varieties are eaten fresh.

About 6 percent of the world crop is dried into raisins. Grapes are also crushed and consumed in the form of unfermented juice. Some grapes are also made into jelly. In the Middle East they are used as sugar; the grapes are crushed and most of the juice boiled off leaving a sirup of high viscosity, which serves as a sweetener for much of the farm population. A few grapes are canned, mostly for fruit cocktail.

Like the banana, the grape dates from prehistoric times. The Old World or European grape, *Vitis vinifera*, has been cultivated so long that its exact place of origin cannot be determined.

Seeds of grapes have been found in the oldest tombs of Egypt. The Egyptians probably grew grapes and made wine 6 thousand years ago. The oldest Hebrew, Greek, and Roman writings refer to grapes and winemaking. Apparently the vinifera grape originated in the region of the Caspian and Black Seas. The Vikings apparently found wild grapes so abundant in North America that they called North America Vineland.

Today's American varieties derive from the native wild grapes; in the South, the Muscadine varieties, from the species, *V. rotundifolia*, and in the North, varieties as the Concord and Niagara from *V. labrusca*.

Many varieties of Europe, which produces nearly 80 percent of the world's grapes, are mostly grown on roots partly or wholly of American stock. The reason is a root louse, phylloxera, which was native to eastern America and was accidentally taken to Europe over a century ago.

Since some American grapes are resistant to this sucking insect, the introduction of American rootstocks saved the European grapegrower from the American insect. Greater frost resistance in Old World grapes is also obtained by crossings made with American varieties.

In California, Old World varieties are grown on American rootstocks in soils where phylloxera is a problem. The most famous wines are made from Old World grapes.

More grapes are produced in Italy than in any other country of the world. France is the next largest producer. Although the production of dessert varieties has been increasing, the bulk of the grapes in those two countries is grown for wine. The production of grapes there has averaged 10.4 million and 7.1 million tons, respectively. Spain is third with 3.4 million tons, mainly for wine.

The United States is next with nearly 3 million tons (2.7 million in California), but in the United States wine grapes do not predominate. In fact, only about one-fifth of American grapes are of the wine type.

Raisin varieties account for well over half of the United States crop, but only about half of them are made into raisins. The rest are used for wine or eaten fresh. This diversified usage in the United States is particularly characteristic of the Thompson Seedless, the variety that we know so well as the light-green, sweet grape of the supermarkets in late summer. It also is much used in making dessert wine.

The Thompson Seedless had its beginning in Turkey, where it is known as the Sultanina. It is widely grown in Australia and South Africa.

Other major grape producers are Turkey, Algeria, Argentina, the Soviet Union, Portugal, Greece, Rumania, and Yugoslavia.

Foreign trade in grape products is much greater than the trade in fresh grapes if we convert world exports of wine and of raisins to their equivalent in fresh grapes.

Thus the grapes needed to make the 670 million gallons of wine exported annually would total about 4.5 million tons. The grapes from which the 360 thousand tons of world raisin exports are made would amount to about 1.5 million tons.

Exports of fresh grapes for table use average 510 thousand tons annually, a poor third to the 4.5 million and 1.5 million tons of grapes that go into wine and raisin exports, respectively. The figures for raisins include the so-called dried currant or Black Corinth of Greece—a dried vine fruit that has been made in Greece for more than 500 years from a small, usually seedless, reddish-black grape.

Algeria has been the world's largest exporter of wine, exporting an average of 362 million gallons annually—more than half the world exports. Most of this wine has gone to France. Far behind Algeria in volume of exports are Spain, Portugal, and France; each ships approximately 50 million gallons yearly. Then come Italy, Morocco, Tunisia, Yugoslavia, Hungary, Greece, Rumania, South Africa, Cyprus, Australia, and West Germany.

France accounts for 450 million gallons of imports a year on the average. Large as France's own production is—about 1.25 billion gallons per year—her imports are equivalent to more than one-third of her vintage. West Germany is the next largest importer. The United States ranks seventh among the wine importers, with an average of 9 million gallons, which has been moving up.

The main table-grape exporting country is Italy. Well behind are the United States and Bulgaria. Spain is next, and well behind Spain are South Africa, France, Hungary, and Greece. West Germany is the biggest importer. Canada and the United Kingdom also import substantial quantities.

There are innumerable varieties of dessert grapes. To mention a few: Regina in Italy; Chasselas and Gros Vert in France; Rosetti and Ohanes (also known as Almeria) in Spain; Rosaki in Greece; and Muscat de Hambourg, Muscat d'Alexandrie, Alphonse Lavalle, Dattier, Ideal, Cardinal, and Emperor in various places in Europe. The Thompson Seedless is number one in the United States for table use. The production of table grapes generally has been increasing.

Only a few countries produce and export sizable tonnages of raisins. In order, they are the United States, Greece, Turkey, Australia, and Iran. Smaller tonnages are produced in Spain, the Republic of Cyprus, South Africa, Afghanistan, and Argentina.

In the term "raisins," we include all dried vine fruits: Thompson Seedless (sultaninas), sultanas (a close relative of the Thompson and important in Turkey, Greece, and Iran), dried currants, muscats, rosakis, and others.

Greece leads the world as an exporter of dried vine fruit, followed by Australia, Turkey, the United States, and Iran.

THE PINEAPPLE (*Ananas comosus*), a native of South America, is one of the most widely grown tropical fruits. It can generally be grown between 25° north and south of the Equator. It is second only to the banana among fruits grown in the Tropics.

A pineapple harvested fully ripe is soft, sweet, and juicy. Its sugar content can increase 100 percent in the last stage of ripening on the plant.

Fully ripe pineapples cannot be shipped very far, so the fresh pineapple we buy in the Temperate Zone was harvested before full maturity and is relatively hard and tart (though still a treat to us who know no better).

Canned pineapple, prized the world over as a dessert, is a cooked fruit.

World production of pineapples is substantially greater than the combined production of grapefruit, lemons, cherries, and apricots. An average world crop in 1951–1955 amounted to 1.7 million tons; in 1957–1961 it had risen to 2.3 million tons.

Hawaii produces nearly half of the world's crop. Brazil, the second largest producer, raises one-fourth as much as Hawaii. Mexico, Malaya, and Taiwan rank third, fourth, and fifth. Malaya and Taiwan have made spectacular gains in production. The Philippines, Cuba, South Africa, and Australia also are heavy producers.

Exports of fresh pineapple average about 85 thousand tons annually. Cuba used to be the leading exporter, but its shipments have declined sharply.

Mexico and Brazil became the largest exporters. Exports from the Azores, a traditional source of fresh pineapple for Europe, amount to 2,500 tons annually—a small fraction of the volume shipped by Mexico or Brazil. Hawaii exports hardly any fresh pineapple.

Exports of pineapple in cans is more important than trade in the fresh fruit. Approximately 400 thousand tons of the fresh fruit are processed into the canned pineapple that enters international trade channels.

As a canner of pineapple, Hawaii outranks other countries. Hawaiian-canned pineapple accounts for more than half of the world's pack. Malaya, South Africa, Taiwan, Australia, Mexico, and Cuba are the other main canners. Hawaii accounts for one-fifth of the world's exports, but Malaya, the Philippines, South Africa, and Taiwan are not far behind Hawaii in the quantities they export.

The United Kingdom, West Germany, and the United States are the big importers. Other substantial importers of canned pineapple are Canada, Japan, France, Sweden, and the Netherlands.

ESTIMATES OF CONSUMPTION of fruit in 12 countries—the United States, Australia, Canada, and nine European countries—have been published by the Commonwealth Economic Committee in London.

The consumption figures are in terms of fresh fruit—processed fruit having been converted to a fresh-fruit basis.

Of the 12 countries for which the committee estimated consumption, Switzerland has had the highest consumption—236 pounds per capita in the 3 years, 1959–1961. The United States usually has been second, with 196 pounds.

Sweden and Canada generally have been third and fourth, about 180 to 190 pounds per capita. West German consumption has been rising rapidly, and in 1959–1961 attained an average of 193 pounds. Swedish and Canadian consumption has also been rising.

The higher the level of consumption, the less is the tendency to increase. Thus, the United States and Switzerland show no gain; Sweden and Canada show slight gains; but countries with a lower base, such as Germany, France, Italy, and Spain, have shown marked gains.

British consumption is lowest of the 12 countries. Australian consumption has been steadily increasing. Dutch consumption has also been increasing to a level of 144 pounds as a 3-year average. Only Belgium, of the 12 countries, has experienced a substantial decline.

Considerable fluctuations in consumption from one year to another are common and are, of course, attributable to variations in the yield because of weather or other conditions, such as insects or plant diseases. Adjustments in the import or export volume often offset only partly the variations in the domestic supply.

Though per capita consumption of dried fruits has been declining, the consumption of other processed fruits, such as canned and frozen, and particularly juices, has been increasing.

Data compiled by the Organization for Economic Cooperation and Development in Paris for 19 countries (mostly European) show that consumption of fresh fruit has expanded in 14 countries, declined in 4, and did not change in 1.

The committee estimated that more than 11 million tons of fresh fruit were used for juice in 1961, "though the conversions involve a wide margin of error." This tonnage includes the fruits used in the making of citrus, pineapple, grape, apple, pear, prune, peach, apricot, passion fruit, berry, currant, and other juices.

The United States dominates world production and consumption of fruit juices, although it is not possible to be too precise in citing the United States percentage of the total.

Probably more than four-fifths of the world's production and two-thirds of the world's exports are accounted for by United States fruit juices. Citrus juices, of course, the most important juices in the United States, average 550 million gallons of a United States total of 770 million. More than 80 percent of the Florida orange crop is processed, and two-thirds of the crop is used for frozen concentrate. Pineapple juice is next most important in the United States. Grape juice is third.

Other producing countries, far behind the United States in volume, are West Germany, Switzerland, Italy, and France. Apple, pear, and grape juices are important in those countries. Citrus juices, especially lemon juice, are important in Italy. Production of juices from deciduous and citrus fruits are expected to continue to increase in many countries.

Countries that export juices include Italy, France, the Philippines, the Republic of South Africa, Israel, Trinidad, Spain, Jamaica, and Algeria. Canada, West Germany, and the United Kingdom lead in imports.

It appears that fruit consumption per person will continue to expand in most countries and that total fruit consumption will expand even more since population is increasing.

Although consumption of fresh fruit has been increasing, probably the same tendency will develop in other countries as in the United States—namely, a shift by consumers to processed fruits, particularly canned fruits and juices and frozen fruits and juices.

Both trends—greater consumption of fruit and a shifting toward consumption of fruit in processed form—would mean an increase in international trade.

STANLEY MEHR *has been with the Fruit and Vegetable Division of the Foreign Agricultural Service since 1954. Upon receiving his master's degree from the University of Wisconsin in 1941, he joined the Soil Conservation Service and subsequently worked in the Bureau of Agricultural Economics and Office of Foreign Agricultural Relations. He concluded his wartime military service as an agriculturist with military government in Austria. Mr. Mehr has made a number of surveys abroad of fruit production and marketing.*

Growing and Using Vegetables

by A. CLINTON COOK

ENOUGH VEGETABLES, including roots, tubers, and melons, are grown to supply an average of 300 pounds for each of the world's 3 billion persons. That would be a total annual harvest of more than 400 million metric tons for food. Besides, starchy root crops, such as potatoes, sweetpotatoes, and cassava, are used in the manufacture of alcohol and starch and are fed to livestock.

Vegetables are nutritious and can supply a large part of one's daily vitamin requirements. A 5-ounce tomato provides one-half the amount of vitamin C and about one-third the vitamin A an adult needs daily.

An acre of tomatoes at a yield of 40 metric tons would supply 700 persons with a medium-sized tomato each day for a year. A yield of 20 metric tons of potatoes would furnish one-half pound daily for a year to 240 persons. (A metric ton is 2,204.6 pounds.) Additional small servings of green and yellow vegetables complete the vitamin requirements. Thus a relatively small acreage of vegetables, reasonably well grown, can provide healthful foods to large numbers.

We eat various parts of vegetable plants—the leaves of cabbage; parts of the flowers of cauliflower and broccoli; the fleshy portion of the roots of carrots, beets, cassava, and sweetpotatoes; and the fruits of tomatoes, peppers, squash, and melons. Tomatoes normally are eaten when they are ripe, but most peppers and squash are harvested before the seeds mature.

Some leafy vegetables, like kale, spinach, mustard, and nonheading lettuce, sometimes are harvested a few leaves at a time.

Most vegetables are consumed fresh, but they can be stored fresh for a few weeks or canned, frozen, or dehydrated and kept for a year or more. In the United States, where fresh and processed vegetables are abundant all year, 50 percent of the vegetables (excluding potatoes) are consumed fresh, 41 percent are canned, and 9 percent are frozen.

About one-third of the food potatoes are processed as chips, dehydrated, and frozen french fries. Much less of the crop elsewhere is processed.

THE CHIEF FACTORS that determine the places and amounts of production are soil, climate, land tenure, marketing facilities, transportation, and government policies.

Nearly all countries can grow a variety of vegetables at various locations at one season or another. Vegetables can grow in a range of climates and soils, but for each kind some conditions are better than others.

Sweetpotatoes and yams are tropical crops but can be grown in temperate regions. Potatoes are best adapted to cooler Temperate Zones but can be grown in tropical regions in winter and at higher elevations in spring. The cabbage family prefers the cooler climates but species are grown extensively in the Tropics. Tomatoes are widely grown but will not set fruit under extreme heat and will not grow where seasons are short and cold. Other vegetables likewise have a wide tolerance, which reflects somewhat growers' skills and the development of strains that fit local conditions.

Vegetables have a wider span of harvest dates than most crops. Cabbage can be cut at 2 pounds or 5 pounds or more. Potatoes can be dug in 60 days or in 100 or more. Sweetpotatoes and yams in tropical places can be dug in 4 months or in 2 years.

Harvest at various stages extends the marketing season, but early harvest of most kinds reduces yields per acre. Such reductions can be offset partly by multiple cropping—planting more than one crop on the same plot of ground during a year.

Since vegetables under the best cultural practices can produce high yields on an acre, growers tend to use intensive methods. Many are grown under irrigation or in humid areas with supplemental irrigation. Growers tend to use large inputs of fertilizer and organic matter when available. Intensification extends to glasshouse culture in cold climates. This system is generally limited to places near large cities and to high-value crops, such as tomatoes, lettuce, and cucumbers.

Hydroponic culture, in which vegetables are grown in a water solution with added plant nutrients, has been tried in a number of places. Under carefully controlled research conditions, yields have been high, but nearly all commercial ventures have failed.

Storage and facilities for preserving them have a major bearing on the tonnage of a crop that is grown in a district. Cabbage, carrots, and beets can be stored for a few months. Potatoes and onions can be held in good condition 6 to 9 months. Canning and freezing will preserve good vegetables a year or more.

Indians in mountain valleys of South America for centuries have used freeze-drying to preserve potatoes. A commercial adaptation of the method has been developed for a number of items. Sun drying also is used. Several kinds of vegetables and potatoes are dehydrated under controlled conditions.

Potatoes, onions, garlic, and soup bases make up the largest volume of commercially dehydrated vegetables.

In countries where transportation is limited, production is concentrated near population centers, but such districts are not necessarily the most efficient in production or (if they are outside the Tropics) suitable for a year-round supply of vegetables.

The use of mountain valleys or other favored districts in less-developed countries for summer vegetables often is restricted because of lack of transportation. Production in the United States and Canada was limited to counties near cities until railways and highways were developed.

Today in the United States and Canada competition is keen among a number of vegetable-growing areas, and production continues to shift to those that can produce crops of high quality more efficiently and deliver them to markets at lowest cost. Some growers have several thousands of acres, and some operate in more than one district.

This trend to a larger production was accelerated by the demand of supermarket buyers for uniformity of grade, size, and packaging and the demand of food processors for raw stock suitable for manufacture of standardized products by machines.

The world's marketing practices range from primitive, open-air markets to chains of air-conditioned supermarkets of the United States, Canada, and Europe. In supermarkets, leafy, salad-type vegetables can be kept several days in good condition in display cases where temperature and humidity are controlled. In the direct sun of a sidewalk market in a hot climate, they may last mere minutes.

Mass distributors demand uniformity in quality, but local gardeners sell their produce as harvested with little or no grading and often in any available used container. Under primitive marketing methods, a producer usually must sell to consumers within a day or two of harvest, while an efficient system permits a transportation and selling time of 10 to 15 days for highly perishable products and 20 to 30 days for those somewhat less so. Production in developed areas thus can be located at great distances from consuming centers.

Trade barriers may influence the production and consumption of vegetables. High duties, import taxes, quotas, and embargoes tend to cause scarcities and high prices within a country. Local growers are expected to produce sufficient quantities to satisfy demand. Often they cannot do so in all seasons; at times, quality is poor and prices are high; and restrictive measures might be continued well beyond the normal storage life of commodities. Such restrictive measures tend to increase cost to consumers, reduce consumption, and discourage shifts to improved methods and to crops best adapted to an area.

THE AMERICAS gave the world several vegetables that now lead in tonnage produced. Potatoes and tomatoes originated in the mountain valleys of South America; sweetpotatoes, squash, sweet peppers in tropical America; and sweet corn and snap beans in North America.

The United States produces more than 10 million tons each of vegetables for fresh market and potatoes. In tonnage, the leaders are potatoes, lettuce, watermelons, onions, tomatoes, and cabbage. Vegetables for processing amount to almost 10 million tons a year; tomatoes, sweet corn, peas, green beans, and cucumbers for pickles are the five leaders. Tomatoes represent more than one-half the tonnage; sweet corn, almost one-fifth.

United States vegetable and potato production is concentrated in a few relatively small areas. California produces 37 percent of the United States vegetables for processing and 32 percent of fresh. Five States—California, Florida, Texas, Arizona, and New York—produce 67 percent of the tonnage of vegetables and melons for fresh market. Idaho, Maine, California, New York, and North Dakota grow 55 percent of the potatoes. California, Wisconsin, New York, Ohio, and Illinois grow 61 percent of processed vegetables.

California and Arizona grow 70 percent of our cantaloups. Florida, Texas, and Georgia grow more than half the watermelons. California, New Jersey, Ohio, and Indiana grow 80 percent of the tomatoes for processing. California, New Jersey, and Washington produce 90 percent of asparagus for fresh and processed use. Much of the mushrooms are grown in Pennsylvania.

THE VEGETABLE season begins with early harvesting of fall, winter, and early spring vegetables and potatoes in Florida, the Lower Rio Grande Valley of Texas, southern California, and Arizona. Production moves northward and ends with late harvest in fall.

Growers strive to improve their competitive position by improving yields, cutting costs of production, and improving grading and handling. Winter-vegetable growers may spread risks from weather hazards by planting in more than one place in the United States or in Mexico and the Caribbean Islands.

Yields per acre have trended sharply upward since 1940—some 100 to 300 percent—because of improvements in cultural practices, improved varieties or hybrids, and a concentration of acreage in districts where yields are well above average.

High costs and shortages of labor have caused United States growers to increase the mechanization of production, harvesting, and handling.

A group of wheatgrowers in Washington and Oregon discovered that garden peas for freezing were well adapted to their district. They modified wheat machinery for peas and ended up with a self-propelled combine for harvesting and shelling the peas as the machine moves through the field. Thus only shelled peas are hauled to the freezer. Much of the lettuce is packed in the field, and half a carload may be unloaded at one time by a giant forklift truck at a vacuum cooler.

Several rows of celery in Florida are harvested at the same time by workers and placed on a moving belt, which carries it through a giant, self-propelled field packing plant, where the celery is washed, trimmed, graded, and packed in shipping containers. It is then hauled to a hydrocooling plant for quick removal of field heat and loaded in rail cars or motortrucks.

A machine to harvest tomatoes for processing has been designed, but its success depends on the development of a low-growing tomato plant on which nearly all fruit ripens at the same time.

Many tomatoes for fresh market are trained on stakes or trellises, an expensive method but one in which yields of marketable tomatoes are three or four times higher than when the plants are close to the ground. Yields may be 30 to 40 tons an acre—even 52 tons in California.

Major improvements in highway and rail facilities in Mexico have meant sizable increases in production of vegetables. A large tonnage of winter and spring vegetables and melons are grown mainly for export to the United States and Canada. About half the tonnage is concentrated in the Culiacan Valley in Sinaloa. The leaders are tomatoes, cantaloups, and watermelons; smaller quantities of onions, garlic, sweet peppers, peas, cucumbers, squash, snap beans, and eggplant are exported.

More than half the tomatoes in 1963 were staked and harvested as vine ripened—as they start turning pink. The vine-ripened tomatoes are precooled to 50° F. and shipped by refrigerated motortruck. The green tomatoes are shipped in ventilated rail cars. Cantaloups are harvested vine ripe and are top iced or refrigerated.

Mexico limits imports of fresh and processed vegetables. Local supplies are adequate most of the year.

Canadian production, limited to summer and fall vegetables because of climate, is concentrated in the Maritime Provinces, Ontario, and British Columbia. Seasonal surpluses occur, but there is a shortage of fresh vegetables in winter and spring.

Since no nontariff barriers exist between the United States and Canada, growers on both sides of the border consider the two countries as one market. Growers in Ontario may be shipping fresh carrots and lettuce to eastern United States markets while western Canada will be importing the same items from the Western States. Canada imports early potatoes from the States and exports seed and table potatoes during the winter.

WESTERN EUROPE and countries of northern Africa bordering the Mediterranean form a production and marketing area. Patterns of production and marketing are like those of North America.

Production begins with winter and spring vegetables in the Mediterranean countries. Since northern Europe has the world's greatest concentration of heated and unheated glasshouses and coldframes, imports of winter vegetables are supplemented by glasshouse crops. The varieties consumed in western Europe are similar to those of North America, but many more are eaten in fresh form.

Consumption of potatoes per capita in Europe is about double that of the United States but has been declining. Production is high, but in some countries—for instance, West Germany— only a third is used for food. Many potatoes are used for livestock feed and for industrial products—starch, glucose, and alcohol. Yellow-fleshed potatoes are preferred in some countries for food.

Northern European countries export seed potatoes to the Mediterranean countries and import new potatoes from them in winter and spring. Trade in potatoes is extensive among these countries in winter and spring, but few potatoes are exported from or imported into the European area.

Onions are grown in all western countries of Europe, but climatic conditions limit production in the Scandinavian countries, the United Kingdom, and Ireland. The four principal exporting countries are the United Arab Republic, Spain, Italy, and the Netherlands. The United Arab Republic, the world's largest exporter, sends most of her crop to northern Europe in spring, and the fall crop is consumed locally. Spain exports the mild-type Valencia or sweet Spanish types, including some new hybrids. Italy grows many red-skinned onions. The Netherlands is a leading supplier of yellow globe onions.

Field-grown tomatoes are produced in northern Africa, the Canary Islands, Spain, Italy, and southern France for local consumption and export in winter and spring. These supplies are supplemented with the glasshouse crops in northern Europe. Processing of tomatoes in Italy, Portugal, Spain, and France has been developing rapidly. Whole tomatoes, paste, and puree are canned.

Cabbages, broccoli, cauliflower, and brussels sprouts are grown extensively in all countries. The largest production is in northern Europe. Cabbages are stored in pits or in common storage or preserved in the form of kraut.

Carrots, parsnips, beets, and rutabagas are widely grown. Many are stored in the ground and harvested as needed. Others are stored in pits for marketing in fall and winter.

The Pharaohs of Egypt 3 thousand years ago monopolized the consumption of mushrooms and considered them much too good for common people. Sometime before 1700, British gardeners had learned to grow them in hothouses. French gardeners later learned the secret of growing mushrooms in caves and cellars around Paris. Paris now is the center of production of fresh and canned mushrooms in western Europe. France exports and uses domestically a high volume of canned mushrooms.

THE NETHERLANDS horticultural industry, the most intensive in the world, developed when the population reached a fairly high level of prosperity.

During 1850–1930, a period of rapid

economic development in western Europe, the Dutch decided on a course of free trade and of specialization in the vegetable crops best suited to their area. In the twenties, an increase in the number of growers led to an even more intensive culture and a rapid expansion of glasshouses. This development was stopped by the agricultural crisis of the thirties, when several importing countries imposed restrictions that adversely affected the market outlets and depressed prices of Dutch horticultural crops. Then the Netherlands took a number of measures to restrict the area of certain crops and established minimum prices and relief programs for growers.

Regulations since that time have been expanded and increased. The Commodity Board licenses growers, and the applicant must demonstrate sufficient skill and capital to operate a holding. The board also fixes the area planted to certain crops, specifies the quality and packages for export, and operates a Minimum Price Fund, which is a means of price stabilization.

Each grower signs a contract to sell all his produce through one local auction company for one year. The auction furnishes returnable containers for local sales, but export vegetables are packed in nonreturnable containers. The Dutch use a unique electrically controlled auction clock. The hand of the clock starts at a high price. When a buyer touches a button at his desk, the clock stops. His assigned number is flashed, and he has purchased the lot of produce offered at the price shown on the clock. This is a rapid method of selling produce.

All persons interested may attend a horticultural school for training in growing, marketing, inspection, and related fields. Qualified students can attend classes at university level for 5 to 7 years.

There are more than a thousand agricultural credit banks in the Netherlands. Growers who cannot qualify for loans from them may secure credit for certain improvements from the Agricultural Security Fund or from the Provincial Horticultural Security Fund.

The government provides research, an advisory group for technical and economic problems, and an inspection service. The government and quasi-government regulations are intended to promote the efficiency of production and marketing and to expand markets by offering high-quality produce to consumers at competitive prices.

The Dutch have a land area about double that of New Jersey, on which they produce more than 1 million tons of vegetables and 4 million tons of potatoes annually.

There are 125 thousand acres of vegetables in open culture and almost 11 thousand acres under glass in the Netherlands. About 69 percent of the glasshouses are heated. The Dutch report production of 22 different vegetables, but tomatoes, onions, cabbage, and cucumbers make up 50 percent of the total. Only 17 percent are processed, compared to 50 percent in the United States.

The Dutch have 25 percent of the world's vegetable glasshouse area.

The maximum number of successive crops in a year under glass is four, but most growers plant two to three.

The annual value of glasshouse vegetables and fruit is 90 million dollars; tomatoes, cucumbers, and lettuce account for 80 to 85 percent of the total. Tomatoes in heated glasshouses may yield as high as 60 tons to an acre, but the Dutch average 40 tons. Yields would probably be higher if there were more sunlight during the growing season.

EASTERN EUROPE, including the Soviet Union, has encountered many problems in producing and marketing vegetable crops.

A survey in Russia in 1961 showed that 65 percent of the potato and 45 percent of the vegetable production was grown on private plots.

Cabbage follows potatoes in importance. It is marketed fresh and from storage. Carrots, beets, turnips, and rutabagas are grown extensively, especially in the northern districts. In the south—the Ukraine, Caucasus, and central Asia—cantaloups, honeydews, watermelons, and peppers are grown for local use and for shipment to northern markets.

The Balkans grow tomatoes, onions, garlic, and many other crops. Poland grows a fall crop of yellow globe onions for export both east and west.

Many wild types of mushrooms are gathered in northern Russia. They are used fresh and sun dried. Dried mushrooms are chiefly used for soups.

A number of vegetables appear to have originated in the land area of the eastern Mediterranean east to the Pacific Ocean. Onions, muskmelons (including cantaloups and Persian melons), eggplant, celery, asparagus, cabbage, carrots, and radishes came from this area.

Excellent cantaloups, Persian melons, and similar types can be grown in several locations in Iran and areas having like climatic conditions and soils. These melons prefer hot, arid climates, with cool nights and an abundant supply of irrigation water.

THE FAR EAST contains more than half of the world's people, with a per capita agricultural land area of half an acre. Thus vegetables are grown on garden plots of far less than an acre. Inadequate transportation tends to concentrate commercial production to districts near cities.

Little or no research is available to growers in many of these countries. Relatively small amounts of chemical fertilizers, insecticides, and fungicides are used, except in Japan and Taiwan. Growers use animal and human waste, ashes, and other materials that can be composted to improve the soils.

Sweetpotatoes, cassava, and potatoes are important, particularly in the countries with a warm climate. Other vegetables are grown intensively with five to eight crops a year on the same plot of ground. This system requires irrigation, careful timing in planting various crops, and the use of transplants for some.

Some areas will grow a crop of staked cucumbers, tomatoes, pole beans, lettuce, cabbage, chinese-type cabbage, onions, peppers, or eggplant in the dry season and a crop of paddy rice in the wet season.

In mainland China, vegetable production declined sharply when the peasants' system of multiple cropping was disrupted. This was partly corrected in 1961 when many people were allowed to cultivate a private garden plot.

In Hong Kong, a commercial vegetable farm for a family is one-third acre. Because Hong Kong is a free trade area, growers concentrate on vegetables that have a short growing season and for which they have a transportation advantage. Vegetables such as lettuce, chinese cabbage, rape, mustard, tomatoes, sweet corn, and cabbage are the principal crops grown. Carrots, potatoes, beets, celery, and turnips are imported.

A Hong Kong grower usually places all of the available waste material and chemical fertilizer in a cistern or pool. The liquid is then hand drawn and carried in pails to the vegetable plants.

Growers deliver produce to the road, where it is picked up by a truck and hauled to one of several wholesale markets. In some other southeastern Asian countries, the produce is transported one or two baskets at a time by a person in a boat, bus, or taxi. A third or more of the sale price is needed to pay the transportation for a distance of 10 to 20 miles.

AFRICA is a land of contrasts, divergent societies, nomadic desert tribes, primitive jungle tribes, and highly developed civilizations in the north and south. The people of the central areas depend on wild plants, cassava, yams, sweetpotatoes, and watermelons. A small volume of other vegetables may be grown near a few of the larger cities for local sales.

The Republic of South Africa has an extensive commercial vegetable industry, which was developed by Europeans. The supply of potatoes and other fresh and processed vegetables is good; nearly all are grown for domestic use.

People on the deserts produce and eat few vegetables.

SOUTH AMERICAN climate ranges from the northern tropical areas to the cool climates of southern Argentina and Chile. Many of the tropical areas have districts at high elevations that can grow a wide variety of vegetables. Often the better locations for vegetable culture cannot be used because of a lack of roads and transportation.

Potatoes, cabbage, tomatoes, and corn are widely grown. Brazil is the only country that prefers yellow-fleshed potatoes, varieties of European origin. The corn consumed fresh is early harvested field corn.

Much of the Indian population uses vegetables for seasoning soups and stews. Onions, garlic, tomatoes, peas, and beans are popular for this purpose.

Many of the vegetable growers in Argentina are of Italian descent. They grow varieties of vegetables brought over from the homeland, such as cherry or pear-shaped tomatoes, broadbeans, zucchini squash, leeks, artichokes, leaf lettuce, and watercress. Cabbage follows potatoes in tonnage produced.

Japanese gardeners near São Paulo, Brazil, supply vegetables for the city. Their farms are small and intensively cropped. Growers formed a cooperative that furnishes tractors for occasional deep plowing; purchases production supplies, such as seeds, fertilizer, and spray materials; and markets the crops. Aside from tractor plowing, nearly all seeding and cultivating is done by hand. Vegetables are hauled to market by truck. Because of the elevation and moderate climate, vegetables are harvested all year in this district.

Nearly all vegetables in the South American countries are grown for domestic consumption, but Chile exports large quantities of onions and garlic to North America and Europe and many honeydew melons to North America.

Processing in South America is generally limited to relatively small processors. The principal products are chili sauces, catsup, peppers, artichoke hearts, and baby foods.

Argentina, Venezuela, and Colombia lead in commercial processing. A few vegetables are sun dried for home use.

Vegetable production could be expanded by making effective use of coastal plains and districts at higher elevations. Until the transportation system and marketing facilities are improved, however, low-income families will continue to use vegetables for seasoning rather than as a basic part of their diet.

THE WORLD'S potential vegetable production is enormous. Under ideal cultural practices, yields per acre are high.

As more vegetables become available, people tend to eat less cassava, sweetpotatoes, and potatoes, in that order.

Cassava is consumed as a vegetable through necessity rather than by choice. Processing increases as the economy of a country improves.

While there is a great need in many countries of the world to expand production of vegetables, particularly the green and yellow vegetables and tomatoes, this will not happen until the economy of the country improves. Increased production requires roads, fertilizers, chemicals, farm equipment, specialized transportation equipment, and facilities for storing and marketing the crops.

A. CLINTON COOK *became Chief, Foreign Marketing Branch, Fruit and Vegetable Division, of Foreign Agricultural Service in 1962. He joined the Department in 1934. He holds degrees from Texas Tech and Michigan State Universities.*

Meat Production and Trade

by DWIGHT R. BISHOP

THE NUMBER OF MEAT animals and the production of meat reflect the prosperity of a country, consumers' incomes, increases in population and living standards, favorable prices, and industrial growth, all of which started to rise at the end of the Second World War.

The world production of meat reached a record 112 billion pounds in 1963 and was about 3 percent larger than the 109 billion pounds produced in 1962 and 38 percent above the 1951–1955 average.

The rise in the production of meat since 1951 more than equaled the rise in population, and meat consumption per capita went up in most countries.

A 4-percent gain in 1962 was the largest on record and was about twice that of population growth.

Other factors also influenced the production and consumption of meat.

Most of the major livestock- and meat-producing countries improved range management, production techniques, and feeding practices.

Examples are the planting of improved grasses and distribution of fertilizer by airplanes in the steep terrain of New Zealand, the construction of tanks for storing water in the arid parts of Australia, the shift from crop production to livestock husbandry in the Southeastern States, and a much higher carrying capacity

obtained by planting alfalfa pastures in the fertile Pampa of Argentina.

Most countries have developed or enlarged programs of research for improving breeds, eradicating livestock diseases, and promoting the sale of meat products in world trade.

Substantial progress has been made in the United States in improving breeds of beef cattle to obtain a more uniform carcass with less waste and with breeds of hogs to yield more lean meat and less fat.

A more uniform lamb carcass has been developed in New Zealand by crossing Southdown rams with ewes of the Romney breed.

The Santa Gertrudis and Brangus have been developed from crosses between Indian and English breeds to obtain an animal that produces meat efficiently in hot climates.

The eradication or control of diseases has lowered livestock mortality.

An example is the extensive and costly eradication program conducted against foot-and-mouth disease in Mexico. The disease broke out in 1946 and was brought under complete control in 1955 at a cost of more than 130 million dollars to the United States Government and a great economic loss to Mexican stockmen.

Slaughterhouses and freezing and processing facilities have been constructed or modernized in Australia, New Zealand, Africa, Central America, South America, the Soviet Union, Yugoslavia, Poland, and elsewhere.

More efficient design and layout of slaughterhouses and their location in the main producing areas have lowered marketing costs in the United States. A greater use of trucks for transporting livestock in other meat-producing countries has reduced loss in weight between farm and slaughterhouse.

THE GREATEST differences in diets in less-developed countries and the more developed regions lie in the use of livestock products.

Poverty has been mainly responsible. The demand for livestock products has risen sharply once incomes began to rise. Estimates based on the expected growth of population and incomes suggest that the demand for meat may grow about 5 percent a year in the less-developed countries.

In general, the number of livestock in relation to the human population was not significantly lower in less developed than in more developed regions, but the small production of livestock products was the result of low productivity per animal.

The output of meat per head of the cattle population in Europe, for example, was estimated to be about 10 times greater than in the Far East and 7 times greater than in Africa. Increased supplies of livestock products in those regions would depend less on increasing the number of animals and more on raising the output per animal.

The difference in productivity was due mainly to bad management, primitive breeding practices, and failure to prevent or control diseases and parasites that lower production.

There were more than a billion cattle in the world in 1964. Since 1950 their numbers have increased about 1.5 percent annually—19 percent above the 1951–1955 average. The main reason was the high prices for beef because of strong consumer demand.

A large proportion of the cattle were unproductive, however, or at a low level of productivity.

The more productive were in the more developed regions of North America, Europe, and Oceania, where the demand for beef and per capita consumption were high.

Asia, despite a cattle and buffalo population of 400 million head, was a meat-deficient area. Cattle numbers during 1959–1964 increased rapidly in those countries because of a rising standard of living, notably in Japan and Taiwan, but in some Asian countries religious objections to the consumption of beef exist.

The cattle in Africa mostly were of poor quality. Cattle in 4 million square miles of Africa are prey to the tsetse fly, which spreads protozoan parasites and prevents the successful raising of cattle.

India had the world's largest cattle population, estimated at 235 million in 1964, but since religious policies prohibited their slaughter, people derived little nutritional benefit from them. The United States ranked second, with 104 million. The Soviet Union was third, with 87 million.

The number of hogs in the world rose in 1963 to 496 million head, 1 percent over 1962 and 43 percent above the 1951–1955 average. Steadily increasing production in all geographical areas since 1956 was the result of a growing population, adequate supplies of feed, and favorable prices. The largest increases were in the Soviet Union, South America, and western Europe.

Sheep numbered 991 million head in 1963, about 18 percent above the average for 1951–1955. Some sheep were produced in almost every country, but 15 countries had three-fourths of the world total.

Australia (160 million head), Russia (140 million), New Zealand (50 million), and Argentina (47 million) had 40 percent of the total in 1963.

Sheep were the main form of livestock in the Near East, where vegetation generally is too sparse for cattle and little pork is eaten. Sheep and goats provide the chief source of meat in large areas of Africa.

In the Sahara and surrounding arid parts of northern Africa, several million people depend on nomadic pastoralism for meat and other livestock products. Sheep, goats, and camels are the only kinds of livestock that are adaptable there, and they must be moved often to new areas in search of pasture.

ABOUT HALF of the world's meat supply in 1963 consisted of beef, 41 percent of pork, and 8 percent of lamb, mutton, and goatmeat. The remaining 1 percent was horsemeat. This proportion has remained about the same for more than a decade.

The United States and the Soviet

Union accounted for 40 percent of the world's meat production. The United States produced twice as much as the Soviet Union and accounted for more than one-fourth of the world supply.

Ten countries in 1963 accounted for about three-fourths of the world's production of 112 billion pounds of meat. The United States led with 31 billion pounds; next was the Soviet Union, with 15 billion. West Germany, France, and Argentina all produced more than 5 billion pounds. The other five—Brazil, the United Kingdom, Australia, Poland, and Italy—ranged from almost 3 billion to more than 4 billion pounds of meat.

Estimates for mainland China are not included in my figures, although China probably was the world's third largest producer. It is estimated that China had 120 million head of hogs in 1963 and a relatively high slaughter rate, but the average slaughter weight undoubtedly was low. Hogs, which can utilize byproducts and waste materials, are the main livestock in China.

Beef output in 1962 totaled 54.7 billion pounds. The United States, the leading producer, accounted for 16.3 billion. The Soviet Union was second, with 5.5 billion; Argentina, third, with 4.7 billion; and France, fourth, with 3.6 billion. The four countries accounted for 55 percent of the world's beef output.

The world output of pork was 44.2 billion pounds in 1962, an increase of 2.5 billion pounds over 1961 and a 35-percent increase within a decade. The United States produced 11.8 billion pounds; Russia, 6.9 billion; West Germany, 3.9 billion; and France, 2.3 billion. The four accounted for about three-fourths of the supply of pork.

The world output of lamb, mutton, and goatmeat in 1962 was 8.7 billion pounds. The 1951–1955 average was 6.3 billion. The Soviet Union produced 2.2 billion pounds. Australia was second, with 1.3 billion. The United States and New Zealand each produced about 800 million pounds.

Horsemeat has dwindled in im-portance. The 1963 output of about 1 billion pounds was 1 percent of meat production in the world. As the use of tractor-powered farm machinery continues to increase, the numbers of horses and the production of horsemeat should decline further.

THE UNITED STATES consumes more meat than any other country—32 billion pounds in 1963. Consumers in the United States ate 33 percent of the world's supply of beef and veal, 28 percent of the pork, and 11 percent of the lamb, mutton, and goatmeat. On a per capita basis, however, the United States consumption of 167 pounds in 1963 was exceeded by New Zealand (233 pounds), Australia (215), Uruguay (213), and Argentina (198 pounds).

The Australians and New Zealanders were the largest consumers of lamb and mutton—99 pounds per person in 1963. Argentina, the major beef consumer, had a per capita consumption of 168 pounds in 1963.

Per capita consumption of meat in Asia was low. It amounted to only 10 pounds in Japan in 1963. Per capita consumption in Russia averaged 65 pounds and was lower than in all countries of western Europe, except Greece, Italy, Portugal, and Spain. In all South American countries except Argentina and Uruguay, per capita consumption was less than 80 pounds.

WORLD TRADE in meat has increased 50 percent since 1953. Many countries had some volume of trade, but relatively few handled the bulk of the commerce. New Zealand, Denmark, Argentina, and Australia accounted for about 60 percent of the world's meat exports in 1963.

The United Kingdom and the United States together imported three-fourths of the world's meat shipments. The United Kingdom alone accounted for more than half of the total.

The United States and the United Kingdom received almost three-fourths of the total beef imports in 1963. The United Kingdom was the market for 70 percent of the pork and more than three-fourths of the lamb and mutton in world trade.

Australian exports were largely beef; 74 percent was marketed in the United States and 17 percent in the United Kingdom in 1962. The proportion going to the United States market has increased sharply since 1958. The 1962 shipments were approximately double those of the previous year.

Beef and veal made up about 85 percent of Argentina's meat exports in 1962. More than half was received by the United Kingdom and most of the remainder by countries of the European Common Market.

Because of United States quarantine regulations that forbid imports of fresh or frozen meat from countries where foot-and-mouth disease is prevalent, Argentine exports to the United States were limited to the cooked or canned products.

New Zealand's meat exports consisted predominantly of lamb and mutton, almost 90 percent of which was sold to the United Kingdom. A substantial amount of beef went to the United States.

The United Kingdom has long been the major importer of meat. Of the 2,650 million pounds received in 1962, 937 million consisted of pork, more than two-thirds of it supplied by Denmark; 789 million consisted of lamb and mutton, more than four-fifths of which was supplied by New Zealand; 733 million consisted of beef, more than half of which was supplied by Argentina.

The United States was the second largest meat importer and the leading beef importer in 1962. Of the 1,253 million pounds of meat received, 971 million consisted of beef, of which Australia and New Zealand supplied two-thirds. Most of the remainder consisted of pork products, largely canned hams from Denmark, the Netherlands, and Poland.

Most of the meat imports into the European Common Market consisted of beef supplied largely by Argentina and variety meats mostly from the United States.

THE AMERICAN livestock industry produces meat almost exclusively for American consumption.

Foreign producers generally have been unable to compete with domestic producers in the production of meat of uniformly high quality that Americans require. Foreign producers, however, have been able to market in the United States a sizable amount of boneless beef and mutton, used for manufacturing, and specialty products, principally canned hams.

The United States has been the only country in which significant numbers of beef cattle were fed grain in order to produce a higher grade of beef than would be obtained from fattening on grass pastures.

Consumption of beef has increased as population and incomes have risen.

The demand for beef has been rising steadily. Annual per capita consumption of beef in the United States has gone from 55 pounds in 1938 to 93 pounds in 1963. A growing proportion of this beef comes from grain-fed cattle. The number of fed cattle produced has increased from 30 percent of total cattle marketed to more than 60 percent since 1935. The cattle-feeding industry has been expanding rapidly. Many new commercial lots have been built, and existing feedlots have expanded capacity.

Beef production has become an attractive enterprise for United States farmers. Beef cattle use roughages that would otherwise be wasted. They require a minimum of labor compared to other agricultural enterprises. Feed prices have been favorable compared with prices of fed cattle. Emphasis on soil conservation has increased the acreage and quality of forages.

These encouraging factors have led to rapid changes in the cattle industry. There have been shifts in production areas of fed cattle.

The States in the Corn Belt have been dropping their share of total output. In 1963, 67 percent of the cattle on feed were in the Corn Belt; 83 percent were fed there in 1930. Most of the shift has been to the West. More than five times as many cattle were on feed in the Western States in 1963 as in 1935. Washington had 16 times the number on feed in the early thirties; California, 12 times as many; and Arizona, 8 times.

Indications are that the South, which in 1963 had a relatively small output of fed cattle, is becoming more interested in this industry. In the Mississippi Delta, the Tennessee Valley, and along the Atlantic coast, improved transportation and favorable prices for midwestern grain has encouraged local fattening of cattle.

The number of cattle and calves on farms has moved up steadily since 1958 and reached a record of 104 million head on January 1, 1963. Even more important is that those kept for beef production totaled 75 million head, a rise of 16 million head, or 26 percent over the 59 million head on farms as of January 1, 1958.

Individual demand for pork has been falling. Per capita consumption of pork declined from 68 pounds in 1947 to 64 pounds in 1963. Nevertheless, because of population increase, pork production in the United States has been increasing and in 1963 was a record 12 billion pounds, compared to 11.4 billion in 1961 and an average of 10.8 billion in 1951–1955.

The demand for lamb in the United States appears to have declined steadily. The average annual decrease in demand since 1947 has been larger than the increases caused by the effects of increases in income and population. Production of lamb and mutton in 1963—710 million pounds—was the lowest since 1958. The number of sheep on farms in 1963 was the smallest since 1950.

Imports of meat into the United States in 1962 reached a record level of 1.8 billion pounds, carcass weight.

Imports of beef in 1962 increased to an alltime high of 1.5 billion pounds, equivalent to nearly 9 percent of United States production. Of the beef imports, 86 percent was frozen, boneless beef, used primarily for manufacturing; another 9 percent was canned beef, a product which is not made to any extent in the United States. Little bone-in or chilled beef, the product that would compete directly with American production, was imported.

Boneless beef is produced largely from overaged cows and bulls. The meat is too tough for use as beefsteaks and roasts and would generally be equivalent to the American Canner and Cutter grade—the lowest grade in USDA grading standards. The bone is removed from practically all of this type of beef entering international trade. It is then packed in cartons and frozen. Meat thus packaged and processed can be shipped and handled more efficiently and economically than in the whole or half carcass form. It can be packed more closely in the holds of ships, and there is a saving in freight costs because the weight of the bones is eliminated.

Boneless beef usually is ground in a meat chopper. It can then be sold as hamburger or blended with other types of meat and processed into frankfurters and other sausage.

Imports of boneless beef supplied lower grade processing meat, which during 1958–1963 was not produced domestically in sufficient quantity to meet a strong demand. Low-grade cows, which provided most of the processing meat, made up less than 10 percent of domestic cattle slaughter in the United States.

Australia and New Zealand supplied three-fourths of the fresh or frozen beef imports in 1963. Ireland and Mexico also were important exporters of boneless beef to the United States. Argentina was the main source of canned beef.

Imports of mutton reached a record 65 million pounds, product weight, in

1962. Imported mutton, all of it from Australia and New Zealand, was used largely in frankfurters and other manufactured products and thus did not compete directly with American lamb. Imports of lamb were relatively small, compared with domestic production. Imports in 1962 were equivalent to less than 2 percent of United States lamb production.

Most of the pork imported into the United States was in the form of canned hams from Denmark, Poland, and the Netherlands. Considered a specialty item, imported hams have usually sold at prices higher than American hams.

The United States has produced a surplus of variety meats, principally livers, kidneys, and tongues. Our exports of variety meats have been increasing steadily, and in 1962 they amounted to 125 million pounds.

The Common Market countries, a leading outlet for variety meats in 1963, bought about two-thirds of total shipments. The United Kingdom imported most of the remainder.

ARGENTINA, a large country, extends across 33 degrees of latitude and covers 1.1 million square miles. About 80 percent of the cattle, 85 percent of the hogs, and half of the sheep were concentrated in the Pampa, a region of about 150 million acres, or 21 percent of the land area of Argentina.

The Pampa, a level plain, extends in a rough semicircle from Buenos Aires to a radius of about 300 miles.

Its fertile soil supports luxuriant, improved pastures, usually of alfalfa, and produces most of Argentina's small grain and corn. The mild climate and well-distributed rainfall make the area an ideal cattle country. Green forage is available yearlong. Rail and highway networks have been highly developed. The country's major centers of consumption, industry, and commerce are in this region.

Patagonia, a rolling, semiarid region, is covered with scrub trees and coarse grass. Winters are harsh. Only hardy types of livestock have proved adaptable. This has been primarily a sheep grazing area, where about one-third of Argentina's sheep, but relatively few cattle, are raised.

North of the Pampa is Mesopotamia—the land between the rivers. This subtropical area has heavy rainfall, gently rolling terrain, and outcroppings of rock. The soils are less fertile than those of the Pampa. Most animals have been raised on unimproved pastures of relatively low productivity. As transportation facilities have not been highly developed, producers must drive livestock considerable distances to loading points. Ticks and tick fever were widespread in this zone. Cattle have been fairly heavily concentrated here; sheep are raised extensively in one part.

To the west of Mesopotamia lies the Chaco, an arid, semitropical expanse of scrubland extending up into Paraguay. This section suffers from periodic droughts and excessive soil salinity. Much of it is almost completely barren, although a fairly large population of cattle was scattered over most of the region. Ticks have been prevalent here also.

Although conditions vary widely from one part of the country to the other, livestock operations have tended to be relatively large. According to the census of 1960 in the Pampa, there were 122 properties, each containing cattle herds of more than 10 thousand head. Approximately 40 percent of the cattle were in herds of more than a thousand. Most of the livestock producers in the Pampa stocked substantial numbers of sheep on their properties in addition to cattle.

In Patagonia, landholdings and herds were large. Livestock operations in Mesopotamia and the Chaco as a rule were somewhat larger than in the Pampa.

Only in exceptional cases has pastureland been used fully. While most ranches were fenced and cross-fenced, the subdivisions were usually much larger than those in the United States.

Full utilization of forage was difficult. Clipping or other mechanical or chemical control of weeds was seldom practiced. Weeds in pastures reduced the stand of grass and lowered the livestock carrying capacity.

The Pampa has a great potential for pasture improvement. Progressive ranchers have been using airplanes for seeding improved grasses and applying herbicides. Many producers replaced old fences and further subdivided pastures. Forage yields on grazing areas in the Pampa that have been carefully and scientifically managed have been among the highest on record.

The Argentine cattle and beef industry has been based on the productive pastures of the Pampa. Steers and heifers were put on special fattening pastures soon after weaning and kept there for about 12 months until ready for market. Alfalfa pastures have been the foundation of this system, although many animals were pastured on rye or other small grains during the winter. Fattening in feedlots, common in the United States, has not been practiced.

Although calf and lamb crops on some ranches were comparable to those in the United States, the average for the country probably did not exceed 60 percent. Disease also took a severe toll of newborn calves.

Disease and deficient nutrition were the two primary factors in this low level of production. Both factors have been recognized by progressive Argentine breeders as serious problems, and considerable research has been conducted.

Argentina has been the world's largest exporter of meat during most years since 1950. Approximately one-fourth of Argentina's meat production has been exported. Exports of livestock and meat products accounted for more than half of the value of all exports in 1962.

Argentine meat production totaled 5.4 billion pounds in 1962, slightly higher than the previous year, and 20 percent above the 1951–1955 average, but a billion pounds below the record 6.4 billion pounds produced in 1958. Beef accounted for 88 percent of the total meat production in 1962, lamb and mutton for 7 percent, and pork for 5 percent.

About 85 percent of Argentina's meat exports were beef. Mutton and lamb made up most of the remainder. About three-fourths of the beef was exported chilled or frozen, and most of the rest as canned beef. The United Kingdom bought about half of the chilled and frozen beef. The Common Market countries received most of the remainder. The United Kingdom was also the major market for lamb and variety meat exports. The United States and the United Kingdom together received about three-fourths of the canned beef.

NEW ZEALAND was a close second to Argentina as an exporter of meat and in some recent years shipped a larger quantity than that country. Meat and other livestock products earned more than 90 percent of New Zealand's foreign exchange in 1963.

Meat production, which had been increasing steadily, was estimated at an alltime high of about 1.7 billion pounds for 1963, compared to a 1951–1955 average of 1.3 billion pounds. About 38 percent of the meat production consisted of lamb, 33 percent of beef and veal, 23 percent of mutton, and 6 percent of pork.

New Zealand has 50 million sheep and has specialized in the production of fat lambs for export. About 95 percent of the lamb production was shipped abroad—more than 90 percent to the United Kingdom. More than 60 percent of the total meat production was exported—about three-fourths to the United Kingdom. Less than 40 percent was required for domestic use, although per capita consumption averaged among the highest in the world.

New Zealand was the second largest supplier of boneless, manufacturing-type beef to the United States, furnishing about one-fourth of total imports in 1963. About 60 percent of New Zealand's total beef and veal shipments were to the United States.

The United States bought only limited quantities of New Zealand mutton because it generally had more fat than was wanted.

New Zealand has sold large quantities of mutton to Japan and other Asian countries since 1960, but the United Kingdom was still the market for more than one-half the exports.

Sheep numbers and production of lambs have increased steadily, but there is a considerable potential for further expansion. Beef cattle usually are run with sheep. Their numbers, in 1963 at an alltime peak, have increased gradually, a trend that should continue as long as there is a good export market for boneless beef in the United States.

The production of sheep, lambs, and wool has been New Zealand's chief industry, and the economy of New Zealand has centered around it.

About 40 million acres of New Zealand's total area of 66 million were used for pasture in 1963, most of it for sheep.

Sheep were widely distributed over both the North and South Islands, but some of the high country in the South Island, covered with sparse native grasses and tussok, carried only one sheep to 10 acres. In extensive areas of the country, improved pastures carried six ewes or more to the acre.

More than 90 percent of the lambs exported in 1963 had been sired by Southdown rams crossed with ewes of the Romney breed. The type of sheep produced and production practices in New Zealand are uniform, although the country spans more than a thousand miles. The fat lamb industry was based on marketing a milkfed lamb, averaging 30–35 pounds, carcass weight, at 4 to 8 months.

The lambing percentage for the country was relatively high. It had not been below 94.3 since 1953, and during the spring of 1958 (September–December) was more than 100 percent.

About 85 percent of the beef cattle were in the North Island. The number of farms keeping cattle in conjunction with sheep has increased since 1953. Some cattle have been kept in areas where land was being cleared. Close grazing by cattle was one means of clearing bracken from new land.

Nearly all of New Zealand is well adapted to beef cattle. More cattle would be produced if this operation were more profitable in comparison with dairying and sheep production. Beef cattle require more preserved winter feed than sheep. The provision of suitable watering places in the pastures is also a problem.

New Zealand's considerable potential for increased production is largely in improvements on existing farms, such as the additional use of fertilizers, clearing of brush, and better husbandry. It will also be influenced by development of new land through clearing and irrigation.

SHEEP NUMBERS in Australia increased by 37 percent and cattle numbers by 23 percent between 1950 and 1964. A further increase is likely, particularly if meat and wool prices continue relatively high.

Australia has had a larger sheep population than any other country. Sheep numbers for 1963 were estimated at 160 million head—nearly five times the United States total. It had 19 million head of cattle, compared with 104 million in the United States.

Australian meat production reached an alltime high of 3.4 billion pounds in 1962, of which beef and veal accounted for 53 percent, mutton for 26 percent, lamb for 14 percent, and pork for 7 percent of the total.

Australia has exported approximately one-fourth of its meat. At one time nearly all of this went to the United Kingdom, but the proportion has gradually declined since the Second World War, and by 1962 the United Kingdom accounted for only 20 percent of the total meat trade.

Shipments to the United States reached the highest level in 1962 and were more than double the year before. Boneless, manufacturing-type beef was the major export and in 1963 accounted for three-fourths of the total meat shipments to the United States. Mutton made up most of the remainder. Beef shipments to the United States reached a record level of 445 million pounds, product weight, in 1962.

The United States has offered a more attractive market for Australian beef than the United Kingdom. Canner and cutter cows, which supply the manufacturing beef sold to the United States, have been bringing about the same price per pound as the better grades of steers slaughtered for the United Kingdom.

Although conditions vary widely from one part of Australia to another, livestock properties generally have been large. In the more developed southeastern part of Australia, they ranged up to 5 thousand acres. Holdings of fewer than 700 acres in many sections are regarded as too small for successful operation. In central Queensland, holdings of 20 thousand acres are common. In northern and western Queensland, properties often exceed 250 thousand acres.

In Northern Territory and in the Kimberley region of western Australia, a number of cattle stations had 5 thousand square miles, or more than 3 million acres. The carrying capacity of this area has been as low as six head to the square mile because of a long dry season. Attempts to operate units of less than 1 thousand square miles frequently have been unsuccessful. Many of the properties were held by large corporations.

In New South Wales and Victoria, the common practice has been to run cattle and sheep together on the same pastures. As the carrying capacity was increased through the use of fertilizers and seeding with clover and improved grasses, the prevalent practice was to increase the number of cattle while

maintaining the same number of sheep. A considerable number of dairy farmers were disposing of milk cows in 1963 and shifting to beef cattle.

Practically all of the cattle have been fattened on pastures. There were a few small feedlot operations on an experimental basis in 1963, but it was the general opinion that the price of grain relative to the price of cattle was too high to make grain feeding economical. Furthermore, there was no market in Australia for highly finished beef.

In the southeastern parts of the country and in the parts of western Australia where rainfall is adequate, a rapid and extensive development of improved pastures has occurred. The area in improved pastures in 1963 was more than three times that devoted to crops. To a limited extent, utilization of dry native grasses was increased by spraying with molasses and the feeding of urea.

Cyclical droughts and irregular rainfall have limited the number of livestock that could be raised in most parts of Australia. The long dry season north of the Tropic of Cancer has been a limiting factor, for the stocking rate was determined by the number of head which can be carried through the dry period.

Rabbits, once a serious pest, have been reduced greatly in numbers, but in some regions measures to curtail rabbits have been costly.

Sheep were not raised in the coastal and northern part of Queensland, Northern Territory, and the Kimberley region of western Australia because of the prevalence of spear grass, whose sharp points penetrate the skin of sheep, and the sheep-killing dingos (wild dogs).

Although production of meat in Australia expanded about 50 percent in 1954–1963, there remained a large potential for similar or even greater expansion in the future. Production could be further increased by enlarging grazing areas, clearing brushland, and constructing roads, which would permit cattle raised in remote areas to be transported to market.

Although livestock were raised throughout the United Kingdom, not enough meat has been produced for the country's requirements. Thus in 1963 about 30 percent of the beef, 60 percent of the mutton and lamb, and 33 percent of the pork requirements were supplied by imports, even though meat production had increased by 40 percent over the 1951–1955 average.

Meat imports in 1962 totaled 2.7 billion pounds, product weight, 35 percent above the 1951–1955 average. Beef made up 30 percent of the imports, pork 38 percent, and lamb and mutton 32 percent.

Relatively few countries supplied the bulk of the imports. Argentina furnished 55 percent of the beef, Denmark 69 percent of the pork, and New Zealand 83 percent of the lamb and mutton in 1962.

ALTHOUGH Common Market countries were 95 percent self-sufficient in meat production in 1963, they were the third most important importer of meat. Most of the imports consisted of beef, of which Argentina supplied about two-thirds, and variety meats, of which the United States supplied more than one-half.

The combined meat production of the six countries—West Germany, France, Italy, the Netherlands, Belgium, and Luxembourg—totaled about 18 billion pounds in 1963, exceeding that of any country except America.

In the Community as a whole, the trend of production kept pace with that of consumption, so that the degree of self-sufficiency over the decade ending with 1963 changed little.

DWIGHT R. BISHOP *joined the Livestock Division of Foreign Agricultural Service in 1959. He has traveled extensively through most of the major livestock producing countries and has prepared a number of publications about them. Previously he was stationed in Brazil, Cuba, and the Congo as agricultural attaché.*

Milk and Dairy Products

by DAVID R. STROBEL and
SAMUEL L. CROCKETT

MILK HAS COME to the modern world from the cradle of civilization as a basic element of nutrition.

Milk was regarded as Nature's most nearly perfect food long before we had the modern science of nutrition. Scientific analysis has made known the nutritional elements that make milk and its products effective components of the human diet.

Most of the milk for human food comes from domestic cattle. Cows produce 90 to 95 percent of the total supply, and goats, sheep, deer, buffalo, camels, donkeys, mares, and yaks the remainder. The world milk production therefore usually means cow's milk.

That does not mean that milk from animals other than cows is not important. Much of it is produced in areas where cow's milk is not available. Milk cows thrive and produce best in the Temperate Zones and may survive only with difficulty in some climates where other milk-producing animals are quite at home.

THE CHIEF producing regions are Europe, North America, and Oceania. The major producers in Europe are France, West Germany, the United Kingdom, Italy, the Netherlands, Denmark, and the Soviet Union. In North America, the United States and Canada have about 95 percent of the total output. Production in Oceania is about equally divided between Australia and New Zealand.

The industry and governments in some countries have had problems of milk surpluses from time to time, but estimated world production (exclusive of mainland China) of milk of all types in 1963 was 735 billion pounds. That was not enough milk to provide each person in the world with a pint a day.

Milk production in western Europe, North America, and Oceania—which have about 20 percent of the world's population—account for about 55 percent of total world production. The developing countries, mainly in Latin America, Africa, the Near East, and the Far East, with more than 60 percent of world's population, produced about 20 percent of the world's milk.

A large part of total milk production (about 45 percent of annual output in the United States and Canada) is used in fresh fluid form. The rest is used mainly for butter, cheese, canned milk, and dried milk.

Consumption of fluid milk in North America is considerably higher than in other heavy producing areas, where distribution facilities have not yet been so highly developed. A rough approximation of milk utilization in 16 of the principal dairying countries, other than the United States and Canada, is that about 30 percent is consumed as fluid milk, 40 percent as butter, 15 percent as cheese, and 2 percent as canned and dried whole milk. The rest goes for miscellaneous uses.

CHEESE is made wherever animals are milked. A part of the milk supply in excess of that needed for fluid use nearly always is used for cheese. Most cheese is made from cow's milk, but smaller amounts are made from the milk of goats, sheep, camels, reindeer, and other animals.

Cheese is nutritious and palatable and contains most of the protein and usually most of the fat, as well as essential minerals, vitamins, and other nutrients of milk.

According to legend, cheese was first made accidentally by an Arabian merchant. Preparing for a long journey across the desert, he put some milk into a pouch made of a sheep's stomach. The rennet in the lining of the pouch and the heat of the sun caused the milk to separate into curd and whey. At nightfall, he discovered that the whey satisfied his thirst and the cheese—curd—satisfied his hunger.

Cheese may have been used as a food more than 4 thousand years ago.

It was made in many parts of the Roman Empire, and the Romans taught Anglo-Saxons to make cheese. Monks in European monasteries did much to perfect the art of cheesemaking. Italy was a cheesemaking center in the 10th century. Cheese was included in the ship's supplies when the Pilgrims sailed for America.

Cheesemaking was largely a farm industry until the middle of the 19th century. The first cheese factory in the United States was built in 1851 in Oneida County in New York. For a long time it remained a center of the cheese industry. Cheesemaking in the leading cheese-producing countries has become largely a factory industry.

Only small amounts are made on farms, largely for home use.

Procedures for making cheese differ as to types and places, but all require care and skill.

Lucius L. Van Slyke and Walter V. Price in a book, *Cheese*, published in 1949, stressed that cheesemakers must be able to think and act quickly in controlling variations in the process caused by climatic, biological, and chemical conditions. They prepared a manufacturing record sheet for cheese processors that listed many essentials for achieving success, such as condition (appearance, odor, taste, temperature, acidity) of milk, the kind of starter used, and ripeness of milk when rennet is added.

While the methods employed in the making of different cheeses vary widely, two sets of processes are involved— production of a coagulum and the curing, or ripening, processes. The beginning process requires a starter of a material containing large numbers of lactic acid organisms. It is added to milk or cream to cause lactic fermentation. A natural starter is prepared in the home or local factory. A commercial starter is prepared under the supervision of bacteriologists and sold to cheesemakers. They are called cultures or pure cultures.

Natural cheese is made directly from milk. Much cheese is consumed as process cheese. The natural cheese or cheeses are mixed with curd, nonfat dry milk, whey solids, or other milk products and combined by processing to produce process cheese. Natural cheeses include brick, Camembert, Cheddar, cottage, cream, Edam, Gouda, Limburger, Neufchatel, Parmesan, Provolone, Romano, Roquefort, Swiss, Trappist, and whey cheese (Mysost and Ricotta). No two are made by exactly the same method.

Cheese Varieties, Handbook No. 54 of the Department of Agriculture, describes more than 400 cheeses.

Many are named for the community in which they are made or for a landmark of the community. For that reason, many cheeses with different local names are basically the same.

Scientific study has given us a better understanding of the bacteriology and chemistry of cheesemaking and has made it possible to control more precisely every step of manufacture to obtain a uniform product.

BUTTER is produced and consumed most extensively in temperate climates. In terms of volume and commercial significance, it is the main manufactured dairy product.

Butter has a long recorded history of usage. In 2000 B.C., the people of India used butter. The Hindus probably were the first to use a twirling churn.

At the beginning of the 20th century, most farmers in the United States and elsewhere had their own churns and made butter for family use and perhaps for sale to the general store or the peddler who made periodic stops at the farm to buy butter and eggs.

Only about 3 percent of total butter production in the United States and Canada now is made on farms. A similar trend has taken place in other dairying countries.

A form of butter known as ghee is made by heating butterfat in an open vat to remove the water. The concentrated product is then filtered and slowly cooled to a granular consistency. Ghee, or a similar product, is made in India, the United Arab Republic, Pakistan, and other Asian and African countries and is used mostly in cooking.

NONFAT DRY MILK is produced in connection with the manufacture of butter. Its volume in some parts of the United States was substantial in the early thirties. At the time of the Second World War its production expanded sharply as the American dairy industry was called on to supply more food for the United States and other countries. From about 250 million pounds before the war, output rose to 650 million pounds in 1946. Extensive use of skim milk powder helped reestablish better nutritional levels in many countries.

Continued heavy postwar demand for relief feeding and changes in the butter production pattern pushed output even higher—to 2.2 billion pounds in 1963. Production of nonfat dry milk expanded also in other countries, but the expansion was not accompanied by an equally impressive growth of a commercial world demand. The United States, therefore, began to donate nonfat dry milk for use by international and charitable organizations overseas. Shipments under the Food for Peace program in 1963 reached approximately 750 million pounds and went to some 80 countries and territories.

An example of the place of nonfat dry milk in programs to improve nutrition is the school lunch program in Japan. The Government of Japan has imported more than 100 million pounds of nonfat dry milk annually, and Japanese nutritionists say milk has been a factor in the general increase in the average weight and height of Japanese children.

Canned milk is produced in most dairying countries, but output of evaporated and condensed milk on a large scale is concentrated in a few countries, principally the United States, the Netherlands, West Germany, and the United Kingdom. Those countries accounted for more than 75 percent of the total output of canned milk in 1963. Output in the United States has trended down since 1955, but in the Netherlands, West Germany, and in France it has made moderate gains.

WORLD TRADE in dairy products consists mainly of the movement of special manufactured items from a few leading suppliers to a limited number of markets.

In order of economic importance, the chief dairy products in world trade are butter, cheese, dried milk (nonfat and dry whole milk), and canned whole milk. Others are ice cream mixes and infant and dietetic foods.

About three-fourths of the butter in international trade is shipped to the United Kingdom. Normally most of it, about 1 billion pounds annually, is supplied by New Zealand, Denmark, Australia, and the Netherlands.

Before 1961, the United Kingdom maintained a free market for dairy products and from time to time imported sizable amounts from France, Ireland, Argentina, Poland, Sweden, Hungary, and Bulgaria. Any country with a surplus of butter could ship to the United Kingdom and dispose of it at some price. Because of the postwar upward trend in butter production and the heavy surplus situation that developed in 1960–1961, the Board of Trade of the United Kingdom announced a quota system that limited imports of butter from all traditional suppliers to specified quantities. Nontraditional suppliers were excluded; no quotas were authorized for them.

Italy and West Germany are the only other sizable importers of butter. Their imports are mainly seasonal and subject to control.

It seems likely that most of world trade in butter will continue to be controlled by a quota or licensing system for some time.

The principal markets for cheese have been the United Kingdom, West Germany, the United States, Italy, and Belgium. The Netherlands generally has been the largest exporter.

New Zealand, Denmark, France, Switzerland, and Italy have been next. Many types or classes of cheese enter commerce, but most of the trade is in Cheddar.

Trade in canned milk is mainly between the Netherlands and the Far East, the Philippines, Hong Kong, Thailand, and Malaysia. Africa also is an important market. About two-thirds of the canned milk in world trade comes from the Netherlands. Other sizable exporters are the United States, the United Kingdom, and France.

Trade in nonfat dry milk is carried on mainly by the United States, New Zealand, and Australia. Most of the shipments from the three go to the United Kingdom, Mexico, the Philippines, western European countries, Japan, and India.

Trade in such products as dry whole milk, anhydrous milk fat, dry ice cream mix, and milk-base infant and dietetic foods has been less important. More and more of the dry ice cream mixes have been shipped, but the importance of dry whole milk to the dairy industry has been declining.

Advances in dairy technology have made it possible to place milk and milk products in the diets of many persons at reasonable cost, but inadequate transportation and physical barriers make it impracticable to distribute milk in some regions unless it is canned or otherwise preserved.

A development of recent years has made it possible to provide a dependable supply of fluid milk far from the cow. This process and product are described in a publication, *Recombined Milk*, issued by the Foreign Agricultural Service in 1955.

The nonfat dry milk is reconstituted with water, anhydrous milk fat is added, and the mixture is processed through standard dairy equipment. The nonfat solids, milk fat, and water are combined in proportions to obtain the desired whole milk with a butterfat content of 2.5, 3, or 4 percent.

Once recombined, the milk can be distributed in fluid form or used to make ice cream, cottage cheese, white cheese, yogurt, and other products.

A publication, *How To Use Recombined Milk Ingredients in Manufacturing Dairy Products*, was issued by Foreign Agricultural Service in 1957.

Because milk in its natural state varies in its content of fat and solids-not-fat and these important composition factors can be changed by manufacturing procedures, it is essential that there be minimum standards of composition as well as regulations that control the sanitary production and manufacture.

THE UNITED STATES has been a leader in the formulation of sanitary rules and regulations and in the formulation of composition standards. The Milk Ordinance and Code (1953 Recommendations of the Public Health Service) for the production of milk issued by the United States Public Health Service has served as a guide to many other countries. The American pure food laws, minimum composition standards for dairy products, and testing procedures are widely recognized.

Recognizing the need for minimum standards for milk and milk products, the Food and Agriculture Organization undertook the development of such standards for voluntary acceptance by producing countries over the world. More than 50 member countries of the Food and Agriculture Organization have accepted the FAO Code of Principles for Milk and Milk Products and Associated Standards. *Milk Hygiene*, published in 1962, cov-

ered many phases of sanitation in the production, processing, and distribution of milk.

IN NEARLY ALL countries, milk has some special national importance. In some countries, usually the more developed ones, there have been problems associated with surpluses and their disposal. In less-developed countries, the problem is more apt to be one of formulating a pricing policy that will encourage greater output and hold prices stable. No entirely satisfactory solution was apparent in 1964.

The dairy industry provides a large share of total farm income in some countries. In a few, exports of dairy products have been leading earners of foreign exchange. Government measures to assist producers have varied. A common scheme has been to support prices in a way that assures producers adequate returns. This has been done oftenest by making direct purchases of dairy products to support the price of milk to producers. Another method utilizes deficiency payments to make up the difference between free market prices and the guaranteed price to the producers.

Many countries have believed it necessary to maintain production at a level high enough to assure minimum supplies in the event of an international crisis.

Japan is an example of a country that has been developing a high-price-structure dairy industry to increase production. The numbers of the dairy cattle in Japan increased from 751 million in 1959 to 974 million in 1962. Japanese producers in recent years have received a higher price than United States producers for milk used for manufacturing purposes. Consumers in Japan, whose per capita income equaled about 430 dollars in 1963, paid as much or more for dairy products than American consumers.

Japan has laws to control imports of dairy products. Domestic butter retails at 66 to 72 cents a pound. (New Zealand consistently exports and sells its butter on the United Kingdom market for about 30 to 40 cents a pound.) Despite high retail prices, per capita consumption of dairy products in Japan has been growing 12 to 14 percent a year.

Domestic market protection at guaranteed levels exists in nearly all countries. In developed countries, such protection tends to hold production at maximum levels and increase exportable supplies.

In developing countries, price supports geared to high-cost production tend to inhibit increased per capita use of milk and dairy products. In many countries, the supply available for domestic consumption to a considerable degree is limited to short supplies of high-priced domestic products by discouraging or virtually precluding imports of lower priced dairy products from world market sources.

World production of milk and dairy products will probably continue to increase. While per capita consumption of certain products will go up in many countries, such gains in total are not expected to keep pace with increases in production.

A gap may continue for some time between world production and effective demand for dairy products. In the developing countries, where there are deficits of milk and dairy products to provide adequate nutrition, milk production has been growing. The rate of increase has not kept pace with population growth, however, and there continues to be less milk available on a per capita basis. In Latin America, the rise in milk production is said to have matched population growth, but the overall consumption remains low in most countries.

Milk production probably will continue to increase in the countries with advanced dairy industries. Consumption of milk and milk products in these countries is at a high level, and further expansion of the market has only limited possibilities.

Continued gains in production may result in larger surpluses of dairy products on the world market. Because of national policies both in surplus (exporting) countries and deficit (importing) countries, market expansion on a purely commercial basis is not expected to develop fast enough to absorb total available supply. Sizable supplies of milk and milk products therefore probably will continue to move under government programs to the enormous potential markets in the developing countries.

From the standpoint of world nutritional needs, total milk production is not excessive, but from the standpoint of effective demand, there is excess production. This situation necessitates a constant review by the advanced dairy countries of national policies concerning efficiency of production and world prices for dairy products.

In the developing countries, where efforts are being made to attain higher production of food products of all kinds, careful consideration should be given to the adoption of policies designed to take full advantage of world supplies of low-priced milk and milk products to improve nutritional levels.

DAVID R. STROBEL *in 1962 became assistant agricultural attaché in Japan in charge of the agricultural office, the United States Trade Center in Tokyo. He previously was Deputy Director, Dairy and Poultry Division, Foreign Agricultural Service; marketing specialist and branch chief in the Dairy and Poultry Division; and technologist in the Production and Marketing Administration and the Agricultural Marketing Service with a major responsibility in the formulation of dairy product standards.*

SAMUEL L. CROCKETT *joined the Dairy and Poultry Division, Foreign Agricultural Service, in 1957. He was appointed Chief of Commodity Analysis Branch in February 1962. He was an agricultural economist in International Cooperation Administration assigned to Managua, Nicaragua, in 1955–1957. Previously he was employed in the Department of State, the Production and Marketing Administration, and the Bureau of Agricultural Economics.*

Fisheries

of the World

by SIDNEY SHAPIRO

THE AMOUNTS of protein the world gets from its fisheries always have been large and are getting larger.

The global catch was 20 million metric tons in 1950 and nearly 45 million in 1962. It may reach 70 million by 1980.

Some experts on marine resources believe that about 90 percent of the ocean's productivity is unused and that utilization eventually can be increased at least fivefold without endangering aquatic stocks. If so, the world's oceans could produce 200 million tons annually with sound management and conservation. Opportunities exist also for increased fresh-water production.

The developing countries, mainly in Asia, Africa, and Latin America, have begun to establish modern fishing industries, because fish and shellfish are primary resources that can be utilized with less capital investment than most other forms of industrial development require. Besides supplying local populations with high-quality protein, such fishery products as frozen tuna and shrimp, canned sardines and tuna, and fish meal and oil earn foreign exchange.

The developed countries also are eager to enlarge their fisheries. Some have extended their fishing to distant waters and foreign coasts. Competition thus has increased, and so have inter-national problems and a need for international cooperation to solve the present and future problems of the development, management, and conservation of aquatic resources.

The global fishery catch is utilized in two main ways—as food for direct human use and by reduction into meal and oil for industrial purposes. Between 1957 and 1962, the amount of fish landed for direct food use increased from 26.1 million metric tons to 31.8 million at an average annual rate of about 4 percent. The amount of fish (excluding offal) sent to the reduction plants increased from 4 million tons to 11.9 million, at an average yearly rate of 25 percent. The major contributor to the increase has been Peru, which increased its production of fishmeal from 64,500 tons to 1,111,400 tons (product weight) between 1957 and 1962. (A metric ton is 2,204.6 pounds avoirdupois; it is the unit used in this chapter.)

AQUATIC animals (excluding whales) supply an estimated one-third of the world production of all types of animals. (Milk and eggs are not included in the comparison since they are the products of land animals.) About 115 million tons of water and land animals were produced in 1961. Of that big amount, aquatic animals contributed about 41 million tons (live weight) and land animals about 74 million tons (mainly carcass weight).

The production of aquatic animals rose 37.7 percent between 1956 and 1961; production of land animals rose 19.9 percent. Fishery products were the largest single category in the world's supply of flesh protein in 1961. The take of 40.6 million tons of aquatic animals in 1961 exceeded production of each of the chief classes of land animals—29.1 million tons of beef and veal, 28.1 million tons of pork, 7.5 million tons of chicken, and 5.7 million tons of mutton and lamb.

These data indicate the magnitude of the supply of each type of flesh protein and must be used with caution.

They are incomplete and are not comparable precisely because of the different weights in which they are recorded. Furthermore, subsistence fishing produces a large but uncounted catch, notably in undeveloped regions.

Fisheries (including those for seaweed but not for whales) shortly after the Second World War recovered their prewar catch level of about 21 million tons in 1938. During the midfifties the global catch rose at a sustained annual rate of about 5 percent and reached 32.5 million tons in 1958. Since then, the annual increase has been faster, about 8.5 percent. The catch reached 44.7 million tons in 1962.

About 90 percent of the total fishery catch comes from the oceans, seas, and tributary waters. The rest is caught in rivers, lakes, or other bodies of fresh water or are cultivated in natural or artificial impoundments. The marine catch in 1962 was 40 million tons; fresh-water production was 4.7 million tons. Statistics from the Food and Agriculture Organization show an increase for the fresh-water fisheries of about 26 percent between 1957 and 1962, compared to 46 percent for the marine fisheries.

About 70 percent of the world's fresh-water production has come from Asia, mainly from the highly developed pond-culture industries of such countries as mainland China and Indonesia. China's fresh-water production was reported as 2 million tons in 1959, or 44 percent of the world's production of 4.6 million.

Possibilities exist to expand the fresh-water fisheries in many places by systematic breeding and artificial cultivation, although climate and other conditions cause considerable variation in production. Average annual yields of about 900 to 1,800 pounds per acre of pond have been attained in China, Indonesia, and the Congo, and maximum yields have been as high as 8 thousand pounds an acre. Average annual yields have been between 180 and 360 pounds an acre in Europe.

Cultivation of fish and shellfish has also been conducted successfully in brackish ponds, especially in Asia. Average annual yields range between 130 and 900 pounds an acre.

Cultivation in wet ricefields, submerged 3 to 8 months of the year, shows promise. Yields have averaged 90 to 130 pounds an acre. Maximum yields have been as high as 1,800 pounds an acre in Japan. One estimate is that 250 million acres of ricefields are available for such cultivation. An annual potential yield of 5 million tons of fish thus is possible, even if yields are based on a modest 45 pounds an acre.

THE WORLD'S MARINE fisheries have been dominated by the developed countries of the North Temperate and Arctic Zones. This pattern has been changing, largely because of the rapid increase in fishery production in Peru. Between 1957 and 1962, tropical areas increased their share of the world's marine catch from 21 to 33 percent; South Temperate and Antarctic Zones increased theirs from 5 to 6 percent. North Temperate and Arctic Zones showed a decline from 74 to 61 percent during this period.

The marine fisheries take a wide assortment of demersal (or bottom) fishes from the ocean floor and pelagic (or surface-swimming) fishes from the upper layers. Certain species in each of these major categories may be taken from intermediate layers of the ocean in certain seasons and localities.

More than 20 thousand species of fish exist in the oceans, rivers, lakes, and other bodies of water, but only a small number are taken in significant commercial quantities.

Fishing effort has been directed so far primarily toward species easily available to present fishing craft and gear or species highly prized in world markets.

Examples of the former are the herring, sardines, anchovies, and similar schooling fishes that for decades have supported major fisheries in the Northern Hemisphere and have become attractive to countries of the Southern Hemisphere.

Highly prized are such species as salmon, tuna, halibut, and shrimp, which have been the goal of too concentrated a fishing effort in some places and the source of problems of overfishing and declining yields.

Herring, menhaden, sardines, anchovies, and many related clupeoids accounted for 33 percent of the world's fishery catch in 1962. Such products as salted or smoked herring, canned sardines, and brine-cured anchovies are traditional in world markets.

Some of those species also are used in the fish-reduction industry to manufacture meal and oil. In this way, Norway, Canada, and Iceland use a part of their herring catches, and Morocco and the Republic of South Africa use part of their sardine catches.

Some clupeoids—for example, the menhaden off the United States Atlantic and gulf coasts and the anchovy off Peru and northern Chile—are used entirely for reduction.

The world catch of clupeoids increased from 7.3 million tons in 1957 to 14.7 million in 1962, largely because of their greater use for reduction.

The next most important group is the cod, haddock, hake, and related species. These bottomfishes contributed 5.5 million tons (or 12.3 percent) to the world's catch in 1962.

A famous member of the group, the Atlantic cod, has long been dry salted to provide a staple food in Portugal, France, and Spain, and is exported by Norway, Canada, and others to Latin American countries. The cod and related species have been taken mainly with trawls from the fishing banks of the vast Continental Shelves of North Temperate and Arctic areas. This group is also known to exist in quantity off Chile and Argentina. Hake has become abundant in the Chilean catch.

The jacks, mullets, sea basses, perches, croakers, and related species are recognized as a single group for statistical purposes. The 4.3 million tons taken in 1962 made them the third largest category in the world catch.

Next in importance were the tunas, mackerels, and related species (2.4 million tons); flounders, halibuts, and soles (1.2 million tons); salmons, trouts, and smelts (550 thousand tons); and sharks, rays, and such (370 thousand tons). Unsorted and unidentified marine fishes accounted for 6.8 million tons.

Shellfish abound primarily on the ocean bottom. This group includes such mollusks as oysters, clams, abalone, scallops, squid, cuttlefish, and octopus, and such crustaceans as shrimp, lobsters, and crabs. Each of the types comprises a large number of important species. About 2.5 million tons of mollusks and 960 thousand tons of crustaceans were taken in 1962.

The world's fisheries also produce lesser amounts (180 thousand tons in 1962) of a large number of miscellaneous aquatic animals. In Oriental countries, the produce of the seas is utilized more fully than in western countries, where mostly selected species are brought to market.

Sea urchins and sea cucumbers are among the more highly prized miscellaneous aquatic animals. Bullfrogs, snails, turtles, and the like are also listed as miscellaneous edible aquatic animals. Among the miscellaneous nonedible species are the sponges and shells, the best known of which enter commerce as mother-of-pearl.

Edible seaweeds find their greatest use in the Orient. Agar and alginates are extracted from nonedible seaweeds. Japan, the largest producer of aquatic plants, accounted for 502 thousand tons of the world production of 660 thousand tons in 1962.

As to methods of capture, the world's fisheries are in a transition from simple hunting to more orderly and efficient harvesting with instruments that search out the fish, shellfish, and the other aquatic animals.

Most of the world's fishermen still use small craft propelled by sail and oar and can be considered hunters who catch the fish indiscriminately or fortuitously. Their combined catch is only a small fraction of the world's total. These fishermen operate mostly in shallow coastal and inshore waters of tropical countries and average a yearly catch of about a ton. Their fishing gear is of an almost infinite variety but primitive in construction and difficult to operate with the rapidity needed to make large catches.

Bilateral and multilateral technical assistance programs have made a good start on upgrading the efficiency and maneuverability of small fishing craft by installing small inboard or outboard motors.

One of the most successful of a number of such projects has been conducted in Ceylon by the Food and Agriculture Organization with the support of a large manufacturer of motors. With British aid, the efficiency of the Hong Kong fishing fleet was upgraded in a short period when semidiesel engines were installed in unwieldy fishing junks.

Most of the world's fishery catch is taken by fishermen who average 100 tons or more per man each year.

These fishermen use four principal types of gear—trawls, gill nets, seines, and lines, each type constructed in a multitude of designs and sizes.

For net webbing and lines, synthetic fibers have become popular, as they are strong and do not rot.

With such gear and with larger, more powerfully motorized vessels, many high-seas fishermen have been able to extend operations into waters on the slope off the Continental Shelf to depths of nearly 2 thousand feet. Some of them have progressed from the hunting to the systematic searching stage.

Modern fishing craft carry advanced echo-sounding and echo-ranging gear. Trawlers use echo sounders to locate schools of fish on the ocean floor. When used in midwater trawling, they pinpoint the exact depth of fish that are in intermediate water layers; the trawls then can be adjusted to the proper depth for catching the fish. This method, yet to be fully developed commercially, has promise of tapping hitherto unutilized or underutilized resources.

Helicopters are used to locate schools of fish on the surface and also (with echo sounders) on the ocean floor.

Progress has been made in a still more advanced stage of capture, that of attracting or guiding fish to an area where they are available to fishing gear.

Electrical attraction as an aid in purse seining or in trawling or in pumping fish directly aboard the vessel has some distinct possibilities, although this is still in an expensive experimental stage. A major difficulty is that the high conductivity of salt water requires great power output.

Simpler guiding devices also show promise. One developed by the United States Bureau of Commercial Fisheries has demonstrated that a curtain of air bubbles will guide small herring, known as Maine sardines, into shallow bays, where they can be caught with purse seines.

Another development is that the building of vessels of larger and larger tonnage has enabled fishermen to extend their operations to high seas thousands of miles from home port. Distant-water fishing has been done for centuries but under difficult conditions for preserving the fish. Western Europeans have fished on the Grand Banks off Newfoundland since the 16th century. The British, Germans, French, Belgians, and others have trawled on the Continental Shelf off Iceland, Greenland, and Spitsbergen, along the Norwegian coast, and in the Barents Sea. The range of the vessels and their length of stay on the fishing grounds were limited, however, because the fish could be brought back preserved only in ice.

Today's higher powered, longer range vessels have better facilities for preserving catches, and also in larger amounts.

Large freezer-trawlers, with stern chutes for handling and bringing aboard huge trawl nets, can catch, fillet, and freeze the fish and bring them to market in excellent condition.

More than 20 countries have vessels with some type of equipment for processing fish at sea. The British pioneered in this field in 1950. The Soviet Union has more than 100 stern freezer-trawlers, averaging about 3 thousand gross tons. United States fishermen had no vessels of that size and type in 1964.

A further advance in integrated fishing on the high seas has been the factory ship fleets of the Japanese and the Soviets. These floating bases consist of small catcher vessels, refrigerated carriers, tankers, supply ships, tugs, and factory ships for processing catches by freezing, curing, canning, or reduction to meal and oil.

Japan has been the leader in fishing for as long as records have been kept. Before the Second World War, Japan sent trawlers into the North Pacific and Indo-Pacific regions and its tuna long-liners into the Southwest Pacific. It conducted distant high-seas fisheries in the Pacific with large fleets of tuna mother ships and salmon and crab factory ships.

After 1952, Japan resumed activities on an even larger scale. Today many of its vessels, individually or in integrated fleets, fish all major oceans. Japanese tuna long-liners up to a thousand gross tons now range as far as the Indian Ocean and the tropical South Atlantic. Fleets of salmon factory ships work in the North Pacific, crab fleets in the Sea of Okhotsk and the eastern Bering Sea, and meal and oil reduction factory fleets in the Bering Sea. A Japanese trawler began fishing in the northwestern part of the Atlantic in 1962.

The Soviet Union had no distant high-seas fisheries until the late fifties, when it began to build large numbers of stern trawlers and fleets of modern factory ships. Besides its 100 stern trawlers, the Soviets had about 15 factory ships, each of 15 thousand to 20 thousand gross tons, in 1963.

Off North America, Soviet freezer-trawlers and factory ship fleets fish on the Grand Banks off Newfoundland and Georges Bank off the New England coast, in the eastern Bering Sea, and in the Gulf of Alaska. The Soviets also operated in the Caribbean and the Gulf of Mexico out of Cuban ports in 1964.

Other Soviet vessels have begun to explore and operate in waters off the west coast of Africa and in the Indian Ocean. Vessels of more than 300 horsepower comprised only 6 percent of the Soviet fishing fleet in 1960 but took 76 percent of the Soviet catch.

THE UPWARD SURGE in world fishery production has been taking place at different rates in different regions.

South America, Asia, Africa, and the Soviet Union have been in the forefront in higher catches. Between 1950 and 1962, fishery catches increased 1,547 percent in South America, 149 percent in Africa, 130 percent in Asia, and 122 percent in the Soviet Union.

The countries of North America and Europe have been leaders in introducing technological developments for better utilization of catches, but increases in fishery production have been less spectacular. Fishery catches in North America increased only 16 percent between 1950 and 1962. The increase in Europe has been 38 percent.

Asia, the largest producer of fishery products, accounted for a catch of 17.5 million tons in 1962—39 percent of the world's total and an increase of 3.9 million tons over the 13.6 million tons caught in 1957. Japan had a catch of 6.9 million tons in 1962—more than double its catch in 1950. Mainland China, India, Indonesia, the Philippines, South Korea, Pakistan, Taiwan, and Thailand also increased their catches.

I have no reliable data on mainland China's production, but its fisheries are said to be large and next to those of Japan and Peru in world production. An estimate is that production was 2.9 million tons in 1948 and about 5 million tons in 1961. China has extensive pond-culture fisheries for carp and allied species. The coastal waters of the Yellow, East China, and South China Seas have large stocks of fish, which can be caught by motorized junks. China has not developed its offshore fisheries and has not built modern vessels.

South America has progressed notably in fishing. Its catch rose from 1.2 million tons in 1957 to 8.1 millions tons in 1962. Peru was second to Japan in world fishery production in 1962.

Chile and Ecuador have increased their production through national development programs and with the aid of technical assistance from the Food and Agriculture Organization and the United Nations Special Fund. Brazil and Argentina have considered similar plans.

The increase in South American fishery production has been mainly in anchovy for the Peruvian fishmeal industry. Chile has started to utilize the same resource off its northern coast, also for production of fishmeal.

The shrimp fisheries of Ecuador, Colombia, Venezuela, and British Guiana have begun to develop, mainly for export to the United States.

Fisheries in Africa have always had an important place in the economies of many countries but on something of a subsistence level. The fishery catch was 2 million tons in 1957—mainly from Angola, the Republic of South Africa, South-West Africa, and Morocco. An increase to 2.6 million tons in 1962 was due mainly to continued expansion of the fish-reduction industry in South Africa and South-West Africa, increased Moroccan production, and the beginning of modern fishing industries in many of the developing countries, especially in western Africa. The fishing industries of the eastern coast of Africa have been somewhat primitive.

The full potential of the fisheries of Africa has yet to be realized. The developing countries have been giving first priority to the modernization of their fishing industries. Plans have been made in many localities for large offshore operations for tuna and other species. Many countries recognize that their inland waters can be used to good advantage in producing fishery products for domestic use and export.

European fisheries have been among the most productive in the world and have used modern techniques to catch and market fish. Scandinavia, West Germany, the Low Countries, the United Kingdom, France, Portugal, Spain, and Iceland always have had good market outlets. Accordingly, their fishing industries, which have concentrated mainly on cod and allied species, flatfishes, and herring, have been substantial.

The concentration has meant, however, that the catches in European waters have not increased very much; sometimes signs of overfishing are evident, especially for bottomfishes in the North Sea. European catches have fluctuated slightly between 7.7 million tons in 1957 and 8.4 million tons in 1962.

Mediterranean countries—such as Italy, Yugoslavia, and Greece—have contributed little to the European catch. Mediterranean waters are not very productive because of the scarcity of plankton, and large fishing industries are not expected to develop there.

Fisheries in North America have been dominated by the industries in the United States and Canada. Mexican and Central American fisheries were almost entirely undeveloped until recently. Mexico during the fifties developed a large shrimp fishery, which accounted for one-third of its total production of about 219 thousand tons in 1962. Central American countries, such as El Salvador and Panama, have also increased production of shrimp, primarily for export to the United States. North American catches have fluctuated between 4 million tons in 1957 and 4.4 million tons in 1962.

United States and Canadian fisheries can be considered mostly as in a static stage. There have been indications, however, of technological advancement which could spark a renewal of growth. Both countries have introduced many improved techniques for catching, processing, and distributing fishery products, but competition from fisheries overseas has hurt domestic producers, especially on the United States market.

THE WORLD's catches have been used in five main ways—fresh, frozen, cured, canned, or reduced to meal and oil.

In the first four are fishery products destined for use as human food. Meal is used for animal feeds. Oil has food and nonfood uses.

Fish are highly perishable, and until we had better freezing and canning methods, use in the fresh form was restricted mainly to coastal areas near fishing grounds. Consequently, for many centuries a large part of the world catch had to be preserved by curing methods such as drying, salting, smoking, or a combination of them or by fermentation.

Suitable techniques made it possible to produce canned fishery products in sizable quantities early in the 20th century. A beginning was made during the twenties in the use of freezing. The trend since the Second World War has been to the greater use of canned and frozen fish, although fresh and cured products still are consumed in the largest quantities.

Since the midfifties, a striking change in utilization has been the increase in the amounts used for meal and oil.

Consumers bought about 16 million tons (36 percent of the world catch) of fresh fish in 1962, compared to 13.5 million tons in 1957. This increase can be attributed to more widespread use of ice and to investment in larger, faster mechanized vessels, a trend which has made more fish available for sale in the fresh, iced state. Concomitant improvements in transport, distribution, and sales have also contributed.

About 7.3 million tons of fish were cured in 1957 and 7.6 million tons in 1962. In Japan, India, Norway, Iceland, and other countries, especially those in developing areas, curing is a traditional and effective way of utilizing a large part of the catch.

Canada, Norway, and Iceland have been the leading exporters of cured fish. The use of cured products has been declining in North America and in most European countries, but in some countries the trend is upward. The demand for dried fish has been increasing in Latin America and tropical Africa. Soviet and Polish consumption of smoked fish is up.

Fermented fishery products, such as South Vietnam's nouc-mam and Burma's nga-pi, have their greatest use in the Orient, a use that can be expected to expand.

About 9 percent of the world catch was canned in 1962. Canning is done in many countries, but its use has been slow in advancing, except in the United States, Japan, and the Soviet Union. Tuna and salmon are most used in canning in the United States and Japan. The Russians can pike, pike perch, bream, eel, and whitefish, largely to feed people in remote nonfarming areas. Sardines and herring are canned in many places, notably in Portugal, Spain, Norway, the United States, West Germany, France, Japan, Morocco, and South Africa. About 2.9 million tons of all species were canned in 1957 and 4.0 million in 1962.

Freezing accounted for about 4.2 million tons of fish in 1962, compared with 2.4 million tons in 1957. The Soviet Union leads in the total amount frozen. Its far-ranging vessels freeze fish in bulk for delivery to home ports, where it is thawed and reprocessed. Japan freezes about one-fourth of its catch. The United States, Iceland, Canada, Norway, the United Kingdom, and Denmark also freeze sizable portions of their catches. Freezing has become a practical means of preserving catches made by the growing fleet of high-seas vessels.

Freezing methods have had their greatest use in countries whose populations have reached a high standard of living. Freezing requires costly investment in the equipment necessary to bring frozen fish from the fishing grounds to the consumer.

The greater use of fish for industrial purposes has accelerated. About 13 percent of the world's fishery catch of 31.1 million tons in 1957 and 27 percent of the catch of 44.7 million tons in 1962 were reduced to meal and oil.

Fishmeal is a vital secondary element in the food supply for people. It is used primarily as an ingredient in mixed feed for poultry and swine.

The fish oils are used as a component in paints, lubricants, and plastic foams, but so far most of the fish oil has been made into margarine. Oil has begun to be used as an energy supplement in animal feeds.

Great emphasis has been put on the development of fish products of better quality and more kinds for domestic use and export. Of potential importance is preserving fish and shellfish by the freeze-drying method, which scientists in the United States and Great Britain have worked on for a number of years.

Freeze drying permits the removal of about five-sixths of the original weight of the fish. The product can be stored in plastic wrappings a long time at ambient temperatures. Freeze-dried shrimp have appeared in some markets, but the high cost of processing equipment has restricted the wide use of the method.

Another promising product is fish protein concentrate. Several countries, including the United States, and international organizations have given increasing recognition to the importance of concentrates in improving the diets of people in countries where animal protein deficiency is prevalent.

Commercially feasible methods of manufacturing the concentrates cheaply need to be devised and consumer markets developed. Then, many fishes now reduced mainly to fishmeal could be utilized more effectively as animal protein supplements for human diets made up largely of vegetables and cereals. Also, species not now utilized could be the raw material for concentrates.

Off the United States coasts, for example, large stocks of hake, mackerel pike, and certain herringlike fishes are almost completely unutilized. Very likely United States production could be doubled if such species were caught up to the limit of their maximum sustainable yields.

INTERNATIONAL TRADE in fishery products is large. Based on data for 127 countries, fishery exports in 1961 totaled 4.3 million tons (product weight), valued at more than 1.2 billion dollars. The combined total catch of these countries was 35.7 million tons. The live-weight equivalent of the exported products was 11.8 million tons. The total international trade was 33 percent of the original catch taken.

The most valuable products entering international trade were fresh, frozen, or canned fish and shellfish, but in quantity the principal exports were fishmeal, fish solubles, and similar ingredients for use in animal feeds.

Fishery products traded internationally for human consumption are mainly high-priced products (destined mostly for the United States, Canada, and northwestern Europe) and low-priced products for special markets in Latin America, Africa, and Asia.

Norway, a leading exporter of fishery products, for example, prepares large amounts of salted, dried cod, which go mainly to South America and Central America. Norway also prepares high-quality canned sardines, primarily for the lucrative United States and European markets.

South Africa has built a large industry based on canned sardines, which are exported mainly to southeastern Asia.

Japan's tuna freezing and canning

industries formerly relied solely on United States markets, but Japan has been successful in expanding the market in western Europe and in Canada.

Exports of dried, salted, and smoked fish have declined since 1945. Formerly dried or salted herring, salted dried cod, unsalted dried cod (stock fish), and dried or salted sardines and anchovies were shipped from countries in western Europe and from Iceland and Canada to many parts of the world, but chiefly to eastern Europe, Portugal, Spain, and Latin America. Some of the importing countries have turned to other types of products or are trying to attain self-sufficiency. To compensate for the decline in markets for cured products, exporters have begun to look to the development of the fish-freezing industry.

Japan, the largest exporter in value of fishery products, exported 415 thousand tons (product weight), valued at 188 million dollars, in 1961. More than one-half was in canned products, such as tuna for the United States and western Europe, and sardines and saury for low-priced markets in southeastern Asia. Next in importance were frozen tuna, salmon, and swordfish.

Norway, Denmark, Iceland, Canada, and the Netherlands have been among the longtime leading exporters. Many other countries have entered the export trade since 1945. The South African fishing industry relies heavily on its export business in fishmeal, oil, and canned sardines. Peru, the largest exporter of fishmeal, shipped almost 1 million tons in 1962, mainly to European markets and the United States. Morocco has built a sizable fishing industry based on sardine canning and fishmeal and oil.

The United States is the largest importer of fishery products. Our imports have increased tenfold in dollar value almost steadily since 1936. We imported edible and industrial fishery products with a foreign export value of 475 million dollars from more than 100 countries in 1962. The increase can be attributed mainly to a growing popula-

tion, lower import duties, improved methods of preservation, and foreign demand for dollar exchange. The principal imports have been fresh and frozen groundfish (cod, haddock, hake, pollock, and cusk), ocean perch, tuna, shrimp, and northern and spiny lobsters; canned tuna and sardines; and fishmeal.

Other principal importers of fishery products have been the United Kingdom, West Germany, France, Belgium, Italy, and the Netherlands.

United States fishery exports are negligible, compared with imports. The United States ranked 12th in 1962 among the countries that exported fishery products. Our exports that year were valued at 36 million dollars. Fish oils were the principal fishery product exported. Canned salmon, mackerel, sardines (not in oil), shrimp, and squid were the other leading exports. Tariff and nontariff barriers to trade, imposed particularly by foreign countries until 1959, have impeded full development of the United States export trade in fishery products.

The changes being brought about by the formation of the European Economic Community may have important significance for international trade in fishery products. The six member countries in 1961 imported fishery products valued at 343 million dollars, or 25 percent of the world total, and exported fishery products valued at 100 million dollars, or 8 percent of the world total.

The United States fishing industry's trade with the six countries in 1963 involved mainly exports of fish oils; they enter the EEC free of duty. Normal trade patterns in other fishery products, however, may be altered by the new level of common external duties and by special arrangements by which member countries propose to support their fishing industries. The averaging of duties could result in declining imports of certain fishery products. For example, Germany's original duty of 10 percent and Benelux's free rate on the imports of fish fillets may be raised eventually to 18 percent. This may force such supplying countries as Norway and Iceland to expand their trade in other markets, possibly in the United States.

It is hard to evaluate the changes being made by the Common Market with respect to the fisheries. If tariff changes alone were being considered, one might predict that the end result could adversely affect many countries, including the United States. But other factors such as subsidy measures, marketing aid programs, and probable changes in the buying habits brought about by a higher standard of living in the Common Market countries may be more important factors.

It is well to note the tremendous increase in canned tuna consumption and the increasing demand for frozen fish fillets, sticks, and portions in the Common Market countries and in other countries of northern Europe. The use of fishmeal in mixed feeds also is increasing because of expanding production of poultry (especially broilers), swine, and cattle. Thus a higher standard of living in these European countries in the end may benefit the world's fisheries through increased consumption of fishery products.

THE UNITED STATES has traditionally been one of the major producers of fishery products. Landings have remained at a high level but have not surged ahead as have the catches of other countries.

Before the war and until 1956, the United States ranked second to Japan in size of catch. American fisheries dropped to third place in 1957, behind the expanding fisheries of mainland China. At that time, the fisheries of Peru and the Soviet Union began to boom, and in 1960 both countries forged ahead, placing the United States fifth among the fishing nations.

United States fishery landings increased from 2.6 million tons (live weight) in 1950 to 3 million tons in 1956. Since then, the catch has tended to level off, fluctuating between 2.7 million tons in 1957 and 2.9 million tons in 1962.

Such increase as has taken place has been in the landings for industrial purposes, principally of menhaden for meal and oil. The fish sent to the United States reduction plants rose from 601 thousand tons in 1950 to 1.1 million tons in 1962, an increase of 83 percent. At the same time, the amount of fish and shellfish caught for human food has been declining. This amount rose to a peak of 2 million tons in 1950 but thereafter declined almost steadily to 1.8 million tons in 1962.

American fishermen have access to many species of fish and shellfish, but their operations have been highly selective.

For food fish, they go for fish that have high market value or wide consumer acceptance. Salmon, shrimp, tuna, oysters, crabs, northern lobster, flounders, clams, scallops, haddock, and Pacific halibut (in order of decreasing value) in 1961 accounted for 73 percent of the total value of the United States catch, but only 43.5 percent of the quantity (live weight) caught.

For industrial use, fishermen have concentrated on species available in enormous quantities in inshore and nearby coastal waters. The principal industrial fish, the menhaden, accounted for 35.8 percent of the total amount of the catch but returned only 7 percent of the total value.

The United States fisheries are predominantly marine and conducted in or near coastal and inshore waters. About 66 thousand tons—2.3 percent of total landings in 1961—came from the fresh waters of the Great Lakes and the Mississippi Basin. Marine landings were nearly 2.9 million metric tons. Of that amount, about 216 thousand tons were taken on the high seas off foreign coasts.

United States fishermen from California fish for tuna, mainly yellowfin tuna and skipjack, off the western coasts of Central America and South America as far as northern Chile.

Part of the shrimp catch (about 20 percent in 1961) was taken off the eastern coast of Mexico, principally from the Campeche Banks off Yucatan. The third distant-water fishery of any significance has been for the bottomfishes off the eastern and the western coasts of Canada. The Atlantic species have been principally ocean perch and haddock, the Pacific species, cod and flounders.

The United States is a much larger consumer of fishery products than its production indicates. Nevertheless, per capita consumption has changed little since 1930. It has been at or near the 10.5 pounds (edible weight) recorded for 1962, even though there has been a declining trend in landings for direct food use.

The total consumption has remained steady because an increasing part of the United States supply has been provided by imports. About 23.4 percent of the United States supply of edible fishery products was of foreign origin in 1950; this share rose to 45.1 percent in 1962.

Imports of industrial fishery products—mainly fishmeal, fish solubles, and sperm oil—have followed a similar trend. About 28.6 percent of our supply in 1950 and 48.6 percent in 1962 were of foreign origin.

United States customs duties on fishery products were established under the Tariff Act of 1930. On practically all fishery products, however, duties have since been reduced by 50 percent or more under the authority of the Trade Agreements Act (enacted in 1934 and since extended), through reciprocal tariff reductions negotiated bilaterally, and through the General Agreement on Tariffs and Trade.

United States duties collected in 1936 on imported fishery products amounted to 15.6 percent of the value of all fishery imports, free and dutiable. The average ad valorem equivalent since has followed a downward trend to 4.3 percent in 1961.

Certain products, including frozen tuna, shrimp, and lobster, enter the United States free of duty. The effective trade agreement rate for imports of whole fish is generally one-half cent a pound; fillets are generally about 1.5 to 2.5 cents a pound. On canned fish products, duties generally range from about 6 to 35 percent ad valorem. Tariff quotas are applied on groundfish fillets and canned tuna in brine. Imports of groundfish fillets up to 28.6 million pounds in 1962 were subject to a duty of 1.88 cents a pound; imports in excess (without limit) were dutiable at 2.5 cents a pound. Canned tuna in brine in 1962 was subject to a duty of 12.5 percent up to a quantity of 59 million pounds, and imports larger than that were subject to a duty of 25 percent.

Competition from imported fishery products at times has seriously affected segments of the American fishing industry. United States markets have been unable to absorb sudden large influxes of imports. Prices have dropped at the ex-vessel level, inventories have built up, and United States catches have declined.

Examples are the New England groundfish industry, the tuna fisheries of California, the shrimp fisheries of the gulf and South Atlantic coasts, and the fishmeal and oil industry. The groundfish industry is still strongly affected by increasing imports. Conditions in the other industries have stabilized somewhat because domestic markets have enlarged sufficiently to absorb increased imports, fishermen have introduced more efficient methods of operation, or our catches have declined and been replaced by imports.

The United States had a relatively large, efficient fishing fleet after the war. Subsequently the industry was adversely affected by competition of imports and a cost-price squeeze. Repairs and replacements in the fishing fleet have been below the minimum necessary to maintain it at efficient operating capability. United States fishermen are unable to take advantage of lower construction costs for fishing vessels abroad, since the law requires that vessels operating in the United States fisheries must be constructed domestically. Important parts of the fleet have deteriorated since 1950; the fleets of other countries have expanded and have been modernized.

The United States fishing fleet consisted of about 77,600 units in 1961. Most, about 60,200, were motorboats of less than 5 net tons and about 5,400 were nonmotorized. The bulk of the United States catch was taken by nearly 12 thousand vessels of 5 net tons and over; the total gross tonnage of these vessels was 400,935, and their average tonnage was 33.5, a low figure by comparison with similar vessel categories (5 tons or more) of other leading fishing nations. Only four American fishing vessels were over 500 gross tons in 1961. The largest was slightly over 700 tons.

The age of the United States fleet also does not compare favorably with that of other fleets. About one-half of the United States vessels were built before 1946. The New England otter trawl fleet exemplifies effects of foreign competition. Few New England otter trawlers have been built in recent years. The oldest of the large trawlers operating in 1961 was built in 1928, and one-half of them were built before 1940. No large trawler was built between 1953 and 1962.

The United States fishing industry does not receive governmental subsidies comparable to those provided for other segments of the economy or to those provided by many countries to their fishing fleets.

A Fisheries Loan Fund has been in operation since 1956. This revolving fund, with a capital in 1964 of 13 million dollars, can only be used for financing or refinancing operations, maintenance, replacement, repair, and equipment of fishing gear and vessels. The construction of new vessels is not authorized unless they are replacements. Interest is 5 percent for a maximum period of 10 years.

The Fishing Vessel Mortgage Insurance Program, introduced in 1961, provides Government insurance for privately financed mortgages. Little use has been made of the program because many banks are unwilling to make loans at 6 percent, the maximum interest rate allowable; are unfamiliar with admiralty law; and have other outlets for their funds. The high cost of vessel construction in the United States, compared with foreign costs, also has impeded the program.

Some assistance was given (beginning in 1961) to vessels that had been determined to be injured by imports. A subsidy was granted to compensate partly for difference in building costs in the United States. The authority expired in June 1963, and less than 1 million dollars was involved in grants under the program.

BECAUSE MUCH of the world's fishing is done on the high seas outside territorial waters, international complications arise as to resource conservation and management, territorial and fishery limits, and competition.

The United States is party to nine international fishery conventions. All of them were in force in 1964, except the Shrimp Convention between the United States and Cuba. The conventions have been effective in rehabilitating fish stocks that have been depleted through overfishing and in taking action to prevent depletion.

In the northwestern part of the Atlantic, the United States and 12 other countries are parties to the International Convention for the Northwest Atlantic Fisheries that entered into force July 3, 1950.

A commission has been established to deal with problems of protecting the fishery resources of the Grand Banks and the Continental Shelf of the Northwest Atlantic. The commission has regulatory powers. Cooperative investigations are conducted by the member countries, principally with regard to reduced abundance and possible depletion of species.

The commission is proving effective in programing research and collecting and exchanging information.

Research on cod and haddock stocks have indicated that their maximum sustained yield can be attained by regulating the mesh size of the trawls used by fishing vessels. Mesh regulations have been adopted for the area covered by the convention, and evidence has accumulated to show that they are effective in producing increased yields of haddock and cod.

In the Pacific, the United States is party to five international conventions—the Interim Convention on Conservation of North Pacific Fur Seals, the International North Pacific Fisheries Convention, the International Pacific Halibut Convention, the International Pacific Salmon Convention, and the Inter-American Tropical Tuna Convention. All have specific conservation objectives and responsibilities for managing resources.

During the 19th century, pelagic (or high-seas) sealing had decimated the main herds that breed in the summer on the Pribilof Islands and then migrate south along the Pacific coast of North America; a part of the herd also moves into the western Pacific to waters off Japan.

A fur seal convention was signed in 1911 by the United States, Great Britain (for Canada), Japan, and Russia. It was terminated in 1941. An Interim Convention on Conservation of North Pacific Fur Seals was signed by the United States, Canada, Japan, and the Soviet Union and entered into force in October 1957. Representatives of those governments in 1963 signed a protocol that would extend the convention with some modification for 6 years. The protocol must be ratified by each of the signatory governments before it becomes effective. The United States Senate ratified the protocol on January 30, 1964.

The Pribilof herds of fur seals have increased since 1911 from an estimated low of 200 thousand animals to about 1.5 million. As a result of the increase

in fur seal herds, the annual harvest has been about 60 thousand to 80 thousand animals.

Japan, Canada, and the United States are parties to the International Convention for the High Seas Fisheries of the North Pacific Ocean, which came into force in June 1953.

That convention established the International North Pacific Fisheries Commission to deal with the conservation of fish stocks in the North Pacific and adjacent seas. The principal species dealt with have been salmon, halibut, and herring.

The convention established a new principle, known as abstention, which provided that member countries abstain from fishing species where it can be shown that one or more of the other countries are fully utilizing such stocks and have them under study and under scientific management. Under this abstention principle, the Japanese agreed not to fish North American halibut and herring stocks, and salmon stocks east of a provisional line established at 175° W. longitude. Certain stocks of herring were removed from the abstention list in 1959.

Difficulties have been encountered with salmon. The provisional abstention line was established at 175° W. longitude until research by the contracting parties could determine more firmly the line of separation between salmon stocks of North American and Asiatic origin. Investigation since has indicated that salmon of North American origin spend a part of their life cycle in waters west of the abstention line, and have been taken by Japanese fishermen. Efforts by the United States to move the abstention line farther west have failed.

In May 1963, Bering Sea halibut was removed from the abstention list on the basis that the United States and Canada were not fully utilizing this species in that area. Halibut in eastern Pacific waters south of the Aleutian Islands remained on the list.

The original North Pacific Convention was to continue in force for 10 years and thereafter, until one year from the date on which a contracting party gives notice of intention to terminate, whereupon the convention would be terminated for all parties. No such notice has been given. In early 1963, however, Japan notified the other parties of its desire to revise the convention, principally to eliminate the abstention principle. Meetings were held in Washington and Tokyo in 1963, but agreement was not reached, and a new meeting of the contracting parties was set for 1964.

The United States tuna fisheries in the eastern Pacific began early in the 20th century and grew rapidly. Among the tunas taken are yellowfin tuna and skipjack, which are caught off the coasts of Latin America as far south as northern Chile. Persons concerned with these fisheries foresaw the need for eventual regulation because of the intensity of fishing. A Convention for the Establishment of an Inter-American Tropical Tuna Commission entered into force in March 1950 between the United States and Costa Rica. Since then, Panama, Ecuador, and Mexico have adhered to it. Colombia has taken steps for similar action.

The tuna commission has authority to gather information useful in determining and maintaining maximum sustained catches of yellowfin tuna and skipjack. It has undertaken investigations for that purpose and has recommended that regulations be instituted to limit the catch of yellowfin tuna. The United States Congress adopted legislation authorizing the Secretary of the Interior to promulgate regulations to carry out the commission's recommendations. The legislation, however, requires that regulations cannot be applied to United States fishermen before a date agreed upon for the application of regulations to all fishermen who harvest the resource. The commission considers that no need exists at present for regulating skipjack fishing.

The International Pacific Halibut Convention between Canada and the United States entered into force in 1924 and was modified in 1931, 1937, and 1953. Soon after the end of the 19th century, the catch of Pacific halibut dropped to a low level and remained so until the thirties because of excessive fishing. Since then, through the efforts of the commission established to study and to maintain the maximum sustained yield of halibut by proper management, the catch has risen and has been restored to about 70 million pounds annually. The commission is now faced with problems brought about by extension of Japanese and Soviet Union fishing operations into the eastern Bering Sea and the Gulf of Alaska.

The International Pacific Salmon Convention between Canada and the United States entered into force in 1937. A commission was established to determine ways of restoring the runs of Fraser River sockeye salmon. The original convention was amended in 1957 to include pink salmon. This convention has been effective in restoring the annual run of sockeye salmon from fewer than 2 million fish to more than 15 million—almost the same as in earlier days.

The Convention on Great Lakes Fisheries between the United States and Canada became effective in 1955. The Great Lakes Fishery Commission was established in 1956. It has dealt with the decline of some of the Great Lakes fisheries and the serious damage to some of them by the sea lamprey.

Scientists of the two countries have developed the electric barrier that prevents the adult lamprey from ascending spawning streams tributary to the Great Lakes. A more successful effort to control the lamprey involves the use of poisons to kill the larvae in the tributary streams.

The commission also has the duties of developing research programs and making recommendations for regulations to be enforced by the participating countries. The commission does not have regulatory powers; they are retained by the signatories.

The only worldwide fishery treaty to which the United States is a party is the International Convention for the Regulation of Whaling of 1948.

It provides for a commission that recommends research programs, reviews scientific findings, sets whaling seasons, fixes whaling areas, and limits the number of whales that can be killed. Seventeen countries were party to the convention in 1964.

Annual meetings of the International Whaling Commission are held primarily to establish quotas for each whaling season. The efforts of the commission have been unsuccessful in preventing depletion of the Antarctic whaling stocks, principally because of the conflicting economic interests of certain member countries and the difficulty of bringing the quotas down to limits that will permit the stocks of whales to recover to their maximum sustainable yields.

AID PROGRAMS in fisheries have been a part of United States economic assistance to developing countries. Fishery advisers on missions have helped plan and execute programs for the development of the fishery resources in Liberia, Peru, Indonesia, Pakistan, Korea, India, and other countries. Technicians have assisted in training citizens of other countries in fishery skills. Persons from nearly every developing country have been trained in fishery biology, fish culture, and fishery technology at United States universities and Government agencies.

Resource surveys have also been a part of American aid programs. An example is the Gulf of Guinea Trawling Survey, conducted under the Commission for Technical Cooperation South of the Sahara (CCTA). Its funds—about 600 thousand dollars—were supplied largely by the Agency for International Development.

The United States aid program also has included development loans to foreign fishing industries. A number of loans have been made for the purchase of fishing vessels and shore equipment, such as processing machinery. Regardless of the method of financing, a criterion for extending loans has been that the end products derived from the aid program should not compete with American fishery products.

The United States is also a strong supporter of multilateral development programs in fisheries. The United Nations and its specialized agencies have had considerable influence on the growth of fishing industries, especially in the developing regions. The chief organization in this respect—the Fisheries Division of the Food and Agriculture Organization—has been a focal point in assisting countries in assessing and developing their marine and fresh-water fisheries.

The Fisheries Division has given high priority to a program for the development and utilization of new fishery products, especially fish protein concentrates. Another program supplies technical information to member governments on promoting optimum utilization of the aquatic resources.

The Food and Agriculture Organization has sponsored and conducted international meetings on the biology of the sardines and tunas, fish in nutrition, fishmeal, the economic effects of fishery regulations, fishing gear, and fishing boats. These meetings have brought together leading experts, and their recommendations have guided the Fisheries Division in planning its activities. Meetings have been planned on such subjects as fisheries oceanography, fish processing technology and marketing, fresh-water fish culture, business decisions in fishery industries, and fishery administration.

The Fisheries Division is the executing agency for United Nations Special Fund fishery projects in Ecuador, Peru, Nigeria, India, Chile, and the Caribbean. Several other countries have submitted requests for similar projects. The fund projects are programed for 4 or 5 years. The aim is to determine whether investment possibilities exist in the fishing industry of a developing country.

Short-term projects—mostly in product development, gear development, and training—have been conducted by the Food and Agriculture Organization with the support of the Expanded Program of Technical Assistance of the United Nations.

Among such projects are a survey and recommendations for the development of the inland fisheries in Guatemala; the implementation of recommendations of previous surveys of the development potentials in the inland fisheries of El Salvador; a survey of the crawfish resources of Eastern Aden Protectorate; a survey to determine methods of building fishing boats on Lake Chad; an assessment of the potential for fishery development in Lake Tanganyika; and the holding in Quezon City, the Philippines, of a regional training center on the technology of processing fish.

Among the councils or commissions established by the Food and Agriculture Organization are five regional bodies—the Indo-Pacific Fisheries Council, General Fisheries Council for the Mediterranean, Regional Fisheries Commission for Western Africa, European Inland Fisheries Advisory Commission, and Southwest Atlantic Fisheries Advisory Commission. The Food and Agriculture Organization provides administrative facilities for those bodies, but they draw their membership from the countries of a specific area. The councils and commissions have been concerned primarily with national and regional development programs in fisheries. Scientific information is exchanged on aquatic resources. The United States is a treaty member of the Indo-Pacific Fisheries Council and has observer status in the other organizations.

Soon after the Organization for Economic Cooperation and Development came into force in September 1961, with the United States as a full member, a fisheries committee was established to consider fishery programs, exchange information, and sponsor consultation on the fishery problems.

Efforts have been made to standardize sanitary regulations, quality standards, statistical coverage, and the like and to remove excessive governmental assistance, trade restrictions, and other obstacles to the marketing of fish.

Another type of international organization is devoted to the exchange of biological and other scientific information and to the coordination of research. One such is the International Council for the Exploration of the Sea. It began in 1902. The United States is not a member because its fisheries are not conducted in the area it covers.

RESEARCH on oceanic food resources and their relation to sea currents, the chemical and physical characteristics of sea water, and meteorological conditions generally has not progressed so rapidly as some other fields.

The United States has taken a leading part in cooperative efforts to enlarge our knowledge of the living resources of the sea. Comprehensive, worldwide research programs of sea exploration are being conducted by many nations under the guidance of the Intergovernmental Oceanographic Commission of United Nations Educational, Scientific, and Cultural Organization and with support and collaboration of the Food and Agriculture Organization. The commission, established in 1960, has sponsored programs such as the International Indian Ocean Expedition and the International Cooperative Investigations of the Tropical Atlantic.

Of vital concern to all fishing nations are the subjects of territorial seas and of fishery limits, or the right of any government to control the sea and its resources within specified boundaries off its coasts.

The United States was a participant at the First Law of the Sea Conference, sponsored by the United Nations in Geneva in 1958, and also at the Second Law of the Sea Conference in Geneva in 1960.

Four conventions dealing with the international laws of the sea were drawn up at the conferences: Convention on the Territorial Sea and Contiguous Zone; Convention on High Seas; Convention on Fishing and Conservation of the Living Resources of the High Seas; and Convention on the Continental Shelf.

The conventions require ratification by 22 nations in order to become binding in full force upon the contracting parties. The United States has ratified all four conventions. The Conventions on the Continental Shelf and Territorial Sea and Contiguous Zone have been ratified by 21 nations and require one more ratification. The Convention on High Seas entered into force in September 1962.

Agreement was not reached at either conference on fishery limits and the breadth of the territorial seas. These questions remain controversial; various countries claim territorial seas and fishery limits ranging from 3 to 200 miles. The United States officially recognizes a 3-mile limit for territorial seas and fishery jurisdiction. Many countries, however, have abandoned the 3-mile limit. Iceland, for example, claims a 12-mile fishery limit. Norway claims a 4-mile territorial sea and a 12-mile fishery limit. The Soviet Union claims 12 miles for both territorial waters and fisheries. Canada in May 1964 extended its fishery limit from 3 to 12 miles. Chile, Ecuador, and Peru claim a fishery limit of 200 miles.

SIDNEY SHAPIRO *has had 25 years' experience in fisheries, mainly in the international field. In 1957 he was appointed Chief, Branch of Foreign Fisheries, Bureau of Commercial Fisheries, the Department of the Interior. He has served on United States delegations to international fishery meetings and to conferences of the Food and Agriculture Organization. He was a marine biologist with the Bureau's Hawaiian staff and the Fisheries Division of the Occupation Forces in Japan. He is a graduate of Cornell University, Columbia University, and the University of Michigan.*

Sugar and Other Sweeteners

by JOHN C. SCHOLL and
LESLIE C. HURT

SUGAR, which we get from sugarcane and sugarbeets, is a major carbohydrate food.

Sugarcane is native to New Guinea and was found there sometime before 8000 B.C. It later spread to India, China, and other areas.

Columbus introduced sugarcane into Santo Domingo (Dominican Republic) on his second voyage in 1494. It spread from there to Cuba and to other West Indian, Central American, and South American areas. The production of sugar from cane became a major industry by 1600 in tropical America.

A German chemist, Andreas Marggraf, proved in 1747 that the sugar in beets and the sugar in cane are identical. A half century later, efforts were made to capitalize on the discovery. The King of Prussia became interested in developing an industry to obtain sugar from beets and financed the first beet sugar factory in 1802.

A few years later Napoleon also saw possibilities in sugarbeets. Beet sugar made at a small factory at Passy provided energy for his armies at a time when a naval blockade had cut off French supplies of cane sugar. He decreed that 79 thousand acres be planted to beets and that six experimental stations be established to help farmers and landowners. The beet used then was the Silesian beetroot, from which modern strains of sugarbeets have developed.

Many small beet sugar factories were built in France, but after Waterloo, in 1815, prices collapsed as large volumes of cane sugar came in from the Indies. A year later only one sugar mill remained in operation. Laws aimed at equalizing competition with the Indies brought a recovery in France.

THE FIRST ATTEMPT to establish sugarbeets in the United States was made by James Ronaldson of Philadelphia in 1830. He was instrumental in establishing the Beet Sugar Society of Philadelphia. Sugarbeets were first grown in the United States in 1838 at Northampton, Mass., and White Pigeon, Mich. Neither venture was successful, although the Massachusetts factory operated until 1841. Fifteen beet sugar factories built between 1838 and 1879 in Maine, Massachusetts, Delaware, Michigan, Illinois, Wisconsin, Utah, and California failed, mostly because of a lack of technical knowledge.

The first successful operation in the United States is credited to E. H. Dyer, whose plant, built in 1870 at Alvarado, Calif., was well established by 1879. The industry then spread to other States. By the turn of the century 30 factories were operating in 11 States. Some 60 factories were operating in the United States in 1963.

SUGARCANE, a tropical plant, is a perennial grass of the genus Saccharum. The commonest species is Saccharum officinarum (the noble cane). The cane stalk grows from the plant cane, or ratoon, each year. New plantings must be made every 2 or 3 years in Louisiana, 5 to 8 years in Cuba, and slightly less often in a few other parts of the world.

Cane customarily is harvested once a year, except newly planted cane and cane in irrigated areas, such as Hawaii, where it is harvested at intervals of about 18 months. Successive plantings are arranged so that only a part of the total crop is planted each year. Planting is usually done by setting out a section of cane stalk, from which a new plant sprouts.

Sugarcane for the production of sirup was first successfully grown in the United States by Jesuits about 1751. Some years later sugar was produced from cane in Louisiana. The plantation system became highly developed around New Orleans. The Spanish-American War dealt sugar a setback in Cuba, and a few years later the mosaic disease seriously affected the industry in Louisiana. Men at experiment stations found ways to control mosaic, and the industry was revived.

Sugarcane needs well-prepared and well-drained soils. The land should be flat, broken to a depth of 6 to 8 inches, and disked into rows 4 to 5 feet apart. Planting usually is done in the United States in late summer and early fall. Fall-planted cane should be covered with 7 to 9 inches of soil to protect it from cold.

In the spring the soil is removed to within 2 to 3 inches of the seedcane. Several shallow cultivations are needed throughout the season to control weeds and provide good growing conditions. Fertilizer should be applied when the cane is 8 to 12 inches high, followed by shallow cultivation. Flame cultivation often is used to destroy young weeds. Chemical weedkillers have been fairly successful.

Sugarcane is harvested in Louisiana as late in the season as feasible to allow the maximum accumulation of sucrose.

In hand harvesting, still practiced in some countries, leaves are stripped, the tops are removed, and the stalks are cut at ground level. Cutting is done with a cane knife or machete. The stalks are cut close to the ground, because the juice from the lower internodes contains more sugar than the middle and top. Cane is milled soon after harvesting.

In Hawaii, Louisiana, and Australia, mechanical harvesters are used widely. Machines for use in many other countries have been developed.

SUGARBEETS are produced in temperate climates. Europe, the Soviet Union, and the United States are the major producers.

Sugarbeets grow on a wide variety of soils at elevations from below sea level up to 7 thousand feet. Beets are relatively tolerant of alkali soils. They improve soil conditions for following crops as their roots extend 6 to 7 feet in the ground. Crop rotations that include beets are beneficial to the soil. Byproducts—tops, pulp, and molasses—are fed to cattle and sheep.

Sugarbeets are cultivated between the plants and between the row. The sugarbeet crop is planted each year.

Thinning of young plants used to be laborious, for many seedlings grow from one seed, but a new type of seed, the monogerm, produces a single plant and saves work of thinning.

The harvesting of sugarbeets in the major producing regions is done mostly by machines. The old way was to loosen the beets with a tractor-drawn beet lifter, pull them by hand, slice off the crown and leaves, and pile them for scooping into a wagon or truck. Machines now handle all steps in one operation. Harvest in most sections lasts about 3 months.

THE FIRST STEP IN MAKING cane sugar is to extract juice by crushing cane between a series of rollers. The juice is strained to remove solid pieces. Clarification, the next process, is the removal of nonsucrose impurities mainly by heat and lime. Most of the juice is then evaporated. The bagasse, or crushed cane waste, usually is used for fuel to operate the mill.

Crystallization occurs when enough water is evaporated from the juice to force the sugar out of solution. The sugary sirup or molasses is then placed in centrifugal machines, where the crystals are separated by centrifugal force. Sugar produced in this way is known as centrifugal sugar.

The centrifugal machine is a perforated drum, which revolves at high velocity on a vertical axle. The drum,

or basket, revolves within an iron casing, which catches the molasses that is spun off. The unwashed sugar remaining in the basket is known as raw sugar. Standard raw sugar is 96 percent sucrose. Most sugar for world trade contains 97 percent or more of sucrose. International trade in sugar generally is in this form, because most importing countries prefer to use their own refineries for refining sugar.

Refining removes practically all the remaining impurities in the raw sugar in the following general steps: Removing the film of molasses from the raw sugar crystals; a repetition of the clarification process that is carried on in making raw sugar; passing sugar liquor through bone char or other types of charcoal to remove color and other impurities; crystallization, to form crystals of sucrose in the juice; separation of sugar crystals from the mother liquor by means of centrifugal machines; removal of remaining moisture by heat.

PROCESSING SUGARBEETS into sugar is somewhat different. The beets are washed at the factory and cut with revolving knives into thin strips, which are known as cossettes, or chips. The cossettes are soaked in hot water in a continuous diffusion process. The products of this process are raw juice and beet pulp.

The raw juice contains numerous nonsugar substances, some of which are precipitated or coagulated in the next stage, clarification, and later removed by filtration. Carbon dioxide gas and lime are used in the precipitation stage. The juice is passed through filter presses, and the lime is filtered out with the coagulated nonsugar substances. At this stage the thin juice is run through evaporators to remove most of the water.

Crystallization is then accomplished by boiling the thick juice in vacuum pans. Sugar crystals are formed by seeding the liquid with a small amount of pulverized sugar. The crystals, when of proper size, are separated from the sirup in a high-speed centrifugal machine. The product is refined sugar. The beet pulp from the first operation usually is dried or stored in wet form and fed to livestock.

DISEASES constantly threaten sugarcane. Some varieties resist disease.

The commoner virus diseases are mosaic, which is transmitted by aphids and is marked by streaks of light-green, chlorophyll-deficient tissue, and ratoon stunting disease, which may be transmitted by cutting knives.

Treatment of plant cane with hot air or hot water helps to control the ratoon stunting disease. Red-rot, a fungus disease, reduces germination; severe infection before harvest reduces the sugar content and lowers the yield.

A number of insect pests attack sugarcane. The most serious, particularly in young sugarcane, in the United States is the sugarcane borer. Others are the gray sugarcane mealybug, corn leaf aphid, sugarcane beetles, wireworms, and a cornstalk borer.

Several diseases are common in sugarbeets. Cercospora leaf spot is caused by a fungus and leads to loss of root weight and lowering of sugar content.

The use of disease-resistant varieties and crop rotations provide the most effective control of leaf spot.

Black root, sometimes called damping off, is especially severe in humid areas. Seed treatment checks the seedborne fungus and protects the young plant from the fungi in the soil. Crop rotation is also beneficial.

Yellows disease was first discovered in the United States in 1951. It is one of the worst, for it reduces yields and sugar content. Control measures used for the yellows disease are spraying to control vectors, destruction of sources of infection, selection of planting dates to avoid infection, and the use of resistant varieties.

Several species of insects may feed on the foliage or roots of sugarbeets, especially in the humid sections. Among them are armyworms, aphids, flea beetles, the webworms, grasshoppers, white grubs, wireworms, and the spinach leaf miner.

SUGAR is of great economic importance. It is a major item of diet in most countries of the world.

The Department of Agriculture prepares sugar production estimates for all producing countries. Sugar is being made somewhere over the world all through the year. In general, most sugarbeets are harvested in the fall and early winter and a large part of the cane in the winter and early spring (Northern Hemisphere seasons).

About 42 percent of the world's centrifugal sugar was produced from beets in 1963. The rest came from cane.

Production of centrifugal sugar reached a peak of 60.1 million short tons in 1960–1961. It meant a substantial additional buildup in the already large world stocks and encouraged many countries, notably in western Europe, to cut production.

Two successive smaller crops followed. Production in Cuba dropped from 7.5 million tons in 1960–1961 to 4 million in 1963–1964. Western Europe had two rather small crops following the bumper 1960–1961 outturn because of a reduction in acreage and, in 1962–1963, bad weather.

The decline in production brought a tightening of free world supplies in late 1962 and in 1963 and sharp increases in world prices. Most of the reduced Cuban crop was committed to the Sino-Soviet bloc.

THE GOVERNMENT of nearly every sugar-producing country controls to some degree the production, refining, and marketing of sugar.

Most producing countries generally require the payment of a minimum price to growers of sugarcane and sugarbeets, and importing countries commonly impose tariffs or other import controls to protect their producers.

Exporting countries often impose export taxes or other means of raising government revenue from the industry. Price pooling to distribute the impact of the different prices in different markets also is common.

Several importing countries have comprehensive trading systems involving preferential arrangements with sugar-exporting countries with which they have strong political ties.

World gross exports of sugar, after remaining fairly stable at 16 to 18 million short tons for a number of years, increased to about 21 million in 1961 and 1962. Many of the importing countries, including those in the European Economic Community, are trying to become more nearly self-sufficient in sugar.

The United States is by far the largest importer of sugar—about two-fifths of its total sugar consumption is imported. Consumption totaled about 9.7 million tons, raw value, in 1963.

About 95 percent of the United States imports of sugar were supplied by Cuba and the Philippines before 1960. Legislation since 1960 has increased to 25 the number of countries assigned quotas—that is, specific quantities for shipment to the United States. Legislation in 1962 established a global quota, representing the quota reserved for Cuba. In 1963 this amounted to about 1.7 million tons.

About two-thirds of the world's sugar exports move under special or preferential marketing arrangements of one kind or another.

Noteworthy is the Commonwealth Sugar Agreement, which represents a long-term undertaking of the United Kingdom to buy specified quantities of sugar from countries with which it has historical ties. Under this plan, the United Kingdom contracts to buy fixed quantities of sugar from supplying countries at prices that are negotiated annually.

Some other European countries have types of preferential arrangements with their former territories. A number of countries engage in long-term contracting arrangements. Most of the sugar shipped by Cuba to the Sino-Soviet bloc has moved under barter arrangements. Sugar moving under preferential arrangements tends to be insulated from other world supplies.

International sugar prices are highly volatile.

The world sugar trade moving under nonpreferential terms amounts to about 12 percent of the total world production and is sometimes referred to as the residual world sugar trade. This is the sugar with which the International Sugar Agreement has been most concerned.

World consumption of sugar was somewhat above production in 1962 and 1963. It had been increasing at the rate of about 2 million tons a year, but the rate of increase was slowed in some countries in 1962, 1963, and 1964 because of high prices.

Consumption is not affected very much by higher prices in industrialized countries. In some low-income countries, especially those that tend to consume less domestically and export more to increase foreign exchange earnings, however, higher prices reduce consumption.

Increases in consumption depend largely on the available supplies and prices. A key element in the future level of world consumption may be the extent to which the Sino-Soviet countries increase consumption.

The annual per capita consumption in the United States has remained constant at approximately 103 pounds (raw value) for a number of years. Approximately two-thirds of our total consumption is through industrial uses. The rest is used in households and institutions.

Sugar is the dominant sweetener in food industries in the United States, but they have been using increasingly larger quantities of corn sweeteners (sirup and dextrose) and noncaloric sweeteners (saccharin and sucaryl).

The amount of corn sirup, a glucose product manufactured from cornstarch, delivered to American food processors increased from 423 thousand tons (dry basis) in 1952 to 705 thousand tons in 1961. Deliveries of sugar to industrial food processors over the same period increased from 3.2 million tons to 4.6 million tons of refined sugar. While the tonnage figures for sugar are larger, the rate of increase for corn sirup exceeded that for sugar by a wide margin. The use of dextrose, another derivative of cornstarch, has also been increasing but at a slower rate.

The fastest increase in the use of corn sirup has been in the canning and dairy industries, where it is used to blend with sugar for certain products. Relative prices influence the extent to which other sweeteners are used in place of sugar. Also, blends of sweeteners enhance the quality sought in some confectionery products, principally hard candies and ice cream.

Saccharin and sucaryl add no calories to manufactured products. Often the market for such products is largely separate from that for products sweetened with sugar—that is, they are purchased mostly by persons, who for reasons of health cannot use products sweetened with sugar.

In other instances, notably soft drinks, noncaloric sweeteners appear to be competing directly with sugar. Trade sources indicate that the uses of noncaloric sweeteners in soft drinks increased from a few hundred cases in 1950 to about 25 million cases in 1961. They were used to sweeten about 1.6 percent of the total output of soft drinks in the United States in 1961.

HONEY competes with sugar in certain uses. It is made by honey bees that gather nectar from flowers and carry it to their hives. The bees store the honey in combs of hexagonal wax cells for their later food needs.

The nectar is a watery solution containing primarily levulose and dextrose, some sucrose, and small amounts of mineral salts, coloring matter, aromatic bodies, and other ingredients. Much of the water in the nectar is evaporated at the hive.

Honey bees belong to the order of insects called Hymenoptera. They are the only insects that gather nectar

in such a way as to make it available to man in commercial quantities. In beekeeping, people merely make it possible for the bees to store more honey than they need for themselves. The surplus is removed for human use.

The Egyptians and the East Indians were familiar with bee husbandry 4 thousand years ago. People probably brought honey bees to Europe and thence to the New World. Honey bees were first imported into the United States during the 17th century.

Honey production in 15 countries, which account for a major part of the world production, was estimated at 570 million pounds in 1962. The United States, West Germany, Argentina, Mexico, Australia, Canada, and France are leading producers. The United States exports and imports honey. Argentina and Mexico are large exporters. West Germany is the largest importer.

The number of colonies of bees in the United States was estimated at 5.5 million in 1963. Production of honey in 1963 was 299.0 million pounds, an average yield per colony of 54.0 pounds. The total farm value of the honey was about 50 million dollars.

American honey is sold as extracted honey or as some form of comb honey. Extracted honey is the liquid taken from the combs. Extracted honey for commercial sale normally is processed and blended to produce a uniform color, flavor, and density, which are prime attributes of quality or grade.

Grades for extracted and comb honey have been established by the Department of Agriculture. Grade A (or Fancy) is the top quality associated with types of extracted honey in consumer-size containers. Grade B (or Choice) is of a slightly lower quality. Most of the honey of commercial beekeepers, as well as that of many smaller producers, is sold to brokers or packers.

MOLASSES is a byproduct in the production of sugar from sugarcane and sugarbeets. The common name for the product from sugarcane is blackstrap molasses. Producers in the beet industry call their product beet molasses. Both are usually referred to as "industrial molasses." They are used principally in livestock feed and in the production of such industrial products as citric acid and yeast.

Before the Second World War, industrial molasses was used mainly in the production of ethyl alcohol. In recent years ethyl alcohol has been produced from petroleum gases at lower costs than from molasses. In some countries, however, molasses is used in the production of alcohol.

Hydrol, a byproduct of the corn wet milling industry, and citrus molasses, a byproduct of orange and grapefruit juice production, compete with other industrial molasses, particularly for livestock feed.

Mills processing sugarcane sometimes produce a type of molasses designated as edible molasses. Only a part of the sugar normally recoverable from the cane is used in producing sugar. The remainder is left in the molasses.

Edible molasses competes with cane sirup, sorghum sirup, and maple sirup. Some of it is blended with maple sirup and sold in that form. Cane and sorghum sirups are produced from the juice of the cane or sorghum; no sugar is extracted from the juice.

The production of cane and sorghum sirup in the United States has declined markedly. With improved economic conditions, people apparently prefer to purchase more of their sweetener in the form of sugar rather than sirup.

The United States is the world's largest importer of industrial molasses. The ratio of molasses to sugar production varies considerably among countries and from year to year. Weather conditions affect the sucrose content of both sugarcane and sugarbeets. Beets or cane with high sucrose content yield a lower ratio of molasses to sugar than when the sucrose content is low.

In some countries, particularly those with only a small production of sugar, molasses is discarded as waste material or used locally, as the expense of storing and transporting may exceed its value.

The output of molasses declined in 1963, and prices increased. Future production of molasses will depend primarily on the output of sugar.

Maple sugar probably was the first sweetener produced in North America. Early settlers found Indian tribes making such sugar. The Algonquin Indians called it "sinzibuckwud"—"drawn from the wood."

Maple sirup and sugar are produced in Canada and the United States from the sap drawn from maple trees, mainly the rock maple (*Acer saccharum*).

Production in early days was a fairly simple operation. An ax was used to gash the tree trunk and the sap caught in troughs hewed from logs. The liquid was then carried in wooden pails to central boiling points and reduced to sirup or sugar in kettles. Refinements and improvements have been made in those methods.

Late in the winter, operators bore holes in the trunks of trees and insert metal spouts for the sap to flow through. Buckets usually are hung on the spouts to gather the sap. The buckets are emptied into larger containers, which are taken to the sugarhouse, where the sap is boiled down to the desired consistency before being poured into cans or drums for marketing. Some of the larger producers now gather the sap by a system of plastic tubing with trunklines running directly to the sugarhouse.

The best time for tapping the trees is said to be during a period of cold, crisp nights when temperatures are near 20° F. and daytime thawing temperatures are in the 40's. A moderate snow cover is also considered beneficial during the tapping season.

The yield of sap varies with the size and age of the tree. Weather prevailing during the winter and early spring largely determines the length of the tapping season.

The sirup is made by simple evaporation of the sap. Maple sugar is produced by further cooking the sirup. About 8 pounds of maple sugar are obtained from a gallon of sirup, which weighs about 11 pounds.

Maple trees used for sugar grow best at altitudes of 600 feet and above. A stand of trees old enough to be tapped and grouped close enough together for economical collection of sap is a sugar bush. Often a bush is a one-family operation.

Most Canadian production is in the Province of Quebec. Canada in 1962 produced 3.5 million United States gallons of maple sirup and 781 thousand pounds of maple sugar. Canada exports much of its maple products to the United States.

The United States production of maple sirup has steadily declined since 1940. The output of maple sugar has declined to such a low level that the Department of Agriculture no longer issues production estimates. The estimated production of maple sirup, including the sirup equivalent of sugar, in the United States in 1962 was 1.45 million gallons, compared with 1.52 million gallons in 1961.

Despite the general decline in production, the maple sugar industry is still a vital part of the economy of hundreds of communities from Maine westward into Minnesota and south to Indiana and West Virginia. The maple season comes when most other farm activities are slowest. The total farm value of the maple sirup produced in the United States amounted to 6.8 million and 7.3 million dollars in 1962 and 1961.

JOHN C. SCHOLL *was named Director of the Sugar and Tropical Products Division, Foreign Agricultural Service, in 1962, a short time after receiving the Department's 30-year Length of Service award.*

LESLIE C. HURT *began his government career with the Federal Crop Insurance Corporation of the Department of Agriculture in 1941. He joined the Foreign Agricultural Service in 1956.*

What's Behind the Coffee Break

by LESLIE C. HURT and
JOHN C. SCHOLL

COFFEE is the seed of cultivated varieties of *Coffea arabica*, *C. liberica*, and *C. robusta*. Green, raw, unroasted coffee is the bean freed from all but a small portion of its hard coating. Roasted coffee is cleaned green coffee that roasting has made brown and aromatic.

Coffee has been used in turn as a food, a wine, a medicine, and a beverage. Its use as a beverage dates from the 13th century. The coffee plant is a native of Abyssinia and probably of Arabia. It grows in the Tropics.

Toward the end of the 9th century, an Arabian physician wrote about the properties and uses of coffee. The legendary discovery of coffee is attributed to an Arabian goatherd named Kaldi 15 centuries ago. Kaldi, it is said, found his animals dancing after eating fruits and tips of certain bushes. He tasted them and was so stimulated that he cavorted with his goats in the Arabian hills. A monk from the sanctuarial spaces below, where later grew up the city of Mecca, came by and talked with the herdboy. The monk tried the fruit, seeds and all, and found them invigorating. The use of coffee became a fad in Mecca.

Some persons believe coffee was cultivated first in Yemen about A.D. 575 and shortly thereafter was grown in Abyssinia and Arabia.

Coffee reached Europe about 1500

and was brought to Italy by Venetian traders in 1615. Invading Turks carried it into Vienna. Holland had already begun a worldwide trade in coffee from their colonies in Java. The Dutch presented a seedling from one of their Java trees to Louis XIV in 1714, and he had it planted under glass in the Jardin des Plantes in Paris. Eight years later a seedling from this tree was carried by Captain Gabriel de Clieux to the French West Indian island of Martinique. This was the source of all coffee plants in the New World, as seedlings were carried throughout the West Indies and the Guiana colonies.

Although jealously guarded in the Guianas, coffee found its way to Brazil in 1728. The story is that Juan de Palheta, a Brazilian emissary, obtained an illicit coffee seedling in a bouquet given him by the wife of the Governor of French Guiana.

COFFEEHOUSES were introduced to colonial America in the 1680's. Around 1700 coffee and tea were for only the well-to-do. Tea gained in popularity faster than coffee, but tea was boycotted after the Stamp Act of 1765 and the tea tax of 1767. After the Boston Tea Party in 1773, coffee became more popular.

By 1882 the United States was importing 3 million bags of coffee a year, and Europe was importing 7 million bags. Imports in the United States had gone up to 13.8 million bags by 1939, compared with 11.5 million in Europe. After the Second World War, the United States became the largest consumer of coffee and has imported more than half of the coffee in world trade.

Arabica and Robusta are the main species. Arabica accounts for about 80 percent of the world's coffee. Most of the remainder is Robusta. Almost all coffee in Latin America is Arabica.

Four-fifths of the coffee grown in Africa is Robusta. Some of each is produced in Asia and Oceania.

Arabica is of two general kinds— "Brazils" and "milds." It is high in acidity and has considerable body. Robusta is more flat. Most coffee the American housewife buys is a blend of two or more coffees.

The coffee plant is an evergreen shrub. It grows 14 to 20 feet high if it is not pruned. Pruning increases the yields. Coffee often is grown under shade but does not have to be. Brazil and Kenya grow practically all of their coffee without shade. Higher yields and more intensive cultivation often characterize the nonshade, or sun grown, coffee. Robusta often is grown in the lowlands, but altitudes of 2 thousand up to 6 thousand feet are better for Arabica.

The Liberica and Excelsa (often classified with Liberica) coffees also are of economic importance. They are exported from western Africa to use as a filler. The Liberian has large beans, grows up to 40 feet tall, and flourishes in the hotter, lower elevations in tropical regions. *Coffea excelsa* grows into a large tree, but the beans are about the size of the Arabica coffee. The Excelsa was discovered near Lake Chad. The Liberian is indigenous to a region near Monrovia, Liberia. The liquoring qualities of the two normally are not high, and they account for a small part of world trade.

COFFEE is grown in tropical areas on a wide range of soils. It does well in friable topsoils over fairly heavy subsoil. Arabica grows very well on rather recent volcanic deposits. Coffee requires soils that have good aeration, some acidity, a good supply of potassium, and humus.

The lateritic soils of the Tropics often are planted to coffee, especially in Brazil. Such soils are rich in nitrogen and humus when first cultivated, but are poor in lime, potash, and phosphate. They therefore are soon exhausted if they are not fertilized. To provide some humus, the ground under the trees sometimes is kept covered with crop vegetation.

Weather has a bearing on the quality and quantity of production. Heavy rains during the normal flowering season have a particularly adverse effect, as they stimulate growth rather than flowering.

Arabica is produced generally in areas of a yearly rainfall of 75 inches. Robusta grows well where the average rainfall is even higher. Moisture requirements for coffee are about intermediate when compared with other tropical crops. The Arabica can withstand prolonged dry periods. More rainfall is needed generally in warm regions, where the soil is thin and lacking in humus and the shade covering is sparse.

The general practice in preparing new land for coffee is to fell and burn vegetation and let the ashes provide some potassium and phosphoric acid.

The trees begin bearing when they are 3 to 5 years old. One may see flowers and fruits in all stages of development, as there may be two or more flushes of blossoms in a year.

Cold winds and hot sunlight are injurious to coffee.

If cultural practices are good, the trees will bear for 20 or 30 years. Trees may yield one-half pound to 8 pounds each year. Two pounds of green coffee is considered a good yield.

COFFEE IS GROWN in various ways.

Seeds may be planted, or seedlings may be transplanted from nursery beds planted a year earlier. The trees are in rows about 8 to 15 feet apart on the square. The average is about 450 trees to the acre. Other trees, for shade, may be spaced 30 or 40 feet apart.

Plantations vary in size. In Cameroon, the holdings may have 50 to 100 trees. Native holdings on the slope of Kilimanjaro in Tanganyika may be three or four times that large. Family farms in Costa Rica and Colombia range from 5 acres to 30. Some plantations in Angola and Brazil cover several thousand acres.

White, fragrant flowers appear when the trees are about 3 years old. The fruit (commonly called cherries) ripens about 6 or 7 months after flowering. It is green, then yellow, and finally purplish-crimson.

Harvest begins in some countries in May; in others, as late as November, according to climate and altitude. In Brazil, the harvesting season is May to September; in Mexico and Venezuela, from November through March; in Guatemala, from October through April. In Uganda there are two crops; one ripens in March and the other in September. Ethiopia also harvests in two seasons—from October through March and from May through June.

Generally the fruit is picked by hand, but in some countries the cherries are allowed to ripen and fall to the ground.

A good picker can pick 200 to 250 pounds of cherries a day—about 40 or 50 pounds of green coffee.

COFFEE IS PREPARED FOR MARKET in two ways.

What we call the wet or washed method includes fermentation and pulping in water, drying in the sun or by artificial means, and cleaning by machine. The outlay for plant, power, and machinery is considerable. The berries are pumped into tanks of water. The green berries, sticks, and leaves float to the top and are skimmed off. Settling troughs catch stones and sand. The berries then go into a pulping machine, where the pulp or outer skin is removed, after which they become identified as beans.

The next step is to run the beans into fermentation tanks. This is the most important step, for it determines the final color and quality of the beans. The fermented beans are washed in washing tanks or by mechanical washers. Then the beans (still in the parchment or the hull stage) are spread out to dry for 4 to 8 days, or even longer, although machines can dry them in 24 to 30 hours.

The other, the dry method, requires little outlay for machinery or equipment. The berries are dried in the sun and then cleaned by hand or machines.

The final step in preparation for market is hulling, or peeling. Hulling, sometimes at the farm and sometimes at the port of shipment, is done by a machine that rubs the beans between a revolving inner cylinder and an outer covering of wire. After hulling, the coffee is cleaned and graded by a machine that drives off dust, shells, and foreign material. Machines then grade for size by sieves, or the coffee may be handpicked to remove undesirable beans.

COFFEE sometimes thrives in the semi-wild state and some is harvested from the wild, but normally it requires regular cultivation. It is susceptible to attack by insects and a number of diseases that are caused by fungi, viruses, and bacteria.

Coffee rust has been devastating in some regions. After Ceylon had been growing coffee for several hundred years, rust forced abandonment, and tea planters replaced coffee planters. When Ceylon was a big coffee producer, England was one of the best buyers and consumed about as much coffee as tea. With the shift to tea production in Ceylon, England shifted to tea drinking and now consumes more tea than coffee.

Another of the leaf diseases is known in Latin America as Ojo de gallo or gotera, and in the Orient and Africa as the American leaf spot. The disease defoliates the plant. It has been severe enough in regions of Brazil, Colombia, Costa Rica, Guatemala, and Mexico to cause abandonment of production. Brown eyespot, a common leaf disease, can attack the fruit, seedbeds, and nurseries. Serious attacks have occurred in Central America, Colombia, and Africa. Leaf deterioration may also be caused by weak spot, or chronic leafdrop.

COFFEE is subject to anthracnose, or infectious dieback, which causes a blackening of leaves, fruits, and stems. Antestia and thrips are dangerous in regions where temperatures are sometimes too high, no shade is provided, and rainfall is sporadic. They are fairly easy to control, but mealybugs and scales, although not so prevalent, are harder to get rid of. Borer beetles, the most feared of all pests, cause damage to coffee everywhere. Stem borers exist in every country, and there is no direct method of control. Good cultivation can be helpful in preventing damage. The Antestia bug is a major pest of Arabica coffee, but does not bother the Robusta.

THE VALUE of world exports of coffee amounts to about 2 billion dollars a year. It is a leader in world trade. For a time in the fifties it was second in value to petroleum and petroleum products of all commodities in international trade. Total world exports were at a level of slightly over 30 million bags (each 132.276 pounds) in 1950 and 49 million by 1963. Most of the coffee is exported as green coffee.

Eight countries in Latin America and Africa—Brazil, Colombia, Costa Rica, El Salvador, Guatemala, Haiti, Ethiopia, and the Ivory Coast—generally receive more than half of their total export earnings from coffee. Many countries depend heavily on exports of coffee to provide revenue for their governments.

The trade is big business; a drop of a cent a pound in export prices means a decline of about 65 million dollars a year in exchange earnings of the exporting countries in Africa, Asia, and Latin America.

Some that have relied heavily on coffee have been trying to move from a one-crop economy by diversification programs. Going out of coffee, a tree crop, and moving into other agricultural production often poses problems.

THE FRUIT of the coffee tree has uses other than to make the beverage. Coffee may be used in candy and the extracted caffeine may be used in soft drinks. Coffee pulp has been used as fertilizer and at times it has been used for cattle feed.

Research work is being continued to find additional uses for byproducts. Attempts have been made to produce synthetic coffee, but only about one-third of the 100 or more components that make the taste and aroma of coffee have been identified.

The world consumed about 62 million bags of coffee in 1963. On a per capita basis, the leading coffee drinkers are in the Scandinavian countries.

The United States is near the top. The per capita consumption of coffee on a green coffee basis in this country in 1962 amounted to almost 16 pounds—the equivalent of about 3 cups a day for each American over 10 years of age.

The coffee break came into its own in the United States in the forties.

It is one reason why Americans account for 40 percent of the world consumption of coffee.

Increases in coffee consumption have been noteworthy, particularly in western Europe. Consumption in Japan was negligible in 1952 but rose to 250 thousand bags in 1962. Italy, Canada, Western Germany, and the United Kingdom also are getting to like coffee more. Rising incomes and growing population were factors.

The producing countries generally have a fairly low per capita consumption. Most of them have been trying to encourage their people to use more of it.

Coffee prices fluctuate a lot. Santos 4's, a basic grade of Brazils, for instance, sold spot New York at 6.75 cents a pound in August 1940, 88 cents in April 1954, and 33 cents in April 1963. Prices of green coffee in early 1963 were at the lowest levels since 1949 but were increasing in late 1963. They reached a peak in 1954, when frost damaged the crop in Brazil. The high prices encouraged plantings; a few years later a surplus cut prices; the lower prices boosted consumption. But the larger volume of exports did not compensate for the decline in prices, and the world export value of coffee declined later.

SURPLUSES began building up following the high prices of 1954, and carryovers increased. By the end of the 1962–1963 crop year, they had reached a level of almost 75 million bags, the equivalent of about 15 months of usual world consumption. The bulk of the surplus stocks have been held in Brazil. Sizable stocks accumulated in Colombia, Angola, and the Ivory Coast.

Many consuming countries impose duties, internal taxes, and other marketing charges on coffee. Reducing them would raise consumption. In early 1964, the European Common Market countries lowered their common external tariff on coffee from the originally announced 16 percent to 9.6 percent ad valorem. Import of green coffee into the United States is on a duty-free basis.

Major exporting countries also impose export taxes, a major source of revenue for many of them. Such taxes mean higher prices to consumers in importing countries.

The United States imports slightly more than half of the coffee entering world trade. The European Economic Community accounts for about 20 percent of total world imports. Other western European countries account for 10 percent; eastern Europe and the Soviet Union, about 2 percent.

The United States in 1963 imported coffee from Brazil, 39 percent; Colombia, 17; Mexico and Central America, 14; other Latin American countries, 7; Africa and Asia, 23.

The European Economic Community has been taking more than half of its imports from Latin America and about one-third from Africa.

Under good conditions, coffee will keep well in storage. Storage is costly, however, and precautions must be taken against deterioration. The United States generally keeps about a 2 months' supply of green coffee in stock. Imports therefore are distributed fairly well throughout the year.

Latin America produces almost three-fourths of the world's coffee.

Brazil continues to be the largest producer, but Africa has had a threefold expansion since 1950. The leading African producer (in some years Angola and sometimes Ivory Coast) ranks third behind Brazil and Colombia. About 25 countries in Africa produce coffee, and earnings from coffee are of considerable importance to more than half of them.

The bulk of African production is Robusta, which is used extensively in the manufacture of soluble coffee. It may be used also as a blend in regular coffee, and then it may compete with Brazilian coffees. Preferential treatment sometimes is given to African producers in the form of guaranteed quantitative imports and subsidies.

About 10 percent of the world's coffee was used to prepare soluble coffee in 1963. The United States processes about 18 percent of its coffee into this form. European countries have been slower to accept the product, but a large part of consumption in the United Kingdom is soluble. On a green equivalent basis, more cups of coffee can be obtained from soluble than from roasted coffee. Many plants have been built in producing countries so as to increase exports as well as domestic consumption. The Soviet Union had one soluble-coffee plant in 1964, and Poland had two. Little soluble coffee was made before 1945.

Soluble coffee is made by a percolation process after blending, roasting, and grinding. After a fixed interval, the water is driven off by a special process. The grounds are removed; they may be burned to provide heat for the percolation. The remainder is the soluble coffee. Nothing is added to it. The weight of soluble coffee may be one-fourth the weight of regular coffee. Soluble coffee therefore is much less costly to ship. Other savings can be made in handling costs. Convenience in preparation is a reason for using soluble coffee, but some of the flavor may be lost in processing it.

From some coffees most of the caffeine has been removed. Caffeine, an alkaloidal substance, appears as long, white, silky needles when it is isolated in the pure form. Removal of the caffeine takes away a good deal of the stimulant. Arabica coffee often contains less than 1.5 percent of caffeine. The Robustas usually contain more than 2 percent. A cup of coffee may contain about 1.5 grains of caffeine; a cup of tea contains less than 1 grain.

The upward trend in coffee consumption has often lagged behind production. This difference was so acute that Brazil burned as locomotive fuel or otherwise destroyed 78 million bags between 1931 and 1944. By 1957 it had again become apparent that world surpluses would be mounting for the next several years. This led to a series of annual Producer Coffee Agreements and finally to the International Coffee Agreement, negotiated at the United Nations Negotiating Conference in 1962.

COFFEE in the cup, then, has a background of much social, political, and economic significance. Few agricultural commodities are so widely grown or universally consumed. The world value and renown of coffee assure that this pleasant drink will have an important place for years to come. The coffee break has become an institution, although few of us think of the intriguing steps from the picking of coffee berries from trees in faraway lands to the final product—the cups of coffee.

LESLIE C. HURT *holds degrees from Virginia Polytechnic Institute and Maryland University. He began his Government career with the Federal Crop Insurance Corporation in 1941. He joined Foreign Agricultural Service in 1956.*

JOHN C. SCHOLL *was named Director of the Sugar and Tropical Products Division, Foreign Agricultural Service, in 1962. His previous experience included an assignment as agricultural attaché in Central America and work with the Department's Crop and Livestock Reporting Service. He is a graduate of North Carolina State College.*

Tea the World Over

by WILLIAM C. BOWSER, JR., and
ARTHUR G. KEVORKIAN

TEA is considered the national drink in most of the major tea-producing countries of Asia and in many countries of the Middle East. The United Kingdom, the world's largest importer of tea, and the Commonwealth countries consume much tea. Tea is drunk in much of continental Europe and the United States, Latin America, and Africa.

Production is concentrated principally in Asia, where it is grown on more than 2 million acres. Africa, second in production, has less than one-tenth of the Asian acreage.

The two main types of tea are designated as black (or fermented) tea and green (or unfermented) tea. Only black tea is of major importance in world trade; India, Ceylon, and Pakistan supply most of it. The demand for green tea is mostly in the countries that produce it, such as Japan, mainland China, and Taiwan. Only a few countries, like Morocco and Afghanistan, import green tea in quantity.

For centuries tea was almost exclusively a Chinese commodity. China had the world's largest supply and trade. Tea was first introduced into Europe by the Dutch, but it did not become popular in Europe until late in the 18th century. Early in the 19th century an indigenous tea was discovered in the Assam region of India, and

production prospered in the British Empire and the Netherlands Indies.

By 1900, the British and the Dutch dominated exports from their expanding plantations.

Total world exports of tea have continued to increase and were valued at about 650 million dollars in 1963.

Thus it was among the top 10 most important agricultural commodities in international trade. Tea is vital to the economies of many developing countries in Asia and Africa, where it provides a livelihood for millions of people and is an important source of government revenue.

Compared with people of the United Kingdom, who average six or seven cups of tea a day, Americans seem rather indifferent consumers. Yet imports of the United States, the second largest importer, in 1963 reached a total of 126 million pounds, valued at 58.2 million dollars. The United States has been importing more tea over the years, but the gains have been less than the gain in population.

Our per capita consumption was highest in 1897 at 1.56 pounds. Increasing use of coffee and other beverages caused a steady decline, and consumption was 0.55 pound in 1945. Tea bags and iced tea have improved the competitive position of tea among beverages. Since 1956, annual per capita consumption in the United States has remained relatively stable at about 0.6 pound.

The Americans' consumption of tea might well be at a higher level were it not for the duty the English levied in 1767 on tea brought into the Colonies. The Boston Tea Party in 1773, similar occurrences throughout the Colonies, and the practice of substituting herbs and roots for tea in many households probably had a continuing effect on the tea-drinking habits of the people of this country in the years that followed.

TEA is the dried leaf of an evergreen shrub, *Camellia sinensis*. Its three primary chemical constituents are the caffeine, tannins, and essential oils. The caffeine content, about 3 percent, provides the stimulating effect of the drink. Tannin supplies the strength or body, and the essential oils the flavor and aroma. Other solid matter in the tea leaf are protein bodies, gummy matter, and sugars.

The origin of tea as a beverage is said to go back some 4 thousand years, but its true beginning is lost in time. One popular Chinese myth places the introduction of tea drinking in the region of Emperor Shen Nung about 2737 B.C. Leaves from a nearby plant fell into a steaming pot while water was boiling. The fragrance and aroma were caught by the Emperor, who, on sipping the "tea," relished its taste and stimulating effect. Early Chinese and Japanese monks and Buddhist priests valued the plant as a medicinal shrub, and Europeans drank tea for its "curative" properties.

The first authentic mention of tea appeared in a biography of a Chinese official who died in A.D. 273. Tea was first alluded to in Japanese literature in A.D. 593, and was first cultivated in that country in A.D. 805. The first handbook of tea, however, was by the Chinese about A.D. 780. The cultivation of tea and its use was spread throughout China and Japan by Buddhist priests in an effort to combat intemperance.

THE TEA PLANT grows naturally 15 to 20 feet high. In general appearance and form of leaf it resembles our crapemyrtle. White flowers, much like apple blossoms, cover the plants. The seeds, three to a fruit, are like hazelnuts in size and shape.

Propagation is usually by seeds. The seeds are placed in nursery beds in rows about 6 inches apart and remain there 9 to 12 months. Then the young plants are transplanted to the tea gardens or estates. The young plants usually are set about 3 to 6 feet apart. The average density is about 3 thousand plants to the acre.

In order to provide the maximum number of leaves he can reach easily, the tea planter keeps his bushes pruned to a height of 3 to 5 feet. He cuts the young plant back to within a few inches of the ground early in its growth. The result is a main stem and side branches similar to the clipped privet hedges in the United States.

The bushes are ready for plucking by the end of the third year, but they do not reach full bearing stage until about the 10th year.

Properly-cared-for bushes yield well for 25 to 50 years. During the season, a good bush will have a number of flushes, or new leaf growth, and yield up to a quarter pound of leaves.

The tea plant will grow in tropical and subtropical areas from sea level up to 6 thousand feet. In the more temperate zones, however, it must be kept to relatively low elevations to prevent killing by frosts.

Most of the world's commercially produced tea is grown within latitudes 42° North and 33° South. The tea production in India has been most successful in the Assam Valley region, where rainfall varies from moderate to high during the monsoons, the temperature is moderate, drying winds are at a minimum, and the humidity is high.

Soil types where tea is grown vary in regions and within countries. Alluvial, sedentary, volcanic, and other types of soils, which usually are deep, friable, well drained, and acid, are suitable for tea growing. The usual tropical red, friable clays normally constitute the preferable tea-growing area of the major producing countries.

THE QUALITY of tea varies at different seasons. The leaves are plucked throughout the year in southern India, Ceylon, Java, and Sumatra. Northern India teas, the China greens, and Japanese and Taiwan teas are seasonal in nature. In all producing areas, however, certain picking months and flushes produce the finest teas.

On the average, a tea plant produces a full set of leaves, or flush, every 40 days. Some planters, however, do not wait for a fully mature flush, and plucking may be done every 7 to 15 days during the season.

Harvesting in most countries is done mostly by women and children, who toss the leaves into baskets slung at their sides or hung on their backs. For the finest teas, only the small unopened bud and the first two leaves are taken. An experienced tea picker using both hands may pluck 30 to 60 pounds of leaves a day, depending on the fineness of the plucking. Ordinarily it takes about 4 pounds of leaves to make a pound of manufactured tea.

DISEASES AND PESTS inflict varying damage to the tea plant. The most devastating is blister blight, which has spread to all tea-growing regions of Asia. This pathological disorder is caused by a fungus, *Exobasidium vexans*, which attacks young leaves and distorts the host tissue and gives the leaf a blistered, enlarged appearance.

The principal tea root disease of Indonesia, Ceylon, and India is the red root disease, caused by *Poria hypolateritia.*

The worst root disease in the African tea sections is root splitting. The culprit is another fungus that is almost omnipresent wherever forest trees or orchard crops are planted. The causal organism is *Armillaria mellea*, which also causes considerable trouble in rubber plantations.

The red spider mite (*Metatetranychus bioculatus*) is particularly serious in northeastern India.

Crickets, beetles, stem borers, caterpillars, grubs, and thrips also do varying degrees of damage.

Research is being conducted constantly to prevent and control diseases and pests of tea plants. Insecticides and fungicides and modern spraying and dusting equipment have been moderately successful. Because the use of chemicals may entail hazards, emphasis is placed on the use of resistant varieties or the use of other biological control methods to limit losses.

THE PROCESSING of black tea has five steps—withering, rolling, roll breaking, oxidation or fermentation, and drying or firing.

The withering phase, which reduces moisture content of the leaf and makes it soft and pliable, is done by sun drying or the use of artificial heat. The newly plucked leaves, spread on bamboo trays, are placed in the sun for a specified period. Indoors, the withering is done by forcing heated air over the leaves until the proper moisture content is reached.

After withering, the still green leaves are passed through the rollers, where the leaf cells are broken and the juices that give the flavor to the tea are liberated. The juices, however, remain on the leaf. Upon exposure to the air, the first important chemical changes take place. Oxidation begins, and the essential oils begin to develop.

The tea leaves emerge from the rollers in twisted lumps, which are broken up by passing over coarse-mesh sieves, or roll breakers.

Oxidation is completed in the fermenting room. The leaves are usually spread on cement or tiled floors and exposed to a cool, damp atmosphere. Here fermentation continues, and the leaves turn to the more familiar coppery color.

The objective of the final processing step is to prevent further fermentation and to dry the leaf evenly. Firing is done in pans or baskets or in automatic drying machines. Careful regulation of the air temperature is essential in the firing process to assure a quality tea.

The tea leaves are now ready for brewing, but they must be sorted into grades for sale.

The two basic grades are leaf and broken grades. For some commodities—but not tea—the term "broken" signifies lower quality. Leaf grades are simply larger than the broken grades. Broken grades constitute roughly 80 percent of the total production and make a stronger and darker tea than the leaf grades. Consumers in many countries, including the United States, prefer the broken grades. Leaf grades are favored in continental Europe and South America. Usually the smaller sized teas bring a higher price. Americans frequently associate "orange pekoe" (pronounced *peck-o*) with quality, but orange pekoe denotes merely a size and style of tea leaf.

Black teas from India, Ceylon, and Indonesia are generally graded by leaf size as follows: Broken Orange Pekoe, Orange Pekoe, Broken Pekoe, Pekoe, Pekoe Souchong, Souchong, Fannings, and Dust. Fannings are generally preferred in the Near East markets. Dust is the grade most widely sold in India for domestic consumption.

THE MARKETING of tea is much the same in some aspects as the marketing of tobacco in the United States—that is, most tea is sold at auction. Major auction centers are Calcutta and Cochin in India, Colombo in Ceylon, Chittagong in Pakistan, and Djakarta in Indonesia.

Many countries ship much of their tea to London or Amsterdam to be sold on consignment. The United States, however, buys most of its tea in the countries where it is grown, although a little comes to us from London and Amsterdam.

Tea usually is packed in plywood chests, lined with aluminum foil, to maintain its quality during marketing and transport. The quantity of tea in each chest varies according to size and type of leaf, but an average net weight is about 100 pounds.

Before an auction, samples are taken from holes bored in each chest to allow examination by the buyers. A buyer ships the tea to fill a standing order or sends samples of his purchases to the major importers for their approval.

Hundreds of American firms are wholesalers of packaged tea. Most of them buy their tea from the importer. A comparatively few firms with national distribution, however, handle the bulk of the tea sold in this country.

When tea arrives at the principal United States ports of entry for tea, it

must await approval by inspectors of the Food and Drug Administration. The object of the inspection is to assure that tea brought into the United States meets the standards of purity, quality, and fitness for consumption prescribed under the Federal Food, Drug, and Cosmetic Act and the Tea Importation Act of the United States.

Tea approved for entry into the United States is blended and packaged, in tea bags or loose, before it moves to the retailer. Many companies blend up to 20 varieties to achieve their own blend. Expert tea tasters determine the formula for a company's blend.

Approximately 80 percent of the tea sold in the United States is consumed in homes; the remainder, in restaurants and institutions. Tea bags and iced tea are peculiarities of the United States market. Of total United States tea sales in 1961, an estimated 35 percent was used for iced tea and 65 percent for hot tea. Instant tea has become a factor in the retail market in recent years, accounting for more than 6 percent of United States sales in 1961.

China was the world's largest producer of tea before the Second World War. Since then, China's relative position has declined. India, with about one-third of world output, has become the leading producer.

More than 90 percent of the world's tea is produced in Asia. Africa produces most of the rest. Production in South America has increased, but its output in 1963 was only 1 percent of the world crop.

World production in 1963 was estimated at 2,270 million pounds, slightly above the record 1962 outturn, and 19 percent above the 1955–1959 average. The principal Asian producers in 1963 were India (760 million pounds), Ceylon (490 million), mainland China (340 million), Japan (179 million), Indonesia (84 million), Soviet Union (88 million), Pakistan (55 million), and Taiwan (45 million).

The largest African producers in 1963 were Kenya, the Federation of

Rhodesia and Nyasaland, and Mozambique. In South America, Argentina produced about 60 percent of the total 1963 outturn. Brazil and Peru produced fairly large crops.

Approximately one-half of the world's tea crop is exported. Nearly three-fourths of the 1962 world exports originated in India and Ceylon. Other Asiatic countries accounted for about 15 percent; Africa, 9 percent; and South America, 1 percent.

Leading exporters in 1962 were India, 466 million pounds; Ceylon, 452 million; Indonesia, 72 million; Kenya, 30 million; Federation of Rhodesia and Nyasaland, 28 million; Taiwan, 27 million; Mozambique, 20 million; Japan, 19 million; and Argentina, 14 million pounds. Exports from China in 1962 may have been 65 million pounds.

The United Kingdom has taken well over 40 percent of the world's exported tea. The United Kingdom imported 563 million pounds in 1963, chiefly from India and Ceylon.

The United States imported 126 million pounds in 1963. About 40 percent came from Ceylon. Other important sources were India, Indonesia, eastern Africa, and Taiwan.

The Netherlands, West Germany, and France are among the leading European importers. Australia, Canada, and New Zealand are large consumers, and per capita consumption is almost as large in Ireland as in the United Kingdom.

Consumption has been increasing in many of the Near East and northern African countries. The United Arab Republic, Morocco, Iraq, Iran, Sudan, Turkey, Algeria, and Tunisia have been importing increasingly larger amounts.

The most notable percentage increase in the consumption of tea, however, has taken place in the producing countries themselves. Domestic consumption in India increased from about 70 million pounds in prewar years to more than 300 million pounds in 1962.

In 1957–1962, world tea has been in a fairly well balanced supply-demand position. Tea prices were relatively stable during the period. During the latter part of this period and in 1963, there was growing concern among producing countries that accelerated trends in tea production might result in significant excesses of production over demand in future years. Not only were the older producing areas increasing production; the newer areas were also expanding to increase foreign exchange earnings from exports.

In most of the Asian countries, tea plantations are being rejuvenated by replacing older trees with higher yielding varieties. The use of fertilizers, fungicides, and insecticides are being encouraged to increase yields per unit area. In the meantime, African production and trade is on the upward trend, as is that of South America. Asia remained the major tea producer and exporter, but its proportionate share of world production is being reduced by the emergence of new producing areas.

UNTIL RECENTLY the United States was one of the few important consuming countries which imposed no import duty on tea. In 1963, steps were taken by the United Kingdom and the European Economic Community for the removal of import duties on bulk tea. Such action should result in some decline in retail price and moderate increases in consumption in those areas. Declines in internal taxes and charges of one kind or another in many major consuming countries similarly would increase consumption somewhat.

WILLIAM C. BOWSER, JR., *joined the staff of the Foreign Agricultural Service in 1951. He obtained a bachelor's degree in agricultural economics from The Pennsylvania State University and a master's degree from the University of Maryland.*

ARTHUR G. KEVORKIAN *is Chief of the Special Studies Branch, Sugar and Tropical Products Division of Foreign Agricultural Service.*

Pepper, Vanilla, and Other Spices

by ARTHUR G. KEVORKIAN

WE USE SPICES to make food taste better, preserve some foods, and make perfumes and ointments.

What we think of as true spices are aromatic substances that come mainly from tropical plants. They include allspice, cassia, cinnamon, clove, ginger, mace, nutmeg, pepper, tumeric, and vanilla.

Other seasonings include aromatic seeds, such as anise, celery, dill, and poppyseed. Culinary herbs, another group of seasonings, are derived mostly from leaves of plants, such as bay, chervil, parsley, mints, and sage. Condiments usually are mixed seasonings, such as catsup, curry powder, and prepared mustard.

Here we consider only true spices, which are important in our meat-packing, bakery, canning, and pickling industries and which come from the stems, fruits, and roots of plants of a number of botanical families all over the tropical world.

PEPPER (*Piper nigrum*), the most important of all spices in terms of usage and value in world trade, is the dried fruit of a climbing vine. It has innumerable uses in flavoring food and preserving meat. It is native to Asia, notably the Malabar Coast of India and the Malayan region. It is produced in only a few tropical countries. India and Indonesia account for about two-thirds of the world output.

Most of the remainder is grown in Sarawak, Ceylon, Brazil, Cambodia, and the Malagasy Republic.

Most of it is grown on small plots of land and gardens. It requires a well-distributed rainfall of about 100 inches a year and rich soil. It flourishes best at lower elevations, usually under 1,500 feet.

Propagation is usually by cuttings. Some shade is desirable for the young vines, but little is required for the mature plant. Hardwood posts or trees are used to provide support. The vine usually bears at 3 or 4 years and gives the most returns when it is 6 to 8 years old. The average yield is 3 to 5 pounds of dry pepper per vine.

In harvest, the berries are broken off the vine before they are fully ripe. If white pepper is desired, the berries are allowed to mature further—black pepper and white pepper are obtained from the same plant, depending on maturity and the method of processing.

The reddish peppercorns are spread on mats to dry in the sun. They shrivel, and the hulls become black. They are then cleaned and bagged for export. Grinding and packaging usually are done by importers.

For white pepper, the more mature berries are placed in bags or other containers and soaked in running water for several days to facilitate the removal of the outer coating. The ripened seeds are then dried, cleaned, and bagged. About 3.6 pounds of black pepper are obtained from 10 pounds of peppercorns. If they are processed into white pepper, the yield is about 2.4 pounds. Ground black pepper contains both light and dark particles, as the entire berry is used in it.

Indonesia once was the largest producer, but India has become the main grower. About 95 percent of the output in India is in the State of Kerala.

Indonesia's output, less than one-half of prewar levels, is concentrated in southern Sumatra and the nearby islands of Bangka and Belitung.

The United States, the largest consumer of pepper, imports all of its annual requirements of 35–40 million pounds.

Other major importing countries are the Soviet Union, the United Kingdom, West Germany, and France. About one-third of India's crop is used locally. Nearly all of Ceylon's output goes for domestic consumption.

Pepper is a highly speculative commodity. It can be stored or withheld from the market for several years without loss of quality. Because major producing areas are localized and the world output is relatively small (150–175 million pounds), trade in pepper is sensitive to cornering operations. Singapore merchants handle about a third of the pepper entering commerce.

Pepper has been subject to wide fluctuations in production and price. When prices are high, growers increase acreage and apply additional fertilizer to existing vines, thus causing an oversupply and lower prices. When prices are low, growers neglect their pepper gardens and may withhold stocks from the market. The results are high prices and short supplies. Average annual prices were 10 cents a pound in 1945, 169 cents in 1951, 36 cents in 1962, and 33 cents in 1963.

The consumer demand for pepper is relatively inelastic, as its price usually is a small item in the family budget. The demand for pepper actually has declined since 1945, probably because of the greater use of precooked foods and new food processing methods.

VANILLA (*Vanilla planifolia*), the fruits or beans of a climbing orchid, is native to southeastern Mexico and Central America.

About two-thirds of the world's vanilla crop is grown on islands off the southeastern coast of Africa—the Malagasy Republic, Comores, Réunion, and the Seychelles. The Malagasy Republic accounts for more than one-half of output. That is less than 10 percent of the countries' total exports, but (as is true of pepper) it is vitally important as the only cash crop of many small growers in the northern part of the Malagasy Republic. Tahiti and Mexico supply much of the remaining world supply.

World trade usually amounts to about 2 million pounds annually, of which the United States consumes about two-thirds.

Vanilla requires a tropical climate, partial shade, ample rainfall, a dry season, and rich, well-drained soil. An altitude of about 1 thousand feet is desirable. Propagation is from cuttings. The plant usually comes into bearing in the third year and remains commercially valuable for 7 years. The vines are usually spaced 5 to 8 feet apart in rows 10 feet apart. The climbing plants, usually on trees, are kept to a height of 4 to 6 feet. Yields average about one-fourth pound of cured beans per plant. Four pounds of green beans yield a pound of cured product.

Since less than 1 percent of the flowers produce beans under natural conditions, hand pollination is necessary in commercial operations. It must be done daily because each flower remains open for only a day or so. Usually not more than three flowers on each raceme are pollinated. Overpollination weakens the vine, makes it highly susceptible to disease, and may reduce the size of the beans.

Most of the vanilla of commerce belongs to the species *Vanilla planifolia*, but significant quantities of the *V. tahitensis* and *V. pompona* are grown. *V. tahitensis*, grown chiefly in Tahiti, brings a lower price because its strong heliotrope aroma makes it more suitable for perfume than a flavoring material. *V. pompona* is cultivated mostly in the West Indies. *V. planifolia* is cultivated chiefly in the Malagasy Republic and the other southeastern African islands and in Mexico.

The vanilla of African origin is known commercially as Bourbon vanilla and usually brings a lower price than the Mexican beans. Many species of vanilla grow wild, but they lack the desired aromatic properties.

The vanilla beans are harvested 4 or

6 months after hand pollination. The beans are picked just when the apex, or blossom end, begins to turn yellow, in order to obtain the highest aroma and quality during curing. If the pods are allowed to become too ripe, a splitting occurs at the blossom end, and the beans bring a lower market price. If beans are harvested before the blossom end yellow stage, the cured beans are also inferior.

The traditional curing process has three steps: Heating or freezing the beans, the killing phase; sweating the beans in the sun during the day and rolling them in woolen blankets at night; and conditioning, which is conducted in tin-lined boxes at room temperature until the characteristic vanilla fragrance is obtained.

Research on the enzymic action in vanilla beans during the curing process done at the Department of Agriculture's experiment station at Mayaguez in Puerto Rico led to the development of a new curing process on a pilot-plant basis. Curing can be done indoors in thermostatically controlled ovens, and the elimination of much hand labor increases curing capacity and cuts costs and time.

The cured beans should be of a uniform dark color and flexible. Beans of a moisture content of 20 to 25 percent are less likely to become moldy during storage and shipment. After curing, the beans are graded according to length, color, and flexibility; tied in bundles of 50 to 70 beans; and packed in tins or tin-lined boxes.

Vanilla is ordinarily used in the form of an extract; 13.35 ounces of beans with a moisture content of not more than 25 percent make a gallon of extract. The extract is made by cutting the vanilla beans into small pieces, which are placed in a solution of not less than 35 percent ethyl alcohol and heated in a percolator. Dextrose, sucrose, or glycerine may be added at the end of the extraction process to prevent precipitation and to preserve the flavor and aroma.

Vanilla is used for flavoring ice cream, chocolate, beverages, as well as sweets and in the manufacture of soap and perfume.

Sharp fluctuations in prices of vanilla beans have kept consumption down and have encouraged the use of synthetic products. Vanillin, the most widely used synthetic, is produced from waste sulfite liquor of papermills, coal tar extracts, and from eugenol, obtained from clove oil. Its price has remained at or near 3 dollars a pound; the prices of vanilla beans have fluctuated between 5 and 16 dollars a pound. Vanillin lacks the oleoresins that impart flavor to the vanilla extract.

The Flavoring Extract Manufacturing Association of the United States has participated in a cooperative project with the Department of Agriculture in Puerto Rico. The aim is to improve cultural practices and to solve problems of disease.

THE CLOVE TREE (*Caryophyllus aromaticus*) is native to the Molucca Islands, or "Spice Islands," which now are a part of Indonesia. Its name comes from the French "clou," meaning nail, which describes the unopened flower-buds used as the spice. Zanzibar (including Pemba) is the largest producer of cloves. Most of the remainder of world production comes from the Malagasy Republic and Indonesia.

We usually think of cloves only as a spice to decorate and flavor foods, but as much as two-thirds of the world's supply of cloves is ground and mixed with tobacco in cigarettes. Indonesia consumes more cloves than the rest of the world combined, mainly in the manufacture of cigarettes. Other major consumers are the United States and India.

The clove tree requires a tropical climate, with a well-distributed annual rainfall of 90 to 100 inches and a well-drained soil. The clove tree usually does not thrive far from the sea. An altitude of a few hundred feet above sea level is desirable.

The trees are usually planted about 30 feet apart. They begin to bear in the seventh or eighth year and may continue in production for more than 100 years. They normally grow to 30 or 40 feet and produce an average of 7 to 10 pounds of spice. Production varies from year to year because the trees have an off-year alternating with a good bearing year.

The unopened or immature flower-buds are the spice of commerce. They are handpicked from the trees and spread on mats in the sun for about a week. Sometimes artificial heat is used in the curing. The greenish buds become reddish-brown or black and lose half of their original weight.

Whole cloves are used in pickling and preserving, as a garnish for hams and salads and in catsup. Ground cloves are used in baked goods, vegetables, desserts, and in some brands of cigarettes.

Clove oil, obtained in a distillation of buds and stems, is used in pharmaceutical preparations, as a flavoring in candy and gum, and in the manufacture of perfume. Eugenol, a constituent of clove oil, is used as a basic material from which synthetic vanilla extract (vanillin) is manufactured. Other uses of eugenol are in the manufacture of perfumes and soap. The use of clove oil or powdered cloves in moth repellants has been studied.

CINNAMON AND CASSIA were known in commerce in Biblical times. *Cinnamonum zelanicum* is the true cinnamon of commerce. *C. cassia*, a related species, has characteristics and uses similar to cinnamon.

The aromatic oils in the bark of these tropical trees determine their commercial importance. They are grown commercially in Asia from southern India and Ceylon to mainland China.

Cassia is considered to be inferior to cinnamon, but is often used as a substitute. The United States processors prefer cassia because of its aromatic qualities and perhaps because it is less expensive than the true cinnamon.

Ceylon and the Seychelles Islands account for the bulk of world produc-

tion. Mexico, the United Kingdom, Japan, the United States, West Germany, and the Netherlands are major consumers.

The spice is used for flavoring bread, cakes and pastries, beverages, candy, drugs, and cosmetic products and for scenting soap and perfumery. Oil of cinnamon is used in medicines.

The cinnamon tree requires a tropical climate; a rich, sandy loam soil; and 85 to 100 inches of annual rainfall. The tree is grown as a low, bushy shrub, usually not over 8 to 10 feet tall, although it may reach the height of 30 to 40 feet in the wild state. Propagation is usually from seed. The first crop can be expected in about 2 to 3 years. Maximum returns are obtained when the trees are about 10 years old. Yields average 150 to 200 pounds an acre.

Harvesting of cinnamon consists of cutting the many-branched, bushy shoots twice a year. The bark is peeled off by hand, scraped, and dried in the sun. Upon drying, the bark rolls into quills. Scraps from peeling and scraping are called chips and featherings and are used to make cinnamon oil through a distillation process. The leaves and roots are also a source of an inferior oil of low value.

C. cassia, or Chinese cinnamon, is also the dried inner bark of an evergreen tree, which attains a greater height than the true cinnamon. This tree has been grown in southern China for centuries. Mainland China, Indonesia, and South Vietnam are major producers.

Cassia trees are allowed to grow for several years before harvesting. Cassia can be grown in areas where cinnamon would not thrive.

The harvesting of cassia includes cutting the branches or the tree, loosening the bark, and stripping and scraping the grayish outer bark. The pieces are then dried in the sun. The resultant quills are tied in bundles and packaged for export. Yields may average about 1,500 pounds of quills an acre.

Cassia oil is obtained by the distillation of the bark and leaves and from the dried, unripe fruits. The cassia buds, or fruit, contain the same essential oil as the bark and resemble cloves.

NUTMEG AND MACE are derived from one evergreen tree (*Myristica fragrans*). Its seed is the nutmeg of commerce. A thin membrane (the aril) around the seed is known as mace. Mace and nutmeg taste somewhat the same.

Indonesia is the largest producer and exporter. Most of the rest comes from the West Indies, mainly Grenada. Ceylon also exports some nutmeg and mace.

Grenada's nutmeg industry was crippled as a result of a hurricane in 1955. Nutmeg and mace prices doubled and tripled as a result of the reduction in supplies. The immediate effect of the damage was eased somewhat as the Grenada Co-Operative Nutmeg Association had sizable stocks on hand.

The nutmeg tree is grown from seed. Male and female flowers are produced on separate trees, and the sexes cannot be identified until they flower 6 or 8 years after planting. To insure an ample number of female trees, which are the only source of fruit, two seedlings are planted a short distance apart. Later all male trees, except one for the pollination of every 10 or 12 female trees, are cut down. Some growers plant only one tree at the proper spacing and bud or graft the extra male trees with female scions.

The nutmeg tree requires a tropical climate. The trees begin to bear after 6 to 8 years and continue in production for more than 50 years. They may attain the height of 30 to 40 feet. The maximum yields of several thousand seeds are obtained when the tree is 15 to 20 years old.

Harvesting the nutmeg usually continues throughout the year. The heavily laden limbs usually are arched with the fruit, which is about the size and shape of an apricot. The ripe, fleshy portion splits open, disclosing the scarlet aril (mace) and the glossy, dark-brown seed.

Some of the nuts fall to the ground, but most remain on the tree. They are usually gathered by raising a long pole, to which a basket and prongs are attached. The average yield per acre is about 1,500 pounds of green or about 720 pounds of processed nutmeg. A 30-year-old tree may yield 3 thousand to 4 thousand nuts. The yield of green mace per acre is about 150 pounds, which yield 35 pounds of dried mace.

The seeds are sun dried until the kernel rattles freely in the shell. The shell is broken, and the nutmeg is removed and ground. The fleshy aril is removed before the drying.

Nutmeg is used in flavoring foods, sauces, and beverages. Nutmeg oil is used in pharmaceutical preparations, confections, condiments, and perfumes, cosmetics, and soaps. Mace oil has similar chemical and therapeutic properties as the oil of nutmeg.

GINGER (*Zingiber officinale*), the root or rhizome of a tuberous, perennial plant, is native to southeastern Asia. The palmate roots are commonly called hands.

India and Taiwan, the largest producers, supply more than three-fourths of the ginger in commerce. Nigeria, Sierra Leone, and Jamaica account for most of the remainder. The United States and the United Kingdom are the major importers.

There are many varieties or types of ginger. Jamaican ginger, which is usually much larger than the Indian, or Cochin, is preferred for making ginger ale, fancy baking, and medicinal purposes. Sierra Leone ginger is used mainly in ginger cookies, gingerbread, and cakes. The Jamaican variety commands a premium price on the world market, and Indian ginger brings a price considerably below that of the Jamaican variety. Ratoon ginger consists of the old roots that are left in the field and dug out at a later time. This type is in great demand in the United States market because of its low cost.

Ginger is cultivated mostly in small home gardens. It needs a hot, moist, tropical climate and partial shade. Since the plants are gross feeders, they require a rich, loamy soil or heavy fertilization. Ginger is grown from sea level to approximately 3 thousand feet.

Propagation is by divisions of the rhizomes, which are usually planted in rows 12 to 18 inches apart. The plant reaches a height of about 3 feet.

Yields average 1 thousand to 2 thousand pounds an acre. The rhizomes are dug, washed, and dried in the sun.

Peeled ginger is prepared by placing the roots in scalding water and then removing the skin with a knife. Preserved ginger is peeled and boiled in a sugar solution. Ginger is usually exported in the form of dried rhizomes and made into extract or ground into powder in consuming countries.

TODAY SPICES ARE OF comparatively minor importance in world agricultural production and trade, but in the few exporting countries, mainly in the Far East and Africa, spices are a major source of foreign exchange earnings. Cloves, for example, comprise about 80 percent of the total value of Zanzibar's domestic exports, furnishing the government approximately one-third of its revenue from all sources.

Spices are of importance to importing countries because the entire population depends on one spice or another to flavor food. The United States' imports of the eight spices in 1959–1963 had an average value of 31.5 million dollars. That is a small fraction of the value of all our imports but a large factor in the production of millions of dollars' worth of processed products, in which spices are essential ingredients.

ARTHUR G. KEVORKIAN, *an economist in the Foreign Agricultural Service, is Chief of the Special Studies Branch of Sugar and Tropical Products Division. He has degrees from the University of Rhode Island and Harvard University. He worked for the Department of Agriculture in Latin America for many years.*

Cocoa and Chocolate

by ARTHUR G. KEVORKIAN and REX E. T. DULL

COCOA is a newcomer among foods and beverages, although Central Americans enjoyed it long before the discovery of the New World. Commercial production of cocoa beans was small until only a half century ago, but has expanded from about 200 million pounds in 1900 to more than 2.2 billion pounds, valued at 500 million dollars, in 1963.

Cocoa beans are seeds of the cacao tree, *Theobroma cacao.* They grow in pods along the trunk and the older branches. The cacao tree, a tropical plant, can be cultivated successfully only in a narrow belt 20° north to 20° south of the Equator.

The cacao tree is native to tropical America. The Indians of Central America and South America grew cacao for many years before the discovery of America. The Aztecs, Toltecs, Mayans, and Incas had various uses for cocoa beans. A favorite was a drink made from the beans, corn, spices, and water. A similar beverage, pinolillo, is still popular in Nicaragua.

Columbus saw cocoa beans but regarded them only as a curiosity.

Cortez, another explorer, found the Aztec Indians of Mexico using them to make a bitter but rather delightful draught. The addition of sugar, vanilla, and cinnamon made this exotic drink more pleasing to the European tastes, but cocoa was so expensive that only the wealthy could afford it.

Cocoa was consumed only as a beverage until a process of making "eating chocolate" was discovered in the 19th century. A Dutchman, C. T. van Houten, in search of a way to improve the palatability of cocoa, which was rich and somewhat indigestible, devised a way to remove part of the fat—cocoa butter—from the bean. He developed "chocolate powder," which made a more digestible drink, by removing most of the fat contents of the beans. The next step was to mix cocoa butter, cocoa, and sugar to make "eating chocolate."

A Swiss manufacturer, D. Peter, later devised a means of adding milk to cocoa to make the milk chocolate we know. Cocoa then became popular throughout Europe, and production was expanded in tropical areas.

The importance of cocoa in the confectionery industry can be noted in the large variety of candies, cakes, cookies, ice cream, and beverages that contain cocoa and chocolate. Chocolate tastes good and has a high nutritional value.

Cocoa was considered a strategic commodity in wartime because of its nutritional value. Candy bars and the K-rations of the Armed Forces included chocolate to sustain energy when other foods were not available.

Spain guarded its secret of cocoa for many years, but in time the monopoly was broken, and the Dutch, Portuguese, British, French, Belgians, and Germans established plantations in their oversea territories.

Plantings were made in the western African islands of São Tome and Fernando Po in the 17th century. Cultivation spread into other areas in Africa.

At the beginning of the 20th century, Latin American countries, mainly Ecuador, Brazil, Trinidad and Tobago, and Venezuela, were producing nearly four-fifths of the world output of cocoa beans. But as Africa was relatively free of cacao diseases, mainly witches' broom, and

offered lower production costs, Africa became the major supplier after the First World War.

The expanding industry suffered a setback during the Second World War because of the lack of shipping and the loss of the European market immediately after the war. Production soon gathered momentum, and new plantings were made. During the fifties, cacao acreage was expanded, and more emphasis placed on the control of diseases and pests, especially in western Africa.

MOST OF THE WORLD'S cocoa is produced in a few countries. Ghana accounts for more than one-third of it. Next are Nigeria, Brazil, the Ivory Coast, Cameroon, Ecuador, and the Dominican Republic. These seven countries produced more than four-fifths of the 1962–1963 world harvest. Most of the remainder was grown in Togo, New Guinea, Venezuela, Colombia, Mexico, Costa Rica, the West Indies, and the islands of Fernando Po and São Tome off the coast of Africa.

Of the many varieties of cacao tree, three are commercially important.

The Criollo produces a "fine" or "flavor" cocoa. The Forastero yields a "base" or "ordinary" grade. The Trinitario is a cross between the Criollo and Forastero.

The Criollo has plump, round, white-to-pale violet seeds. The pods are 6 or 8 inches long and about half as wide. The fruit wall is fairly soft and easily split. The surface of the fruit wall has 10 furrows; the ridges between them are rather warty and irregular.

The Forastero is classified on the basis of fruit form into four basic types: Angoleta, Cundeamor, Amelonado, and Calabacillo. The first two have deep ridges and are rather warty. The others have shallow ridges and are less warty. Because the shapes of the fruit vary, another classification divides the Forastero complex of varieties into the Amazonian Forasteros (which represent the four types we mentioned) and the Trinitarios, a type, originally found in eastern Venezuela, that is said to be hybrids of the South American Criollos and Amazonian Forasteros.

The shifting of the center of production from Latin America to Africa has brought about a sharp reduction in the Criollo flavor cocoas and the predominance of the Forastero variety. The latter variety was preferred for new plantings, as it was hardier and had greater yields than the Criollo. Flavor cocoas now constitute less than 10 percent of world production.

The cacao tree needs temperatures between 65° and 95° F. The tree flourishes best at altitudes of less than a thousand feet, although most plantings in Ceylon are at about 1,500 feet. In the Cauca Valley of Colombia, cacao is grown at elevations of more than 2 thousand feet.

Rainfall may vary from 50 to 80 inches, usually with a distinct rainy and dry season. In regions of long dry seasons, clay soils that retain water well and have ample humus are desirable. The level of the water table also is important. High rainfall and a high water table may be detrimental.

The Criollo types have a somewhat upright growth and can be planted close together. The Forastero types are more spreading and require wider spacing. Plantings can be closer spaced on sandy soils than in rich alluvial soils, where growth is more vigorous.

In many countries, cacao is grown under shade to reduce the amount of direct sunlight. Sometimes windbreaks are needed for protection. When seedlings are transplanted from a nursery, they are usually grown under temporary shade crops, such as bananas, plantains, and cassava, which provide shelter as well as cash returns while the cacao is developing. Permanent shade is provided by planting leguminous trees, whose long taproots will not interfere with the cacao. In some countries, notably in western Africa, few shade trees are utilized, although in some districts cacao is planted as an intercrop with the Hevea rubber tree.

The cacao tree usually begins to bear in about 3 to 5 years and continues in production for nearly 50 years. A mature tree may reach a height of 12 to 18 feet.

The pods usually contain 30 to 40 beans each.

In the Republic of Ghana, Federal Republic of Nigeria, and Republic of Ivory Coast, cocoa usually is grown on small native farms in groves of only a few acres. Spacing is unusually close, and shade trees seldom are used. The older trees, which comprise the major portion of the plantings, were planted 30 or 36 inches apart. Those trees produced only 10 or 12 pods each; plantings with shade and a spacing of 10 to 12 feet yielded 50 to 80 pods in Cameroon and 70 to 85 in Fernando Po.

Cacao is usually grown in Latin America on large plantations. Varieties and hybrids are mixed. The trees are shaded and generally are of the more vigorous type. Normally they are spaced 8 to 15 feet apart.

New plantings in both hemispheres were derived from vegetatively propagated clones or selected seed from trees obtained in the Amazon region of South America.

The late Dr. F. J. Pound, an eminent cacao technologist who worked in the Department of Agriculture in Trinidad, traversed the Amazon area of Brazil, Colombia, and Ecuador in search of disease-resistant cacao. From the clonal nursery that was established on the basis of his collections, healthier, more productive trees were developed through selection and hybridization.

In the western African cacao areas, these Amazonian types have been planted at intervals of 4 feet. Such crowding could result in moisture conditions conducive to serious losses due to pod-rot disease. Officials in Nigeria, for example, have recommended that farmers thin the trees after several years of production when overcrowding is obvious.

CACAO has to be harvested by hand. The mature pods usually are cut from the trees with a machete or with a hook. Pods must be removed carefully from the trees, lest the flower cushions and immature pods are injured. The pods are then gathered into heaps and opened. The extracted seeds or beans are taken to some central place for fermentation.

In the Ivory Coast and other parts of Africa, the first step in fermentation is to put the sticky seeds in containers and cover them with leaves for several days. The beans and their coatings are stirred from time to time until the right degree of fermentation has taken place. Then the beans are placed on platforms and allowed to dry in the sun. Grading and sacking follow, and the cocoa is transported to collecting centers for sale. On the plantations of Fernando Po, fermentation is accomplished under shelter. A mass of beans is shifted from one fermentation box to another every day in order to have a uniform fermented product.

The time of fermentation varies as to the country, climate, and potential market. For example, Spain prefers slightly fermented beans; the plantations of Fernando Po therefore use a 3-day fermenting period. Drying is also accomplished under shelter at the plantations of this island. Large platforms are artificially heated, and automatic stirrers travel back and forth every 5 minutes. Drying usually takes 2 days.

Fermenting boxes and artificial heat are also used in the Western Hemisphere, but a large part of the beans in South and Central America are fermented on raised platforms or on wooden trays and sun dried. The beans are covered at night and before rains.

MANY DISEASES and pests may attack the roots, stems, leaves, flowering cushions, and pods of cacao trees, but only a few of them are of economic significance. Without adequate control measures for these, there would be a scarcity of cocoa and its products.

The black or brown pod-rot disease, caused by the fungus *Phytophthora palmivora*, is present in all cacao districts and is worst in wet and humid areas. In 1962–1963, it caused losses of less than 10 percent in the drier areas of Africa but up to 100 percent in parts of Cameroon.

Considerable losses are caused by *Monilia roreri*, another pod-rot fungus that is related to the brown rot of peaches in the United States. The disease first appeared in Ecuador in the early 1900's and has spread to parts of Colombia, Venezuela, and Panama.

The witches' broom disease of cacao, caused by the fungus *Marasmius perniciosus*, spread from Surinam to Trinidad and Tobago and all the cacao areas of South America, except Brazil. In 1964 it was not known to exist in the other islands of the Caribbean, Central America, Mexico, or the Eastern Hemisphere.

The Imperial College of Agriculture and the Department of Agriculture in the island of Trinidad pioneered in investigations on the disease. Dr. Pound traveled extensively over the Amazon Basin in search of resistant wild cacao trees. In the upper reaches of the Amazon region he found trees that appeared to have some resistance. These were tested, and clonal material with considerable resistance was found. Resistant trees were sent to growers and research workers elsewhere.

Scientists of the United States Department of Agriculture and the Agency for International Development have worked cooperatively with Ecuadorans to perfect strains resistant to witches' broom under Ecuadoran conditions. The resistant strains that were developed have been used for replantings in Ecuador.

The swollen shoot disease has been troublesome in Ghana and nearby countries. It is caused by a virus that has many strains, a number of which can kill a tree. It is transmitted by mealybugs, which can carry it to a healthy tree a few hours after they feed on an infected tree.

Control measures developed by the Ghana Cocoa Research Institute at Tafo consist of cutting out diseased and exposed trees and replanting. Millions of trees have been eliminated in Ghana in attempts to control the disease—a costly operation that caused considerable discontent among growers, even though they received compensation for lost trees and had government assistance in replanting. Amazonian hybrids have given signs of having some tolerance to the swollen shoot disease. Swollen shoot disease is not known to exist in the Western Hemisphere.

Cushion gall disease, which affects the floral cushions of the cacao tree, is prevalent in Central America and is known to occur in most of Africa and South America. Research as to its causal agency, life history, dissemination, and control has been concentrated at the Inter-American Cacao Center at Turrialba, Costa Rica.

The major insect pests of the cacao tree are capsids, which have been especially devastating in western Africa. Their eggs are usually placed in the bark near the feeding punctures and are hard to reach by spraying. The staff of the Ghana Cocoa Research Institute and several teams of specialists have done work on control measures. Their success will affect the size of future crops in Ghana and elsewhere in Africa.

Research on cocoa has been mainly concentrated in three areas. By the turn of the century cocoa production in the Western Hemisphere was threatened by the witches' broom disease. The Imperial College of Agriculture in Trinidad consequently placed its major emphasis on identifying the causal agency, testing chemical sprays to control the malady, and determining the existence of resistance in the various species and varieties available. It is logical that the basic investigation of this disease was conducted in Trinidad, since it only occurs in parts of South America and the island of Trinidad.

Investigations at the Ghana Cocoa Research Institute and the station in Nigeria have been made part of government-sponsored agricultural research activities. The work has centered on swollen shoot disease and the capsid bug, since only these problems are known to exist, and cause serious reduction in cocoa production in western Africa.

The Inter-American Cacao Center was established at Turrialba, Costa Rica, in 1947 as a cooperative venture of United States manufacturers of cocoa and chocolate products and the Inter-American Institute of Agricultural Sciences. Investigations there are concentrated on black or brown pod-rot and cushion gall diseases.

As cocoa is primarily a cash crop, almost all of it is exported as beans or semiprocessed products—cocoa butter, chocolate, and cocoa powder. In a few countries, such as Peru and Colombia, the entire crop is used at home.

Cocoa exports account for almost two-thirds of export earnings of Ghana and nearly one-quarter of the earnings in Nigeria, Ivory Coast, and Federal Republic of Cameroon.

In most of the producing countries in western Africa, cocoa is marketed through government-controlled marketing boards. In Ghana, for example, the board fixes seasonal prices to be paid to producers, determines purchase arrangements, issues licenses to buyers, and maintains arrangements for purchasing, shipping, and selling.

THE MARKETING boards offer some protection to the growers from the fluctuations in cocoa prices. When world prices remain above a fixed level, the surplus is deposited in the board's reserves; a subsidy is paid when prices fall below a fixed level. The reserves of the boards may be used for research, training farmers in improved practices, and buying new seedlings, spray machines, and insecticides and fertilizers.

Nearly all of the world's production

of cocoa is consumed in Temperate Zone countries. Most of the crop is processed and consumed in the United States and western Europe. The United States usually takes about one-third of the total world imports. The value of United States imports of cocoa beans and semiprocessed cocoa products is about 170 million dollars to 200 million annually. The annual per capita consumption in the United States usually is 3.5 to 4 pounds.

Any appreciable change in world supplies has an immediate effect on prices and sometimes on governments. Manufacturers have been quick to shift to cheaper cocoa-butter substitutes and extenders when prices were exceptionally high. Others have reduced the size of their chocolate bars and thinned the chocolate coatings.

EFFORTS HAVE been made through the Food and Agriculture Organization of the United Nations to develop an international arrangement to provide stability for supplies and prices.

A Cocoa Producers Alliance was formed in 1962 by the five leading cocoa-producing countries, which account for about three-quarters of the world output. Among its activities have been the exchange of statistics and other information, conferences on problems of production and marketing, and efforts to encourage greater consumption.

Tariffs and taxes in many countries make chocolate a luxury. The United States has no duty or quantitative restrictions on the importation of cocoa beans and has small tariffs on imports of semiprocessed products.

The production and consumption of cocoa could be increased if prices were stabilized at a level that would be fair for producers and would allow more consumers to buy it.

ARTHUR G. KEVORKIAN *and* REX E. T. DULL *are economists in the Sugar and Tropical Products Division of the Foreign Agricultural Service in the Department of Agriculture.*

Production, Trade, and Use of Tobacco

by HUGH C. KIGER,
FRANKLIN S. EVERTS, and
EDWARD J. EISENACH

TOBACCO, *Nicotiana tabacum*, from humble beginnings in the Americas has become a crop of economic importance and is grown in nearly every country.

Most producing countries grow more than one type of tobacco and supplement their own production by imports of other types required by the domestic industry. Some countries are nearly self-sufficient in tobacco. Others produce a surplus and export large quantities. A few countries in western Europe grow no tobacco on a commercial scale and purchase from other countries the kinds of leaf they require.

From the grower to the ultimate consumer, because it is such a good producer of revenue, tobacco is under the surveillance of governments around the world.

We can group tobaccos into eight categories—flue-cured, burley, other light air-cured (including Maryland), light sun-cured (excluding oriental and semioriental), oriental and semioriental, dark air-cured (including cigar), dark sun-cured, and fire-cured—on the basis of characteristics due to genetics or breeding, the influence of soil and climate, and the method of curing.

A great increase in cigarette smoking since 1920 raised the demand for the kinds of tobacco suitable for cigarette manufacture, principally flue-cured, light air-cured, and oriental. Production of flue-cured tobacco, which totaled about 300 million pounds in 1913, rose more than tenfold to well over 3 billion pounds in 1963. Other light types of leaf, particularly burley and oriental, have also gone up in importance. Because of the lessened importance of smoking tobacco, cigars, chewing tobacco, and snuff, the dark tobaccos used primarily in their manufacture dropped in relative importance.

CURING is important in leaf production. During most of the period since Columbus learned about tobacco, air-curing, a natural process, was by far the predominant method. The Indians learned that leaf hung to dry near campfires where it would be impregnated with smoke could be kept longer. During the past century, the flue-curing process was developed in the United States and has spread because of a demand for this kind of leaf in making light types of cigarettes.

Changes in the relative importance of curing methods reflect the changing pattern of the uses of the leaf.

Flue-cured tobacco has a thin leaf, lemon to red in color. It is cured by heat from a firebox, which is circulated through flues throughout a barn of special construction. It usually requires 4 or 5 days to cure a barnful. Flue-cured is used primarily in cigarettes. It often is used exclusively in the so-called straight Virginia cigarette or mixed with other light leaf in blended cigarettes.

Flue-cured tobacco is produced in some 50 countries—from tropical areas to such northerly regions as Poland and Canada, and in the Southern Hemisphere in Argentina, the Republic of South Africa, and Australia. The United States always has been the major producer of this kind of tobacco.

Since 1935, world production increased from less than 1.3 billion pounds to about 3.2 billion in 1963. The United States once accounted for more than two-thirds of the world crop; in 1963, the figure was 41 percent. Big gains in flue-cured production have been reported, especially in Southern Rhodesia, Zambia, India, Canada, Brazil, and mainland China. Others are Japan, Australia, Argentina, Venezuela, Italy, Poland, Indonesia, and the Republic of Korea. Flue-cured in 1963 accounted for 35 percent of total world production, compared to 20 percent in 1935–1939.

Burley leaf is rather thin. It usually is yellowish tan, but variations depend on the position of the leaf on the stalk. Burley tobacco is wilted in the sun. It is moved into the curing barn, where it remains for several months, while the leaves undergo the yellowing and browning stages. Burley is used primarily for blending with other tobaccos in cigarettes. The heavier, darker leaves usually are used for smoking tobaccos.

The United States accounted for more than 90 percent of the world total in 1935–1939 and 80 percent in 1963. About 40 countries produced burley tobacco in 1963—double the number in 1950. Important producers include Spain, Italy, Japan, Mexico, Venezuela, Southern Rhodesia, Zambia, Malawi, and Canada. Greece rapidly stepped up its crop of burley for export in the early sixties. The growing interest in expanding production in many countries is indicative of the growing popularity around the world of American-type blended cigarettes, in which burley is an ingredient.

Other light air-cured tobacco includes Maryland-type tobacco and native varieties. Most other light air-cured looks like burley. Curing methods are much the same. Maryland is used primarily in cigarettes, but considerable amounts go into pipe mixtures, chewing tobacco, and cigars. Major producers, aside from United States, whose production of Maryland is substantial, include Italy, Nigeria, the Malagasy Republic, and the Republic of South Africa.

Light sun-cured leaf includes a number of types of native or native-improved tobacco, named after the practice of curing it in the sun. Sometimes it is left to cure almost completely in the sun, but often it is placed under cover as soon as it is yellowed. Light sun-cured leaf is used for both cigarettes and pipe mixtures.

Major producers of light sun-cured include mainland China, Japan, India, Mexico, South Korea, Pakistan, and Paraguay. World production of this kind of leaf remains relatively stable. The United States does not produce light sun-cured leaf.

Oriental leaf has small leaves, spaced far apart on the stalk. It is cured in the sun. Some may be air-cured. It is known for its aromatic qualities. Semioriental is cured by the same method as oriental, although the leaves are somewhat larger because of crossing with other varieties. Both oriental and semioriental varieties are used largely in cigarettes—sometimes alone and sometimes in a mixture of other light cigarette types.

World production of oriental and semioriental varieties was about twice as large in 1963 as in 1935–1939. The main producers include Turkey, Greece, Bulgaria, and the Soviet Union. Substantial amounts are grown in Yugoslavia, Italy, Syria, and Lebanon. Other producers of oriental leaf include Hungary, Poland, Cyprus, Iran, and Iraq.

Oriental tobacco, next to flue-cured in world trade, accounts for about one-fifth of the total. The United States alone imported about 130 million pounds annually for blending with domestic leaf for cigarettes in the early sixties.

Dark air-cured tobacco, including types used for cigars, is less important in world production than formerly. It is grown to some extent in practically every tobacco-producing country. It includes many different varieties that have a high content of nicotine. The uses of dark air-cured include every form of smoking. Cigar types of dark air-cured are quite important in international trade. Other types are used in dark cigarettes in South American

countries and in several countries in western Europe.

Major producers of dark air-cured leaf include the Soviet Union, with its substantial crop of Makhorka; Brazil, with the Bahia cigar types and native twist tobacco; France; Indonesia; the Philippines; Pakistan; the United States; Colombia; and China.

Dark sun-cured tobacco is cured completely in the sun and, like dark air-cured, is used to some extent in all forms of tobacco products. Most dark sun-cured leaf is grown in Asia, the Caribbean area, and (to a lesser extent) Africa. Major producing countries include India, mainland China, Burma, Pakistan, Thailand, and Cuba. A little dark sun-cured leaf is grown in the United States.

Fire-cured leaf is dark in color, rich in gum, and has a pronounced smoky odor. It is cured over open fires at a moderate temperature and is subjected to a maximum amount of smoke. Fire-cured leaf is used chiefly for the manufacture of snuff, specialty cigars, smoking tobacco, and dark cigarettes in a few countries.

Fire-cured tobacco used to be one of the major kinds of leaf, but its relative position in world production and trade has declined considerably. The United States remains the world's leading producer and exporter. Other significant producers are Malawi, Southern Rhodesia, Italy, and Poland. Less important are Argentina, Mozambique, Uganda, Tanganyika, Ceylon, and Pakistan.

THE WORLD HARVEST of tobacco in 1963, 9.2 billion pounds, was a record—6 percent above the 1962 crop and 18 percent larger than the annual average for 1950–1954.

Flue-cured production in 1963, at 3.2 billion pounds, was about the same as that for 1962. Smaller 1963 harvests of flue-cured tobacco in the United States and in Southern Rhodesia just about offset increases in Brazil, Italy, India, and Bulgaria. The United States crop of flue-cured in 1963, 1.4

billion pounds, was 3 percent smaller than the 1962 harvest because of a cut in acreage allotments. The crop of flue-cured in Malawi, Zambia, and Southern Rhodesia, 199 million pounds, was 16 percent below the record of 237 million produced in 1961, because of unfavorable weather. Canada harvested a crop of 188 million pounds—equal to 1962 production—despite a sharp cutback in acreage. India, another major flue-cured producer, harvested a crop a little above that of the previous year. The Japanese crop reached about 190 million pounds in 1962 and 1963. There were increases in Brazil, Italy, and Bulgaria.

World production of burley tobacco totaled a record 885 million pounds in 1963—5 percent above 1962, and 28 percent above the 1950–1954 average. Larger harvests were recorded in 1963 in practically all countries. Nearly all countries had record burley crops in 1963. Exceptions were Italy and West Germany. The United States crop of burley in 1963 was a record 710 million pounds.

World production of oriental tobacco also totaled a record of nearly 1.3 billion pounds in 1963. This was one-fifth larger than the 1962 harvest. If blue mold had not reduced the harvest in a number of Near and Middle Eastern countries, the final outturn might have been at least a third larger than in 1962. All oriental producing countries, except Bulgaria, Cyprus, Israel, and Syria, harvested larger crops in 1963. Significant increases were reported for Greece, Turkey, Yugoslavia, and the Soviet Union. Yugoslavia's harvest was a near record, and Greece achieved a record crop of 257 million pounds.

Crops of dark air-cured tobacco (including cigar leaf) totaled 1.9 billion pounds in 1963—up from 1.7 billion the previous year. Larger harvests of dark air-cured in Brazil, Paraguay, Colombia, and the Dominican Republic partially reflect anticipation of a larger market in the United States for cigar filler tobaccos.

ALTHOUGH THE GREATER portion of tobacco production of the world is consumed in the producing countries, a considerable amount, about one-fifth in recent years, enters international trade, either in the form of leaf or products to supplement deficient supplies in some countries or to provide total requirements in others.

International trade in tobacco products amounts to less than 10 percent of total free-world exports of leaf tobacco. Much is manufactured locally because of the protectionist policies of governments favoring their own manufacturers, growers, and laborers. Only the United States and the United Kingdom have relatively important exports of cigarettes and other tobacco products.

Free-world exports of leaf tobacco amounted to 1.7 billion pounds in 1963, compared with 1.1 billion in 1935–1939. That was an increase of 60 percent, in contrast to the 38-percent rise in world production of leaf tobacco. This development reflects the rapid rise in consumption in western Europe, which needed proportionately larger imports than could be acquired from domestic production to equate the rising leaf requirements of manufacturers.

The principal free-world exporters of flue-cured tobacco include the United States, the former Federation of Rhodesia and Nyasaland, India, and Canada. Other exporters include Italy, Brazil, Japan, Thailand, the Republic of South Africa, Pakistan, and mainland China. Bulgaria also ships some flue-cured tobaccos to the other Soviet-bloc countries.

The United States is the largest exporter of burley, but such countries as Greece, Mexico, Italy, and Japan have increased their export shipments. Practically all of the Maryland-type tobaccos entering foreign trade come from the United States, the Malagasy Republic, and Italy. Turkey, Greece, and Yugoslavia are the principal free-world exporters of oriental tobaccos.

Changes or shifts in consumer demand for the different kinds of products have an effect on trade. Many times, shifts in manufacturing, other than consumer demand, are mostly due to the fluctuations in domestic supplies or foreign availabilities, rising prices of leaf supplies, and changes in internal taxes.

Fixed retail prices, in conjunction with rising internal taxes, often hampers selective buying of quality grades when raw leaf prices are advancing, thus causing a modification in a present blend or the complete elimination of a brand from the market. Import trade restrictions in many nonmonopoly countries also affect the different kinds, types, and blends of tobacco products. These usually consist of high import duties, along with variable or preferential rates on leaf tobacco and internal variable excise rates, which tax products made of imported leaf at a higher rate than products made from domestic leaf.

The introduction of filter-tipped brands in the fifties has also brought about some changes in world cigarette leaf trade. Filter-tipped production permits the use of lower qualities or grades of cigarette leaf tobaccos, requires less leaf to manufacture a given number, and increases the number of cigarettes smoked daily by consumers. Also, the use of the filter and the various flavorings as new techniques in production has definitely facilitated the greater use of the medium and lower grades of cigarette tobaccos and fosters the possibility of even further substitution among different kinds or types of cigarette tobaccos.

The introduction of specialized machines, which utilize stems, midribs, small leaf particles, and such and transform them into homogenized sheet or microflake filler, has cut the costs of raw materials and increased the volume of finished products from a smaller amount of raw leaf.

Before the war, quality leaf was essential in the manufacture of specific types of cigarettes. Cigarette leaf was assessed and priced according to the special characteristics of quality—a suitable rate of burn, low nicotine content, desirable flavor and aroma, and chemical composition.

There is no world price or standardized grades for tobacco entering world trade. Each of the many types and varieties has its own grade designations, which are marketed at different prices, usually according to supply and demand. Also, the price varies for the same type and variety according to the area or district of growth.

The difference in climate and soil conditions in an area or district gives the special quality characteristics to the leaf. The export price may reflect the interplay of free market forces, modified in various ways or forms by efforts of governments to support growers' incomes, retain high foreign exchange earnings, and reduce unemployment in rural areas.

Trade barriers tend to limit imports and direct trade toward specific suppliers. The barriers take the form of high import duties, import licenses, foreign exchange regulations, bilateral agreements, mixing regulations, guaranteed purchase arrangements, and preferential duties.

TOBACCO is used in one form or another in all parts of the world. Smokers are numerous in every country.

Cigarette smoking is the most popular form of tobacco consumption, but there have been some marked changes in the preferred method of smoking in recent years. Only about one-third of the tobacco consumed in 1935 was in the form of cigarettes. It was estimated that more than three-fourths of world consumption of tobacco in 1963 was in the form of cigarettes.

The most important cigarette blends in the world are American, English, oriental, dark, and Maryland. Climate, income of consumers, and the availability of leaf influence the type of blend produced. Many countries influence the type of blends by monopoly control, tariff policy, price policy, and various trade restrictions.

The American-blend cigarette is the most popular in the world. As produced in the United States, it consists of about 55 percent flue-cured, 35 percent burley, 1 or 2 percent Maryland, and 8 or 9 percent oriental leaf. Casing, such as sugar and flavorings, help standardize the taste. Tobaccos used in this blend are normally aged 2 to 3 years before use. In most other countries the ratio of flue-cured to burley is usually higher than in the American blend.

The English blend, second in popularity, normally contains only flue-cured leaf, which is packaged fairly dry. A high-quality leaf with a good, bright color is used to produce it.

Dark blends in most countries are made primarily from dark domestic tobaccos. This blending varies widely from one region to another because of the wide differences in the dark types of tobacco available. Government policies in many countries are designed to encourage the consumption of domestic-grown dark tobaccos. Flavors and spices are sometimes added to dark blends. Important consuming countries for dark cigarettes are Spain, Cuba, France, Colombia, Indonesia, and Brazil, all of which produce dark types of tobacco.

Blends made solely from oriental leaf are smoked mostly in the Balkan countries and Middle East. Oriental tobaccos are used extensively in other parts of the world in American and modified oriental blends. Leading consumers of oriental blends are Greece, Turkey, Yugoslavia, Iraq, Iran, and Syria. Modified oriental blends, which use oriental tobacco as a filler, are popular in West Germany, Austria, and Italy.

The Maryland blend, made from a light, air-cured tobacco of the same name, comprises about one-half of the cigarette sales in Switzerland. Sizable amounts of this blend are sold in France.

About 10 percent of the world's tobacco is smoked in pipes. Pipe smokers in most countries have a wide choice in blends—some mild, some strong, and some heavily sauced.

Chewing tobacco is available as sauced leaf scrap, natural leaf twists, and heavily sauced plugs. Chewing tobaccos are usually heavy grades of leaf.

Snuff could be considered a variation of chewing. It consists of a dry, fine powder, which is used for dipping and tucking under the lower lip.

The principal producers of chewing tobaccos and snuff include the United States, Sweden, India, Algeria, South Africa, West Germany, France, Norway, Denmark, Italy, and the Dominican Republic. These products account for about 5 percent of the consumption of tobacco.

Cigars and cigarillos account for about 4 percent of world tobacco consumption. They are of many types, flavors, blends, shapes, and sizes. The principal producers include the United States, West Germany, the Netherlands, Denmark, Colombia, Indonesia, Belgium, Switzerland, India, Italy, Cuba, and Canada.

Other specialty tobacco products include water pipe tobacco, tombac, kerf, and hookah. They are produced primarily in the Middle East, southern Asia, and southeastern Asia.

World cigarette output increased from an average of 1,616 billion pieces during 1951–1955 to about 2,388 billion in 1962.

Americans older than 15 years smoked an average of 3,985 cigarettes in 1961. In some other countries: Canada, 2,960; Australia, 2,760; the Netherlands, 1,840; the United Kingdom, 2,835; Belgium, 1,655; India, 150.

In 1962 cigarette output in North America and Central America was about 630 billion pieces, representing about 26 percent of the total world output. The United States accounted for about 85 percent of the production in North America and Central America and 22 percent of world production.

Production of cigarettes in South America in 1962 totaled 127 billion pieces. The largest producers were Brazil, Argentina, and Colombia, whose output accounted for 83.5 percent of the total output for the area.

Cigarette production in Western Europe in 1962 was 460 billion pieces. The largest producers in Europe were the United Kingdom, Italy, West Germany, and France. The English-type cigarette predominates in the United Kingdom; however, in the rest of western Europe large quantities of the American blend, the modified oriental blend, and dark blends are produced.

Production of cigarettes in Africa in 1962 was 68.1 billion pieces. The United Arab Republic and South Africa were the major producers in this area.

Cigarette output in Asia in 1962 totaled 682 billion pieces. The major Asian producers were mainland China, Japan, Indonesia, and India. Most of the cigarettes were made from native leaf; however, American-type cigarettes were gaining in popularity. Production of cigarettes in Oceania totaled 22.7 billion pieces in 1962.

The production of filter-tipped cigarettes has been increasing. In 1955 they accounted for about 10 percent of the output; they accounted for about one-third of the world output in 1962.

Higher retail prices, the smaller quantity of leaf required, and publicity linking smoking to health problems caused a sizable shift to filter cigarettes.

HUGH C. KIGER *became Director of the Tobacco Division of the Foreign Agricultural Service in 1961. Previously he was Chief of the Foreign Marketing Branch of that Division. He joined the Department of Agriculture in 1949.*

FRANKLIN S. EVERTS *became Chief, Commodity Analysis Branch, Tobacco Division, Foreign Agricultural Service, in 1956. He joined the Department in 1942.*

EDWARD J. EISENACH, *a supervisory agricultural economist in the Tobacco Division of Foreign Agricultural Service, joined the Department in 1952.*

Forests and Forest Products

by ALBERT A. DOWNS

FORESTS once covered about half the land area of the earth. They were absent or rare only in ice-capped polar regions, barren mountains, deserts, and dry grasslands.

People over the centuries have cleared forests for farming and have overcut and overgrazed and burned forests, so that now about one-third of the earth's land surface is in forest or is classified as forest land.

A long period of extensive and indiscriminate clearing and abuse is nearing its end, and people are beginning to conserve the forests.

Many governments recognize the value of forests in furnishing timber for industry and the home, a refuge for wildlife, and recreation for people; in regulating streamflow; and in checking soil erosion.

Abuses by the uninformed, however, outweigh proper uses in some countries. In Iraq, for example, some public and private planting programs, preceded sometimes by expensive work to control erosion, have been offset by overgrazing, shifting cultivation, frequent fires, and destructive cutting by Kurdish tribes in remote mountain forests.

Of the total of 11 billion acres of forest lands that remain in the world, one-third is unlikely to be commercially valuable, at least in the near future, because adverse climate or soil conditions make the stands too open or too scrubby. Another third is commercially valuable and in use. The remaining third is potentially commercial but may not be in use or is inaccessible.

The forests are fairly well distributed regionally. Although Europe, except the European part of the Soviet Union, has less forest than other physically larger regions, it is 30 percent forested—better than Africa (25 percent) or Asia (19 percent). The two most densely populated areas, Asia (without Asiatic Soviet Union) and Europe, however, have a per capita forest area of only 0.8 acre, compared with 17 acres in South America and 13.6 acres in the Soviet Union.

Slightly more than half the world's forest area is deemed accessible by existing waterways, roads, railways, or other transportation. Nearly all forests in Europe are accessible and in use, but other regions have large tracts of inaccessible forest, particularly the Amazon Basin and the northern parts of the Soviet Union and North America north of Mexico.

The accessible forests not in use are not necessarily a ready reserve from which rising timber requirements will be met in the future. Generally, these forests are not in use because they grow on poorer sites, are less well stocked, or are stocked with less desirable species than those in use. Often they are noncommercial. Stands of scrubby alpine birch in Norway and the sparsely wooded savannas in Tanganyika and the Republic of the Sudan, for example, produce little but fuelwood.

Much of the inaccessible forest in the North Temperate Zone is also noncommercial, especially in places where climate limits growth, as in northern Canada and the Soviet Union, in high mountains, and in dry areas. Inaccessible areas in the Tropics are likely to contain good timber stands, as in the Amazon Basin, the Andes, middle Africa, and southeastern Asia.

Most forests—especially the inaccessible and the less desirable accessible forests—are publicly owned. More than three-fourths of the accessible forests are owned by the state or public entities.

Private ownership of accessible forests is most marked in Europe (55 percent), in South America (45 percent), and in North America (43 percent). Nearly all forests are publicly owned in the Communist countries. There is a tendency toward public ownership of forest land in less-developed regions.

CONIFERS OCCUPY a little more than one-third of the world's forest area; broadleaf species, slightly less than two-thirds. Conifers occur mostly north of the Tropic of Cancer.

On an area basis, 98 percent of the coniferous forests, composed mainly of pines, spruces, firs, and larches, is in the Northern Hemisphere. Conifers in the Southern Hemisphere, mainly araucarias, podocarps, and dammarpines or kauris, generally are mixed with broadleaf species and are not abundant. An exception is a fairly large area of an araucaria, known as Paraná pine in the trade, which occurs in fairly pure stands in southern Brazil and has been heavily exploited.

Plantings of the useful conifers have been made in the Southern Hemisphere. Conifers have been the mainstay of large-scale wood industries for generations, because they are adaptable for many purposes, notably construction, packaging, and pulp and paper. Oddly enough, the most widely planted conifer, Monterey pine, is an import from the United States, where it occurs in a restricted area along the coast of central California and is not utilized extensively. Monterey pine has been planted in New Zealand, Australia, Chile, and South Africa.

Despite the predominance of broadleaf species, somewhat more than half of the forest area in use is coniferous, nearly all in the Soviet Union, North America, and Europe. The use of broadleaf forests is geographically more evenly distributed, but more than two-fifths of the broadleaf area in use is the temperate broadleaf forests of North America, the Soviet Union, and Europe.

Vast tracts of tropical broadleaf forests in Latin America (including Mexico and Central America), Asia, and Africa are not in use, because of inaccessibility and the bewildering number of species.

Unlike temperate forests, tropical forests are generally a mixture of a great many species with a low volume per acre of any one species. In the mahogany-bearing part of the Amazon rain forest, the number of merchantable mahogany trees probably is less than one to the acre.

Indonesia has at least 4 thousand species of native trees that reach saw log size. Indonesian foresters estimate that about 400 will become commercially important because of useful wood properties or abundance. Only a few of these species are now known in foreign markets, and not many more are used domestically, because the properties and proper use of most of these timbers are unknown or because steady supplies cannot be guaranteed.

THE VOLUME of growing stock in forests in use is estimated at 5.5 trillion cubic feet—two-thirds coniferous and one-third broadleaf. Volumes of growing stock in North America, Europe, and the Soviet Union have been estimated at 4.1 trillion cubic feet.

The volume in all forests is probably twice that of forests in use. Because a large part of the forests not in use is in the Tropics, the proportion of volume in broadleaf species is large.

Gross annual growth is estimated at 1.8 percent of the growing stock, equal to about 100 billion cubic feet. The drain on forests in use (removals, waste in the forest, and losses from fire, insects, disease, shifting cultivation, and transportation, especially in rafting and in floating) has probably been less than the gross growth since 1955.

There appears to be no wood shortage for the world at present consumption rates, but the uneven distribution of forests, lack of conifers locally, current quality and species requirements, high transportation costs, and waste in the woods and at processing plants produce timber shortages in places.

The Soviet Union, Europe, and North America, with less than one-third of the world's population, have two-thirds of all forests, have nine-tenths of the coniferous area in use, and account for two-thirds of all removals. This roundwood volume includes more than four-fifths of the world's output of industrial wood.

Timber removed from the world's forests totaled about 62 billion cubic feet in 1960—37 percent saw and veneer logs; 15 percent pulpwood and pit props; 6 percent other industrial wood, such as poles, posts, and piling; and 42 percent fuel and charcoal wood.

Wood for fuel accounted for nearly three-fourths of removals in the less-developed regions—Africa, Latin America, and Asia-Pacific—but less than one-fourth in North America, Europe, and the Soviet Union. Although a little more than half of all removals is coniferous, three-fourths of the industrial wood is coniferous and four-fifths of the fuelwood is broadleaf.

Coniferous forests generally are utilized more completely and efficiently than broadleaf ones. Greater usable volumes per acre in coniferous forests—because of the prevalence of pure stands and the economic usability of small trees and logs—favor mechanization in logging and close utilization.

Rather low usable volumes per acre in broadleaf forests, particularly in the Tropics—because of the mixture of species of widely varying wood properties, utility, and marketability—favor low-investment animal logging and wasteful utilization. Logging in broadleaf stands in Latin America and Asia is primitive and expensive in many places, and only choice logs of desirable species may be brought out. Other logs are left to rot in the woods. Sometimes the best logs, such as butt logs, are also left, because they are too big to handle manually.

Major processed forest products are lumber, plywood, fiberboard, and particle board—panels made from scrap wood. The order cited corresponds to the order in which those industries developed in the course of time. It also corresponds to the present order of importance, as measured by roundwood consumed, value of output, or direct employment afforded.

The sawmilling industry employs two-thirds of the forest industries labor force, uses about two-thirds of the industrial roundwood, and furnishes nearly half of the gross output value of all forest industries. The pulp and paper industry employs one-fourth of the forest industries labor force and uses about one-fourth of the industrial roundwood, but it furnishes more than two-fifths of the gross output value.

Capital invested by the pulp and paper industry is three to four times that of the sawmilling industry. Plants tend to be larger and more mechanized, and they yield a much higher gross value per unit of raw material used. Compared with these two giants, the wood-based panel industries—plywood, fiberboard, and particle board—are comparatively minor.

World lumber output in 1960 was estimated at 140 billion board feet, four-fifths of it coniferous. Because the wood of conifers can be readily sawn and planed and is strong in relation to its weight, it is preferred for many purposes. The Soviet Union, Europe, and North America produced most of the coniferous lumber and two-thirds of the broadleaf lumber. Temperate broadleaf species, such as oak, maple, birch, and black walnut, are well known.

They are used mainly in furniture, flooring, and a great variety of other high-value wood products.

Tropical woods vary greatly in physical properties. Balsa, mainly from Ecuador, is lighter and softer than cork. Local species of ironwood are extremely heavy and so hard that they turn nails.

United States imports of lumber or logs of tropical broadleaf species consist mainly of specialty woods.

They include fine woods, whose ornamental grain and desirable physical properties make them suitable for furniture and cabinetwork. Among them are true mahogany from Latin America, African mahogany, and some Philippine dipterocarps.

We also import some others whose unusual properties make them outstanding for other uses. They include lignumvitae from Central America, one of the hardest and heaviest of woods. It has the unique property of being self-lubricating. It is especially good for bearings under water, and is widely used for bearing or bushing blocks lining the stern tubes of propeller shafts of ships. Lignumvitae wears better than metal and needs no lubrication in such uses.

Teak from southeastern Asia is one of the outstanding woods of the world. Its strength, durability, and dimensional stability under varying moisture conditions make it ideal for many uses, particularly in shipbuilding.

WORLD OUTPUT was 70 million short tons of pulp and 82 million tons of paper in 1960. North America and Europe accounted for more than four-fifths of the production.

Somewhat less than a third of the pulp was mechanical woodpulp, mainly for newsprint and fiberboards. Nearly two-thirds was chemical and semichemical woodpulp used chiefly in papers other than newsprint and for paperboard and synthetic materials, such as rayon, plastics, and films. About 6 percent of the pulp came from nonwood sources—straw, bamboo, bagasse, and grasses, such as esparto in Spain and northern Africa and sabai in India.

About 90 percent of the woodpulp is made from the long-fibered conifers, but the use of broadleaf pulp has been increasing, usually mixed with coniferous pulp.

Paper production was 19 percent

newsprint; 18 percent printing and writing paper; 30 percent other paper, including tissues, wrapping paper, cigarette paper, and wallpaper; and 33 percent paperboard, largely for corrugated containers, cardboard boxes, and food containers.

More than half of the world's plywood output (544 million cubic feet in 1960) is produced in North America, largely from the conifer Douglas-fir. It is destined for construction and general utility purposes.

Most of the plywood produced in the rest of the world is broadleaf and destined for furniture, cabinetwork, or paneling. Broadleaf plywood in Europe and the United States is faced with choice domestic species, such as black walnut and birch, or ornamental woods from tropical Latin America and Africa, such as mahogany and okoume.

Japan, a major producer and exporter of broadleaf plywood, operates largely on lauan veneer logs imported from the Philippines.

The plywood category includes other products, such as blockboard, battenboard, and cellular wood panels. Blockboard and battenboard consist of a thick core composed of blocks, laths, or battens glued together and surfaced with veneer. In cellular wood panels, the core consists of battens or laths spaced one from the other either parallel or in lattice form.

Fiberboard production in North America and Europe accounted for four-fifths of the world output (4.7 million short tons) in 1960. This was three-fifths hardboard (compressed) and two-fifths insulation board (noncompressed). North America makes more insulation board than hardboard, but the reverse is true for other regions.

Two million tons of particle board were produced in 1960, two-thirds in Europe. This board is a sheet material manufactured from small pieces of wood (chips, flakes, or shavings) agglomerated by an organic binder and heat and pressure. The major uses

of particle boards so far have been core stock for plywood, flooring, facing for concrete forms, and paneling.

NONWOOD FOREST products include a multitude of items collected for industrial and home use, medicine, and food. Some products are important only locally, but many enter international trade. The United States imported in 1962 crude or slightly processed nonwood forest products valued at more than 100 million dollars.

Bamboos are an essential of existence in parts of eastern Asia. Complete houses are built solely of bamboo and without nails. Other uses include fencing, weapons, furniture, clothes, paper pulp, bridges, road surfacing, baskets, mats, domestic utensils, containers, tool handles, farm implements, binding material, fishing equipment, fuel, and food. With some exceptions, especially Ecuador, bamboos have not been extensively utilized in the Western Hemisphere. Bamboos are giant perennial grasses. Some species grow more than 100 feet in height and up to a foot in diameter. Like other grasses, the culms, or stems, attain total height and diameter in one growing season.

Cork, the dead outer bark of the cork oak native to the Mediterranean region, was used extensively by the ancient Greeks. Cork is stripped from the trunks periodically. If the operation is carefully done with no injury to the live inner bark, the trees are not harmed and continue to produce.

Many gums, resins, and latexes are obtained by tapping or wounding the live inner bark or the live sapwood. Gums are commoner in trees of drier regions and are used in adhesives, paints, candies, and medicines, and in the printing and finishing of textiles and the sizing of paper. Gum arabic, gum tragacanth, and karaya gum are the most important and better known gums.

Resins include a host of substances, such as copals, dammars, lacquer, turpentines, balsams, and elemis, which have many uses, particularly in the paint and varnish industry. The turpentine industry in the southern pine region of the United States is the world's largest producer of turpentine and rosin. The flow of pine resin is often increased by spraying the chip or wound with sulfuric acid.

Guttapercha and chicle are best known among the many latexes tapped from wild trees. One of the important uses of guttapercha is in the construction of submarine cables, and no suitable substitute has been found. Guttapercha is a poor conductor of electricity. It is resistant to salt water and pliable and yet has the right amount of rigidity. Chicle is the basis of the chewing gum industry.

The production of some products, such as some tannins, drugs, and essential oils, involves destruction of the tree.

Tannin extracts are prepared from the whole bark of many species, especially wattles and mangroves, and from the wood of quebracho trees in Argentina and Paraguay. Tannin also comes from the fruits of myrobalan trees in southeastern Asia and divi-divi and tara trees in tropical America and the acorn cups of the valonia oak of Asia Minor.

Quinine, valuable in the treatment of malaria, originally was extracted from the whole bark of cinchona trees, native to the Andes of northern South America. Most quinine now comes from large cinchona plantations in the Far East, particularly Java.

Curare, the arrow poison of some South American Indians, is extracted from the bark, roots, and woody stems of certain lianas. Various alkaloids found in curare are used in medicine. The demand for the fragrant sandalwood and sandalwood oil, an essential oil, has been so great that sandalwood has been nearly exterminated in many parts of the East.

Palms furnish fibers for brushes, cordage, hats and mats, and baskets; fatty oils expressed from the nuts; and important waxes scraped from the leaves. Carnauba wax, chiefly from northeastern Brazil, is valuable, because it is hard and has a high melting point.

Rattans, stems of climbing palms which may attain a length of 200 feet or more, are used for furniture, ship fenders, and canes and in plaiting or coarse weaving of many articles. Rattans occur in many tropical rain forests, but the most pliable and best quality whole and split rattan comes from southeastern Asia.

Some nuts, such as brazil nuts, pistachio nuts, and chestnuts, still come mainly from wild trees.

The preferred beverage of millions of South Americans is maté brewed from the leaves of Paraguay tea, a tree of the highlands of Paraguay and southern Brazil.

INTERNATIONAL TRADE in wood and wood products is large, mainly because forests in use are unevenly distributed in relation to population density and forest industries are concentrated in North America and Europe.

Densely populated Europe is a heavy net importer of roundwood, processed wood, and woodpulp, but a major exporter of paper and paper products. Although the Soviet Union and North America are net exporters of wood, their different degrees of industrialization is reflected in the kind of exports— the Soviet Union exports mainly lumber and roundwood and North America, which is a net importer of roundwood, exports woodpulp, paper, and processed wood.

The less-developed regions tend to be net exporters of roundwood and net importers of manufactured wood products, particularly paper.

Because of the need for a variety of products and because the flow of raw materials in (for processing) and out (after processing), the two highly industrialized areas, North America and Europe, account for about four-fifths of international trade in wood.

The United States in 1960 was the world's largest producer, importer, and consumer of industrial wood products on a value basis. As an exporter, it ranked behind Canada, Sweden, and Finland.

Per capita consumption of wood is highest in North America. The industrialized areas, North America, Europe, and the Soviet Union use much more industrial roundwood per person than fuelwood, but the reverse is true in the less-developed regions, Latin America, Africa, and Asia-Pacific.

The consumption of industrial wood products varies tremendously from country to country, depending chiefly on the degree of industrialization. In some less-developed countries, nearly all the wood used goes into fuelwood. Per capita consumption of industrial wood in the United States thus is more than 300 times that of Ethiopia, but fuelwood consumption in Ethiopia is 6 times that of the United States.

Some forest-rich countries like Finland, the Soviet Union, Sweden, and Norway use lumber as lavishly as the United States and Canada, but none comes close to North America in the use of plywood and paper. North American per capita consumption of paper is 3 times that of Europe, 12 times that of the Soviet Union, and 50 times that of Africa.

TRENDS in world production since 1955 indicate that outputs of all wood products except fuelwood will probably increase in the next decade.

The output of lumber has not kept pace with the rise in general industrial output or with the increase in population. As a result, per capita consumption has been decreasing.

The pulp, paper, fiberboard, and particle board industries, unlike the sawmilling industry, are able to operate on small-size timber and frequently on less valuable species. Furthermore, they are to an increasing extent utilizing wood residues from sawmills and veneer and plywood plants and even residues from forest operations. The percentage increase in outputs of these products has been double or more of that of lumber.

The particle board industry, able to operate on the cheapest raw material and almost unknown in 1950, has grown rapidly; output in 1960 was four times that of 1955.

The plywood industry has also grown rapidly. The output in 1960 was 2.5 times that of 1950. Although large, good logs are needed for at least the face veneer, plywood has several advantages over lumber. It does not split, warps little, and can be made in large, easily used panels.

Lumber is being displaced by wood-panel products as well as by masonry, metals, and plastics in construction, furniture, and other end products and by paperboard in packaging.

Although man, in the near future, will probably clear some land suitable for agriculture, such deforestation will tend to be balanced by the reforestation of denuded forest land near population centers to avoid the expense of opening up inaccessible areas and of the high transportation costs. Tropical forests contain huge supplies of wood, but increasing use of these areas will be slow because of problems of accessibility, utilization, and marketing. The increasing demand for wood products will probably quicken the current trend of better and more intensive management of forests now in use and greater utilization of what was formerly considered unavoidable waste in the woods and at the processing plants.

The man in the street (as well as governments) is becoming more conscious of the multiple uses of forests—wood, water, forage, recreation, wildlife, and protection from floods and soil erosion. As this understanding grows, forests, a renewable resource, will be more wisely managed for the benefit of all people.

ALBERT A. DOWNS, *a research forester in the Forest Service, became Chief of the Foreign Forestry Resources Branch in 1958. Before 1950 he did research in timber improvement, forest management, and tree genetics. He received his undergraduate training at The Pennsylvania State University. He died April 2, 1964.*

Fibers Are Universal

by HORACE G. PORTER

ALL PEOPLE, except maybe a few primitive tribesmen, use fibers. Nearly all countries produce one or more fibers.

Fibers and manufactured products containing fibers enter the international trade of practically all countries.

Thousands of plants and animals give us fibers. Most of them are unused.

Many are used on an essentially noncommercial basis and only in the neighborhoods where they grow. Only a few-score natural fibers are articles of commerce; they are as basic in our lives as food and shelter.

Most natural fibers—cotton, silk, wool, linen, sisal, and many more—have been in use for hundreds or thousands of years for clothing, coverings, cords, and countless other useful items.

Manmade fibers—rayon, nylon, Dacron, and so on—are new. Their commercial production was small until the twenties. Work to develop them in latter part of the 19th century apparently was aimed at producing commercially profitable substitutes for silk and chiefly involved ways of handling cellulose—the woody part of trees and other plants—in the form of continuous filaments. Some countries wanted to lessen their dependence on imported textile fibers; rayon staple fibers were developed and placed in large-scale production.

The results achieved with cellulosic fibers and the lure of financial reward believed awaiting anyone who could produce at a reasonable cost any fiber with desirable characteristics led many firms and individuals to join the laboratory searches for new fibers. Their successes have been phenomenal.

But the direct and indirect search for substitutes for natural fibers has gone much further than the development of manmade fibers.

We have seen how cotton cement bags first lost out to paper bags; the paper bags have now lost ground to bulk handling. On American farms, the shifting from the grain binder to the combine has reduced the use of binder twine in grain harvesting. In American homes, paper towels and napkins, plastic place mats, and automatic dishwashers have cut the use of cloth towels and napkins.

FIBERS perform so many services that we tend not to notice some of them.

We may forget that fibers are used in our paper money; cigarette papers; pillows, mattresses, and box springs; upholstered furniture and slipcovers; artists' paintings; window blinds and shades; carpets and carpet pads; electrical cords; umbrellas; shades and felt bases for lamps; hairnets; bandages; ironing board pads and covers; shoes; brushes; tea bags; twine, cord, and rope; bookbinding; door mats; flags and pennants; stuffed animals and other toys; fire, garden, radiator, and vacuum cleaner hoses; belts for automobiles and appliances; automobile interiors and tires; laundry bags; luggage; typewriter ribbons; projection screens; awnings; furniture; the backing of linoleum and wallpapers; tents, packs, and other camping equipment; boats and fishing equipment; and fine writing papers.

An upholstered chair is an illustration of the ways several fibers—each with its own characteristics—are combined to serve mankind. Such a chair may contain webbing of jute from Pakistan or India; twine made from Italian hemp to tie the springs; linen thread (to sew upholstery) that may be made of French flax that was retted and scutched in Belgium and spun in some other country; padding that may consist of some combination of Spanish moss, cotton linters, animal hair, sisal or flax tow, coconut or palm fibers, or foam rubber; and an upholstery fabric of cotton, linen, mohair, silk, manmade fibers, or some blend of fibers.

No attempt is made here to compete with recognized textile or general dictionaries concerning matters of definition or to compete with such works as *Matthew's Textile Fibers*, which devotes nearly 1,300 pages to the subject of textile fibers and on which this and the following chapters on fibers have drawn rather heavily.

It is adequate for our purpose to think of a fiber as the raw material out of which yarns, cords, ropes, cloth, felt, brushes, and the like are made. Generally speaking, they can be spun into yarns and knitted or woven, twisted into ropes, matted into padding, or cut and fashioned into brushes and whisks, although some (such as kapok) are too weak to be spun and are used largely as stuffing materials.

Fibers vary in physical and chemical characteristics and their uses. People therefore have classified fibers in various ways at one time or another.

One is to divide them on the basis of origin—whether they are natural or manmade; whether the natural fibers are of vegetable, animal, or mineral origin; and whether the manmade fibers are of a cellulose, silica, or a chemical origin.

Fibers customarily spun and woven into fabrics often are referred to as apparel fibers. Others, such as abaca or sisal, are known as cordage fibers or as industrial fibers.

Such a system of classification by use can accommodate some of the major fibers, but it is not all-inclusive, and it tends to imply an understatement of the versatility of many fibers.

The discussion of the families of fibers in the next chapters follows the classification by origin. Natural fibers are subdivided into those of vegetable and those of animal origin, and each is further broken down according to systems that are explained as the need arises.

THE FAMILIES of fibers of vegetable origin have a greater volume than the total of fibers of animal, manmade, and mineral origins.

Cotton and jute are the leaders, but many other vegetable fibers—each with its own characteristics—serve mankind.

Some vegetable fibers, such as cotton, kapok, and milkweed, are hair fibers that are produced in the seed pod of the plant. Others, like jute, flax, hemp, and ramie, are stem fibers; the fibers lie between the outer bark and the woody central cylinder of the stem. Generally the seed and stem fibers are in the group of soft fibers, as contrasted with the hard fibers, like sisal, henequen, and abaca, which generally are characterized as leaf fibers.

Asbestos, a mineral fiber, was formed under intense heat and pressure. Commercially important deposits exist throughout the world, but the largest volume is mined in Canada, Southern Rhodesia, the Republic of South Africa, and the Soviet Union. The main deposits in the United States are in Arizona and Vermont.

Of the six types of asbestos of commercial importance, one, chrysotile, is used in textile processing. About 65 percent of the world's supply of this type is mined in Quebec.

Asbestos will not burn; it remains stable under high heat. It is used to manufacture safety clothing and for industrial uses where heat resistance is essential. Asbestos fibers one-quarter to three-quarters inch long are used for spinning into yarns. Because the fibers are so short, pure asbestos yarns are weak unless asbestos is blended with cotton or manmade fibers.

HORACE G. PORTER *is Chief, Foreign Competition Branch, Cotton Division, Foreign Agricultural Service.*

Cotton, King

of Fibers

by VERNON L. HARNESS and
HORACE G. PORTER

THE ORIGIN of cotton is lost in the darkness of unrecorded time, but there is strong evidence that man's use of cotton—this king of fibers—was well developed at least 5 thousand years ago. Despite the deep inroads that competitive fibers and other materials have made in many of its traditional uses, cotton still serves more people in more ways than ever before.

Bits of cotton fabric and string dating from 3000 B.C. were found in 1929 in Pakistan. Even at that early date, the art of dyeing fabric was practiced. Today the manufacture of cotton cloth continues to dominate the utilization of cotton. Estimates are that the total number of uses to which cotton in its various forms has been put exceeds a thousand. The list grows constantly.

Cotton is man's servant universally because of its adaptability to many uses and its inexpensiveness and because it can be grown around the world and converted into useful items on highly standardized equipment.

The fiber can be woven into cloth one-fourth inch thick or so sheer and delicate as to have been referred to as "webs of woven wind."

A pound of cotton can be spun so coarse that it would extend not more than a few hundred yards, or so fine that it would reach from Washington to New York. Cotton cloth can be woven so tightly as to be waterproof. Chemical processes can make it resistant to flame, oil, rot, mildew, heat, and scorch. Modern cotton fabrics can be truly wash and wear. Cotton yarn and fabric can also be processed in such a manner as to retain considerable give or stretch.

COTTON is the name applied to the elongated epidermal cell of the seed-coat of certain species of the genus *Gossypium*.

Most countries produce cotton as an annual crop, and most commercial varieties are capable of producing a good crop in a single crop season. In places where the plant is not killed by frost, however, the cotton plant will live for some years and will develop into a small shrub. Some cotton produces on a satisfactory commercial scale as many as 3 years in Peru. Some cotton is replanted only every 7 years in northeastern Brazil.

Cotton is native to many regions of the world. There are a number of species of cotton. Some have 13 pairs of chromosomes, and others have 26 pairs. Only a few species, however, are of broad economic significance.

G. hirsutum, one of the tetraploid species with 26 pairs of chromosomes in the germ plasm, may have had its center of origin in southern Mexico and Central America. The cultivated varieties of American Upland cotton arose from this parental stock. Such Upland varieties now comprise about seven-eighths of the cotton produced in the world.

G. barbadense, another tetraploid species with 26 pairs of chromosomes, is believed to have originated in western South America. It is the parental stock of other cultivated varieties. This group includes the so-called Egyptian-type cottons of the United Arab Republic (Egypt), Republic of the Sudan, Peru, the United States, the Soviet Union, and a few other countries.

The third and fourth major groups of cultivated cottons, the so-called Asiatic types, are annual-type cottons that have as their parent stock the diploid species with 13 pairs of chromosomes, *G. arboreum* and *G. herbaceum*, which were native to ancient India. These Egyptian and Asiatic types account for the remaining one-eighth of the cotton produced in the world. The Egyptian types are considerably more important from a quantity standpoint than the Asiatic types.

Each of these broad types contains considerable dispersion with respect to staple length; the Egyptian type accounts for nearly all the extra-long staple cotton, or that having a staple length of 1.375 inches or longer. Most of the remaining Egyptian-type cotton is only a little shorter.

The Asiatic-type cottons tend to be the shortest. Much of it is shorter than three-fourths inch. Upland-type cottons account for the large volume of medium staples, although they partly overlap both the Egyptian-type and Asiatic-type cottons.

COTTON has been grown in the United States since early colonial times. Before 1793, when Eli Whitney invented the cotton gin, the lint had to be removed from the seed by hand, and the cotton was used largely at home.

Production was only 6 thousand bales the year before the gin was invented, 100 thousand bales in 1801, 5 million in 1878, 10 million in 1897, 15 million in 1911, and 19 million bales in 1937.

Exports first exceeded 100 thousand bales in 1806 and 1 million in 1837. They exceeded 5 million bales for the first time in 1890, and in 1911 and 1926 exceeded 11 million bales.

Consumption in the United States was about 100 thousand bales in 1820, 1 million bales in 1870, 5 million in 1908, and more than 11 million during the Second World War.

During the 5 crop years 1958–1962, the United States produced annually about 13.9 million bales, exported 5 million, and used 8.7 million bales. These quantities represent 30, 31, and 19 percent, respectively, of world total

levels—far in front of any other country.

The consumption of cotton in the United States has been holding up well in many end uses but has slipped badly in some. In fact, aggregate consumption of cotton for men's, women's, and children's clothing and for household items has been trending upward. Industrial usage has been declining.

The National Cotton Council of America has estimated that nearly 11 million American workers and their families depend on cotton for much of their livelihood. Another 11 million have livelihoods connected more remotely to cotton.

Cotton is grown on one-third of the farms in the Cotton Belt and accounts for more than one-third of cash receipts on those farms. Cotton brings in one-half to three-fourths of the cash farm receipts in some States.

World cotton production in 1963 climbed to 49.6 million bales—the equivalent of 24 trillion pounds. That is 3 percent larger than the record crop a year earlier and 5.9 million bales larger than the 1955–1959 average.

The area devoted to cotton in 1963 rose to about 80 million acres, and yields were at the exceptionally high average of about 296 pounds an acre. The high yields were attributable to generally favorable crop conditions in nearly all producing countries.

Production outside the United States seems likely to increase, for almost all producing countries have programs to maintain or increase output. Production incentives include direct encouragements (such as guaranteed prices, direct subsidies, and below-cost fertilizers and insecticides) and more indirect methods, like government-sponsored research and breeding services, free or low-cost development of irrigation, and marketing services.

All or most of the increase in production may occur outside the United States.

Government cotton programs in the United States have been designed to protect the income of producers at the same time that a major effort is being made by means of production controls to improve the world balance of supply and demand.

Indeed, the 1963 cotton crop in the United States of 15.5 million bales was actually below this country's production just a few decades ago. In 1926, for example, the record cotton crop was just short of 18 million bales.

In line with the efforts of the United States to restrict cotton production, acreage has been curtailed—14.2 million acres were harvested in 1963, compared with 44.6 million in 1926. A sharply rising trend in yields, however, has offset much of the drop in acreage.

For example, before 1940, average yields of lint seldom exceeded 200 pounds an acre; the average in 1963 was 524 pounds an acre.

COTTON is produced commercially in more than 75 countries. The crop is grown as far north as the 42d parallel in the Soviet Union (about as far north as Chicago) to as far south as the northern part of Argentina and southern Australia.

Cotton is grown in many different soils and under widely varying degrees of climate and technology, but all producing areas have a common characteristic—hot summers.

Twelve countries had cotton production in 1963–1964 that exceeded 640 thousand bales. They—the United States, the Soviet Union, mainland China, India, Mexico, Brazil, the United Arab Republic, Pakistan, Turkey, the Sudan, the Syrian Arab Republic, and Peru—accounted for 89 percent of total world production. The other producing countries together produced approximately 5.7 million bales.

Only the United States, the Soviet Union, and mainland China produce as much as 5.0 million bales of cotton per year. An indication of the competitive strength of the smaller producers is that their total production in 1963–1964 was more than double the corresponding level during 1950–1954,

while the total for the 12 larger producers increased only 19 percent.

IN SOME SECTIONS of the United States and in several other countries, the latest scientific achievements are applied to the cultivation of cotton.

The land is carefully broken with the latest equipment. High-quality seed of the best variety is planted. Weeds are controlled by preemergence chemical treatment, fire, oil, or other modern cultivation methods. Insects are suppressed. Irrigation is carried out where necessary and possible. When harvesttime arrives, mechanical equipment does the work of many men.

In some countries, however, techniques have advanced little in recent generations. Seed of poor quality may be dropped at random—sometimes intermixed with other crops—in soil scarcely scratched with a stick. The plant may be allowed to grow semiwild with little attempt to control weeds and insects. In some regions, a hoe with a short handle still is used. Finally, the small plot may be harvested by hand and carried to market in a bundle on the head. Most of the work in many places is done by women and children.

Wide variations exist in the sizes of cotton operations in many countries, including the United States, but not in others, such as Uganda, where most cottongrowers have only small patches, often less than an acre. Some farmers grow little else and thus rely on their cotton crop to produce all of their income with which they buy most of their food. Others give first attention to producing enough food for their needs and only devote extra land and effort to producing some cotton as a cash crop.

THE CULTURE of cotton in the United States normally follows such steps as the following.

The residue from the previous crop or the winter cover crop is plowed under, and the seedbed is leveled or ridged into rows. Fertilizer is frequently placed under the row.

A mechanical planter then opens a small furrow in the row, drops and covers the seed, and packs the earth. The amount of seed planted per acre is determined by many factors, including germination rate, seed type, soil, rainfall, type of planting pattern used, and later cultural practices. If the seed has not been planted at the proper rate, the young plants are thinned to the right number.

Much of the effort spent on the crop between planting and harvest goes into the control of grass and weeds.

One or more hoeings by hand may be necessary in connection with the use of mechanical cultivators, which loosen the soil and uproot weeds.

Other methods to control weeds make use of flame and chemicals. Several nozzles, two per row, mounted near the ground shoot out a continuous flame, which sears the young grass and weeds and leaves the tougher cotton plant undamaged.

Because flame cultivation cannot be used until the cotton is several inches high and able to withstand heat, however, the farmer must be prepared to use hand methods or other mechanical or chemical methods or all to combat grass and weeds.

One way is to apply a preemergence chemical in a band over the seedbed at the time of planting. The young cotton plant is not harmed by the chemical, but the germination of grass and weed seeds is delayed.

A postemergence chemical may be used; a band of chemical is sprayed on each side of the young cotton plant to kill grass and weeds. Care must be taken, for too much of this chemical will kill the cotton also.

Major insect enemies of cotton in the United States include the boll weevil, thrips, cotton leafworm, cotton bollworm, cotton fleahopper, lygus bug, cotton aphid, spider mite, and pink bollworm. The farmer's choice of insecticides depends on weather conditions, degree of infestation, and the method of application—whether by tractor equipment or by plane.

The cotton plant blossoms about 3 weeks after the square, or bud, appears. The blossom, which at first is creamy white or yellow, then pink, and finally red, falls after a few days and leaves the tiny ovary on the plant.

The ovary develops into a pod, known as a cotton boll. Fibers inside of the boll grow out from each seed and expand the boll until it is mature. The mature, unopened boll is about an inch in diameter and an inch and a half long.

Usually 45 to 65 days after blooming, the cotton boll bursts open like a clean, white powder puff. The fibers are called lint.

HARVEST may be by hand or mechanical equipment.

Hand methods generally are used in the eastern part of this country. Mechanical harvesting is used more in the central and western part.

In hand harvesting, the cotton may be picked from the bur, or the entire bur (the stalk part of the boll) may be pulled or snapped from the plant.

There are two types of mechanical harvesters. One picks the seed cotton. The other pulls the bur. The picker consists essentially of vertical drums equipped with revolving, barbed, or roughened wire spindles, to which the cotton adheres while it is pulled from the open boll. The stripper pulls the entire boll off the plant with rollers or mechanical fingers.

Since cotton is grown on both sides of the Equator in the Tropics as well as Temperate Zones, it is actually planted, and similarly harvested, over a large part of the year. Most cotton is produced in the Northern Hemisphere, however, and the peak harvesttime in the United States is also the main harvesttime for a substantial share of the world crop. World cotton statistics therefore are based on a marketing year starting August 1.

The harvested cotton is transported to a gin, where the lint is separated from the seed. A saw gin is used mainly for American Upland and

Asiatic cottons. Most extra-long staple cotton is ginned with a roller gin. Roller ginning is slower and more expensive than the saw gin but causes less damage to long fibers.

A typical saw gin has several stands, each of which has a series of circular saws mounted on a horizontal shaft. The saws reach between steel ribs, and as seed cotton is fed into the stand and comes within reach of the revolving saws, the lint is pulled from the seed and carried into a separate compartment, where the lint is removed from the saws by brushes or air suction. The lint is conveyed to the press, where it is baled. Most gins are equipped to remove excessive moisture, trash, burs, and foreign matter from the cotton.

The ginned lint is pressed into bales of about 500 pounds gross weight. The bales are covered with jute cloth held firmly in place by steel straps. Each bale is given an identifying number. The raw cotton is then ready for storage, shipment to domestic mills, or further compressing for export.

The identity of each bale is retained as it moves in trade. The owner who places a bale in a warehouse gets a receipt for the particular bale and not a receipt that is exchangeable for just any bale of the same weight and quality.

The practice in the United States is for the farmer to have his seed cotton ginned, and he, in turn, is the owner of the bale of cotton until such time as he disposes of it. Some foreign countries follow this practice, but in others it is customary for farmers to sell their cotton as seed cotton.

Cotton fibers vary greatly in physical characteristics. Because the individual fiber is the unit that determines spinning values—and there are 100 million or more fibers in each pound—a uniform method of describing the specific properties within each bale is necessary.

Factors like length, strength, fineness, and maturity are governed largely by the variety of the seed planted, weather, and farming practices. Characteristics such as color, leaf, and ginning preparation are affected largely by weather after the boll opens and by harvesting and ginning.

To measure its quality, a sample of fiber is taken from each bale after it is ginned. The sample is then classed according to grade and staple length, which materially affect the ultimate utility and market value of each bale.

COTTON TEXTILE manufacturing is divided generally into three operations—preparation; spinning, which results in yarn; and weaving, or knitting, which results in fabric.

Preparation consists of opening and blending cotton from several bales. Blending is important for there must be a maximum uniformity of fibers if a uniform quality product is to be obtained. Machines remove some impurities and foreign matter and form the lint into rolls, called laps, which are 40 to 45 inches wide.

The laps, which resemble huge rolls of absorbent cotton, are fed into carding machines, where the process of straightening or paralleling the fibers is begun. The fiber leaves the carding machines in a sliver, a round strand about the size of one's thumb. The sliver then passes through drawing equipment, where the straightening process is continued. The cotton is then formed into drawing slivers.

Either of two processes may follow—a breaker drawing or a finisher drawing. After drawing, the cotton passes through a roving frame. The fiber is slightly twisted and drawn into strands.

An alternative is to produce combed yarn, whereby slivers are carried through combing operations before roving. This removes more short fibers and impurities. Combed cotton generally is used in finer cotton textile products than the cotton that is only carded.

The roving strand finally is fed into a spinning frame, where it is drawn out and twisted into yarn of specific sizes and wound onto bobbins.

At this point, consideration must be given as to whether the yarn is to be used for lengthwise or crosswise yarns in a fabric. Lengthwise yarn, called warp, requires more twist than crosswise, or filling, or weft yarn, which undergoes less strain in weaving. Sometimes two or more yarns may be twisted together to form yarn of a given ply. For example, two yarns twisted together become two-ply.

Basic weaving principles have changed little through the years. It consists of simply interlacing the warp and filling yarns through each other at right angles.

Weaving is done on a loom, which has two or more harnesses for separating the warp yarns in such a way for the passage of the shuttle that the desired weaving pattern will result. These motions occur at high speeds. At a speed at which the shuttle makes 180 trips a minute, only 12 minutes are needed to weave a yard of fabric that requires 60 trips to make an inch.

After weaving and inspection, the cloth is ready to be bleached, dyed, printed, or otherwise finished before it is made up into one of the thousands of cotton products people use.

Cotton yarn is processed into several types of end products other than woven fabrics. Some yarn is used in knit goods, hosiery, underwear, sweaters, and so on. Softer yarns are used for this type of processing, by which the yarns are interlooped rather than interlaced. Knit goods generally have more stretch than woven goods.

Cotton yarn is also processed into thread by means of a high degree of twisting, which adds a great deal of strength. Further strength is imparted by plying the highly twisted yarns.

Cotton twine, sash cords, and such are made by still other processing techniques from the basic yarn made in the spinning stage. Some cotton is used in the unspun form for such products as surgical cotton.

WORLD TRADE in raw cotton may be expected to resume its long-term uptrend, after slipping to about 15.5 million bales in 1961 and 1962 from

the record of 17.7 million in 1959–1960.

Striking changes have been taking place in the sources of the world's supplies of cotton, however. Even though world consumption should rise considerably, the increase in world trade may not keep pace because of the likelihood that many producers of raw cotton will use more of their product at home.

The United States exports more cotton than any other country and accounts for about one-third of the world total. On the basis of their 1950–1954 average exports, the other nations among the top 10 exporters were the United Arab Republic, the Soviet Union, Mexico, Pakistan, Brazil, British East Africa, the Sudan, Peru, and Turkey. These countries accounted for 86 percent of total world exports of 12.5 million bales, but the total for the smaller exporters, although only 14 percent of the world total, was greater than any individual country other than the United States.

In 1961–1962, the world total of cotton moving in international trade was 15.5 million bales, or 25 percent above the 1950–1954 average level. The group of larger exporters expanded exports during this period by 16 percent, and the increase was distributed among 8 of the 10 countries. During the same period, the smaller countries expanded exports by 81 percent and raised their share of world trade from 14 percent in the earlier period to 20 percent in 1961–1962.

Exports from the cotton-producing countries are competing for markets among the changing group of net importing countries. The old traditional cotton textile producing and exporting countries are being pressed by a growing number of newly developing textile industries, especially in the Far East, the Middle East, southern Europe, and Africa. Some of these countries fill a large share of their raw cotton needs from domestic production.

Spain, once a large importer of raw cotton, has become self-sufficient in most qualities and has begun exporting small amounts of raw cotton. Spain has developed sizable exports of cotton textiles since 1950.

Japan continues as the world's largest importer of raw cotton—she often takes one-third of our cotton exports.

Other large, long-established buyers of raw cotton include France, West Germany, Italy, and the United Kingdom, where imports in 1963 were near the lowest level in this century. Hong Kong, Taiwan, and the Philippines have built up their textile industries rapidly and have stepped up imports of raw cotton.

The patterns in cotton textile trade also are shifting. No longer does the United Kingdom ship huge quantities of textiles to members of the Commonwealth and elsewhere. New exporters are arising.

As a natural sequence to the upsurge in textile production in foreign cotton-producing countries, exports of textiles represent an alluring chance to gain additional foreign exchange, provide employment, and, in some instances, a chance to save foreign exchange by using the homegrown product.

Prime examples of countries that export much domestically produced cotton in the form of textiles are the United Arab Republic, Pakistan, India, and Spain. They also export raw cotton.

The textile industries of Hong Kong, Korea, Taiwan, and the Philippines have expanded, even though they are largely or entirely dependent on imported raw materials.

The decade of the fifties was dynamic in various respects. This was true of the production of raw cotton and the export availabilities of various countries. It also was true of cotton textile manufacturing and in the sources and destinations of cotton textiles moving in international trade. Developments in these various areas have placed heavy burdens of adjustment upon the raw cotton and cotton textile industries of many countries.

The Long-Term International Cotton Textile Arrangement was negotiated in 1962 by the major cotton textile exporting and importing countries.

The major objectives of the understanding, which was negotiated under the general auspices of the General Agreement on Tariffs and Trade, were to maintain an orderly access to markets where imports were not subject to restrictions at the time the international arrangement was negotiated, to obtain increased access to markets where restrictions did exist, and to secure from exporting countries, when and where necessary, restraint in their export of cotton textiles to avoid market disruption in import markets.

Competition is sharpening between cotton and manmade fibers. The world has consumed larger quantities of textile fibers in nearly every year during the past decade. However, though it is still by far the world's most important textile fiber, consumption of cotton has not kept pace with the rise in the use of all fibers.

Total consumption of apparel fibers will likely continue to expand in the world as levels of living and populations rise. Output of manmade fibers as well as cotton will expand, and keen competition for the consumer's favor will continue.

VERNON L. HARNESS *joined the Foreign Competition Branch, Cotton Division, Foreign Agricultural Service, in 1963. He has worked in the Commodity Analysis Branch of the Cotton Division and the Department of Agricultural Economics at Auburn University.*

HORACE G. PORTER *became Chief, Foreign Competition Branch, Cotton Division, Foreign Agricultural Service, in 1957. Previously he worked on cotton and other fibers with the European Headquarters of the Marshall plan in Paris and with the Bureau of Agricultural Economics of the Department of Agriculture.*

Bast, the Textile Fibers

by CECILLE M. PROTZMAN

BAST, OR STEM, fibers are soft, pliable, and fine. Some of them are known to have been used in Europe and Egypt 5 thousand years ago.

The principal bast fibers, known as textile fibers, are in two general groups. Some, such as flax, ramie, and hemp, mainly are spun into yarn and woven into fabrics for clothing, household, and special industrial uses. The other group—jute, kenaf, sunn—mostly is woven into coarser fabrics for bagging and protective coverings.

Most bast fibers, however, are also used in threads, twines, and cordage, and each has important uses other than the principal ones. Each is used often with various other fibers or substituted for them.

Most bast fibers are in dicotyledonous plants that grow from seed and thrive in climates ranging from temperate to tropical.

The fiber lies between the outer bark and the woody central cylinder and gives the stem strength and flexibility. It is usually obtained by pulling the plants from the ground or cutting them near the base.

Some process of natural retting (or rotting) or chemical process is used to weaken the gums and connective substance that hold the parts of the plant stem together. This usually precedes but sometimes follows actual separation of the fiber. The fiber is separated, scraped, washed, straightened, and dried. It is then baled for marketing.

JUTE (*Corchorus capsularis* and *C. olitorius*), of the Tiliaceae family of plants, is a soft, lustrous, textile fiber, ranging from grayish white to almost red and obtained from the stems of cultivated plants.

It is an ancient fiber, but it entered the commercial world later than most of the other most commonly used vegetable fibers. Jute fiber now is the most widely used of the long vegetable fibers and is second only to cotton among all the natural plant fibers.

The jute plant may have originated in the Mediterranean area, but early records of the Bengal area of India-Pakistan mention it as a well-established plant there as early as 800 B.C. India and Pakistan produce the bulk of the current world supply.

An English firm made the first yarn spun by machine in 1820. Firms in Dundee, Scotland, began experiments with jute on their established flax machinery in 1832. Whale oil was introduced soon afterward as a softening agent for the fiber. These developments started the industry on a long period of prosperity. The use of jute increased when new processes were discovered for bleaching and waterproofing it and mixing it with any of many other fibers for special purposes.

By 1855 jute had replaced flax on most of the spindles in Dundee, which became the world center for the import and manufacture of jute.

Calcutta, India, erected its first jute mill and introduced power looms in the 1850's. The Indian industry soon replaced Dundee as the jute manufacturing center. Thus India, almost the only producer of jute fiber, became an exporter mainly of manufactured goods rather than of the raw fiber.

World production of jute reached a peak of 5,545 million pounds in 1961 and was 4,855 million pounds in 1963. The peak was 27 percent more than the average annual crop in the preceding 5 years and 61 percent more than the average in 1935–1939. Demand for jute continues to increase, even though competition has been strong from other fibers, materials, and methods of handling products.

Pakistan and India accounted for 96 percent of the world crop in 1963, when Pakistan produced 2,400 million pounds of jute and India produced 2,240 million pounds. Brazil ranked third, with 106 million pounds.

The leading jute-growing area was in the eastern part of India, especially in the hot, humid, valley lands of the Bramaputra and Ganges River Basins. The jute mills have been centered in Calcutta, a port city.

When Pakistan and India were separated in 1947, at least two-thirds of the jute-growing area was in Pakistan, and all the mills were in India. Trade was negotiated between the two countries, and a new trend began in the industry. India encouraged an increase in production of raw fiber to supply its mills and thus save foreign exchange on imports. Pakistan built mills to manufacture its raw jute and reap the benefit of increased value of its exports.

Indian production of raw jute increased 113 percent from the 1947–1951 average to the 1961 level of production. Production in Pakistan increased 25 percent during the same period, but Pakistan sales of manufactured jute goods, which began in 1951, grew to a value of 21 million dollars a year by 1960.

Brazil began growing jute in commercial quantities in the Amazon Valley in 1937 and ranked third in 1963.

The fiber is 6 to 10 feet long, smooth, and pliable. It takes dyes readily. It is adaptable to machine manufacture. Bags and coverings of jute cloth are strong and resist tear in shipping. Wherever bulky, strong fabrics and twines are required, jute is almost universally accepted because of its relatively low unit price, although it is not so strong as flax or many other soft fibers. It deteriorates rapidly, especially when exposed to moisture.

Jute is used mainly for items that support or protect other goods—burlaps, sacking, bagging, other protective coverings, backings, support webbings, twines, and felts.

A growing use is in backing cloth for carpets, linoleum, and oilcloth and alone or mixed with other fibers in the manufacture of carpets, rugs, matting, tapestries, curtains, upholstery, and novelty fabrics for dresses, coats, and trimmings.

The oldest use of all, cordage, still exists in twines, small cordage, binding thread for carpets, rugs, certain types of shoes, and core material for various cables. The coarse butt ends of the fibers are manufactured into cheap sacking, cotton bale covering, and pulp for paper.

Jute plants are herbaceous. Their slender stems grow 5 to 15 feet tall. Branches at the top bear bright, green leaves, small yellow flowers, and distinctive seed pods. They grow best in a hot, moist climate.

Several varieties are grown to some extent in many countries, but the rich alluvial soils of the river deltas and other conditions in northeastern India and East Pakistan lend themselves best to extensive production. The low cost of labor in that area allows the crop to be processed and marketed at a price that discourages competition from fiber of other countries.

Jute is a small-farm crop centered in rice-growing areas. The two crops compete for land in proportion to the ratio of their prices. Jute occupies only 5 percent of the total cropland in East Pakistan but is the most valuable cash crop. A total of 94 percent of the jute in East Pakistan is on farms of 1 to 25 acres; 44 percent of all the farms raise some jute along with other crops.

About 2 million acres of jute are grown in each of the two main producing countries, India and Pakistan. About 85 thousand acres are grown in Brazil.

Cultivation methods are rather primitive in most Far Eastern countries. Most of the work is done by hand.

The fields are plowed and harrowed, often with crude, oxen-drawn implements, and the clods are broken up with mallets. Seeds usually are broadcast, although sowing in rows has become accepted as a better method. The crop is thinned and weeded several times by hand.

The grower sells his small lot of jute to the local collector, who is usually a moneylender as well as middleman for the crop. He grades it and collects it into large bundles of about 80 pounds and sells it to the next middleman. After further grading and sales, it is finally baled into loose kutcha bales of about 300 pounds each, for domestic consumption, or in pressed pucca bales of 400 pounds each, principally for export.

India, with more than half of the jute looms of the world, consumes its own large crop of fiber and is the largest manufacturer and exporter of jute goods. Jute manufactures are the country's largest earner of foreign exchange and represent 22 percent of the total of all exports.

The value of exports of jute manufactures was 319 million dollars in 1962–1963. Pakistan exports the major part of its jute as fiber. Brazil manufactures practically all of its jute for domestic use.

The Indian jute industry has been organized and controlled to a large extent for many years, but the growers and laborers had little organizational activity until recent years. Mills belonging to the Indian Jute Mills Association have 94 percent of the looms of India.

India had a virtual monopoly on jute for many years, and through the association had considerable influence in stabilizing prices of jute by sealing a designated percentage of looms on the basis of changes in the relationship of supply and demand for jute goods. Since the separation of India and Pakistan, however, the mill organization has lost some of its effectiveness on world prices. The association, alone and in cooperation with government agencies, engages in quota buying, controlling mill stock by designating how many months' supplies must be bought ahead, and fixing prices.

The Indian Central Jute Committee and Jute Buffer Stock Agency work in cooperation with the Indian Jute Mills Association. The Jute Buffer Stock Agency buys surplus stocks at a set price when supply exceeds demand and prices fall below a set level. The East India Jute and Hessian Exchange has power to regulate futures markets.

Modernization of Indian mills became necessary to compete with the new mills of Pakistan and the modern mills of Europe. Modernization, begun in 1955, has meant the replacement of many old spindles and looms. Indian manufactures of jute goods reached 1,074,000 tons, or 51 percent of the world total of 2,107,000 tons in 1959–1960. Consumption of raw jute by domestic mills that year was 1,243,000 tons, or 45 percent of the estimated world consumption.

Pakistan supplies almost all the jute used in mill consumption of nonproducing countries, and its exports have been increasing. Jute has accounted for more than half of the country's foreign exchange in some years.

The Government of East Bengal controlled jute acreage as a means of stabilizing prices during 1940–1960, and since then has advised farmers as to the advisable acreage to plant.

Most phases of jute cultivation and marketing in Pakistan are controlled somewhat by government ordinances and the Pakistan Central Jute Committee. The Pakistan Industrial Development Corporation has been instrumental in setting up new mills in Pakistan and, through special trade agreements, in some neighboring countries to use raw jute from Pakistan. In the first 10 years of industrialization, Pakistan acquired 14 mills with more than 8 thousand looms, and its consumption increased to 800 million pounds of raw jute fiber. The Second 5-Year Plan had a target of 12 thousand looms by 1965.

Exports of jute and manufactures from East Pakistan and India reach all major countries of the world either for domestic use or as containers or wrappings for imported commodities.

Pakistan, the principal exporter of jute fiber, shipped 65 percent of its 1,734 million pounds of jute exports in 1962 to European countries, with 320 million pounds going to the United Kingdom, 203 million to Belgium, 146 million to France, 112 million to West Germany, and quantities of 85 million or less to each of the other European countries.

Only 101 million pounds were shipped to the United States, but small amounts went also to many of the other countries of the Americas, Asia, Africa, and Oceania. However, most countries with large agricultural trade, or with an industrial economy, import large quantities of manufactured jute goods.

The United States imports most of its jute needs in the form of manufactured or semimanufactured goods.

The popularity of jute in most countries rests largely on its relative initial cheapness. When it is priced on a level with other industrial fibers, it loses its market to the stronger or more readily available fiber, to paper, or to the other methods of handling products, and the consumer often does not return to using jute.

Jute has had strong competition from cotton or paper in bags for such commodities as fertilizers, cement, and flour and in tying twines; from plastics and other manmade materials in bags for vegetables, and in tarpaulins or covers for such items as machinery, loads of commodities, and commodities in bulk. The bulk handling of many commodities, such as the grains, agricultural lime, commercial fertilizers, mineral ores, and coal, has made large inroads in that part of the market for jute.

KENAF (*Hibiscus cannabinus*) and roselle (*H. sabdariffa*, var. *altissima*), similar jutelike bast fibers, are known also as mesta, Deccan hemp, Ambari hemp, Bimlipatam jute, and Bombay hemp.

Together they are the chief competitor of jute and are adaptable to a wider variety of growing conditions, but they rarely compete with the best grades of jute because they are somewhat coarser.

Kenaf and roselle, or mesta, are grown extensively in India, where they are used along with jute in the hessian and bagging mills, and to varying extents in many other Asian, African, and American countries of the warm zone.

There are two kinds of roselle plants—one is grown for fiber and one for fruit.

World production of kenaf and roselle is hard to estimate because many countries do not report the amounts they produce. Production in India was reported at 640 million pounds in 1963. In Thailand it was 551 million pounds. It probably reached 535 to 540 million pounds by 1959 in mainland China.

Producing countries use nearly all their crop of fiber in domestic manufacture of bags, burlaps, and other coarse fabrics for protective coverings. The use of kenaf and roselle has been increasing, and many countries have experimented with the fiber, especially in years when the jute prices were exceptionally high.

FLAX (*Linum usitatissimum*) is the first and most valuable of the long vegetable fibers to be spun and woven into cloth.

It is the long, soft, fine, and lustrous textile fiber that some believe was woven into the fine linens of the Pharaohs of Egypt 4 thousand years ago. Old Biblical records refer to it as a symbol of purity.

Some gossamer linens discovered in ancient tombs are far finer than any linen available in the modern world. Linen was used by the prehistoric Lake Dwellers of Switzerland.

The Egyptian art of weaving flax yarn into linen spread slowly to India, where many of the castes wore linen before they began to wear cotton. It was carried to various parts of Europe, Turkey, and the Western Hemisphere. It came to the United States with the early colonists.

Flax was one of the two leading vegetable fibers during the Middle Ages. Hemp was the other. The spinning of flax and the weaving of linen have long been associated with feminine graces of noble women and humbler women, much of whose time was spent at the task in order to supply household fabrics and clothing for their families.

The widespread use of linen for household fabrics for so long gave us our misleading names of "bed linens" and "table linens" for articles made of cotton, ramie, rayon, and other manmade fibers, and even silk, but rarely of linen anymore, except in some flax-producing countries.

Flax lost its priority among textile fibers to cotton after invention of the cotton gin. Jute further displaced flax by being economical in coarse wrapping materials. Manmade fibers now compete seriously in materials for clothing and trimmings.

Flax, because of its length, strength, and beauty, has many uses. It is made into cloth—the finest and sheerest of handkerchief linen, ducks and drills, material for suits and dresses, bedding, napery, curtains, upholstery, drapery, cushion covers, wall coverings, hand towels, and decorative articles.

Flax threads are strong and are used for sewing threads, button threads, fish and seine lines, shoe threads, harness and sacking twines, and upholstery twines. Other uses are in parachute harness webbing, uppers for women's shoes, paddings, and linings.

Large acreages are now grown for seed, and seed-flax straw is used in fine paper, such as cigarette paper.

World production of flax fiber, other than the Chinese output, was estimated at 1,357 million pounds in 1962.

Flax will grow in many temperate regions, but the Soviet Union, the largest producer, is averaging 907 million pounds a year. Poland, Belgium, France, and the Netherlands, with 56 to 103 million pounds each, have been important producers for many years.

Belgium has been noted for a thousand years for the high quality of its retted fiber because of the peculiarly favorable characteristics of the water of the River Lys, which is used for retting the flax straw.

Canada produced flax fiber from 1940 to about 1955 and shipped much upholstery tow to the United States, Australia, and New Zealand. The northwestern United States and other countries produced fiber during the Second World War but later abandoned it as unprofitable in peacetime.

The flax plant for fiber is tall, slender, and branched at the top. Some varieties of flax are grown especially for fiber, some especially for seed, and some for either seed or fiber. Close planting is best for fiber production, because it discourages branching and causes the stem to grow longer and smoother and thus produce a longer fiber.

The flax fiber is obtained from the stem in somewhat the same manner as jute but with some important differences. Often stalks are pulled by hand, even though pulling machines began to be used about 1940. After rippling to remove the seeds, flax retting may be by any of several methods; namely, tank retting (usually with controlled temperature of the water), stream retting in sluggish running water, or dew retting on the grass. The first method is the commonest. All the processes require experience, skill, and judgment.

The flax straw must be dried after retting, and the fiber is separated by machines. The stalks may be dried in drying rooms or by air drying on the grass, either spread or sitting up in loose shocks until dry.

The dry stalks are put through breaking and scutching machines first to break and crush the woody parts of the stems that have been loosened by dissolving of the connecting gummy substance during retting, and then to scutch or scrape away these nonfiber parts called shives. Combing (or hackling) is necessary on the long (line) fiber before it can be spun into yarn.

The short fibers that are broken in the scutching process are kept separate and are known as scutching tow. Hackling or machine tow, sometimes called flax noils, is short fiber resulting from further combing and manufacturing processes and is cleaner and finer than scutching tow.

Tows are used in coarse fabrics, rope, and sometimes for upholstery stuffing. The long fiber is known as scutched flax, or line, and is sorted according to length and bundled and baled for shipment. Sometimes flax is scutched without retting, and the dried green fiber is made into straps or coarse cloth. It is coarser and stiffer than the retted fiber.

The Netherlands and France export much flax straw to Belgium for its specialized retting and import some of the scutched fiber in return, but France has been encouraging domestic processing of the straw.

Northern Ireland and the Irish Republic once had 260 thousand acres in flax but had only about 200 acres each in 1961. The famous Irish linens are now manufactured almost entirely from imported flax—much of it from Belgium. The United Kingdom, however, imports some flax fiber from the Netherlands, France, and the Soviet Union.

All the large producers of fiber flax export both fiber and tow in some form, and most of them manufacture flax goods, also for export. Both fiber and goods are imported by many countries.

The use of flax has declined because of the increase in production of cheaper natural fibers, especially cotton, and the manufacture of manmade fibers. The advance in fiber finishes to make cotton wrinkle resistant or waterproof and to change the characteristics of various fibers has furnished cheaper fabrics with many of the characteristics of linen. The trend among countries toward self-sufficiency in domestic fibers also has reduced the demand.

HEMP (*Cannabis sativa*) is nearly as old as flax and is nearer like flax than any of the other vegetable fibers. It is native to central Asia, and has been cultivated for thousands of years.

A Chinese emperor of the 28th century B.C. taught his people to cultivate for fiber a plant of two forms called ma. China still produces ma, its name for hemp.

This bast fiber is 40 to 80 inches long, lustrous, and pliable. It is stronger than flax but less fine. It may be creamy white or gray and sometimes brown. It suffers less damage from heat, moisture, and friction than any other soft fiber, except flax. Although it resembles flax, it is more adapted to cordage, and flax is better for clothing and fine linens.

Hemp was the first important cordage fiber. The name "hemp" is sometimes erroneously and confusingly applied to other fibers that are used for cordage. Consequently, we find the name applied to various agaves, sansevierias, Fourcroyas, yuccas, Sidas, and others, but never to flax, the fiber it most nearly resembles.

If a prefixed name is not used, such as in "sisal hemp," "New Zealand hemp," or "bowstring hemp," and only the term "hemp" is used, statistics can become hopelessly confused. Even with the qualifying name, such as in "Swedish hemp" or in "Cuban hemp," there can be considerable misunderstanding, because many fibers that carry the false name of "hemp" are hard fibers and are quite different from the soft true hemp.

Hemp grows throughout the Temperate Zones wherever the climate is warm and rainfall moderate. Unlike many other fibers, it has names in nearly every language. It is known as canamo in Spanish, canhamo in Portuguese, chanvre in French, canapa in Italian, hanf in German, hennup in Dutch, and kenevir in Turkish.

Hemp is still mainly a cordage fiber, but its specific uses have changed with changing conditions. It was once about the only cordage fiber of the civilized world and was the chief fiber for marine cordage until abaca came into use in the 19th century.

Sisal also began soon afterward to take over the duties of hemp in larger ropes, fishing lines, yacht cordage, marlines, rigging, and carpets. Other soft fibers came into use for homespuns and the so-called "linen" crash, which was formerly made of hemp rather than linen. The modern "hemp" ropes are almost never made of hemp or even a soft fiber, but of abaca, sisal, henequen, or possibly some other hard fiber. ·

Present uses of hemp are in small, usually tarred, ropes up to 1 inch in diameter, nets, canvas, warp of carpeting material, a substitute for flax in some yarn sizes, cores for wire cables, and many kinds of twines for tying, seines, sacking, mattresses, upholstery, hats, alpargata (sandal) soles, bookbinding, and lashings.

The tow, or short fibers, goes into oakum, packing for pumps and calking for boats. It has competition in these uses from tow of hard fibers such as sisal and coir and from other soft fibers such as sunn. Short fibers are also spun into yarns, and machine waste is used as stuffing for upholstered goods.

The hemp plant also yields an oilseed. Various parts of the plant yield narcotic drugs, the major one being marihuana, derived from the flower.

The cordage industry was one of the first and largest industries in the colonial United States because of the large use of ropes in sailing vessels. A cordage factory was set up in Boston in 1642 with hemp as the raw material. Cordage factories are still an important industry in New England. Much of the work was hand done until the first quarter of the 19th

century, when machines were invented for practically every process of combing and twisting the fiber into yarn, laying the strands, and winding the finished rope on large spools.

Abaca and other fibers have now largely replaced hemp in this country, however, and the crop is no longer grown for fiber in the United States.

Hemp was native to central Asia and has long been cultivated in Persia (now Iran), China, and India for both the fiber and a drug, and in many other warm countries principally for the fiber. Many countries prohibit or severely restrict cultivation of the plant because of the strong narcotic substances.

The Soviet Union, which ranks first in production, manufacture, and consumption, produces about 250 million pounds of scutched hemp fiber out of a world total of about 625 million pounds, and consumes most of it domestically. Yugoslavia, Turkey, and Italy also produce large quantities. Italian hemp is considered to be best in quality.

The chief exporting countries are Yugoslavia, with an average of 90 million pounds, the Soviet Union, and Italy. West Germany and the United Kingdom are the chief importing countries.

The hemp plant grows 6 to 8 feet tall. It is dioecious—male and female flowers are on separate plants. It, like flax, can be grown for either seed or fiber. It is planted in early spring.

Harvest for fiber comes in most countries about 4 months after planting, or when the staminate flowers begin to open and shed pollen.

Cutting is done by hand in some places, but reapers, or hemp harvesters, have become common.

The straw must be processed. The fiber is used without hackling or combing for coarse yarns, but mills hackle some of it to obtain finer, better, and more expensive yarns. These specially separated yarns are as fine as the coarser grades of flax and can be mixed with other fibers in fabrics for clothing.

The processed long, or line, fiber comprises about two-thirds of the total output. The rest is short-fibered tow.

SUNN or San "hemp" (*Crotalaria juncea*), also called San Pat, Indian hemp, Madras hemp, or Bombay hemp, is a soft fiber that grows abundantly in India and parts of Ceylon.

It has been used in southeastern Asia since prehistoric times as a cordage fiber and is used in the United Kingdom especially for paper but also in mixture with other fibers for ropes, cables, twines, and nets.

The chief use in the United States since 1940 has been in the manufacture of cigarette papers and other tissue papers, because of the high cellulose and low ash content.

Sunn can substitute for jute or true hemp. It is also made into carpets and fishing nets. Sunn makes cattle fodder.

Indian cultivation of sunn in 1962 included 482 thousand acres for fiber, 169 thousand acres for green manure, and 135 thousand acres for fodder—altogether, a total of 786 thousand acres. Fiber production was 172 million pounds.

Production fell in the second quarter of this century because of a big drop in exports to the United Kingdom, where other fibers were replacing sunn in cordage manufacture.

Sunn requires moderate rainfall and a light and moderately deep soil. Cultivation, harvesting, and processing methods for sunn are the same as for jute. The processed fiber is soft, ranging in color from gray to brown.

India is the chief exporter as well as producer of sunn fiber. Exports in 1962 amounted to 18 million pounds, worth 1.7 million dollars. Of this quantity, 46 percent was to the United Kingdom and 39 percent to other European countries. The remaining 15 percent went to the United States, Canada, Japan, and other countries.

RAMIE, Rhea, or China grass (*Boehmeria nivea*), of the Urticaceae or nettle family, yields a lustrous, white, silky,

textile fiber. It has been known since ancient times.

The white ramie was first recognized in fabrics exported from China to England as China grass cloth. This species is also common in Taiwan and India. The green ramie (*B. nivea*, var. *tenacissima*), often called rhea, is a more tropical and less hardy plant that grows mostly in Malaya, Africa, Mexico, and the East Indies. The white ramie fiber is finer but not so bright as the rhea.

The distinguishing names by color stem from the different colors of the undersides of leaves of the two species, but the fibers are similar.

Because the degummed ramie fiber has favorable characteristics, many attempts have been made to process it economically by machine.

Ramie is soft, lustrous, silky, nearly as fine as flax, and stronger than other natural textile fibers. It has excellent bleaching qualities and elasticity. It is resistant to rot in dampness and water. It can be processed to resemble wool or cotton.

The fibers are difficult to separate from the stem and from each other, however, and they are not obtained by water retting, like jute, flax, or hemp. Final degumming of the decorticated ribbons is usually a chemical process.

Ramie fiber is manufactured mostly into fabrics in mixture with cotton, wool, silk, manmade fiber, or other fiber and into napery and specialties.

Its possibilities are many. In China, where it is prepared almost entirely by hand as a home industry, it is made into grass cloth and other fabrics and yarns for clothing, mosquito nets, and fish nets. The Japanese make it into seine twines, mosquito nets, shirting, suiting, and manmade fibers, such as rayon. The uses in Germany range from shoe threads to tapestries, trimmings, and various woven fabrics.

Gas mantles once required large quantities of ramie. Ramie has also been used in banknote paper, cigarette paper, fish lines, and nets.

The ramie plant, native to the

Orient, grows well in any hot, moist climate whose soil is rich, damp, and well drained. Commercial production is in China, the East Indies, Japan, Taiwan, India, and the Philippines. Small-scale or experimental production has spread to many countries.

The plant differs from most bast fiber plants in that it is a perennial and lasts 6 or 7 years. New stalks grow up as old ones are cut. A mature plant is 3 to 6 feet tall and has numerous straight stalks bearing heart-shaped leaves. Propagation is usually by rootstocks.

Establishment of a good stand requires about 2 years. Stalks are cut several times during the first 2 years to induce more branches. Then harvest for fiber begins. Cuttings several times a year can continue during the life of the plant. Harvest continues in China from late May until frost each year.

Ramie plants are subject to a variety of hazards, including early or late frost, high winds, excess moisture or drought, lack of fertilizer or cultivation, root rot, insects, and diseases.

The chief deterrent to expanded cultivation was the difficulty in obtaining the cleaned fiber by economic mechanical means without damaging it in the process. The fibers are arranged in bundles that extend the full length of the stalk, and they are held together with gums that must be subjected to a chemical degumming process.

The fiber at this stage dries harsh, wiry, and difficult to separate, so a final treatment with a special emulsion is added during drying to leave the fiber soft, pliable, strong, and gleamingly white.

Most of the commercial production of ramie is in southern China, and about half of the production is exported. The Philippines and other Asian countries also produce commercial quantities.

Japan, the principal importer, sometimes imports the ribbons for processing and manufacture and then exports the finished goods back to the country of origin as well as to other countries.

MALVACEOUS FIBERS are obtained from the stems of many species of the hibiscus, sida, and other groups of plants. Most resemble jute in appearance, performance, and the methods of cultivation and preparation. Kenaf and roselle (discussed previously) are the most generally known.

Urena probably is second in importance. Other fibers are most commonly used in their countries of origin.

Urena lobata, a plant of the Malvaceous family, is indigenous to China but is grown in exportable quantities in the Congo and has been carried to the Western Hemisphere, where in tropical areas it has developed into a native weed.

It is known by many names, and is the Congo jute in Africa and in the export trade from the Congo, paka in the Malagasy Republic, cadillo or cadilla in Venezuela, bolo-bolo in western Africa, grand mahot cousin in Martinique, and Caesar weed in Florida and some other parts of the Americas. Also it is the cadillo, guizazo, or malva blanca of Cuba, and the guaxima vermelha, carrapicho, or aramina (little wire) of Brazil.

Urena lobata grows wild in most of the countries where the fiber is collected and prepared as a cordage fiber or jute substitute.

The Republic of the Congo and Brazil produce the fiber in commercial quantities, but the former is the only exporter.

Brazil has had large-scale production from both wild and cultivated plants since 1900. Output was 29 million pounds in 1961, and peak production was 44 million pounds in 1956. Most of it is manufactured into coffee bags.

Congo (Léopoldville) produces 25 to 30 million pounds a year of *Urena lobata* and punga (*Cephalonema polyondrum*), a similar fiber, and exports 4 to 6 million pounds of urena and 2 to 3 million pounds of punga.

Urena is grown and retted as jute is. The fiber is 3 to 8 feet long. It is used locally in producing countries in cordage, bags, packing materials, sail-cloth, and handmade twines. Importing countries (mostly Belgium, West Germany, and Angola) use it as they do jute.

Many other malvaceous fibers are used to a limited extent, especially in the countries where they are produced. They are generally most suited to cordage or bagging and coarse cloth. I name a few.

Common okra (*Hibiscus esculentus*) of India is used in crude twines and cordage. Indian mallow or Chinese jute (*Abutilon avicennae*) of China is white, glossy, and strong but has little economic value. Mexican Indians use the highly durable fiber from *Abutilon incanum* for hammocks, ropes, and nets. Indian hemp (*Apocynum cannabinum*) is a native fiber of the United States which resembles flax and was used by the Indians for all purposes, but has not been exploited commercially. The Brazilian native pacopaco (*Pseudabutilon spicatum*) is cultivated as a substitute for jute. Rama fibers (*Hibiscus lunarifolius* and *Urena sinuata*) of western Africa are jutelike fibers used domestically.

Sida fibers, also of the Malvaceous family, are used in many countries instead of jute. *Sida acute* is a Mexican fiber harvested from both wild and cultivated plants. It is light colored, even, and slightly harsh to the feel and has good tensile strength. The *Sida rhombifolia* is a good fiber common in most tropical countries. The *Sida tiliaefolia* is an excellent fiber cultivated in China. Other sida fibers are used in Brazil, the Philippines, Canary Islands, West Indies, parts of India, and in northern Vietnam and Laos.

Nettle fibers are malvaceous fibers, which include many besides ramie or China grass, but most of the others are derived from stinging nettles. The great nettle (*Urtica dioica*) is a perennial and yields the most fiber, but the fiber is of considerable thickness. It was used in "nesseltuch" or nettle cloth especially in Germany and France before cotton was introduced into Europe, and has been used

some since during periods of cotton shortage. The small nettle (*Urtica urena*) is a smaller fiber that somewhat resembles flax.

Nettle fibers have been produced since ancient times in Germany, the Soviet Union, Hawaii, and Sweden. They were used in Italy and France during the Middle Ages. Nettle goods were a part of the trade of Germany, Sweden, and Picardy early in the 19th century, but cotton crowded out nettle fibers, except for some local use and a few specific uses.

The fibers are obtained by retting and scraping or decorticating by machines, such as are used for ramie.

TREE FIBERS include the paper mulberry fiber, an unusual bast fiber, which is extracted from the inner bark of a small tree *Broussonetia papyrifera*.

The South Sea Islanders make a fabric known variously as tapa, kapa, or masi from it without first spinning or weaving it. After the fiber has been extracted and cleaned, it is laid evenly in several layers while still wet and allowed to dry overnight. They adhere in one piece when dry. This piece of webbing is laid on a smooth plank and beaten with a wooden tool until it spreads and mats together into cloth as thin as muslin or thick like leather, according to the desire of the worker. Pieces can be joined in the same manner so as to make large pieces of this characteristic cloth. The fabric can be bleached white or dyed or printed.

The same type of fiber is used in Japan, where it is cut in strips, twisted into yarn, and used with a warp of hemp or silk to make cloth. The Japanese also use it in papermaking.

CECILLE M. PROTZMAN, *an agricultural economist in the Sugar and Tropical Products Division, has been with the Foreign Agricultural Service since 1934. She has served since 1942 as a fiber specialist working with the world's vegetable fibers other than cotton. She received a Certificate of Merit Award in 1960 for her work in these fibers.*

Structural, or Leaf, Fibers

by CECILLE M. PROTZMAN

STRUCTURAL, or leaf, fibers (mostly known as hard fibers) include principally the cordage and brush fibers.

As a class, they are long, coarse, harsh, and strong.

Some (such as sisal, henequen, abaca, and some istles) are most suitable for twisting into coarse twines and cordage. They also are used extensively in floor coverings and locally in bags. Others (such as piassava, some istles, and magueys) are bulky, stiff, and suitable for brushes. A few are fine and soft (such as pineapple fiber) and are used locally in fabrics.

But all hard fibers have the same general characteristics of growth and methods for obtaining the fibers. Many of them originated in the Americas. The henequen of Yucatan was probably the earliest vegetable fiber used in the Western Hemisphere.

Hard fibers form the veins that carry water and food within the plant and furnish strength and support for the leaves and leaf stems of certain perennial plants.

They usually are obtained by a process of mechanically crushing the green leaves and scraping away the pulpy and other nonfibrous material.

Most of them grow best in tropical climates and are reproduced by vegetative propagation. A few are grown from seed. Harvest for many of them is a continuous process in a large field or plantation, as only the mature leaves or stalks are harvested and new growth continues from the same rootstock for some years.

Common names of fibers are often confusing, as one fiber may be known by different names in different countries. Indeed, the same name may be applied to several different fibers. *Phormium tenax*, for example, is known also by the common names of "New Zealand flax" or the "New Zealand hemp." Conversely, the name "hemp" is applied frequently to abaca, henequen, and sisal, as well as the true hemp (a soft fiber), with only the identifying country of origin as a clue to the type of fiber indicated. Pita and maguey are commonly used to designate several different fibers of Latin American origin.

Sisal and abaca are invaluable for their use in cordage. They were designated as strategic fibers during the Second World War and are stockpiled in countries of large consumption. The United Nations Committee on Commodity Problems endorsed in 1962 a Study Group for Hard Fibers (principally sisal, abaca, and henequen) to collect and exchange statistics and other information among all important producing and consuming countries in the hard fibers market.

SISAL (*Agave sisalana*) is most important of the hard fibers and is the principal cordage fiber.

It is used principally for manufacture into cables, ropes, binder and baler twines, and other tying twines for farms and industry. In some countries it also is used in bags for handling and storing agricultural, mineral, and industrial commodities. Sisal floor coverings and padding for upholstery also represent significant uses of sisal.

The manifold minor uses include novelty products and such items as pulp for papermaking, which uses mostly short fibers, tow, and waste fiber. Sisal is not the preferred fiber for ropes exposed to salt water, despite its durability in other uses.

Sisal originated in Central America and the Yucatan Peninsula, where Indians were using it along with henequen when the Spaniards discovered Mexico in 1509. It was named from the old seaport town of Sisal, Yucatan, from which most of the exports were shipped after the fiber entered commerce in 1839. Plants were taken to the Florida Peninsula about 1836 and from there to many other countries. They reached Tanganyika in 1893, and before 1939 that country had become the largest producer of sisal.

World sisal production was 1,445 million pounds in 1963, an increase of 185 percent over the 1934–1938 average of 507 million pounds.

The producers in 1963 were Tanganyika, 476 million pounds, or 33 percent of the world total; Brazil, 424 million pounds, or 29 percent; Angola, Kenya, Mozambique, and other African countries, with a combined total of 443 million pounds, or 31 percent; and Haiti, Taiwan, Indonesia, and Venezuela, with most of the remaining 7 percent.

Indonesia had ranked second, next to Tanganyika, in world production before 1940, and its fiber was of the highest quality, but wartime destruction and neglect followed by the breakdown of the plantation system of sisal production were factors in the decline of fiber output from 214 million pounds in 1941 to 9.2 million pounds in 1963.

Sisal is a tropical plant of the Amaryllis family. Each well-developed plant usually produces at least 200 long, stiff, fleshy, dark-green leaves, which grow in a rosette from the central bud at the base of the plant.

Older leaves are about 3 to 6 feet long, 4 to 6 inches wide, and nearly 1 inch thick at the center and thicker at the base. Each has a sharp, terminal spine nearly an inch long.

The plant requires temperatures above the frost level, moderate humidity, and annual rainfall of 30 to 70 inches. It is often grown in poor, dry, rocky soil, but grows faster and more luxuriantly in rich, well-drained, limestone soil.

Successful commercial production of sisal fiber requires a central cleaning machine within easy distance of the fields, plentiful water for washing the fiber, a place for waste disposal, sufficient labor supply, and means of transportation to market.

The growth habit of sisal lends itself most economically to large plantations of at least 2,500 acres and plantings of 1 thousand up to 2 thousand plants to the acre, according to the soil and climate.

Only the more mature, lower leaves are harvested at a time, but plants usually continue to produce new leaves for 10 or 15 years, according to local conditions, including the 6 or 7 years of peak production.

Leaves are harvested periodically as long as growth is economically sufficient. A pole, or flower spike, develops as the plant becomes older. It grows to a height of 15 to 20 feet and bears flowers and the bulbils or buds from which new plants are grown. After poling, the plant dies and is replaced.

Laborers cut the mature leaves from the plant with a heavy, curved, knife-type implement, remove the terminal spines, and tie the leaves in bundles that weigh about 90 pounds.

The bundles are hauled to the decorticating plant, where the fiber is extracted by machine, preferably within 48 hours after cutting. Workers lay the leaves parallel to each other and crosswise on a conveyor belt, which feeds them through revolving, corrugated crusher rollers to soften the leaf mass. Then in a cleaning process, during which the leaves are clamped firmly, revolving drums with beater blades scrape away the broken and softened epidermis and pulp surrounding the fiber, while water is sprayed over it to wash away the waste.

Leaves are sorted according to length and freedom from damage before being fed into the decorticator, and the fiber is graded as it comes from the machine and further sorted with each handling. The clean, wet, greenish fiber from the decorticator is hung over lines to dry and bleach in the sun. The dried fiber is creamy white and ready for brushing and baling according to grade. It runs about 3 to 4 percent of the green-leaf weight.

Sisal is graded principally according to length, color, and cleanliness. Each country's fiber differs somewhat in quality for a specified grade. Consequently the purchasers buy not only according to grade but also according to origin.

Major producing countries have organizations of producers or exporters, or both, for handling and marketing the sisal and promoting the general welfare of the industry. Some major producing countries have organizations for hiring laborers and setting terms of contract between producers and laborers. Labor unions began to organize in British East Africa soon after 1950. Workers often have their families with them. The large plantations provide living quarters and facilities for community life and entertainment, such as schools, churches, and recreation centers.

The chief producing countries are also the chief exporting countries. Exports range from more than half to nearly all of the crop, according to the country.

Tanganyika has ranked first in both production and export of sisal. The fiber is the major commodity in the country's cash economy and is its most valuable export. The United Kingdom is the major buyer. The United States, Japan, Belgium, and the Netherlands are next. These five countries take two-thirds of Tanganyika's sisal exports.

Brazil, second in production, exported four-fifths of its 1962 crop, and shipped it principally to the United States and to the Netherlands, West Germany, and elsewhere in Europe.

Kenya sisal goes mostly to the United Kingdom, West Germany, Japan, Belgium, the United States, and other European and Asian countries. Angola ships more than a third of its sisal to Portugal and sizable amounts to Spain, the United States, and other European countries. Mozambique sends a third to the United States. The Malagasy Republic sends two-thirds of its sisal to France.

The exporting countries export their crop mainly as raw fiber, with 15 percent of the total destined for the United Kingdom in 1961, 55 percent to other European countries, 13 percent to the United States, and most of the other 17 percent to Asian countries and Australia. Products manufactured in industrial countries from imported sisal fiber are not only for domestic use but also for export to all parts of the world.

The price of sisal generally is determined more by fluctuation in demand than by fluctuation in production. The length of time between planting and the first harvest and the long producing period make sisal production fairly resistant to sudden large changes in production. Sudden demands for ropes for military emergencies or for twines to handle unusual grain crops, for example, may deplete stocks and force prices to levels that encourage the use of substitutes. This happened when prices reached an alltime peak average of 29.7 cents (for British East African No. 1, landed New York) in 1951, compared with a prewar average of 5.1 cents a pound in 1935–1938 and a postwar low of 9.4 cents in 1957. The level was 18.9 cents through the last 4 months of 1963.

Hecogenin is derived from sisal juice after dry decortication of fiber and is valuable in the partial synthesis of cortisone.

HENEQUEN (*Agave fourcroydes*) is second to sisal as a cordage fiber.

Its principal use is in binder and baler twines, but it can be substituted for sisal quite satisfactorily in many types of cordage up to about 1 inch in diameter. It is also softened, spun, and woven into sacking, other coarse cloth, floor coverings, and novelty items. It is somewhat longer and coarser than sisal, but sisal has a greater average tensile strength.

Henequen originated in Mexico, where it has been used since prehistoric times and where more than 90 percent of the world total is now produced. Considerable confusion in names derives from lack of recognition in its early history of the difference between henequen and sisal. Sisal was the one that spread to the Eastern Hemisphere; henequen became the main hard fiber of Mexico and Cuba, but henequen is often erroneously called Mexican sisal or Cuban sisal.

World production of henequen was 330 million pounds in 1963—slightly less than the peak of 375 million pounds in 1960 and 34 percent more than the annual average of 247 million pounds during the prewar years.

Mexico has maintained its early position as principal producer, and the bulk of its henequen is grown in the dry, limestone soils of the Yucatan Peninsula. Mexican production was 340 million pounds (92 percent of the world total) in 1962. Cuba was second with an estimated 22 million pounds.

Henequen plants look much like sisal, except that the color is more nearly bluish-gray. The leaves have sharp, slightly hooked prickles along both edges and, like sisal, a dark terminal spine about an inch long. As with sisal, a leaf-scarred trunk develops as the lower leaves are cut in successive harvests and new leaves develop in the center. Leaves yield about 4 percent in fiber.

The large-plantation system, with all facilities for growing and processing the fiber and for care of the laborers, is the traditional system in the commercial henequen regions of Mexico, but a change began to develop about the middle of the 20th century. In the following 10 years, the Government took steps to restrict the acreage of large plantations and set up organizations to finance and establish workers on small, individual farms or on parts of larger, communal-type

areas. Mexico has been purchasing decorticating plants from plantation owners and building new plants for the use of small and large producers.

The methods of cultivating, harvesting, extracting of fiber, and marketing of the baled product are essentially the same for henequen as for sisal. Henequen plants tend to grow a little slower and live a little longer than sisal plants. They may live for 20 to 25 years, but the useful life is barely more than half that time.

Henequen withstands a dry climate better than most plants, but prolonged drought adversely affects quantity and quality of production. The land in many of the Yucatan fields is so dry and stony that it is necessary to make planting holes with a pick and prop the young plants up with stones until they become well rooted. Weeding must be done by hand in such fields.

The first cutting is usually in the sixth or seventh year, as in Mexico, or the fourth year, as in Cuba, largely according to the amount of rainfall. Cutting continues at intervals of about 6 months for the next 10 to 12 years.

Dried fiber is 2 to 5 feet long and is reddish yellow to nearly white. Length, color, and cleanliness determine the grades. The standard bale is about 400 pounds, but the weights vary among processing plants.

The henequen industry—production, manufacture, and export—is the chief factor in the economy of the Yucatan Peninsula. Yucatan factories consumed about 80 percent of the domestic henequen fiber in 1962. Increased demand for cordage to handle unusually large grain and other crops meant a 7-percent increase in mill consumption of fiber in 1961. Another 3-percent increase in 1962 raised consumption to 266 million pounds. The cordage factories of Yucatan were consolidated into one corporation in 1961.

Mexico exports 88 to 90 percent of its henequen products. The United States receives 95 to 98 percent of Mexican exports of raw fiber and about 90 percent of the exported manufactured products. Baler twine is by far the largest item. The balance of raw fiber is shipped principally to Japan and Europe, but the other manufactured goods go chiefly to Central America and South America.

Henequen prices are normally a little below those of sisal. Grade A Mexican henequen, landed New York, was 11.4 cents a pound at the beginning of 1963. Its postwar peak was the annual average of 24.5 cents in 1951.

ABACA (*Musa textilis*), of the banana family, provides the strongest and best of the cordage fibers. It is one of the few hard fiber plants that is not native to the Western Hemisphere.

Spanish and Portuguese explorers of the 16th and 17th centuries found Filipino natives wearing clothing made of abaca fiber. In modern times it is considered primarily as a cordage fiber, and it is the preferred vegetable fiber for the best grades of commercial ropes and cables and for marine cordage because of its resistance to salt water and small amount of swelling when wet. Some of the finer fibers are woven into cloth. Large quantities are made into pulp for strong, high-quality paper and specialty items, tea bags, and mimeograph mats.

Abaca is indigenous to the Philippines, where more than 95 percent of it is grown.

The fiber is often called by the trade name, Manila hemp, even though it is not a hemp and very little is grown as far north as Manila. It received the unrepresentative common name from Europeans who found it in the market of Manila when they first went to the Philippines in 1697.

True hemp had been the recognized cordage fiber before that time. It was understandable that the newly found fiber that was so suitable for cordage should be called hemp and differentiated from the familiar true hemp by using the name of the port city—Manila—where it was first discovered.

It soon became recognized in England as an important fiber for good cordage. Production spread to Indonesia, North Borneo, Malaya, and smaller islands of the Pacific, but met with little continuing success outside the Philippines and Indonesia.

Most early attempts to grow it in the Americas were unsuccessful. It was introduced into Central America in 1925 through efforts of the United States Department of Agriculture and the United Fruit Co. These experimental plantings were developed into a source of emergency supply to the United States while Philippine supplies were cut off during the Second World War. The plantations were abandoned later for economic reasons.

World production of abaca was 260 million pounds in 1963. This represented 13 percent of the combined production of sisal, henequen, and abaca, the three principal cordage fibers. Peak production of abaca was 428 million pounds in 1935. Peak production in postwar years was 318 million pounds in 1951.

Philippine production was 416 million pounds in 1935. Wartime damage to Philippine plantations in 1941-1945, the removal of Japanese producers, and some migration of the native population who were not familiar with abaca cultivation from other parts of the islands to the abaca regions during the war and in early postwar years all worked together to reduce production. Also, infestation by mosaic disease and the rising cost of production continued to keep abaca from regaining its prewar eminence. Philippine production in 1963 totaled only 247 million pounds.

The principal fiber obtained from the abaca leaf is 7 to 14 feet long. The fiber from the outer leaf sheaths of the stems is strong, coarse, and brownish in color. Fiber from inside leaf sheaths is finer and white, but has lower strength.

Some of the best Philippine fiber is combed, carefully drawn out in single fibers, and knotted to make a long, continuous strand, called knotted abaca. This is woven by hand into a cloth, called sinamay, that is used for clothing in the Philippines.

Abaca of good quality can be grown most economically as a plantation crop in a consistently warm, humid climate with well-drained, fertile soil.

A mature abaca plant resembles a banana plant and consists of 10 to 30 stalks growing in a cluster. Each stalk grows to a height of 10 to 20 feet.

Its leaves, about 12 inches wide and 3 to 6 feet long, extend from long, sheathlike stems that grow out of a central base and overlap to form a false trunk 6 to 15 inches in diameter. The broad, green leaves appear to grow from the top of this false trunk, although the leaf sheaths form it.

Harvest begins about 2 years after the suckers are set out. The entire trunk of the tallest stalks is cut down for fiber. Shorter stalks are left to continue growing.

After a field is established, it can be harvested two or three times a year for 10 to 15 years. A trunk weighs 35 up to 120 pounds, but only 2 to 3 percent of its weight is usually recovered as fiber.

The worker separates the leaf sheaths from each other and with his knife pulls off the outside layer of the leaf in tuxies, or ribbons, that are 2 to 3 inches wide and the length of the leaf. This is done in the field.

All pulp is scraped away in a stripping shed. The fiber is extracted from the tuxies by pulling them under knifelike scrapers, operated by hand or by crude or semiautomatic machines.

The work is heavy, and a laborer using the hand method can handle only about 500 strips a day and obtains about 25 pounds of clean fiber. The fiber is dried on long lines in the sun.

A few plantations use large machines, like sisal decorticators, which can extract up to 1 thousand pounds an hour and recover a larger portion of fiber. The decorticated fiber, classed as deco, lacks sheen, but is becoming acceptable in the trade as equivalent to hand-cleaned fiber. Deco fiber is dried in automatic dryers.

All fiber for export is graded under government supervision and pressed into bales that may weigh about 279 pounds. The domestic industry of the Philippines uses mostly loose bales of noninspected, or unbaled, fiber, which was 14 percent of the crop in 1962.

Cleaned abaca fiber is mostly cream colored, glossy, stiff, and tenacious. It is 3 to 14 feet long. All the fibers grow in the outer layer of the leaf sheaths, but those near the margins are shorter. Those from leaf sheaths near the outside are stiffer and darker colored.

The basis for standard grading of Philippine fiber was set up with help from the United States Department of Agriculture and became effective in 1915. Abaca is classified into many grades. It is designated according to the island where it was grown, and fiber of each origin is classified as to degree of cleanliness, color, uniformity, and strength.

Exports of Philippine abaca fiber fell from an annual average of 370 million pounds in 1935–1939 to 208 million pounds in 1962. It goes principally to the United States (29 percent in 1962), Japan (26 percent), the United Kingdom (15 percent), and the other European countries (19 percent).

The Philippines produced 35 million pounds of unbaled or noninspected fiber in 1962 for domestic manufacture into cordage, and factories also used 2.5 million pounds of inspected fiber.

A large share of the cordage was exported, and it was shipped chiefly to the United States, other North American and South American countries, and Asia.

Abaca ordinarily commands a better price than other cordage fibers because of its superior strength, appearance, and stability in salt water. Abaca (Davao I) was being quoted in the New York market at 23.2 cents a pound in 1962 when Mexican henequen (grade A) was selling at 9.4 cents and British East African sisal (No. 1) at 12.7 cents.

The three principal cordage fibers—abaca, sisal, and henequen—each has

its own normal place in use preferences. Abaca (the highest priced) is
used in cordage of the best quality.

Henequen (priced the lowest) is used
in ropes of lesser value and twines.

Sisal is used for the great range
of cordage of various grades and
sizes in between.

The lower grades of abaca and the
better grades of sisal, however, are
readily interchanged in most rope
uses and are often thus substituted
when any change of supply or price
relationship may warrant. Likewise,
lower grades of sisal and better grades
of henequen may be interchanged.

Cotton, jute, hemp, and paper twines
compete with the cordage fibers.

Lesser known native fibers compete
in every category of use when price
relationship, ready availability, or
government policies of self-sufficiency
favor the substitution. Wire and steel
straps and steel cables have gained
importance in such fields as binding
bales and reinforcing packages.

Nylon entered the cordage field
about 1940 and polypropylene somewhat later. They seem established in
certain uses where their higher initial
price is justified by their properties,
such as endurance and light weight.

THE ISTLE FIBERS include principally
certain fibers of the Amaryllis and Lily
families.

They are used in bags of various kinds, other protective coverings,
brushes (especially scrubbing brushes),
wrapping twines, small ropes, novelty
items, and many twine and fabric
items for use about the home or farm.

Mexican Indians have long used the
istle plants for food, clothing, beverage,
and means of livelihood.

Istle (pronounced *issel*) is the angli-
cized name for "ixtle," the name
used in Mexico, where most of the
world supply originates. Some istles
receive their common or trade names
from place names of the region where
they are found in greatest abundance.
But common names are not applied
consistently and often overlap.

The most important istles are lechuguilla, Jaumave, and palma. Lechuguilla (*Agave lophantha* var. *poselgaeri*,
formerly known as *Agave lecheguilla*)
belongs to the Amaryllis family and
is the most important istle. It is known
also in trade channels as Tula istle or
Tampico fiber, but the latter designation includes also zamandoque (*Hes-
peraloe funifera*) and some other similar
fibers of the same region.

The plant of lechuguilla istle resembles a small sisal but does not form a
trunk. It grows wild on the arid, limestone mesas of northern Mexico, and
in parts of southern Mexico, but the
fiber of commerce is obtained from the
northern growths. Lechuguilla grows
best at 3 thousand to 6 thousand feet,
where the climate is temperate.

Lechuguilla istle fiber, in general, is
the coarsest and stiffest of the commercial agaves and is especially suited
to use in scrubbing brushes, but the
grades range from fine and soft to
hard and stiff. It is round, tapered,
creamy to green in color, and 7 to 20
inches long.

The tallador, or gatherer of istle,
gathers cogollos (central stalks) about
once a year after the plants are 6 to 10
years old. The cogollo is composed of
6 to 15 new, tender leaves wrapped
closely together in an elongated ball,
and the fibers are extracted from them.
The leaves are up to 20 inches long
and somewhat less than 2 inches wide.

The worker uses a stick with an
attached iron ring to hook over the
cogollo and pull it off. He can gather
65 to 90 pounds a week, from which he
can extract 6 to 8 percent as fiber. He
obtains the fiber by scraping the leaves
with a heavy knife against a block of
wood. He takes the results of his week's
work to a central collection station,
where fiber is collected, bought, sorted,
graded according to length and color,
and pressed into bales of about 110
pounds. Both collecting and marketing
of istle is controlled by government
through cooperative societies.

The tallador uses some of the istle he
collects to make his rope basket to

carry the cogollos and also ropes to tether cattle, bags for many purposes, rugs for his hut, saddle blankets, and brushes for his family's use. He receives barely a living from his sale of fiber, and the work is difficult and the living hard in the hot, semiarid regions of the istles. Consequently, less istle is collected in years when rainfall favors other crops.

Mexico produces 25 to 30 million pounds of commercial lechuguilla istle annually and uses about 15 to 20 percent of it in domestic manufacture of cordage. The other 80 to 85 percent is exported—principally to the United States, the Netherlands, and other European countries.

The short fibers are curled by twisting before being baled and used in upholstery and pads for under carpets and car mats. Exported brush fiber is sold almost entirely on order; each lot is cut, dyed, and bunched according to the buyer's specifications.

Lechuguilla has to compete with palm or palm-type fibers for use in stiff brushes, but it has greater competition from nylon and other manmade fibers.

Jaumave istle (*Agave heterocantha*), formerly known as *Agave funkiana*, of the Amaryllis family, is third in commercial importance among the istles, but the fiber is superior in quality and brings the highest price.

Production, though small, is entirely for export, mostly to the United States, where it is used in high-quality brushes.

The plants grow only in the semiarid, limestone soil on the sides of mountains in Tamaulipas, Mexico. They differ from lechuguilla in that the leaves are straighter and longer.

MAURITIUS FIBER or Mauritius hemp (*Furcraea gigantea* or *Furcraea foetida*) is a member of the Amaryllis family.

It is another hard fiber for cordage and bags that has a common misnomer. It is quite different from the true hemp and is not native to Mauritius, where it was introduced about 1790. It is used for sugar bags in Mauritius and ranks next to the sugar industry in importance to the island.

It originated in eastern Brazil, where it is known as piteria; from there it spread to Mauritius, St. Helena, Madagascar, Australia, the West Indies, southern Asia, and Africa.

The fiber is known in Mauritius and in the trade as aloe fiber, although it only slightly resembles the true aloe of Africa. Production of Mauritius and similar fibers is relatively small—only 2 million or 3 million pounds annually—but is important to each producing country as a source of fiber for domestic use in cordage, bags, and various other local uses.

SOME LEAF, or structural, fibers have many characteristics of stem fibers and are relatively pliable. These include phormium, caroa, banana, and pineapple fibers and the sansevierias, or bowstring hemps.

Phormium (*Phormium tenax*), from the *harakeke* lily plant of the Lily family, is often known as New Zealand flax or New Zealand hemp because of its softness, even though it is a leaf fiber and differs considerably from both flax and hemp, which are stem fibers.

Captain Cook, when he visited New Zealand in the late 1700's, found the New Zealanders using the leaves for making their baskets and the fiber for clothing and cordage. They used phormium as the first article of barter with the Europeans.

Cultivation spread from New Zealand to St. Helena, Chile, the Azores, and Argentina. Phormium is the only commercial hard fiber found outside the Tropics. Attempts to introduce it into western Europe, some African and other South American countries, and California have met with small success commercially.

Production has been fairly steady since 1957 in the main producing countries. All of the New Zealand production of 9 million pounds and most of Argentina's 9 to 10 million pounds are consumed domestically. The crop of 2 million pounds in St. Helena is exported.

New Zealand began to export phormium in the 19th century, mostly to the United States, Australia, and the United Kingdom. Competition from sisal caused exports to decline to negligible quantities during the next half century.

The fiber is tan or creamy white, soft, quite flexible, and lustrous. It is stronger than henequen but not so strong as sisal. At 4 to 8 feet it is next in length to abaca.

Its use is restricted because it deteriorates rapidly in color and strength when wet.

Fiber is obtained from wild and cultivated plants, but the latter yield the finer fiber.

The principal use of phormium in New Zealand is for manufacture into bags and wool packs, but in other countries it is used chiefly for rope and binder twine, alone or mixed with sisal or abaca. Some is made into floor coverings. It has stiff competition in the world market from other natural fibers, especially sisal.

The African or Guinea bowstring (*Sansevieria metalaea* or *guineensis*) is probably best known of the sansevierias. The common house plant, Spanish bayonet, is one of this group.

Fibers of this group are soft, long, strong, fine, and silky white, but somewhat brittle, and are used especially in cordage, fish nets, native bowstrings, mats, and coarse cloth.

All species grow in Africa, southeastern Asia, and Latin America, mostly where the climate is warm and moist and the soil is sweet.

Extraction of fiber is similar to that for sisal, and is from leaves of either wild or cultivated stands. Production is relatively small, and use is insignificant beyond the areas of origin.

Caroa (*Neoglaziovia variegata, Mez. Bromeliaceae*) has long been used in Brazil, where it grows wild on millions of acres in the hot, dry, northeastern section of the country. Only a small part is harvested.

Caroa leaves are thorny and are 3 feet or more in length. They are cut from the wild plants by hand with stout knives and tied into bundles of 90 to 110 pounds for transport by burro to the nearest processing station.

The fiber is similar to pineapple fiber, long, silky, white or light tan, finer than sisal or abaca, and stronger but somewhat harsher than jute.

It is manufactured into cordage, threads, nets, fish lines, and bags, or mixed with other fibers for use in cloth. It is a satisfactory source of pulp for manufacture into lightweight paper for airmail or cigarette papers. Large quantities are used in bags for coffee and other Brazilian commodities, especially when jute prices are relatively high, but its tendency to deteriorate hampers more widespread use.

Production was 8.6 million pounds in 1961. Peak production averaged about 25 million pounds during the war years, when jute was hard to obtain. Brazil now grows its own jute and is dependent on neither imported jute nor domestic caroa for bags, but the population of the caroa region continues to use the local product and export some fiber and manufactures.

Pineapple fiber (*Ananas comosus*) is obtained from leaves of the plant that produces the pineapple fruit. The plant is indigenous to Brazil and Paraguay, but it has spread to many other parts of the tropical world, including the Philippines, Hawaii, Indonesia, Puerto Rico, and Cuba.

The fiber is not produced in significant quantities for export.

Banana fibers can be obtained from several varieties of the banana or plantain plants. Unlike their relative, abaca, most of them lack sufficient strength for satisfactory commercial use in competition with other fibers. Their use is quite limited.

CECILLE M. PROTZMAN *is an agricultural economist in the Sugar and Tropical Products Division, Foreign Agricultural Service. She holds a bachelor's degree from Kansas State University.*

Other Vegetable Fibers

by CECILLE M. PROTZMAN

OTHER VEGETABLE fibers include leaf and stem fibers and also such widely different types as kapok, from inside seed pods; coir or coconut fiber, from the husk or shell of the coconut; broomroot fiber, from the roots; redwood bark fiber, from the bark of trees; Spanish moss, or vegetable horsehair, and luffas, or vegetable sponges, which are the whole fibrous framework of the plants or their fruits.

Sometimes a whole part of a plant is used as a fiber, such as the broomcorn whisks or strips of the leaves of the toquilla. Some are used worldwide. Others are of interest because of their special uses.

KAPOK (*Ceiba pentandra*), of the Bombaceae family, is best known of the tree fibers and follows cotton as the most valuable of the seed fibers.

It is a short fiber, averaging about three-fourths inch long. It is silky, lustrous, fluffy, weak, yellowish in color, and light in weight.

Kapok has considerable buoyancy, springiness, and resilience. It is well adapted to use in stuffing and padding, but does not lend itself well to spinning because of its smoothness and weakness.

It formerly was used extensively in lifejackets, marine padding, furniture upholstery, cushions, and mattresses, but it has been replaced in importing countries to some extent by manmade foam products and glass fibers. Many producing countries, however, still use kapok or similar fibers for mattresses, padding, and stuffing.

Kapok trees grow to 30 or 40 feet or even to 100 feet and are among the largest in the tropical forests. They are found from sea level to nearly 4 thousand feet and can withstand extremes of rain and drought. Their origin was in Mexico and Central America, but they now grow principally in Indonesia, Thailand, elsewhere in southern Asia, and tropical Africa.

The principal producing countries grow kapok trees along the roadways or set out in plantations at about 144 trees to the acre, but much of the commercial crop of the world is harvested from wild forest trees. The quantity collected depends on demand and price.

Trees bear seed pods after the third year and produce the best crops after the sixth year. Trees may live 100 years. The pods mature about 10 months after the blossoms fall. They are 4 to 8 inches long and about a third as thick as they are long. The outer shell is soft enough to be crushed by hand.

The fiber grows mostly along the membrane surrounding each of the five groups of seeds within the pod. Men use long bamboo sticks with a hook at the end to gather the pods and often have to climb high into the tall trees to reach them.

Women and children usually beat out the seeds with sticks or separate the fiber with a simple machine. The fiber is pressed into bales of about 80 pounds for shipment. Java kapok from Indonesia is considered to be best in quality.

World exports of kapok reached 61 million pounds in 1961. Thailand, Indonesia, and Cambodia are the main exporting countries. About one-half of the world exports is to the United States, the Netherlands, Malaya, and Japan. Most of the remainder goes to the European countries, Australia, and New Zealand.

A similar kapok fiber is obtained from the Indian kapok tree (*Bombax malabarica*), which is smaller than the tree of Java but bears more fiber. This kapok is more brownish than the other and less resilient.

Other flosses of a kapok type and known variously as tree cotton, vegetable wool, ceiba cotton, silk cotton, paina, pochote, and samohu are obtained from other trees of the Bombaceae family, which grow throughout the Tropics of the Eastern and Western Hemispheres.

Ecuador is the most important producer of the Western Hemisphere. Many tropical countries collect kapok for domestic use, but only a few produce sizable amounts for export.

PALM and palm-type fibers are a special group of hard fibers obtained from leaves or leaf stems.

They differ from other hard fibers in many characteristics of fiber, growth development, and method of processing. Most of them are coarse and stiff and are classed as brush fibers.

Many palm trees yield fiber, but only a few are of commercial importance. These are principally the coir, crin vegetal, the piassavas, palmyra, kitul, and palmetto.

Coir (*Cocos nucifera*) is obtained from the hard, fibrous husk of the kernel of the coconut.

The coconut palm grows in most of the coastal regions of the Tropics, but only a few varieties yield suitable fiber. Few countries produce it on a commercial basis.

It is used for cordage, matting, rugs, doormats, brushes, brooms, bags (especially for tea leaves), insulation, and soundproofing. The fibers resist rot.

The coir fiber industry is centered in Ceylon and along the Malabar Coast of southwestern India. World output is estimated at 450 million pounds annually. Indian production is estimated at 290 million pounds of fiber annually, from which 1.5 to 3.5 million pounds are exported as fiber and the rest is spun into about 270 million pounds of yarn. Exports account for 100 million pounds of this yarn a year. Germany, the Netherlands, the United Kingdom, and Italy are India's best customers for coir and coir products.

Ceylon exported 130 million pounds of mattress fiber and 40 million pounds of bristle fiber, 900 thousand pounds of yarn, and 67 thousand pounds of bags, mats, and mattings in 1962.

The United Kingdom and the Commonwealth countries, Japan, Germany, and other European countries received most of both the fiber and manufactures.

Coconut palms usually are 60 to 70 feet tall and have no branches. The man who gathers the nuts must climb the trees with the aid of a rope looped around his ankles. He cuts one cluster of nuts at a time and lets them fall to the ground. Before the fiber can be extracted, the husks are removed from the coconuts by thrusting the nut against a stationary metal spike. A man can husk about 2 thousand nuts in 8 hours.

The best fiber is from husks retted in brackish backwaters. The retted husks are beaten and torn apart—or decorticated—by hand or by a crushing breaker and spiked drum machine.

Three types of fiber are produced from the coconuts. The longer and stronger of the decorticated fibers are cleaned, hackled, made into hanks, and pressure baled for shipment. These are bristle fibers and are used mostly in Europe. They are graded according to color and length and are manufactured mainly into brushes. The yield of fiber is about 225 pounds of bristle fiber and 450 pounds of mattress fiber from 2 thousand husks of good quality.

The torn and broken fibers discarded from the decorticating process are sifted again and baled as mattress fiber for use in stuffing and padding.

Coir yarn, the third type, is spun from the finer grades of fiber and is manufactured into ropes, mats, and a coarse cloth. Yarn production is a cottage industry. Most of it is in India.

Fibers that compete with coir for various uses are manmade fibers, other palm-type fibers, and other hard rope fibers. Coir is meeting its competition, however, and exports of coir and coir products from Ceylon more than doubled from 1938 to 1959. Exports from India increased 83 percent.

Crin vegetal (*Chamaerops humilis*) is fiber from the base of the leaf stem of a dwarf fan-palm that grows abundantly in the northern African countries of Algeria, Morocco, and Tunisia and some parts of southern Europe.

It often is called vegetable horsehair or vegetable curled hair because of its resemblance to the animal product and its curly nature after it has been prepared for market.

Exports of crin vegetal are principally from Morocco to Germany, France, and other European countries. Morocco exported an annual average of 204 million pounds in 1958–1962, despite competition from manmade materials and other fibers.

PIASSAVA or bass fibers (also spelled piassaba or piacaba) are mostly long, coarse, resilient, tough, dark, and water resistant.

They are used mostly in coarse, heavy-duty brushes and brooms, whisks, cordage, mats, baskets, hats, tying twines, and novelties.

Piassava is obtained from the leaf stems or sheaths of many kinds of palms. Each is used extensively in the region where it is grown. Some of the fibers are exported in sizable quantities.

Bahia piassava, or the Bahia fiber (*Attalea funifera*), is used mostly for brushes for sweeping streets. The finer ends of the fibers go into house brooms and scrub brushes. Natives use the finer fibers for cordage, twine, baskets, hats, and tying materials. The trees grow wild and abundantly in the swampy, sandy soils of Bahia in Brazil and north into Venezuela. They grow 30 to 35 feet tall. Their feathery leaves of 10 to 17 feet grow from the ground in a cluster.

Para piassava, or the monkey bass (*Leopoldinia piassaba*), also of Brazil, is used commercially in strong brushes, such as those for grooming horses, but is fashioned into ropes, baskets, and twines for local use. It is too brittle and permeable to compete successfully in the heavy-duty brush market, and production is relatively small. The trees grow wild in the sandy soil along the tributaries of the Amazon River above Manaus and along the Orinoco River in Venezuela.

Piassava ranks as a poor second to cotton in the Brazilian production of vegetable fibers. Output was 38 million pounds in 1961, compared with 16 million pounds in 1951, but exports remained fairly constant at 7 to 8 million pounds during the 10-year period. About half of the exports were to the United Kingdom and Portugal, and a fourth to West Germany and Belgium. The United States, the Netherlands, Denmark, and Spain took most of the remainder.

The West African piassava, or African bass fiber (*Raphia vinifera*), is obtained from the wine-palm that grows abundantly in the valleys along the Atlantic coast of western Africa. The name also includes fiber of the *Raphia hookeri* of the Ivory Coast, which grows abundantly but is not used for fiber export.

This brush-and-broom fiber was first introduced to European markets from Liberia in 1890, but also Sierra Leone, Nigeria, and the neighboring countries became important exporters. It is obtained in the same manner as other piassavas. It is brownish red to deep brown in color, 3 to 4 feet long, stiff, and wiry. It is graded according to the port of shipment because the fiber from each region has certain distinguishing characteristics.

The Calabar, or flexible bass, is the coarsest and heaviest of the African piassavas and makes the best quality brooms. Mixed with Bahia, it is used in railroad track brooms and rotary street sweepers.

Sherbro from Sierra Leone is tough,

lighter in weight than Calabar, rougher, and less flexible. Prime Sherbro is shipped from the same port but is smoother and darker than Sherbro, has a wide range from fine to very coarse, and is used in brushes.

Madagascar piassava (*Dictyosperma fibrosa*) is a rich, brown fiber, 18 to 24 inches long, finer and more flexible than Brazilian piassava. It entered the European market in 1890, but exports have remained comparatively small. It is used in sweeping brooms and for special purposes.

Palmyra fiber (*Borassus flabellifera*) is a bristle fiber extracted from the leaf stalks of a tall, fan-leafed palm indigenous to Ceylon and the eastern coasts of India, Burma, and Africa. It is known as bassine after it has been graded according to size, dyed, dressed, and cut to specified lengths. It is processed in the same way as most other palm-type fibers. It is brown, 9 to 24 inches long, strong, and wiry. It is used mostly for ropes, twines, and baskets. India exports about 5 million pounds annually.

Kitul (*Caryota urens*) is finer, softer, and more pliable than piassava and palmyra. It is dark brown or black, 7 to 28 inches long, strong, elastic, tough, glossy, and somewhat like horsehair. It is obtained from the kitul, jaggery, or Toddy palm, which grows in the hotter parts of India, Ceylon, Indonesia, and the Malay Peninsula. Asians make it into fish lines, nets, and mats, but the export trade is for large cables, ship hawsers for ocean vessels, scrubbing brushes, horse brushes, and some other similar brushes. People in Ceylon use it in ropes to tether elephants. It is more expensive than other fibers used for these purposes.

PALMETTO FIBER (*Sabal palmetto*) is from the cabbage palm, which has a central bud somewhat like a cabbage head. It grows wild in the Bahamas, Bermuda, Cuba, Mexico, and the coastal areas from the Carolinas to Florida. Palmetto fiber and broomcorn are the only commercial brush fibers produced in the United States. Processing consists of softening the boots, or leaf sheaths, by boiling and crushing before scraping, then hackling and oiling the fiber. The fiber is 8 to 30 inches long, a reddish brown, durable, elastic, and resistant to water. It makes excellent clothes brushes, scrubbing brushes, and horse brushes, and is used in ropes and mats.

Toquilla (*Carludovica palmata*) is a palm-type plant. The fiber is called the Panama hat fiber, or jipijapa, which denotes one of the districts in Ecuador where hatmaking is centered.

The fan-shaped leaves are about 3 feet in diameter and deeply divided. The stems, 3 to 10 feet long, grow from the ground in a cluster without a trunk. Toquilla grows throughout the coastal regions of Central America and northwestern South America. It is especially abundant in Ecuador and Colombia, where the hats are made from wild as well as from cultivated plants.

The misnomer, "Panama" hat, originated from the fact that California gold-rush prospectors who returned by way of Panama bought the Ecuadoran-made hats there and gave them the name. They normally were exported through the port city of Panama.

Preparation of the fiber differs from that of most palm-type fibers. The unfurled leaves are gathered, stripped of the coarse veins, and treated with boiling water. The leaves are then separated into strips with a fingernail or a comblike instrument. As the strips dry slowly, they roll into fine, cylindrical strands, which are bleached in sulfur smoke, washed, and used mostly by the hatmakers. Some palm fiber hats are called Panama hats, but the fiber in them is flat and heavier than the toquilla.

Hatmaking is a cottage or home industry. Each hat is made with a specific design in the center of the crown to indicate the locality of the maker. The hat is formed by working outward from this design. The straw is kept damp while being worked. The finest hats often are made in early morning, late evening, or in rainy weather in order to insure better and more even manipulation, and require 3 to 6 months for completion. The worker weaves about 4 hours a day.

Very little toquilla straw is exported, but the hats have been exported almost from the time Francisco Delgado of Ecuador made the first one about 1630. They reached the United States about the middle of the 19th century, but at that time it seemed more profitable for Ecuador to export straw than hats. In 1941–1945, however, exports of 3.2 million hats (representing roughly 1.6 million pounds of straw) ranked second only to rice in Ecuadoran export value.

Peak exports of 4.9 million hats in 1946 were followed by a decline to 800 thousand hats in 1962 and represented less than 0.5 percent of total exports. About two-thirds of them were shipped to Italy, Paraguay, the United States, and Cuba.

TREE-BEARD or Spanish moss (*Tillandsia usneoides*) is a fibrous, mossy plant that grows on trees as an epiphyte in humid or swampy regions along the Atlantic and gulf coasts from southern Virginia to Texas and in Mexico. It is collected from the limbs of trees or from the ground after it has been blown down by strong winds and is piled into heaps and soaked for curing. Afterward, it is taken to a moss gin for removal of the outer scaly layer, packed into bales, and sold for stuffing of furniture, cushions, and mattresses. It is a curly, black, resilient fiber that resembles horsehair except that it is branched. It is one of the best substitutes for the hair. Relatively small amounts are produced, and it is in competition with manmade paddings and some of the hard fibers.

The broomroot, or raiz de zacaton (*Epicampes macroura*), known also as rice root, is a coarse bunchgrass that grows especially in Mexico. The plant is pried out of the ground, and the outer coating scraped off of the tough, crinkly roots. They are treated with sulfur fumes, graded, and sold for brushes and brooms. Mexico exported 5.4 million pounds of broomroot in 1962, 74 percent to the United States.

Broomcorn fiber (*Sorghum vulgare* or *Holcus sorghum*) is the brush or whisk of panicles of seedheads of these sorghums, which are grown in temperate climates, such as in the United States and Italy, and used for house brooms and whisk brushes. The panicles are cut when at least 15 inches long and while green, to prevent brittleness and coarseness, and are then dried in the shade and sorted for market.

MILKWEED BAST FIBER is obtained principally from the swamp milkweed (*Asclepias incarnata*). The fiber somewhat resembles flax. Small quantities are produced, but western Europe has shown interest in it a long time.

Milkweed floss is obtained mostly from several species of the common milkweed (*Asclepias syriaca*). It was used extensively in the United States during the Second World War as a substitute for kapok.

Luffas or loofas (*Luffa aegyptiaca*) are gourds. They are fibrous and, after being retted and cleaned of pulp, are used intact as oil filters, strainers, and household sponges. Japan is the principal exporter.

Smaller varieties of luffas are grown in other parts of the Orient and in Mexico, Central America, and Caribbean countries. Japan in 1951 exported 4 million of these vegetable sponges—3 million to the United States—but competition from manmade sponges reduced the trade in the vegetable product to a negligible quantity. They are used extensively, however, in the countries of production.

CECILLE M. PROTZMAN *has served since 1942 as a fiber specialist working with the world's vegetable fibers other than cotton. She joined the Foreign Agricultural Service in 1934.*

Wool and Other Animal Fibers

by HORACE G. PORTER and
BERNICE M. HORNBECK

ANIMAL FIBERS are the hair, wool, feathers, fur, or filaments from sheep, goats, camels, horses, cattle, llamas, birds, fur-bearing animals, and silkworms.

Let us consider silk first.

A legend is that in China in 2640 B.C. the Empress Si-Ling Chi noticed a beautiful cocoon in her garden and accidentally dropped it into a basin of warm water. She caught the loose end of the filament that made up the cocoon and unwound the long, lustrous strand. She was eager to create a fabric of the lovely fiber and prevailed on the Emperor to let her try. She is said to have developed the methods of reeling, spinning, and weaving silk that form the basis for the techniques used today.

Growing silkworms and producing silk were a Chinese monopoly for many centuries. Death was the penalty for trying to steal the secret. Silk fabrics are thought to have reached Europe about 75 B.C., when a Roman general brought some home from China. By A.D. 126, a "silk road" nearly 6 thousand miles long was opened to enable the transport of silk from China. At the end of the camel-train path was Damascus, the marketplace where East and West met. Silk cloth was in great demand in Greece and Rome.

By A.D. 300, the Japanese had learned about sericulture. Presumably it was introduced into India in the fourth century under the romantic circumstances of a marriage between Chinese and Indian royal families.

At the request of Byzantine Emperor Justinian in A.D. 552, two monks made the perilous journey and risked smuggling silkworm eggs out of China in the hollow of their bamboo canes, and so the secret finally left Asia.

Constantinople remained the center of Western silk culture for more than 600 years, although raw silk was also produced in Sicily, southern Spain, northern Africa, and Greece.

As a result of military victories in the early 13th century, Venetians obtained some silk districts in Greece. By the 14th century, the knowledge of sericulture reached England, but despite determined efforts it was not particularly successful. Nor was it successful in the British colonies in the Western Hemisphere.

There are three main, distinct species of silkworms—Japanese, Chinese, and European. Hybrids have been developed by crossing different combinations of the three.

The production of silk for textile purposes involves two operations: Sericulture, or the raising of the silkworms, and the processing of the silk filament from their cocoons.

The commercially cultivated silkworm species (which is actually a caterpillar—not a worm) is the *Bombyx mori*. The moths are made to lay their eggs on sheets of paper and, if they are to be for breeding, in cells.

The eggs are kept cool and dry until spring, when mulberry trees have their leaves, on which the larvae feed. Then the eggs are hatched in an incubator or in the sun.

Villages of China and Japan have community incubators, but the larger silk farmers have their own facilities.

Larvae are one-eighth to one-fourth inch long and about as thick as a hair when they emerge from the eggs. During the 5 weeks to 2 months that the larvae eat, they grow about 70 times their original size, change skin

4 times, and consume several thousand times their own weight in mulberry leaves—perhaps 200 pounds to produce a pound of silk.

In their early stages, silkworms must be fed five times during the day and twice a night. At full growth the silkworm may be 2 to 3.5 inches long.

During this period, silk glands along each side of the caterpillar's body are filling with sticky fluid. When the larvae is full grown, it ceases to eat and begins swinging its head about. Then the silkworm farmer provides a cell for each in a framework, which becomes the support for the cocoon.

Fluid issues from two spinnerets at the front of the silkworm's head, forms into one strand, and is spun about the larvae in figure-8 patterns. At the end of this process, the silkworm is about half of the weight that it was at the beginning.

A few carefully selected cocoons are permitted to mature into moths that are later to lay the eggs. Moths develop from cocoons in 2 to 3 weeks. Moths have no mouth and cannot eat and live only a few days. They mate, and the female lays about 500 eggs.

Except for those selected to mature for breeding, the life of the silkworm is ended in the chrysalis stage by steam, boiling water, or dry heat. Cocoons are graded as to quality.

The next step is reeling, which usually is done by machinery at filatures, or reeling factories.

The cocoons are prepared for reeling by the removal of an outer layer of floss by brushing after boiling in a tank. The equipment includes a reeling basin, a thread guide, a device for crossing the threads, and a reel, a hexagonal drum of laths on which the silk filaments are gathered. In the reeling operation, a number of cocoons are placed in warm water, which softens the gum that binds the tiny threads together.

The ends on several cocoons are assembled, passed through a fine eye of glass, porcelain, or polished metal, fastened to the reel, and so unwound from the cocoons onto the reels. The number of filaments brought together depends on the fineness of the raw silk thread desired.

There may be 300 to 1,600 yards of reelable filament on each cocoon. They are so fine that a pound of thread made of three to five filaments together would reach a thousand miles.

The amount of reelable silk and its quality depend on the care with which the operations are conducted, the variety of silkworm, and the region in which it is grown.

The technology of silk production (except the reeling process) has changed little over the centuries. In the beginning, reeling always was done by hand.

Once the silk is removed from the cocoons, the remainder of the processing at the filature consists of cleaning, drying, and preparation into skeins for shipment to textile centers of the world. The product of the reeling process is called by several names—raw silk, silk yarn, silk thread, grege.

An average batch of fresh cocoons weighing 1 thousand pounds will yield about 360 pounds of dried cocoons and 137 pounds of filament, which includes raw silk and silk waste.

Something less than 10 percent of Japan's cocoon crop consists of double cocoons, which produce dupion silk, one cocoon produced by two larvae. It is difficult to reel, although it produces a slubby yarn much in demand for novelty fabrics.

The only other major type of silk produced commercially is the wild, uncultivated silk known as tussah. It comes from worms that feed on the leaves of oak, castor, cherry, and uncultivated mulberry. The filament is flat, hairy, and several times thicker than silk from the *Bombyx mori*.

Several types of other wild silks are found in Japan, India, Asia, and in America and parts of Africa, but they are not of commercial significance.

Attempts have been made to commercialize production of spider silk. It has been found to be not practical for textile uses, but is used for cross-lines for optical instruments.

Sea silk, sometimes called pinna silk or fish wool, is obtained from certain types of mollusks and is used in Italy and France for making braids.

Another silk product of commercial importance is silk waste, which is produced in the rearing of worms, the reeling of raw silk thread, and the process of converting raw silk into yarn, thread, and fabric. Silk waste may be 3.5 to 6.5 inches long and is used for spun yarns. Lengths below 3.5 inches are called noils, and are used mainly to mix with wool.

Raw silk sometimes is used for weaving without further twisting, but it is generally advanced by throwing, which consists of several operations: Cleaning, first twisting (also known as spinning), doubling (the twisting of two or more threads together), and the second twisting.

The first and second twistings are in opposite directions, and the number of turns per inch is determined by the use to which the silk yarn is to be put.

The several basic types of silk yarn are singles, tram, organzine, crepe, and grenadine.

The harder the twist, the better the quality of silk required. The throwing process adds greatly to the strength of the silk filaments and reduces the raveling of the yarn.

About 73 million pounds of raw silk were produced throughout the world in 1962. Japan produced about 60 percent, or about 44 million pounds. Mainland China, also a large producer, accounts for more than 20 percent of the world's total production. Other major producing countries are the Soviet Union, India, Italy, Korea, and Turkey.

Japan is also the largest domestic consumer and the largest exporter of raw silk and silk products. About one-fourth of the raw silk produced in Japan is exported in the form of raw silk. In 1962, exports from the silk markets of Yokohama and Kobe totaled 10 million pounds of raw silk,

800 thousand pounds of thrown silk, and about 7 million pounds of silk fabrics and other goods.

Japan also exports silk cocoons, silk waste, spun silk yarns (yarns made of short silk fibers, usually waste) and other types of made-up goods. It has been estimated that about 25 percent of the raw silk that is processed in Japan eventually moves into international trade channels.

Japan's export trade in raw silk, silk fabrics, and silk products of other kinds was valued at more than 100 million dollars in 1962, about one-half of which was raw silk. Other large producers of raw silk also ship to export markets.

The United States is the largest import market for raw silk, silk yarn, fabrics, and made-up goods. Other leading silk-importing countries are Italy, France, Switzerland, West Germany, and Great Britain. Several of these countries, particularly France and Switzerland, export large quantities of made-up silk goods.

Raw silk for the American market is put up in standard skeins, which are about 58 inches in circumference and weigh 2.4 ounces. About 30 skeins are formed into compact bundles called books. About 30 books are combined to make a bale of 130 to 135 pounds.

Silk is extremely strong, quite elastic, and smooth and lustrous. Its major end use is in apparel and homefurnishings, but it also has some industrial applications. Hosiery was once an important use for silk in the United States, but this market has been virtually taken over by nylon.

Silk is one of the most valuable textile fibers and in 1963 sold in the American market at prices above 5 dollars a pound for the standard grade and size. At such prices, it is a luxury fiber in some countries.

WOOL is widely produced. Sheep are raised in at least 80 countries. In 1963, there were about 991 million sheep in the world.

Fifteen countries each had 20 million

or more head and accounted for nearly three-fourths of the estimated world total. Australia and the Soviet Union, with 160 and 140 million, respectively, account for nearly one-third of the world total. Argentina, the Republic of South Africa, India, mainland China, and New Zealand each has roughly 40 million to 50 million sheep. The United States, Brazil, Uruguay, Spain, the United Kingdom, Ethiopia, Iran, and Turkey have about 20 million to 30 million.

The five principal wool-exporting countries are Australia, New Zealand, Argentina, South Africa, and Uruguay. They account for 32 percent of the world sheep numbers and about 80 percent of the wool in world trade.

The domesticated sheep appear to have been related to the urial and moufflon types of wild sheep. Early domesticated sheep were hair covered, and the wool was merely a short, downlike covering next to the skin.

The Phoenicians are believed to have introduced sheep into Spain hundreds of years before the Christian Era. With the passage of time, finer wool types were brought to Spain from various countries surrounding the Mediterranean, and between A.D. 1400 and 1700 these various bloodlines were fused into the famous Spanish Merino sheep, from which most of the fine-wool sheep in the world today trace their ancestry.

For many years, Spain would not permit the export of Merino sheep, but breeding stock found its way into a number of countries in the latter half of the 1700's.

Variations in climate and breeding objectives in different countries have caused differences in fineness of wool and fleece weight within strains of Merinos.

Since the Middle Ages, the Spanish sheep industry has had keen rivalry from that of Great Britain. The British climate was not suitable for Merinos, but Merinos were crossed with native stock, and a number of breeds have emerged there.

The wool of breeds that produce long, coarse wool is known commercially as carpet wool. Carpet wool breeds include the fat-tailed sheep that are common in the Middle East and occur elsewhere, karakul sheep, and various breeds of mountain sheep.

Economics and climate determine which breeds are grown where. For example, in most of western Europe and the Eastern States, feed tends to be abundant and good. Cities are close, and the demand for lamb and mutton generally is good. Market conditions and competitive forces that affect the use of land there dictate that sheep production be rather intensive and mainly for meat; wool is secondary.

Breeds or crosses are favored that produce a good carcass, as farmers usually get four to six times as much return from the lambs for market as from the sale of wool.

In dry rangelands, where sheep have to feed on a large area, the more profitable operation often is wool production. Merino sheep predominate in such regions, although Merino crosses are not uncommon where it is feasible to also produce feeder lambs. In such cases, the Merino ewes will produce a good crop of fine-grade wool, and their crossbred lambs produce a good carcass.

Most wool produced in the world is shorn—that is, clipped from the live animal. Wool, known as pulled wool, also is obtained from the pelts or hides of dead sheep. Wool is generally sheared annually in the late spring or early summer, but it is quite common in Texas and California to shear twice a year.

In its natural state, a bale of raw wool contains considerable grease and foreign matter, which is removed by scouring. Relatively high scoured yields are had in places where the fleece remains fairly free of foreign matter. The scoured yield may be only half as high in areas where much sand and dirt become embedded in the fleece.

Most wool moves in trade as fleece

wool in the grease despite its extra weight. The practice arises partly out of the wide range in quality both between fleeces and within a fleece; besides, many users prefer to sort their wool into batches for various uses before it is scoured. Some wool also moves as scoured wool and some as pulled wool. Normally only the very dirty wool would be scoured before it is exported, but some low-value lots also may be scoured before being exported.

The United Kingdom, the United States, Japan, France, Italy, West Germany, and Belgium imported about 2.6 billion pounds of wool in 1961 and 1962 and accounted for more than 80 percent of total world trade. Each of them produces some wool but has to import wool.

The United Kingdom imported 626 million pounds in 1962; Japan, 472 million; France, 388 million; the United States, 363 million; Italy, 310 million; Belgium, 242 million; and West Germany, 223 million.

The Soviet Union has been a large net importer of wool, despite a marked increase in numbers of sheep and wool production per sheep. The Soviet Union imported about 121 million pounds in 1961.

The quality of wool depends on breeding, locality, care in handling, and other factors. Designations of quality are based primarily on fineness but also on length of fiber.

The British have major subdivisions based on fineness for merino, fine crossbred, medium crossbred, and coarse crossbred. They are further subdivided by numbers that are at least loosely related to the fineness of the worsted yarn into which they can be spun.

The numbers are based on the number of hanks of worsted yarn 560 yards in length that can be produced from a pound of the scoured wool. The numbers range from 100's or more down to 20's—the higher the number, the better the quality of wool. Thus, the merino wools cover the range 60's and finer; the fine crossbreds, from 56's to 60's; medium crossbreds, from 50's to 56's; and the coarse crossbreds from 36's to 48's.

United States wool grades are fine (counts of 64 and finer); half-blood (58's to 62's); three-eighths blood (56's); quarter blood (48's and 50's); low quarter blood (46's); common (44's); braid (36's to 40's).

The terms refer only to the fineness or the diameter of the wool fiber. Other terms are used to describe length. For example, the finer wool—64's and finer—is normally separated into three length groupings that are commonly accepted by the trade—strictly combing, which has a length of more than 2.5 inches; French combing, which ranges from 1.5 to 2.5 inches; and clothing or carding wool, which is less than 1.5 inches in length. In the coarser grades, only two length groupings are customary—combing and clothing.

THE GOAT FAMILY supplies several important textile fibers—mohair, cashmere, and common goat hair.

Mohair is the main specialty hair fiber used by the textile industry. It is the long, strong, lustrous hair of the Angora goat, which originated in Turkey. For many years Turkey supplied the world's needs for mohair. The growth of the textile industry in the early 19th century created demands that Turkey could not supply. Herds of Angora goats were established in South Africa and the United States before the middle of the 19th century.

Annual world production of mohair has been 50 million to 60 million pounds in recent years. The United States, the largest producer, accounts for about 45 percent of the world production. Turkey accounts for about one-third. Most of the remainder is produced in the Republic of South Africa. Basutoland, ranking fourth, accounts for about 2 percent of world production.

Within the United States, Texas accounts for 97 percent of all production of mohair. The remainder is produced in Arizona, New Mexico, California, Oregon, Utah, and Missouri.

The United Kingdom has become the largest user of mohair. In the United States, the use of mohair in automobile and furniture upholstery fabrics and certain other items has declined, and more has gone into woolen and worsted clothing fabrics and knitting yarns.

Among other large users of mohair are Japan, Italy, France, and the Netherlands.

Because the United States has raised production and lowered the consumption of mohair, increasing amounts have been exported.

Most mohair is produced on ranges where goats have access to plants they can browse and graze.

There has been a steady gain in average clip per goat from about 4 pounds in the thirties to about 6.5 pounds in the sixties.

In the United States and the Republic of South Africa, it is customary for Angora goats to be clipped twice a year. The length of fiber then is 4 to 6 inches for a half year's growth. If it is clipped only once a year, the length is 8 to 12 inches.

Because of the fineness of kid mohair, each of the first three shearings of young goats is marketed separately from those of adult goats.

Cashmere, a luxurious animal hair, is obtained from the cashmere goat, which originated in Tibet and is now produced mainly in the northwestern provinces of mainland China.

The cashmere goat is smaller than the Angora goat and is covered with straight, coarse, long hairs, about 1.5 to 5 inches long, under which is a fine undercoat, or downlike wool. The undercoat is valued especially.

The undercoat and some of the outercoat are shed through molting each spring. For several weeks through the shedding season, each goat is combed regularly.

At the time of combing, much of the long hair is removed from the down and the two are marketed separately.

Nevertheless, varying amounts of coarse hair are still mixed with the high-value wool or downlike cashmere when it is marketed. The yield of the mixture per animal has been estimated at not more than one-half pound per animal.

Common goat hair is used seldom in worsted or woolen goods but sometimes in place of kemp in fabrics to be used in ladies' wear.

THE CAMEL FAMILY includes true camels and the various members of the llama family. Each produces distinctive hair that is valued in the textile industry.

The camel hair moving in international trade and used in the wool textile industry of the United States and other industrialized countries is grown chiefly in Mongolia, Chinese Turkistan, and the northwestern provinces of mainland China. It comes mainly from the Bactrian-type camel, which has two humps and is native to those northern areas. Some comes from the dromedary, or one-hump, camel, which may be native to southwestern Asia.

In the spring as warmer weather arrives, instead of being sheared or plucked as with other fleece-bearing animals, the camel hair begins to form matted strands and tufts. They are gathered as they fall off the animal's head, sides, neck, and legs. Most camel hair is shed in the spring but some is shed throughout the year.

One camel may yield about 5.3 pounds of hair a year.

Each caravan usually is followed by a trailer, who gathers the tufts and places them in baskets, which are strapped to the last camel in the caravan. The contents of the baskets are sold at the first opportunity, and the camel hair may change hands several times before reaching a shipping point, where it is sorted and graded for export.

The camel has an outer coat of coarse, tough, and wiry hair, which can be as long as 15 inches. The under layer is a soft, woollike down of fine fibers 1 to 5 inches long. The two types are normally separated by processing through combing machines. Most camel hair is used undyed in overcoat fabrics. Some is used to make soft brushes used by artists.

The llama family comprises four distinct and two hybrid species that grow in the mountains of South America.

The llama and alpaca have been domesticated for probably 1,200 years. The guanaco and vicuña are wild. The hybrids are the huarizo (progeny of a llama father and alpaca mother) and the paco-llama, or misti (the offspring of the reverse cross).

Except for the guanaco, which exists chiefly in Patagonia and the rocky islands south of the Strait of Magellan, the members of the llama family are principally in the high Andes of southern Ecuador, Peru, Bolivia, and northwestern Argentina.

The llama, mainly a beast of burden, has a thick, coarse coat. Its fleece is valuable as fur, and its hair is a mixture of fine hair and kemp.

The alpaca is more important to the textile industry. Its hair normally is 8 to 16 inches long but may grow to 30 inches if it is not sheared. Its fleece is fine and strong. The alpaca normally shears 4 to 7 pounds every 2 years.

The fleeces of the huarizo and misti are less fine and valuable than those of the alpaca.

The vicuña, the smallest member of the llama family, produces the finest and rarest woollike fiber. It is wild in Peru at elevations to 16,500 feet. The vicuña fleece averages about a pound. Only a few thousand pounds are obtained in a year.

THE HAIR COVERING of fur-bearing animals has been used in textiles since ancient times.

Chinchillas were used by early natives of South America to make a soft fabric. In Europe, the hair covering of hares and rabbits has been mixed with other fibers for years.

Textiles utilize the fur fiber of hares, rabbits, muskrats, nutria, beavers, fox, wolf, mink, skunk, and many others.

Brush fibers—bristle and hair—are obtained from the tails or bodies of various animals. Bristle from hogs is used mostly in stiff paint, hair, and clothes brushes. Brush-quality hair is taken from the tails of squirrels, kolinsky (a mink found in the Far East), fitch (from Europe and the Far East), skunk, and civet, and is used for artists' and optical brushes. Hair from all parts of the badger is used.

Down sometimes is mixed with other fibers for textiles. Goose down is best. Duck down and the finer feathers of the ostrich, chicken, and turkey also are used. Down also is used as a stuffing material. Feathers are too coarse and resilient for easy spinning and weaving, but the finer ones are used in bedding.

Fur-bearing animals have two types of hair coverings. The relatively long, spikelike guard hairs are the animal's raincoat. The short, soft inner hairs keep the animal warm. The soft fibers grow silkier and finer in the fall. In spring, these inner hairs are molted, and the longer guard hairs become more prominent.

Garments are made from some pelts. The hair from scraps of such pelts and most rabbit pelts become felt for hats. The guard hair, which is not used in making felt, is sold for spinning. The fur fiber also is blended with nearly all other apparel textile fibers, to which it imparts a soft hand, or feel.

HORACE G. PORTER *has served with the European Headquarters of the Marshall plan and with the Bureau of Agricultural Economics of the Department. He became chief of the Foreign Competition Branch, Cotton Division, Foreign Agricultural Service, in 1957.*

BERNICE M. HORNBECK *worked in other branches of Government in the fields of textiles and international trade before joining the Foreign Agricultural Service in 1956. She holds a bachelor's degree from the University of California at Los Angeles.*

Fibers Made

by Man

by BERNICE M. HORNBECK

MANMADE fibers—which people call synthetics and sometimes miracle fibers—are the infants of the family of textile fibers, but in terms of volume and variety they are well established.

Manmade fibers are important from a consumer's standpoint because of the great variety of their characteristics. They are important from an economic viewpoint because of the competition they afford natural fibers.

The basis of the industry was the work of several Europeans. Count Hilaire de Chardonnet went beyond the work of others by concentrating upon a commercial process for manufacturing rayon.

The development of the first artificial fiber was based upon the use of cellulose, mostly from cotton linters and woodpulp. After de Chardonnet's product was exhibited at the Paris Exposition in 1889, a number of factories using several different processes were built in Europe. The first successful plant for the manufacture of rayon by the viscose process in the United States opened in 1910.

All of the early types of manmade fibers were produced in filament form, simulating raw silk, and were called artificial silk. In the late twenties, rayon was chopped into short lengths and used on the cotton and wool spinning systems. These short fibers are known as staple.

Production of rayon expanded in the twenties, and by the midthirties the level of production in Germany, Italy, and Japan brought manmade fibers into keen competition with cotton and wool.

The governments of those countries fostered the rapid expansion at that time in order to lessen their dependence on imported raw materials—mainly cotton and wool.

Manmade staple fiber sometimes is spun alone, but often it is blended with other manmade or natural fibers in spinning.

Manmade fibers offer intense competition to natural fibers. They also compete with one another. This is perhaps best illustrated by the use of various fibers in automobile tires in the United States. Originally, cotton had this entire market. Cotton lost the market to high-tenacity rayon, and more recently, nylon has offered intense competition to high-tenacity rayon.

Manmade fibers are of two major types—cellulosics, which are based on the use of cellulose found in plant life, and noncellulosics, which are manufactured from chemical raw materials.

There are some manmade fibers that are not generally included in either the cellulosic or noncellulosic groupings. Among them are glass fiber, the most important, and various protein fibers.

Cellulosic fibers also are of two basic types, called rayon and acetate in the United States. Within these two major groups are a number of variations, each with its own distinct attributes. Viscose rayon in appropriate sizes can be given either cotton-like or woollike characteristics. Newer modified types of viscose rayon have overcome some of the weaknesses of regular rayon. Both types of viscose rayon are used alone or in blends.

Cuprammonium is a rayon made by different processing methods from the viscose type. It is fine, lustrous, and supple, and it is used oftenest for women's sheer apparel fabrics.

Acetate fibers are made from cellulose mixed with chemicals to form cellulose acetate. It does not resemble cotton. It is less absorptive, but it is pliable and supple. Acetate fibers are used for curtains and draperies and some types of clothing.

Noncellulosics are produced by large chemical companies by complex manufacturing processes. The first of commercial importance was nylon, a polyamide type. Research was started by the Du Pont laboratories in 1926, and commercial production of nylon started in 1938.

Polyamide fibers are synthesized from the basic chemicals found in coal, oil, water, corncobs, oats and rice hulls, bran, gas, and petroleum.

The nylon fibers are strong, smooth, elastic, and nonabsorbent. Nylon is used alone or in blends with natural fibers. The versatility of nylon is indicated by its application to a wide spectrum of apparel, household, and industrial uses.

Some very fine nylon fibers are used for women's hosiery. Stronger and stiffer nylon is used for cordage, tires, and bristles for brushes.

Many other commercially feasible types of noncellulosic fibers have been developed, which are known by a profusion of trade names. In the United States, there are Dacron, Fortrel, Vycron, and Kodel of the polyester types; Creslan, Acrilan, Zefran, and Orlon of the acrylic types; and several other generic types for which the trade names are not so well known.

Polyester fibers are made from chemicals derived from coal, air, water, and petroleum. They are resilient and nonabsorbent. They may be set to shape by the application of heat and hence are suitable for "permanent" pleats and creases in apparel. Polyester fibers may be spun alone or in blends with cotton, wool, or other manmade fibers.

Acrylic fibers are made from the elements found in coal, air, water, petroleum, and limestone. Their outstanding characteristics are their bulking power, or fluffiness, and light weight, which result in both warmth and resiliency of the finished products.

Acrylics have made inroads into markets once held by wool, such as sweaters and blankets, but acrylics are also used in cottonlike products. They also are blended with both cotton and wool.

The polyvinyl fibers are made from materials manufactured out of salt water and petroleum. There are several varieties of polyvinyl fibers. One is polypropylene. They do not absorb moisture and retain their size and shape even when exposed to changes of the weather. The early types were made in heavy filaments that were used in tapes for outdoor furniture, auto seatcovers, and such. Finer filaments and staple are now produced. Polypropylene staple, which is relatively inexpensive to manufacture, has been blended with wool for clothing, but technical difficulties may limit its use largely to industrial applications.

Protein fibers are made by processing meal from corn, soybeans, and peanuts. They are usually blended with other fibers, to which they impart their high moisture absorbency and softness.

Textile fibers also are made from glass. Their special characteristics are fineness, high tensile strength, and incombustibility. Glass fiber has many applications in electric insulation and other industrial uses. It has also gained wide acceptance for decorating fabrics and wallpaper.

The basic manufacturing process for both cellulosic and noncellulosic types, as well as glass, is the preparation of a solution from cellulose, synthesized chemicals, regenerated protein, or glass.

The solution is forced through fine holes in a spinneret and solidified in air or in a solution. The spinneret somewhat resembles a shower head. In manufacturing a continuous filament yarn, the spinneret contains the number and size of holes that match the number and diameter of filaments desired in the particular yarn.

In the manufacture of staple fiber, on the other hand, a spinneret may contain thousands of holes of the desired diameter. After coagulation, the filaments are chopped into predetermined lengths, generally 1.5 to 3 inches (for use on cotton spinning systems) or 2 to 7 inches (for use on the woolen and worsted spinning systems). Staple fiber is packaged into bales.

MANMADE FIBERS are produced in all industrialized countries.

World production of manmade fibers in 1963 totaled about 9.9 billion pounds, a new record high. This represents a gain of about 10 percent over production in 1962, which also was a record.

Production of rayon and acetate, totaling about 6.7 billion pounds, was 6 percent above the previous high of 6.3 billion pounds in 1962. The production of filament yarn increased to 2.7 billion pounds, a gain of 1.5 percent over 1962, while staple increased to 4 billion pounds, a gain of 10 percent over 1962.

Noncellulosic manmade fiber production reached 2.9 billion pounds in 1963. This new record was 20 percent above the 1962 level, which was also a record. Of the 1963 production, filament yarn accounted for 1.7 billion pounds, and noncellulosic staple and tow production accounted for 1.2 billion pounds. These represent gains over 1962 of 18 percent and 22 percent.

The United States accounted for 27 percent of the world total production of all manmade fibers in 1964. Its share of cellulosic fiber production was 20 percent; cellulosic filament yarn accounted for 27 percent of the world total and staple fiber and tow 15 percent. The United States accounts for 41 percent of total noncellulosic production. The United States' share of noncellulosic filament yarn is 45 percent and of staple fiber and tow 35 percent.

Japan ranks second to the United States as a producer of manmade fibers, accounting for 15 percent of the world total; West Germany ranks third with 9 percent; the United Kingdom and the Soviet Union rank fourth and fifth, respectively, with 7 percent of world production each, and Italy ranks sixth with 6 percent. In the aggregate, these six countries account for 71 percent of all manmade fiber production, 66 percent of all rayon and acetate, 84 percent of all noncellulosic production, and 88 percent of all glass fibers.

Although total world capacity for the production of cellulosic fibers is relatively stable, world capacity for the production of noncellulosic fibers continues to expand rapidly.

With the exception of India and Japan, most of the countries where expansion of cellulosic production facilities has occurred in recent years have not been large producers of manmade textile fibers. On the other hand, the expansion of noncellulosic capacity has continued largely in countries with well-developed industrial economies—in western European countries, Japan, and the United States.

Many of the major producers have become large exporters. Western European countries export in fiber form about 30 percent of their rayon staple production, more than 25 percent of their rayon filament production, and about 5 percent of their noncellulosic production. The bulk of their exports are to destinations outside of western Europe.

The United States exports about 5 percent and Japan only about 10 percent of their total manmade fibers as fiber, although about one-third of Japan's total rayon production is exported in the form of fabrics, mainly to markets in southeastern Asia and in Africa.

BERNICE M. HORNBECK *has been with the Cotton Division of the Foreign Agricultural Service since 1956. She has made a number of studies on interfiber competition and international trade in cotton textiles.*

The Evolution of Competitive Markets

by HARRY C. TRELOGAN

FARM GOODS in the United States move from producer to user in a system that grew from a series of preceding systems and continues to grow and change as new technologies, products, and practices are subjected to the tests of competition.

Market arrangements represent modifications of earlier patterns adjusted to modern conditions. Marketing institutions are often perplexing in the absence of knowledge of their antecedents. Complexity, arising from growth of an economy that employs more and more specialized methods, obscures fundamental relationships that are evident in elemental forms.

When we trace developments from the past to the present, therefore, we and traders overseas can understand better the domestic distributive system from which our foreign trade stems and the problems and possibilities of developing countries.

BEFORE THE American Revolution, political, military, and trade policies of European powers determined the distributive and productive patterns of our country. The policies and patterns have been superseded, but they influenced profoundly the structure on which our marketing rests.

In the same way, the recent and current policies of a country in its onetime possessions and colonies very

261

likely will influence for a long time their marketing structures.

Spanish influence following the discovery of America developed slowly.

The Capilla de San Marcos in St. Augustine, Fla., founded in 1565, is a vestige of the earliest trading era. This fortification protected and succored treasure ships riding astride the Gulf Stream as they passed through the Bahama channel, where they were vulnerable to pirate attack on their way from Mexico and South America.

Spanish policies of exploitation of accumulated riches and native labor met with little success in Florida, with its infertile soil, paucity of minerals, and relatively uncultured and inhospitable inhabitants. Maintenance of forts and surrounding settlements to prevent French and English intrusion was a drain on the Spanish treasury. A self-sustaining economy could not be established. The dollar as a unit of currency is a reminder of Spanish influence on United States commerce.

English colonial policies designed to foster mutually profitable trade left more durable imprints. Fort Ticonderoga, built in 1765 at what now appears to be an obscure point between two lakes in northern New York, symbolizes the penetration of trade routes into the interior. It protected canoes carrying provisions across Lake Champlain and Lake George on their way to inland trading posts to supply trappers, hunters, and frontier farmers. The French, who settled farther north, vied with the British for military control to advance imperial and commercial ambitions.

The British emerged triumphant after a century of struggle. Their colonial policies soon ran into conflict with the colonists, but their cultural, political, legal, financial, and commercial institutions remained as a heritage from which our distributive system has evolved. Their joint-stock companies were forerunners of the modern corporations that characterize the capitalistic business enterprises of our distributive system.

British policy, unlike the Spanish policy, recognized that all participants must benefit if trade is to be sustained. Nevertheless, dissatisfaction with the assessment of costs and distribution of benefits imposed on the American colonists by the English Crown led the Colonies to rebel.

Independence opened the way to arrange new terms of external and internal trade.

External trade was influenced by efforts to expand agricultural exports as a means for obtaining exchange and credit for industrial development and to protect infant industries by discouraging imports.

Internally, each colony assumed independent control of its monetary system and trade policy, but agreed in the Articles of Confederation to submit to Federal direction only in military matters. The articles were drafted shortly after Adam Smith published *The Wealth of Nations*, which advocated laissez faire and warned that the government that governed least governed best.

Trade among the Colonies was disrupted as local interests sought protection from competition from other colonies. It soon became plain that such a system would so weaken the economic strength that joint military protection would be ineffective. A Constitutional Convention, convened in 1787, took significant action, which determined the course of the American distributive system.

The commerce clause ranks high among the provisions of the Constitution that favor the free flow of goods between States and national economic growth. The grant of power to the Congress to regulate interstate commerce did not completely negate State control, which has been persistently proposed and tried ever since. But the Supreme Court has delimited State control sufficiently to regard the United States as a market entity with relatively unfettered opportunity for distribution within it.

The breadth and scope of this market and its single monetary system helped create a mass-production factory system. Before that phenomenon matured, however, other developments, particularly in transportation, led to successive distributive systems, each of which had a part in molding the present system.

DISTRIBUTION CENTERS were established first at eastern ports.

Boston, New York, Philadelphia, Baltimore and Savannah and New Orleans became gateways through which exports of grain, tobacco, and fibers were shipped in exchange for equipment, clothing, and supplies, mainly from Europe and the Indies.

As agriculture spread westward, trade routes generally followed the waterways, which were interconnected by trails, roads, turnpikes, and canals.

The major ports harbored domestic manufacturing and consuming centers and wholesale receiving and distributive markets.

Secondary markets became established inland at the confluences of rivers, lakes, canals, and roads. Goods moved through Hartford, Albany, Buffalo, Pittsburgh, Cincinnati, Louisville, Atlanta, and St. Louis to and from port cities.

This geographic pattern of distribution that evolved when agricultural products moved in raw and bulk forms has endured to a substantial degree. Investments made in warehouses, elevators, stockyards, and other handling facilities augmented natural water transport advantages in keeping trading centers fixed unless or until lower cost alternatives appeared. Barges moving bulk grain down the Illinois and Mississippi or up the Cumberland and Ohio Rivers represent a carryover from the water transport era.

Except for products destined for other countries or originating in other countries, assembly and distribution were mostly localized and decentralized. Grain moved in bulk on wagons to water. Livestock was driven or taken in boats to abattoirs. Fresh produce was sold in municipal markets. Farmers carried supplies back home from market towns. Village retailers accepted home-produced eggs, butter, cheese, and preserves from nearby farms, in exchange for coffee, sugar, molasses, tools, and clothing. Peddlers carried sundries to outlying farms.

As urbanization developed in the United States, the Industrial Revolution, pioneered shortly before in England, caused processing and fabricating activities to be transferred slowly out of homes and off farms into factories, but rural distribution methods changed relatively little until the 20th century.

RAIL TRANSPORTATION brought a modification of marketing. Railroad lines that stabbed out from the port cities brought new farm areas within reach of markets and expanded the territory for profitable distribution of manufactured goods. Domestic industries were placed in better position to compete with oversea sources.

Dependable and economical overland freight transportation was particularly advantageous to areas having limited access to water routes. Such inland distribution centers as St. Louis, Omaha, Minneapolis, and Memphis became important as distributive centers. Some, including Chicago and Atlanta, surpassed previously predominant port cities, especially those that depended on intercoastal shipping.

Major seaboard ports maintained their importance because of export and import trade, augmented by domestic distribution to adjacent populous areas. Growth of trade with other parts of the world, aided by rail transport, brought new ports, such as San Francisco and Seattle, into prominence. Although domestic trade assumed a paramount position that persists to this day, these ports still vie for international trade.

Centralized assembly and distribution were oriented about markets at rail terminals on routes from producing to consuming areas. Supplies moved into the terminals from country elevators, gins, creameries, and stockyards, which bought goods from farmers near the rail shipping points. The local assembler endeavored to ship produce in carlots. At the terminal, wholesale receivers stored and sorted the stocks to fill orders from exporters and distributors in metropolitan consuming areas. For the domestic trade, wholesale receivers forwarded carlots to jobbers, who broke the shipments down to supply smaller quantities to retailers.

The flow of goods back to rural areas came from importers or domestic industrial plants to wholesalers in the terminals, who distributed to wholesalers and jobbers in subterminals. They in turn delivered the goods to retailers. Mail-order houses shipped goods directly from terminals to consumers by parcel post, mail, and express, carried mostly by railroads.

Canners, millers, seed crushers, creameries, and textile factories located their plants at or near terminal markets. There they could choose raw materials best suited for their purposes and convert them into less bulky, less perishable products for less costly distribution to consumer markets.

Thus Chicago, the greatest rail terminal of them all, in the words of Carl Sandburg, became "hog butcher for the world." Boston, in the middle of the New England textile industry, became the dominant wool market and received the raw wool from home and abroad. Minneapolis and Buffalo became leading milling centers, thanks to their location at strategic points in the flow of grain across the Nation and the ocean.

Railroad rate schedules were devised to facilitate centralized storage and processing. Shipments originating at country points were given stopover privileges at the terminals and advantageous through rates to their final destination in raw or processed form.

Specialized facilities were adapted to the needs of giant terminal markets. Huge grain elevators, stockyards, and packinghouses were more obvious but no more effective contributors to the system than organized commodity exchanges, banking houses, and insurance firms whose services were tailored to the requirements of the trade.

These institutions retain their influence in seaboard markets handling shipments abroad. Rates for rail and water transportation and handling facilities often determine which seaport is patronized.

Mechanical refrigeration exemplified technological innovations that altered the times and places for the performance of marketing services so as to favor centralized distribution. It eliminated the cumbersome, expensive harvesting, holding, and shipping of natural ice. It permitted eggs, formerly held from summer to winter in farm icehouses, to be stored in massive refrigerated warehouses at terminal markets. It reduced the need for daily slaughter in abattoirs near butcher shops in every community. Upon its adaptation to railroad freight cars, it enabled packers to ship dressed meat instead of cattle from Chicago to the eastern markets. It broadened the distribution of fresh fruits and vegetables, thereby leading to more concentrated production areas supplying ever-widening markets over longer seasons.

Advertising was another adjunct in the growth of centralized processors and distributors. It was used to stimulate demand for branded products easily identified by housewives in numerous consumer markets that could be supplied from a single rail terminal point.

CONCENTRATIONS OF POWER and control accompanied concentrations of stocks of commodities and volumes of business in the hands of corporate managements operating in the central markets.

A few processors, handlers, or bankers could exercise great influence in determining, if not dictating, the terms of trade implemented through prices paid and charged, rates and fees fixed, and trading conditions and methods maintained.

Centralized marketing consequently was not universally accepted by farmers and consumers as an unmixed blessing, even though efficiencies and conveniences were derived from it.

As activities at terminals grew more specialized, these markets drew farther apart from assembly and retail, so that some misunderstandings enveloped them in the eyes of farmers and consumers who depended on them.

Because the public had a great stake in the food and farm products handled through the centralized distributive system, the Federal Government was called upon to draft rules that would supplement State and local regulations.

The commerce clause of the Constitution provided legal foundation for many of the rules, but new legislation extended the range beyond earlier concepts. Laws were enacted dealing with public health and safety (food and drug, meat inspection, and public carrier safety laws); economic protection (railroad rate, antitrust, and Commodity Exchange Acts); and public information (crop and livestock estimates and market news).

Laws and marketing services subject to voluntary acceptance contributed to an environment in which trading could be conducted with confidence. Such an environment was essential to a distribution system in which trading took place between distant markets and between huge impersonal corporate firms and small dealers. Because individual farmers and country assemblers usually had to rely on brokers, commissionmen, and auctioneers to handle their transactions in terminal markets, the integrity and responsibility of these agents had to be defined and enforced.

The encouragement of farmer cooperatives was another approach toward alleviating inequities of trade. Through cooperatives, farmers were able to manage some marketing services themselves, and to pool their sales to achieve more effective bargaining power in negotiations with buyers in central markets.

THE MOTOR AGE brought revolutionary changes.

One of the first impacts was on roads, always considered primarily a responsibility of local government. Earlier, the responsibility often was turned over to private companies, which usually were financed by the sale of stock, with the intention of recovering investment from tolls. A tendency was general for privately operated roads, ferries, and bridges to be taken over by governmental agencies to provide free public use.

Roads built with Federal funds were few and for military purposes. An exception was the National Road, built to encourage settlement of the Northwest Territory and to provide a way for settlers to get their products to eastern markets.

Concepts of responsibility for roads began to change in 1893, when the Congress established a Federal office to consult and advise States on their road programs.

Invention of automotive vehicles brought demands for improved roads and streets that overwhelmed local tax sources. Consequently, the Congress enacted legislation in 1916 for sustained assistance to States in support of primary roads. Sufficient coordination was achieved by 1921 to initiate a system of highway identification and maintenance that led to the development of an integrated system of interstate highways. Motortrucks began to compete with railways for interurban freight movements in small lots.

Federal assistance was granted to farm-to-market roads beginning in 1932. These secondary roads effectively extended the distribution system to every town and hamlet and to most farms. Only a short haul to a railroad siding or a highway confronted most producers and local shippers and receivers.

The number, size, and performance of trucks have increased tremendously, along with the capacity of highways. The main impediment to over-the-road transport has been variable State regulations and licensing applied to the vehicles, which interfere with trucks and trailers crossing State lines. With additional Federal support of substantial proportions for straightening, leveling, and enlarging highways, with greater uniformity in State regulation of traffic, and with still further advances in truck and trailer equipment, motor transport has been challenging the railroads for more and for longer distance freight movement.

DIRECT MARKETING began to develop because terminal markets were slow to accommodate the trucks that brought shipments to them. Unloading equipment for railcars had to be altered or duplicated. Narrow city streets became congested. Valuable land was required for parking space and service facilities. Some processors found it easier to locate plants in rural areas closer to sources of supplies. Meatpackers with plants near producing areas could compete successfully with the large terminal market packers. Farmers could truck hogs and cattle to them directly from the farm. The trucks were easily unloaded, no selling agents had to be paid, and net returns compared favorably with those received elsewhere.

Dressed meat shipped from country plants directly to points of consumption bypassed terminal markets, often reaching the destination faster and cheaper. Such direct marketing of hogs made inroads on the previous system, beginning in the thirties. Rising costs of labor and land and taxes in the big terminal cities caused decentralized marketing to spread to other commodities, as trucks broadened the areas from which plants could draw supplies directly from farmers.

THE RETAIL end of the distributive system was also undergoing changes.

The corner grocery and general store supplied from independent wholesale houses typified food retailing in town and country until chainstores began to change the pattern in the early 1900's.

Cash-and-carry stores, under central management and supplied largely from company-owned trucks and warehouses, offered urban consumers fewer services and lower prices. When the stores introduced self-service for the customers some 25 years later, their competitive position was augmented.

The supermarket, a large, compartmentalized store offering wider selections of groceries, meats, and produce at still lower prices, was conceived during the depression of the thirties. It attracted mass sales at a location easily reached by automobile. Home facilities, such as electric refrigerators, increased the ability of housewives to hold food for their families and engage in once-a-week shopping.

Chainstore companies eschewed supermarkets until the success of these independently operated competitors forced them to reconsider some 10 years later. After the chains began consolidating their small stores into supermarkets, a concerted effort was exerted to adapt a greater share of the store business to self-service. Meat and fresh produce departments were the last to adopt consumer packaging sufficiently to dispense with clerks at each counter.

The bargaining power of buyers for supermarkets, enhanced by the large volumes handled, is used to achieve objectives of the firm. Each company tries to stock products and provide services that will attract patronage within the competitive area served by its stores. The effort is made to display products in demand by consumers that will sell fast enough at sufficient profit to bear a share of the store operating expenses proportionate to the allotted shelf space.

Food processors often advertise their products to assure favorable reception by stores as well as customers. But supermarkets do not rely entirely on purchases of processor-branded products if the quality, margins, or prices are not satisfactory. Some establish their own processing plants to package products for sale exclusively within their stores. Some contract with processors to pack products according to their specifications for distribution under their own labels. Some send buyers to assembly markets in concentrated producing areas to bid at auction or to negotiate private sales of fresh produce prepared and packed to meet their inspection requirement. Some purchase products on Federal grades, especially when the output of more than one packer is required to supply the amount needed. Some engage in farm production when adequate supplies of the quality of products wanted are not available through normal market channels.

These arrangements permit delivery from the packing plant directly to the local chainstore warehouse thousands of miles away and, where volume is sufficient, even directly by truck to the retail store.

Intricate scheduling of purchase and delivery is sometimes done to enable supermarkets to place advertisements for fresh produce in large city newspapers on Wednesday or Thursday, stating the quality and price of products that will be available in their stores over the next weekend.

AGRICULTURAL ADJUSTMENTS accompanied changes in the distributive system.

Farmers found markets for their production to fulfill the needs of a rapidly growing industrial nation and to provide exports needed by a debtor country until the end of the First World War. Difficulties in disposing of farm output, encountered by the now creditor nation in the twenties and thirties, were not resolved fully with attempts to expand domestic consumption or to curtail production.

A reversal of foreign trade policies, set in motion in 1933, enabled the United States to take the initiative in getting countries to lower trade barriers, but the trend toward international trade freedom alleviated the problem of farm surpluses only slightly before war again brought shortages.

Expansion of farm output for the Second World War was attained despite a decline in farm labor through improved mechanization and cultural practices. The greater capacity to produce, together with subsiding exports following the war, led to resumption of relative abundance. Distributors contended more for customers than for suppliers of farm products. They exercised greater discrimination in their purchases and became more exacting in their demands for products that could be handled efficiently and be used to curry favor of customers. The processing, packaging, handling, and advertising methods they employed required more uniformly high-quality products. Farmers were faced with the necessity of submitting to these demands and of reducing costs.

The response of farmers was to introduce technological innovations involving greater capital equipment investments conducive to larger scale, more highly specialized farm production.

The adjustments made farmers dependent upon the marketing system for additional services.

Functions formerly performed on farms were transferred to the market agents. Mechanically harvested cotton called for more cleaning at the gins than handpicked cotton. Mechanically dug potatoes required more careful handling at storage and packinghouses. Combined wheat had to be conditioned at the elevators. Commercial enterprises were formed to sell mixed feeds and inorganic fertilizers and provide crop dusting and artificial insemination services.

Advances in farming and distribution were mutually interdependent and had to be closely synchronized.

This dovetailing proved to be extremely difficult to arrange between independently managed farms and firms.

The answer that emerged was called vertical integration; that is, the bringing together of successive production processes under unified management, in distinction from horizontal integration, or a centralized management of companies performing the same functions, such as chainstores.

Either by acquiring ownership of farms, or more often by contractual relationships with the farmers, market agents use integrated methods to direct and control farm production to fit their processing and merchandising programs.

Broiler chicken production is an example of a highly integrated industry. In the large, specialized producing areas, market agents, that is, feed dealers, hatcherymen, or poultry processors, contract with farm producers to raise most of the chicks. The contractors provide the chicks plus the feed and the vaccines, which are administered in accordance with directions given to the farmers. Decisions on where to sell and when and for how much to sell are made by the market agents, who assume most of the investment and risk costs.

Efficiencies achieved with these integrated methods enable the dealers to ship frozen ready-to-cook broilers in consumer packages directly to oversea markets to compete successfully with locally dressed fresh poultry.

PRICE STABILITY, long sought by agriculture, is promoted by the Federal Government through a number of approaches. Early steps were designed to help the established distributive system cope with problems that limited its ability to avoid excessive seasonal price fluctuations. For instance, the Federal Reserve Bank system was designed in part to facilitate the flow of funds to agricultural areas for purchase of crop harvests.

Efforts to reduce year-to-year fluctuations included loans to foreign governments for the purchase of farm products and loans to farmer cooperatives to promote orderly marketing through the carryover of stocks from large crop years.

Government intervention became more direct in the thirties, when price-support loans were made to farmers with the option of either redeeming the loans or of delivering the commodities to a Government agency within specified time periods. Responsibility for storage and disposition of the stocks fell to the agency when title was transferred. The Government, in effect, became a third outlet for staple commodities, auxiliary to the privately operated domestic market and the export market.

The Government has also acquired an auxiliary relationship for storage and distribution. Private distributors occasionally purchase from the Government to replenish seasonally depleted stocks, but the bulk of surplus commodities are given to domestic agencies for relief or school lunch feeding, or are sold or donated to needy foreign countries. The storage is sometimes accomplished with Government-owned facilities, but more often through contractual arrangements with privately owned firms.

Strenuous efforts are made to encourage foreign trade, but also to minimize Government involvement in handling the sales and deliveries by subsidizing or otherwise helping private business to make export sales before the products get into Government ownership. A high proportion of exports receive either direct or indirect Government assistance under a wide range of programs.

ARRANGEMENTS FOR EXPORTING agricultural products from the United States may be considered as an addendum to the domestic system.

Few products are produced with an export destination in mind. Major exceptions include such staple commodities as cotton, wheat, and tobacco.

For most products, the foreign market serves as a residual outlet that can be enlarged when crops are abundant. Thereby they serve as a price-stabilizing force.

Exports are diverted from domestic trade channels when it becomes apparent that a foreign market outlet is advantageous. The diversion may oc-

cur at any of several stages of marketing, but the tendency is to export
products in raw and bulk forms. They
leave the distributive system before
processing and packaging and entry
into wholesaling and retailing operations that are essentially oriented to
domestic distribution. They tend to
move from central markets to shipside
on rail, barge, or truck facilities.

Recent technological innovations
have been altering this general pattern. Since the opening of the St.
Lawrence Seaway in 1958, extensive
grain shipments originate from Great
Lakes ports instead of seaboard ports,
thus reducing time and costs to reach
European markets. Tank car and pipe-
line movements of vegetable oils and
other liquids also reduce costs of shipment from inland points to shipside.
Airfreight is being used to ship highly
perishable fresh produce, such as
strawberries, to luxury markets abroad.
More precise environmental controls
in ship holds permit fresh fruit shipments overseas. Processing and packaging advances are enabling more
dealers to emulate the broiler shippers
in penetrating foreign markets with
prepared end products in consumer
units. Presumably the same techniques
offer opportunities for reciprocal trade
to enter American markets.

With international arrangements for
freedom of commerce, the world may
be regarded as a potential market
entity with quite as much validity as
were the early American States.

The American experience suggests
that open competition offers higher
standards of living wherever it may be
allowed to flourish.

HARRY C. TRELOGAN *became Administrator, Statistical Reporting Service, in
1961. Previously he was Assistant Administrator, Agricultural Marketing Service,
and Assistant Administrator, Agricultural
Research Administration, in which positions
he directed the marketing research programs
in the Department. He has served the Department of Agriculture since 1938 in a
variety of responsibilities.*

Changes in Market Structure

by HAROLD F. BREIMYER

THE SYSTEM for marketing and distributing farm products in every country is large, complex, and important.
It is expected to do many things and
do them well. It is called on to function with a roller-bearing efficiency,
clockwork regularity, and thermostatic
dependability. It is a basically self-
regulating system, an early automation
that long predated the electronic com-
puter and photoelectric cell.

In the United States the marketing
system assembles the products of more
than 3 million farms. It transports,
stores, and processes them. It exchanges ownership and arrives at price
at each step along the way. It delivers
the final products to consumers—135
million tons of foodstuffs each year,
worth more than 60 billion dollars,
and nonfoods worth several billions.

A function as vast and vital as the
marketing of farm products can only
be carried out by an orderly system of
processes, techniques, and organizations. Marketing never can be done
satisfactorily by haphazard methods
and irresponsible agents. Even the
most primitive market economy has a
semblance of organization.

To the system of organization by
which the marketing of farm products
of any country is conducted, we apply
a broader term, the structure of the
market, which includes transportation,
warehousing, grading services, and

other facilities and services. It is more than that; in marketing, the whole is more than the sum of its parts. The marketing system is an interdependent system, and market structure is concerned with the manner in which that interdependence is achieved.

The marketing system has a dual obligation. It must move and transform products physically. It also must provide for exchange of ownership and thereby arrive at price.

In a freely competitive economy, price is the primary regulatory device.

By it, services are called forth and supplies are apportioned. Price also determines the rewards to producers and the cost to consumers.

The marketing of farm products is carried on principally by private trading, but invariably it uses some services of government. They are ordinarily designed not to replace private trading so much as to supplement it or to make it work better.

The market structure therefore includes not only facilities and services but also the practices, customs, laws, and private and governmental regulatory services—all the institutions by which marketing is converted from a disorderly melee to a highly organized and efficient procedure that repeats itself day after day, week after week, year after year.

Market structure has national and international significance because there is universal concern for it, it differs so much among nations, and it is subject to dynamic changes.

Although all countries face comparable tasks of devising a marketing system that meets tests of efficiency, fairness, and orderliness, by no means are they equally successful in attaining it.

The contrast in men's weapons, ranging from lance to atomic missile, is no sharper than in his farm markets. In parts of Africa, cassava may be sold directly to consumers in raw form and seasonal supply. Likewise, cereal grains in Central America. In the United States and in western Europe, highly processed foods are available in spotless, refrigerated showcases the year around.

A country's success in improving its marketing seems to be related closely to the stage of development of its economy. The more developed countries generally have intricate systems for marketing the products of their farms. Less-advanced nations can show only cruder systems.

The correlation is not one of chance. J. C. Abbott, of the Food and Agriculture Organization of the United Nations, pegs an adequate system of markets high on the list of conditions essential to the development of agricultural economies. Often it is underrated; direct aids to production, such as putting more capital equipment on farms, often get priority.

FORCES OF CHANGE in the structure of the market may be generated consciously or they may be incidental to other events. That is, countries striving for development may make the improvement of their markets a specific goal, as Argentina has sponsored a replacement of its costly, wasteful bag handling of grain by bulk handling.

Elsewhere, changes may be initiated from other parts of the economy, as some of the trends in marketing in England reflect demands made by the new retail supermarkets, which differ from the small shops that did all retailing in the past.

Change can be overglorified, too. Not everything that is new is better. Often an improvement in one spot in the marketing system creates or accentuates a problem in another. Some new nations have successfully promoted new foreign markets for their products, only to lose them through failure to standardize quality in the products shipped.

Current trends in the United States are an example. Through mass handling and advance contracting for supplies, some large distributors are attaining efficiencies in cost and performance. In doing so, they often circumvent the competitive trading that has been the protection of producers, market firms, and consumers.

The process of change, valuable as it often can be, by no means justifies a less critical attitude toward the structure and operations of the marketing system.

Wherever an economic progress is sought, attention will be paid to the marketing of farm products and to efficiency so that there can be economy in cost and use of resources. It will extend to the exchange side of marketing, because a sound system of pricing is necessary to insure equity and fairness and so insure that producers receive enough return to encourage them to produce. Often in backward regions, so little of the final sale value of farm products gets back to the farmer that he has slight incentive to try to increase his production or the quality of his output.

SEVERAL FEATURES of farm products make their marketing so complex and the attainment of a good marketing system so difficult.

First, in all countries outside the Soviet bloc, farm products are produced in small quantities on widely scattered farms. In places where agriculture is self-sufficient rather than commercial, and most markets are local, that is no big handicap. But during the industrial growth most countries aspire to, people collect themselves in cities. To feed them, foodstuffs must be assembled from wide areas and transported far.

Second, most farm products, both crops and livestock, are produced seasonally. But consumers must be supplied with food the year around, and they resist too much seasonal change in their diets.

Seasonal marketing means also that farmers get their income only a few times during the year and that prices at the seasonal harvest are depressed below their average the rest of the year. If farmers are not well financed, they are in danger of being exploited

by lenders who advance funds in anticipation of harvest and are defenseless against the low prices at harvest.

As a third feature, some time elapses between the planning of production and the marketing of products. In this respect, agriculture differs from industry, in which current production often can be adjusted according to current rate of sales. Misjudgments farmers may make in estimating their market can lead to instability. Farm products, once produced, must be sold, regardless of the wisdom of the original decision to produce them. Nor can any new decision as to production in the future have much influence on the prices that can be obtained for them in their sale. In other words, neither their own production history nor concurrent production plans becomes an element in bargaining for sale of farm products.

Fourth, many farm products are perishable. Perishability adds to expense in handling. It also is an important factor in the pricemaking part of marketing. Anyone who holds products that are perishable finds himself in a disadvantaged position in negotiating for a satisfactory price for them.

Fifth, it is difficult to control the quality of farm products and the exact timing of their marketing. As products of nature, they possess a certain variability and unpredictability in their readiness for market that is sharply in contrast with the products of industry. It is hard to standardize the products of the farm, and they become "ripe," "fat," or otherwise ready for market pretty much at their own pace.

This feature of farm products is increasingly in conflict with the demands of the market. Especially in the larger industrial nations that have highly formalized marketing systems, marketing firms beg for a steady flow of supplies of reliable quality. They do so for two reasons: Consumers with high incomes insist on dependable quality, and the handlers and processors themselves want to take advantage of the economy of mass handling, for which regular supplies of fairly uniform quality are essential.

A sixth attribute is that the individual farmers who produce and sell have only little bargaining strength. Farms typically are comparatively small economic enterprises. Farmers have neither the specialized skill in marketing nor the financial capacity to exercise much bargaining power. They are handicapped by the seasonal bunching of supply, perishability of product, and the other features I mentioned.

Farmers are especially conscious of their inferior bargaining power because they customarily sell to firms that are larger and have greater power. Nevertheless, differences in marketpower are found throughout the marketing system. The place where most power rests varies by commodity and by country.

In the United States early in this century, power often centered in processing. Several processors of farm products became targets of trust-busting, which was the Government effort to influence market structure in those days. More recently, power concentration has tended to move forward, to the retailing of food.

Wherever foodstuffs and other farm commodities are traded under less than perfectly competitive conditions—that is, where there are not many buyers and sellers in close touch—an uneven balance of marketpower is likely to be found.

Finally, farm products are characterized by the remoteness of their producers from the ultimate consumers. This distance—this separation—puts a heavy strain on the marketing system if demands of consumers are to be the source of directional signals in production. Consumers' wishes, transmitted through the pricing system of the market, will reach the producer only if the market is a good communication medium.

Ironically, the long line of communication and the chance that it may be faulty are most apparent in the more developed nations. In simple agricultural economies, farmers sell most of their produce directly to local consumers. In larger industrial countries, the farmer never sees the final consumer, who is distant by many miles and several steps in the marketing-and-distribution sequence.

Data on relative values paid by consumers and received by farmers emphasize the wide gulf between the two. In the United States in 1964, original producers received less than 40 cents of each dollar the consumer spent for food. When nonfoods, such as cotton, wool, and tobacco, are included, the farmer's share was less than 30 cents.

THE FORM the marketing system takes at various times and places can usually be explained by the several characteristics of farm products, by the state of technology, and by the goals that are sought in a good system.

In medieval times, a high proportion of farm products was sold at local markets or fairs. If many sellers and many buyers came together there on announced trading days—and if the sovereign's announced rules of trading were observed—a reasonably good market emerged. The method of trading gained wide acceptance. Even scholars of the day took note of it, and from it they derived their theories of how impersonal forces of supply and demand can interact to the common good.

A big weakness remained, however. It was the lack of close touch between the several local markets. One market therefore could labor under oversupply. Another could suffer a shortage.

Development of a network of transport proved the key to good regional and national marketing systems. Late in the 19th century and early in this one, railroads became the big common carrier of farm products. Ribbons of rail lines reached out radially from each center, and trunklines linked the centers. It was the era of great terminal markets for farm products. The system was especially prevalent in Canada, the United States, western Europe, and parts of South America. Farm products were collected and sold in open-market trading at the great rail centers. Usually sale took place by some form of auction.

At those central markets, many buyers met many sellers, some of whom were commissioned agents of the original producers. Therein were the "ideal" conditions of medieval fairs replicated, giant size.

Moreover, the entire system that was built around central markets was comparatively simple, straightforward, and orderly. It was a system of a well-defined marketing sequence. The successive stages came to be called strata, like layers of rock seen in geologic cross section. The farmer sold his produce at the local market. Much of it went to a central assembly market. It may have been directed next to a processor. At the other end of distribution, it likely passed through wholesalers to retailers to consumers.

It may not have been the most efficient market system, but it was visible and understandable. It conformed to the democratic value of being easily accessible to everyone.

Furthermore, that system lent itself well to the marketing services that were developed to make it work better. Some of the services were performed privately, but others became the responsibility of government—in most countries they were divided or carried on jointly between provincial and central governments.

Market information perhaps underpins all market services. In the United States and all modern countries, elaborate statistical reporting services publish data on supplies and prices of farm products in daily trading—the familiar market news reports that may go out by radio or television almost as fast as trading occurs. Those services also collect and disseminate information on acreages, yields, average prices, and other subjects. Sometimes statisticians project economic trends into the future, in order to help farmers and

market firms to make their production and marketing plans for years ahead.

Less-advanced places may lack elaborate facilities but not originality.

In India and Pakistan, for example, blackboards and loudspeakers at the entrance to local markets are a way to inform farmers and traders. The market committee at Montgomery in West Pakistan was even more ingenious. It sent a messenger on bicycle to schools in the district to leave slips on which the current wholesale prices were written. The headmaster gave the slips to the pupils, who took them home to their farmer parents.

Grading of farm products—their classification into uniform categories of quality—has come to be a mark of an up-to-date marketing system. If, as I noted, it is impossible to produce farm products to exact specification, the next best course is to sort them into classes after they are produced.

Many large processors and distributors have their own systems for grading, but most reliance is usually placed on government grading, which normally is standard nationwide and is conducted impartially.

Oftener than not, grading is voluntary. Some countries, however, are sufficiently concerned about preserving a good national reputation in their export markets that they make grading and inspection mandatory.

Grading occasionally is made compulsory for domestic markets. Seattle, Wash., is known for its law calling for federally graded beef. In Calcutta, all ghee brought into the city must have been graded under the Agmark system.

Inspection of farm products for quality carries grading one step forward. Grading merely sorts, but inspection is done in order to reject any unacceptable lots or specimens. Some inspection is for the purpose of protecting consumers against unsanitary or contaminated products. Examples are compulsory inspection of meat and poultry for sanitation and wholesomeness, which is now commonplace in many countries.

Regulation of market practices has been a guardian of the interests of buyers and sellers for many years.

Markets are regulated in order to make them more freely competitive or to protect the public interest in the absence of adequate competition.

Farmers particularly have wanted regulatory action. As farmers enter marketing with little individual bargaining power, they have been highly sensitive to the degree of competition exhibited among their buyers.

By setting rules of trading and by guarding against monopoly, regulatory agencies can help to assure that the market for farm products is at least reasonably competitive.

Where there are built-in monopoly conditions, the regulatory agency can take protective measures.

The public livestock markets in the United States are regulated under the Packers and Stockyards Act. The agricultural markets of India are similarly subject to that country's Agricultural Produce Act.

Markets in many other countries operate under similar authority.

Closely related are overall antimonopoly policies, which relate to marketers, processors, and retailers of farm products as well as to all other corporate business. The best known legislation in the United States to that purpose is the Sherman and Clayton Antitrust Acts.

Another kind of regulation is aimed at preventing any trader from cornering the market in wheat or corn or other product, either in spot or future trading. In the United States, this is carried out under the Commodity Exchange Authority.

Market research, although a less direct service to marketing, is no less significant than others. Research is applicable to nearly all phases of the marketing of farm products. It can be designed to search out better ways of meeting the dual goals of marketing, those of high physical efficiency and of equity in the system of exchange.

All these market services relate to the improvement of the system by which farm products are marketed.

Their meaning is the same in all countries. Just as the fundamental function of marketing is everywhere the same, so do the actions and services undertaken to facilitate it fall into the same broad categories.

Furthermore, the drive toward better marketing is worldwide. It is part of the restless pursuit of economic advancement, of a better life for all.

In less-developed regions, the initial need may be for the simplest facilities, like roads and storage pits or barns.

Often the most pressing requirement is to break away from established customs. Producers in many parts of the world are virtually forced to use traditional trading channels. They may be indebted to traders, local customs may be binding, or laws may be compelling. In some Italian cities, food must be sold wholesale on the local market. In some Latin American towns, only meat from slaughterhouses inside the city can be sold. Elsewhere, products may be permitted to cross city boundaries but must pay a toll. Often the collection of the tolls is awarded to private persons by auction, a system that invites extortion.

The means of solving such problems usually are not hard to discover. The experience of advanced countries usually can be drawn on as a guide to policy. Action is needed.

In the more developed nations, the United States not the least among them, the challenges to marketing are of a different sort. They may not be more difficult, when measured against resources. They are more likely to be novel. Therefore, unlike the problems of less-advanced areas, they must be dealt with without the advantage of prior experience or precedent.

CHALLENGES to marketing in those countries come from two sources.

One is pressure from without, from both consumers and producers, that marketing do a better job.

Consumers are becoming more insistent, not less so, that foods and other farm products reach them in beautifully prepared form, uniform quality, freedom from adulteration or infection, and round-the-calendar regularity.

Farmers are more impatient than before with fluctuating and undependable incomes. Their attitude partly reflects the trend toward a more commercial agriculture, with its greater cash expenditures that must be met. But it is due also to their sharing in a general desire for stability and security.

This urge toward more constancy in economic affairs seems to be extremely pervasive, making few distinctions among lands, peoples, or classes.

The other challenge to the traditional market structure of independent firms that buy and sell at successive market stages is in the system itself.

It is sometimes technological in nature, but often it arises also in a search for marketpower. Some of the changes taking place in marketing do not bear on competitiveness, but others clearly are in the direction of reducing the traditional competitiveness wherein many buyers meet many sellers in close communication.

A few changes have been toward eliminating market exchange entirely, replacing it with the contractual or ownership relations known as vertical integration.

In one of the earlier changes, the fairly orderly system built around central markets was upset by the arrival of paved highways and the motortruck. They brought a decentralization of some markets. At about the same time, direct trading began to increase. In it, processors or retailers buy products directly from producers, bypassing local assembly markets, wholesalers, or other market stages.

Neither decentralized nor direct trading is necessarily a poorer marketing system, especially with the telegraph and telephone at hand for instant communication. But they do interfere with providing many of the auxiliary services that were designed for central markets.

Another change has been an increase in concentration among market firms. A small number of firms dominate the processing of several farm products. The greatest growth in concentration, however, has been in retailing, in which corporate chains and voluntary and cooperative organizations have gained a size and influence not known a generation ago.

Increase in size of market firms sometimes is grounded in the economy of mass handling. Often, though, we can attribute a continued increase in size to competitive advantages of size alone. Whatever its origin, great size poses a problem of its exercise of unwarranted marketpower.

THE DEMAND for better marketing and the challenges to traditional market structure keep the marketing system in a state of flux.

Over the years, and today, a significant development has been growth of cooperative marketing. Although privately initiated, cooperation has had the blessing and help of government. The twenties were the period of brightest faith and fastest growth in farmer cooperatives in America.

Various kinds of cooperation have been utilized even more in some foreign countries than in America.

For example, Denmark through its cooperatives exercises broad controls over the production and marketing of hogs, including the control of breeds, quality, prices, and export trade.

Other Scandinavian countries are noted for the extent to which they employ cooperatives in the marketing of livestock.

La Coopérative Fédérée de Québec is a highly centralized and integrated cooperative organization that markets 30 percent of all livestock produced in the Province, 20 percent of poultry and eggs, and a third of all dairy products; it sells 30 percent of grain and feed bought, 20 percent of farm machinery, and one-third of the fertilizer and pesticides.

A Provincial law in Ontario sets up

a system of telegraphic auction selling of hogs that requires no personal inspection of the animals. The system is aided by a Dominion rule calling for carcass grading of all hogs and paying a premium for the higher grades.

Cooperatives frequently have been successful in the Orient, although they must sometimes be organized along clan lines. Japan, Taiwan, Thailand, and other Eastern nations have had many successful experiences with cooperatives. In Thailand, for instance, 114 rice marketing societies had a membership of 67 thousand in 1958.

Cooperative marketing for export is fairly common among exporting countries. Any export trading monopoly that is granted ordinarily is under the direction of the central government.

In the United Kingdom, consumer cooperatives handle about 20 percent of the food trade.

Still another form of cooperation, but one that is hardly conventional, is cooperative or group bargaining. This is group negotiation, as distinguished from any pooling or cooperative associations that take title to the product. Groups organized for the purpose are often called bargaining associations.

Several States have enacted laws facilitating the organizing of associations of farmers for the purpose of joint negotiation with buyers of their products. Often the products are crops for processing, such as fruit or vegetables for canning, that are produced and sold on contract. It is almost essential that the price of those crops be arrived at before harvest, and the bargaining association is a means by which producers attempt to present a common front in negotiation.

It is too soon to pass a lasting judgment as to the success of efforts at voluntary group bargaining. The practice is significant chiefly as an effort by farmers to resolve their dilemma wherein a competitive exchange market is not possible and they otherwise would lack bargaining power in arriving at negotiated prices.

THE SEARCH for a solution to problems of marketing farm products has led often into market programs sponsored or conducted by a central government.

Those programs are of two broad categories. One is the enforced marketing by a single agency, with or without floor prices. The second is government effort to add to demand.

Single-agency marketing often is directed by producer marketing boards. Their characteristic feature is that they provide in some manner for participation by all producers of a commodity in a specified area.

Producer marketing boards may be called quasi-governmental, for (whatever their administrative relationship with the government) they act under governmental authority and usually government supervision.

One of the more modest versions of this broad class of programs is the market orders and agreements of the United States. These have been applied to the marketing of fluid milk, several kinds of fruit, vegetables, and tree nuts, and a few specialty crops.

Seldom do they control the total supply of the product as such, but many of them regulate quality of products shipped as well as the rate and allocation of marketings throughout the season.

Federal market agreements were first authorized in the Agricultural Adjustment Act of 1933. In 1964, 83 milk orders and 45 agreements and orders for fruits and vegetables were in force.

Several States have similar provisions, sometimes of broader scope than the Federal ones, including provisions for bargaining associations of producers. Market agreements and orders are a marketing device of much meaning to market structure.

Some producer marketing boards exercise strict control over the marketing of a product, either by taking title to the entire supply or by regulation via some system of certificates.

For more than 25 years, all the grain of western Canada that moves across

Provincial boundaries or into export has been controlled by the Canadian Wheat Board. The Board came into being largely by virtue of Canada's large export trade in wheat. It not only directs exports; it has the benefit of a separate government authority that sets floor prices.

Producer marketing boards in various countries utilize several different measures to assist their producers. Diversion of a part of the supply to a secondary domestic market is common. Another two-price program is to divert part of the supply to a lower priced foreign market, thereby holding prices at home above the export price.

The United States Government establishes floor prices for several crops, milk to be processed, and wool. (For wool and sugar, direct payments may supplement market prices.) The Canadian Government and a number of other governments have similar programs. Floor prices may lift and stabilize prices in general, and they protect against a farmer's having to accept depressed prices at harvesttime. Somewhat less common is the United States program of discretionary Government buying, under the so-called section 32, of commodities that are in temporary oversupply.

Government efforts to supplement or strengthen demand for food and other farm products are of more recent origin and more limited application. They are nonetheless significant. India calls for selling some bread and food grains at low prices through fair-price shops. Iran similarly required wholesalers of wheat to sell some at a concessionary low price. The United States has inaugurated a pilot Food Stamp program to achieve the same objective of stretching the food dollar of families with low incomes.

The Plentiful Foods program of the United States Department of Agriculture is an informational service that directs attention to foods that are in plentiful supply. To be sure, private promotion of foods is enormous. In addition to conventional advertising, a number of producer and trade groups engage in joint promotion of their products. Often they step up their efforts when surplus occurs or impends.

A PROFOUND change in market structure during the late fifties and early sixties was the trend toward replacing market exchange with various contractual and ownership arrangements, known by the term, vertical integration. It has been most prominent in the United States but is not absent elsewhere. If the experience in the United States proves to be only a forerunner, it will become a major feature of marketing in many countries.

Vertical integration can take many forms, but their common quality is that the supplies used in farm production, or the products produced, are not bought and sold in market exchange. Instead, they are negotiated for, and the terms arrived at are usually binding for a period of time.

Vertical integration is important of itself, but it has special meaning to market structure because it typifies efforts to graft the modern industrial techniques of mass handling, mass processing, and mass merchandising upon the production and marketing of farm products. It proclaims bright promise of technical efficiency.

To the critical observer, however, it also raises sober questions about its relation to competitiveness in markets. Vertical integration may add to concentration at any market sector, putting trading in even fewer hands; but its greater significance lies in its enveloping the successive steps in the marketing sequence and putting them under one single management. As another consequence, when vertical integration reaches to the farm, as it does in many broiler contracts, it may change the management status of farmers from entrepreneurial to contractual status.

Isolated instances of vertical integration naturally have little bearing on market structure, but its widespread adoption can have a great deal.

As the most radical of all departures from traditional competitive markets, it wholly removes the opportunity for buying and selling on open markets and presents a new dimension in market regulation. Regulation has related chiefly to structure or practices in markets defined horizontally—that is, in markets performing the functions of only one stage in the sequence.

An example of such regulation is an antitrust action in the United States to block a national dairy firm from acquiring other similar firms. On one of the few early occasions when vertical integration threatened, a packers' consent decree restrained meatpackers from integrating backward into operation of stockyards or forward into retailing of meats. A market firm that holds power in its own sector may be able to extend that power greatly by reaching forward or backward. Unquestionably, the historical attitude as to market structure has been unfriendly to large vertical combinations.

Vertical integration, like any new entrant on the marketing scene, does not become a question of yea or nay, of unqualified approval or absolute disapproval. It may serve as a lens to reveal flaws in the existing marketing system, including inadequacies of market services.

For example, it may show that the higher degree of precision and exactness now called for is not being met by present market news and standardization and grading. If so, a signal flare should go up, insisting on updating of those services.

But again, as is true for anything new, ways must be found to take fullest advantages of the strengths of vertical integration and to minimize its weaknesses. In some instances, regulatory restraints may be necessary. Several of the traditional market services may find it necessary to adapt further to new market structure. If interests of farmers are threatened by monolithic vertical firms, the two possible courses of action are to break up or regulate those firms, and to help farmers to organize into a common front of their own. Much wisdom will be required to make the best choice in each instance.

Whatever policy action as to vertical integration may eventually be chosen in the United States and elsewhere, the message comes through loud and clear.

The structure of the market for farm products is more than a mere listing of the several physical functions, such as assembly, transport, and processing, that are carried out. It includes an understanding of the manner in which those functions, together with the processes of pricemaking in exchange as aided by the various auxiliary services, are combined into an interlocking mechanism.

The structure of any market is viewed and judged according to how well it adapts to the several characteristic features of the farm products with which it begins, and accomplishes the ends of fairness, equity, efficiency, and overall orderliness it is expected to serve.

Moreover, the setting is dynamic. Market structure must be flexible and capable of incorporating new technologies available to it and of accommodating new demands made upon it. And yet it must have the gyroscopic ability to continue to fulfill at all times, and despite all interruptions, the central purpose and mission with which it is charged.

HAROLD F. BREIMYER *became staff economist in the Office of the Administrator, Agricultural Marketing Service, in 1961. For 2 years he was staff economist for the Council of Economic Advisers in the Executive Office of the President. He interrupted his assignment in Agricultural Marketing Service during the school year 1963–1964 to be visiting professor of agricultural economics at the University of Illinois. Mr. Breimyer's earlier career was in price analysis and marketing of livestock, and he drew on his United States and oversea experiences for some of the information and illustrations presented in this chapter.*

Supermarkets Around the World

by R. W. HOECKER

THE FOOD SUPERMARKET was exclusively American until the midfifties. Since then, the apparently simple idea of offering for sale many items on a self-service basis in one store has been adopted in many countries.

Our interest in it here is not that it is American or big or widespread, however. Rather, we view it as a force in helping to develop the food distribution system in developing countries and in regions where it has become established as the best export outlet for American grown and processed food products. The successful adaptation of the supermarket to foreign economies may succeed in raising their living standards and furnish more markets for American farm products.

Low-cost mass distribution requires a dependable supply of good items, adequately packaged, transported, and advertised, and a highly organized marketing system that starts at the production level and ends in the consumer's home.

Supermarkets increased their share of the United States food sales from about 40 percent in 1950 to more than 70 percent in 1964. The average supermarket stocks about 7 thousand items. Today's "discount house" may carry more than 20 thousand items—more than half of them nonfood goods.

Nearly 90 percent of the total food sales in the United States are made by corporate chains or independents affiliated with groups of wholesalers or cooperative retailer associations of retailers. Both types of organizations usually make use of highly coordinated marketing systems from the producer to the retail store.

A corporate chain is defined as an operator with 11 or more retail stores. Many independent foodstore operators have now affiliated with wholesale suppliers. This step has enabled many of them to equal or surpass the corporate chainstore in prices and scale of operation. As a result, lower priced food is available to consumers.

About one-half of the 28 thousand supermarkets (annual sales of more than 500 thousand dollars) in the United States are operated by corporate chains. About one-half are operated by affiliated retailers.

The proportion of the total sales of food made through corporate chains increased from 31 percent in 1931 to 40 percent in 1962. The proportion made through affiliated independents increased from 29 percent to 49.

Many wholesalers have become complete supply centers. Instead of separately owned and specialized meat, produce, or grocery wholesalers, one firm handles nearly all of the retailers' needs. Relatively few large retail outlets, whose wholesalers supply all their merchandise, have replaced the large number who got their goods from many wholesalers.

THE PATTERN of food distribution in industrialized countries, as in Europe and Australia, has followed the one in the United States.

The growth of self-service in several countries has been especially fast since 1956. West Germany, which had no self-service stores in 1948, had 1,380 in 1956, and 30,680 in 1962. Great Britain had 130 self-service stores in 1948, about 3 thousand in 1956, and 10 thousand in 1962.

Supermarkets in Europe are stores with a minimum size of 4 thousand square feet and sell a full range of food.

The first supermarkets appeared in Europe in the midfifties. There were 206 in Italy in 1962, 140 in France, 400 in Germany, and 900 in Great Britain. The number increased rapidly during the early sixties because the prerequisites for expansion existed in many places.

Potential customers of European supermarkets have a high standard of living; good transportation, so they can transport home relatively large quantities from a distance; refrigeration in the home, so that perishables can be stored; and a desire for a wide range of food items, many of which are ready prepared.

The European supermarket operator has fairly accessible large and regular supplies of standard-type products; items packaged in uniform containers; good transportation; effective advertising; and a fairly well organized distribution system. A high level of employment has created an effective demand. Progress in marketing and food distribution is making possible mass distribution.

Suppliers who recognize the product requirements of the supermarket are likely to find a ready demand for their output.

THE INDUSTRY takes on characteristics of the countries in which it develops.

In 1961, for example, 72 percent of the self-service retail outlets in the Netherlands were owned by independent retailers, 23 percent by chains and department stores, and 5 percent by consumer cooperatives.

The corresponding percentages for Great Britain were: Independent retailers, 21 percent; chains and department stores, 36 percent; and consumer cooperatives, 43 percent.

The voluntary groups and the consumer cooperatives are much more active in Europe and Australia than in the United States. The pattern of food distribution in Australia and New Zealand has paralleled closely the pattern in Great Britain.

Since the midfifties, the European distribution industry has been taking the American system and adapting it to its own situation. This period was nearly complete in 1964, and the distributors began to develop distinctly European characteristics. Centralized packaging of meat for retail, for example, was just beginning in the United States, but in Germany almost 40 percent of the meat retailed in packages was packaged at a central place. The one-way flow of ideas became a two-way flow.

RETAIL FOOD DISTRIBUTION outside North America, Europe, and Australia usually has been done through many little shops with small capital investments, limited stock, high margins, and personal selling. Thousands of pushcart operators, on-foot peddlers, also sell food, and small agricultural producers retail all or part of their production. Most consumers buy on a hand-to-mouth basis: People may buy one egg, one cigarette, or one razor blade at a time because they have little money, no place to store food at home, and no good way to transport large amounts of anything. Habit is another reason.

The American-type supermarket does exist in many of the less-developed countries, but it serves only a small part of the population. Usually it is in the capital or a large city and serves American and European nationals and the nation's wealthy class. Most of the nonperishable packaged food and nonfoods may be imported; perishable products are produced in the country.

A big problem is to develop and maintain reliable supplies of perishable and nonperishable goods. Another is the gap between few high-income customers and the many low-income consumers. The number of supermarkets in a country has been said to be an index of the size of its middle class.

The number of supermarkets has been growing in such Latin American cities as Mexico City, San Juan, São Paulo, Rio de Janeiro, Lima, and

Bogotá. The countries have been developing their own sources of supply, a packaging industry, and an integrated marketing structure. As the demand for more and better food grows, because of the growth of a middle class of good incomes, refrigeration, and transportation, we expect further growth of supermarkets. Many people, however, will continue to buy their few staple items at small grocery stores and their perishable foods from open-air markets, without refrigeration or grading and with much waste.

Methods of food distribution in Japan, the Philippines, and India in many respects resemble those in Latin America. The essential differences appear to reflect principally the per capita income of the countries.

The Philippines has a number of supermarkets and a well-integrated food distribution system. India has lower per capita incomes and has no significant number of American-type supermarkets. The Japanese in 1962 had 383 supermarkets, of which 194 sold mostly food and 189 had most of their sales in nonfood items.

It is possible that modern food distribution, as symbolized by the supermarket, will expand in the less-developed countries, but it may be a long time before the bulk of the food is distributed through anything but the small retail stalls.

In Africa, limited diets and low incomes may delay any large expansion in the number and size of supermarkets.

Nairobi, in Kenya, for example, in 1964 had one large supermarket and six small self-service stores, the only self-service stores in Kenya. Nairobi is a tourist center, and many foreign representatives are stationed there. More than 90 percent of the customers of self-service stores are of European extraction.

Kampala, the capital of Uganda, had one small American-type supermarket and two small self-service stores in 1964—the only ones of their kind in Uganda. Dar es Salaam, the capital of Tanganyika, had one large supermarket.

Most of the wholesaling in the developing countries is performed by small operators and is characterized by many handlings. Often the wholesaler's main function is to extend credit. Some of the primary wholesalers offer storage and transportation.

The spread between producers and consumers often is wide. The large number of middlemen, poor transportation, and the great amount of waste conduce to high costs. Products may cost five or six times as much in the city markets as the producer received for the product. In some places where the supermarket has replaced the traditional store, the margins have dropped substantially. For example, operators of two self-service stores in Nairobi reported they reduced their margins from about 30 percent before self-service to about 15 percent. Retail prices for perishables are usually lower than in the United States, because the perishables are locally obtained; prices for nonperishables are higher, because most nonperishables are imported.

THUS THE SUPERMARKET is not a stranger to any part of the world. Poverty limits its spread.

Much can be done to improve distribution practices throughout the world so that people may get food at lower cost and of better quality. Some of the needs are: The development of grades and standards; uniformity of weights and measures; availability of low-cost credit; storage and refrigeration facilities; improved transportation and better sanitation; packaging machinery and materials; improved handling practices; and training in the fundamentals of wholesaling and retailing.

R. W. HOECKER *became Chief, Wholesaling and Retailing Research Branch, Agricultural Marketing Service, in 1950. During 1948 and 1949 he was professor and head of the Marketing Division, University of Maryland.*

Regulating Trade Amid Changes

by CLARENCE H. GIRARD

COUNTLESS regulatory laws of the Federal Government, the States, and thousands of localities influence trade and commerce among the States and with other countries. The laws reflect efforts to protect health and safety, maintain orderly marketing, and preserve free competition in this rapidly changing economic world.

The United States Department of Agriculture administers a wide variety of regulatory laws. Each is specialized in design because of the infinite variations that exist in agriculture and in the marketing of agricultural commodities and products.

Many of the statutes administered by the Department are so-called standardization and inspection laws. Some are permissive and others are mandatory. They provide for establishing official standards of description and require official inspection under certain conditions. Their purpose is to eliminate the confusion that had developed in the use of variant terms to describe quality and condition of farm commodities. They establish uniform standards that are adapted to long-distance transactions and to distribution nationally or internationally.

The first was the Cotton Futures Act of 1916. It levies a tax of 2 cents a pound for each contract for future delivery made on any exchange, board of trade, or similar institution. The tax need not be paid when cotton delivered in settlement of futures contracts conforms to official standards promulgated by the Secretary of Agriculture and when such cotton has been classed and certified by him.

This authority was not applicable to spot transactions. Accordingly, in 1923 the Cotton Standards Act was passed. It also provides authority to establish official standards and makes it unlawful to describe cotton by grade in any transaction in interstate or foreign commerce unless the description conforms to the official standards. The act does not prohibit sales on the basis of individual samples, nor does it require official classification of all cotton traded in interstate or foreign commerce.

The United States Grain Standards Act (1916) authorizes the Secretary of Agriculture to establish official standards for grain and requires the use of the official standards whenever grain is sold by grade. It does not prohibit the sale of grain by sample or by type, or under any name, description, or designation that is not false or misleading as long as it does not include in whole or in part the terms of the official standards. The act goes further than the Cotton Standards Act and requires that grain shipped, delivered, offered, or consigned for sale by grade shall be inspected by an inspector authorized by the Secretary to inspect grain, provided the grain moves from or to a place where an official inspector is located.

These are examples of programs that provide for both permissive and mandatory official inspection. For many other commodities, such as fruit, vegetables, and dairy, meat, and poultry products, official inspection for grade or quality mostly is on a permissive basis. Official inspection for wholesomeness and adulteration is required of meat and poultry in interstate commerce, however.

The Tobacco Inspection Act (1935) deals with official inspection on a somewhat different basis. About 90 percent of the tobacco marketed by producers is sold at public auctions. Because the grading of tobacco requires a degree of skill most farmers do not possess, they were largely at the mercy of buyers as to information on the quality of tobacco they offered.

Under the Tobacco Inspection Act, the determination whether tobacco is to be inspected is left up to the tobacco growers. The act requires that before inspection of tobacco shall be mandatory at a designated market, two-thirds of the producers voting in a referendum must approve mandatory inspection. After the market has been approved and designated, no tobacco can be offered for sale there unless it has been inspected and certified by authorized representatives of the Secretary according to standards established under the act.

Other laws specify official inspection and authorize minimum standards of quality and the specifications for containers.

The shipment of apples, pears, grapes, and plums to any foreign destination is prohibited unless the shipments are accompanied with a certificate showing that the fruit is of a Federal or State grade that meets the minimum quality established by the Secretary for shipment in export.

The Standard Containers Acts of 1916 and 1928 provide specifications for standard barrels for fruit, vegetables, and some other agricultural products, and standard baskets, round stave baskets, hampers, splint baskets, and some other containers. Containers that do not conform cannot be transported in interstate commerce.

Another group of laws is intended primarily to prevent unfair practices. Notable among them are the Packers and Stockyards Act, the Commodity Exchange Act, the Perishable Agricultural Commodities Act, the United States Warehouse Act, and the Federal Seed Act.

The Packers and Stockyards Act (1921) is one of the early major entries of the Federal Government into the regulation of trade practices. It makes it unlawful for meatpackers and live-poultry dealers and handlers to engage in unjust discrimination or deceptive practices; apportion supplies among packers if doing so tends to restrain commerce or create a monopoly; manipulate or control prices; or conspire to apportion territories, purchases, or sales.

The act authorizes the Secretary of Agriculture to regulate the rates, charges, and practices at stockyards in interstate commerce. A person engaged in buying or selling livestock as a commission agent or dealer at any posted stockyard or in interstate commerce must register and furnish bond. Accurate weighing of livestock is required. Consigned livestock must be sold under competitive conditions. Commission firms and livestock auctions must account fully and correctly to their principals. Persons subject to the act must not engage in unfair, deceptive, or discriminatory practices.

Cease-and-desist orders may be issued against violators, reparation orders are authorized, and registrations may be suspended.

FUTURES trading has developed into a vital part of our marketing system.

Future contracts are standardized contracts—with respect to the purchase and sale of a commodity to be delivered in a specified month—in which the terms, except price, are fixed by the exchanges.

The seller, or "short" in the present-day futures contracts, agrees to deliver in a specified month a definite quantity of a commodity. The purchaser, or "long," agrees to accept and pay for the commodity when it is delivered. If, for example, a May wheat futures contract is executed in February, the short has agreed that he will deliver 5 thousand bushels of wheat on any business day in May. The corresponding long has agreed that when the wheat is delivered he will accept and pay for the wheat. The price is determined either by the short accepting a bid to buy at a certain price or the long accepting an offer to sell at a certain price. After the purchase and sale on the exchange have been executed, a portion of the contract price (referred to as the initial margin) is deposited by each party with the clearinghouse of the exchange, which substitutes itself as the seller to the buyer and the buyer to the seller.

A short who delivers the cash (actual) commodity on his futures contract has consummated the contract, and his position in the futures market is thereby liquidated; he is no longer in the market.

The long who accepts and pays for the commodity has also consummated his contract, thereby liquidating his position in the market.

In practice, however, actual delivery of the commodity seldom occurs. About 99 percent of the contracts are offset on the exchange by making an opposite futures transaction; that is, the short in the example becomes the purchaser of a May wheat futures contract, and the long becomes a seller of a May wheat futures contract. So they liquidate their positions. The contractual provisions for delivery nonetheless are a necessary factor in establishing and maintaining the relationship between futures prices and the prices of the cash commodities.

In general, the principal terms of a futures contract provide for a standard unit of trading—for example, 5 thousand bushels of wheat; any one of a number of grades of the commodity to be deliverable in fulfillment of the contract at premiums or discounts from a basic grade; the commodity to be deliverable only from an approved storage facility; the commodity to be graded and weighed by licensed inspectors; the commodity to be deliverable only during a specified month; and the seller to have the option as to the grade delivered and the day of the month on which delivery is made.

The commodity exchanges provide a continuous market to the buyers and sellers of agricultural commodities.

The Supreme Court has stated: "The sales on the Chicago Board of Trade are just as indispensable to the continuity of the flow of wheat from the West to the mills and distributing points of the East and Europe, as are the Chicago sales of cattle to the flow of stock toward the feeding places and slaughter and packing houses of the East."

Trading in futures also provides a pricing basis for commodities sold throughout the country and serves as a hedging facility that permits merchants and manufacturers to transfer the risk of price changes to speculators.

The first attempt to regulate futures trading was the Future Trading Act in 1921, which was declared unconstitutional as an improper use of the taxing power. Shortly thereafter the Congress enacted the Grain Futures Act, which was similar to the Future Trading Act, but based on the commerce clause of the Constitution.

The Grain Futures Act was substantially amended in 1936 and renamed the Commodity Exchange Act. The primary purpose of the act is "to insure fair practice and honest dealing on the commodity exchanges and provide a measure of control over those forms of speculative activity which too often demoralize the markets to the injury of producers and consumers and the exchanges themselves."

The act regulates futures trading in cotton, rice, mill feeds, butter, eggs, white potatoes, wheat, corn, oats, barley, rye, flaxseed, grain sorghums, wool tops, fats and oils, cotton, cottonseed, cottonseed meal, peanuts, soybeans, soybean meal, and wool. It prohibits manipulations or attempts to manipulate the price of these commodities. Corners or attempts to corner are also prohibited.

The act provides that the Secretary of Agriculture, the Commodity Exchange Commission, and the respective exchanges or boards of trade can regulate futures trading.

The Secretary of Agriculture, among other things, licenses boards of trade, future commission merchants, and floor brokers; suspends or revokes licenses of future commission merchants or floor brokers; suspends the trading privileges of persons who violate the act; and issues rules and regulations.

The Commodity Exchange Commission is a commission consisting of the Secretary of Agriculture, as chairman; the Secretary of Commerce; and the Attorney General. The Commission fixes trading limits, suspends or revokes the licenses of boards of trade, reviews refusal by the Secretary to license a board of trade, determines whether a board of trade may exclude a producer cooperative from membership or trading privileges, and issues cease-and-desist orders against boards of trade.

The act recognizes the right of the exchanges to issue rules and regulations and to enforce their requirements. It leaves the exchanges virtually free to admit members and select officers, to discipline offenders, and expel members; determine delivery months and contract terms; fix limits of fluctuation in prices, margin requirements, and brokerage fees and commissions; and exercise other prerogatives.

THE PERISHABLE Agricultural Commodities Act is designed to suppress unfair and fraudulent practices and promote more orderly marketing of fresh or frozen fruit and vegetables, including cherries packed in brine.

The act makes it unlawful for any commission merchant, dealer, or broker handling fresh or frozen fruit and vegetables to engage in interstate commerce in such commodities without a license from the Secretary of Agriculture.

The act prohibits such unfair practices as rejection without reasonable cause; failure to deliver without reasonable cause; making false or misleading statements and making incorrect accountings on consignments; failure to pay promptly for commodities purchased or received on consignment; misrepresenting the grade, qual-

ity, or State or country of origin; and altering Federal inspection certificates.

The act authorizes the issuance of reparation orders for damages resulting from violations of the act. Disciplinary proceedings leading to the suspension or revocation of licenses are also authorized.

THE UNITED STATES Warehouse Act authorizes the Secretary of Agriculture to license and bond public warehousemen storing agricultural products; license weighers, graders, and samplers of such products; and supervise the operations of those licensed to assure compliance with the act.

The primary objectives of the act are to provide protection for producers and others who store their property in federally licensed warehouses; facilitate the credit required to maintain large stocks of stored products and to assist in their marketing; and to set and maintain a standard for sound warehouse operation.

Licensing under the act is optional with warehousemen, but after a warehouseman has elected to become licensed he is subject to severe penalties for violation of the act and the regulations. To be eligible for licensing, he must have a facility suitable for storing the commodities to be handled, minimum financial assets, ability to obtain a bond, and willingness to conform to the regulations.

A licensed warehouseman is prohibited from mingling fungible goods of different grades. He is also prohibited from making any unreasonable, discriminatory, or exorbitant charge for services rendered. He is required, in the absence of some lawful excuse, to deliver without unnecessary delay the agricultural products stored in the warehouse upon appropriate demand by the depositor or receipt holder. He must also maintain in his warehouse products of the quantity and grade called for in all receipts he issues.

The Federal Seed Act requires the labeling of agricultural and vegetable seed shipped in interstate commerce.

The label must show such information as the kind of seed, the percentage of weed seeds, and the percentage of germination. Before they enter into the commerce of the United States, all imports of seed must be inspected and meet the requirements of the act.

Various farm products are also subject to a number of acts that provide minimum standards to protect public health, curtail misrepresentation, and require informative labeling. The foremost of these is the Food, Drug, and Cosmetic Act.

Another set of minimum standards is administered under the Poultry Products Inspection Act, the Federal Meat Inspection Act, and the Imported Meat Act. Federal inspection is required. Meat that is diseased or fails to meet sanitation requirements is condemned. The labeling of such products must be informative. Misrepresentation is prohibited.

These acts raise standards of safety. Because of labeling requirements, they also improve the consumer's effectiveness as the final arbiter in free markets.

MANY OF THE regulatory statutes I mentioned merely enumerate certain prohibited acts or require for the most part minimum but compulsory implementation by Government officials. The Agricultural Marketing Agreement Act of 1937 is different in this respect. It is enabling legislation, which imposes no regulation or obligation. Instead, it authorizes regulation only when justified by the evidence at a public hearing. Even then, such regulations cannot be made effective unless they receive the requisite approval of affected producers.

The principal purpose of the Agricultural Marketing Agreement Act is "to establish and maintain such orderly marketing conditions for agricultural commodities . . . as will establish, as prices to farmers, parity prices" and protect the interest of the consumers.

With respect to milk: Whenever the Secretary finds that the parity price is not reasonable in view of feed prices and supplies and other economic conditions that affect market supplies and demand for milk in the marketing area under consideration, he is authorized to fix minimum prices to producers, which will reflect such factors, insure a sufficient quantity of pure and wholesome milk, and be in the public interest.

The act authorizes the Secretary to enter into marketing agreements with processors, producers, associations of producers, and others engaged in the handling of any agricultural commodity or the product thereof.

On the other hand, the issuance of marketing orders is limited to the commodities specified in the act.

Among them are milk, fruit, tree nuts, vegetables, hops, honey bees, turkeys, tobacco, and certain other commodities. Excluded are honey, cotton, rice, wheat, feed grains, sugarcane, sugarbeets, wool, mohair, livestock, soybeans, cottonseed, flaxseed, poultry (except turkeys), and eggs.

The provisions applicable to the regulation of milk are quite different from those applicable to the other commodities.

Marketing orders for fruit, vegetables, and specialty crops do not fix prices. Instead, these marketing orders may provide, among other things, for the regulation of shipments by grade, size, or volume; the allotments of quotas among handlers or producers; and the establishment of reserve or surplus pools.

Marketing orders that regulate grade, size, maturity, or quality provide that each shipment of the commodity or product subject to regulation must be inspected before shipment by the Federal-State Inspection Service. Also, whenever a marketing order regulates the grade, size, quality, or maturity of tomatoes, avocados, mangoes, limes, grapefruit, green peppers, white potatoes, cucumbers, oranges, onions, walnuts, dates, or eggplant, the importation of any such commodity is prohibited, unless it complies with the grade, size, quality, and maturity provisions of such order or comparable restrictions.

Milk marketing orders may provide for the classification of milk in accordance with its use and fix or provide a method for fixing the minimum prices for each such use classification that handlers shall pay for milk purchased from producers or associations of producers. Such minimum prices must be uniform, subject only to adjustments for volume, market, production, grade, quality, or delivery locations.

The marketing orders for milk provide for marketwide pools or individual handler pools. Under a marketwide pool, the producers and associations of producers throughout one milkshed receive a uniform price for milk delivered to all handlers, subject only to the adjustments authorized by statute. Under an individual handler pool, the producers and associations of producers delivering milk to the same handler receive a uniform price for all milk thus delivered by them. It likewise is subject to specified adjustments.

THE BASIC antitrust laws—the Sherman Act, the Clayton Act, and the Federal Trade Commission Act—also exert a substantial regulatory influence on the marketing of agricultural products in domestic and foreign commerce. These laws prescribe the rules of free competition.

The heart of our national economic policy long has been a belief in the value of competition. It arises out of our belief that free competition promotes economic growth and political and social freedom, and that it yields the best allocation of natural resources, the lowest prices, the highest quality, and the greatest material progress.

Free competition does not mean a license to compete as one pleases. Unfair, deceptive, exclusionary, restrictive, oppressive, and monopolistic practices destroy competition, restrain trade, and create monopoly.

The underlying rationale of the antitrust laws is to eliminate these private restraints upon United States and foreign trade and to prevent one firm or a group of firms from monopolizing such trade. The laws seek to preserve competition on the theory that the public interest is best protected from the evils of monopoly and price control by its maintenance.

The Sherman Act of 1890 was the first of the antitrust laws. Section 1 makes unlawful every contract, combination in the form of trust or otherwise, or conspiracy in restraint of trade or commerce among the several States or with foreign nations. Section 2 provides that: "Every person who shall monopolize, or attempt to monopolize, or combine or conspire with any other person or persons, to monopolize any part of the trade or commerce among the several States, or with foreign nations, shall be deemed guilty of a misdemeanor, and, on conviction thereof, shall be punished by fine not exceeding fifty thousand dollars, or by imprisonment not exceeding one year, or by both said punishments, in the discretion of the court."

The Clayton Act (1914) was based on the assumption that the broad provisions of the Sherman Act were inadequate and that more specific rules against incipient monopoly and restraints of trade were required.

The act contains a number of provisions outlawing specific practices. Section 2, frequently referred to as the Robinson-Patman Act, forbids price discrimination that may lessen competition substantially, injure competition, or tend to create a monopoly. It also forbids the payment of brokerage fees to buyers as well as furnishing services to customers or making payments to them except on proportionately equal terms.

Section 3 of the Clayton Act contains a provision against exclusive dealing contracts or tying arrangements, whereby a customer agrees not to purchase the goods of the seller's competitors, if such arrangement may lessen competition substantially or tend to create a monopoly.

Section 7, also known as the Celler-Kefauver or the Antimerger Act, forbids the acquisition of shares or assets of other corporations if such acquisition may substantially lessen competition or create a monopoly.

Section 8 makes it unlawful for anyone to be a director in two or more competing corporations, any one of which has the net worth of 1 million dollars or more.

The Federal Trade Commission Act, also enacted in 1914, established the Federal Trade Commission and described its functions. Section 5 declared that "unfair methods of competition" and "unfair or deceptive acts" are unlawful.

Under the Sherman Act and certain provisions of the Clayton Act, the Department of Justice may obtain injunctions ordering companies to follow certain practices or to desist from others. If these injunctions are not obeyed, fines and imprisonment may be ordered by a court.

Under the Clayton and Federal Trade Commission Acts, the Federal Trade Commission is authorized to issue cease-and-desist orders. Violations of such orders after they are final are punished by civil penalties.

Exemptions from the application of the antitrust laws are provided by a number of statutes.

The Capper-Volstead Act of 1922 authorized farmers to join together in cooperative associations and to have common marketing agents. If the Secretary of Agriculture finds that prices are "unduly enhanced" by virtue of monopoly powers exercised by such an association, however, he can order the association to cease monopolizing or restraining trade.

The Agricultural Marketing Agreement Act of 1937 permits the Secretary of Agriculture to enter into marketing agreements with producers, processors, and handlers of agricultural commodities. Such arrangements are exempt from the antitrust laws.

The Fisherman's Collective Marketing Act of 1934 exempts associations of fishermen from the antitrust laws. The Secretary of the Interior, however, may issue cease-and-desist orders if he finds that the action of any association has "unduly enhanced" prices.

Other exemptions are provided for certain types of organizations of small business, associations of marine insurance companies, lessees of Federal oil and coal lands, labor unions, and participants under interstate compacts.

The same antitrust statutes that prohibit restraints and monopolization of domestic commerce also apply to commerce with foreign nations.

Section 1 of the Sherman Act provides that "every contract, combination or conspiracy in restraint of trade or commerce . . . with foreign nations . . ." is illegal. Section 2 makes it a crime "to monopolize, or attempt to monopolize, or combine or conspire with any person or persons, to monopolize any part of the trade or commerce . . . with foreign nations."

The Wilson Tariff Act reinforced the Sherman Act by making it applicable to the importation of goods.

The Clayton Act also applies expressly to United States foreign commerce. Sections 2 (a), (b), and (f) of the Clayton Act (forbidding price discrimination) and section 3 (prohibiting tie-in and exclusive dealing arrangements where there is the required anticompetitive effect) apply only where the goods are for use, consumption, or resale within the United States. Accordingly, these provisions are not applicable to exports. However, sections 2 (c), (d), and (e) of the Clayton Act, which concern discriminations in brokerage allowances, advertising allowances, and services in connection with sale, are not so limited by the statute.

Section 7 of the Clayton Act affects mergers between corporations engaged in commerce (defined to include foreign commerce) "where in any line of commerce in any section of the country, the effect . . . may be substantially to lessen competition, or tend to create a monopoly."

The Federal Trade Commission Act also applies to foreign commerce. Under its section 5, "unfair methods of competition and unfair or deceptive acts in commerce" have been held to include actions that also violate the Sherman Act.

Activities that take place outside the United States are only subject to the United States antitrust laws if there is a substantial effect upon the foreign commerce of the United States. For example, price fixing solely within a foreign country and only affecting the internal commerce of that country does not fall within the prohibitions of the United States antitrust laws unless it is part of some larger conspiracy. An agreement relating exclusively to trade between two foreign countries does not violate our antitrust laws.

There is a generally recognized exception to the antitrust laws with respect to acts of a sovereign government within its own jurisdiction. This exception has also extended to private parties who are required by a foreign government or by foreign law to do certain things within that country. The fact that a person engages in a restraint of United States foreign trade because of pressure from foreign business interests or with the acquiescence of a foreign government, however, is not a defense against a charge of antitrust violation.

Restraints under the Sherman Act are to be tested by the "rule of reason," which means only restraints that unreasonably restrain interstate or foreign trade are violations of the antitrust laws. Some restraints have been held by the courts to be unreasonable in and of themselves, or unreasonable per se. These offenses include arrangements by competitors to fix prices, divide markets, and control or limit production or output. Also included in this category are boycotts or patent-tying clauses.

The rule of reason has a limited application to enterprises that occupy a dominant or monopolistic position within their particular industries. A firm is guilty of monopolization if it has the power to fix prices or exclude competitors, combined with an intent to use that power.

Most international arrangements violating the United States antitrust laws have involved an arrangement among competitors to allocate territories or to fix or stabilize prices. Such agreements may also involve a limitation of production and restrictions upon patents or industrial activity.

The Webb-Pomerene Act permits exporters to form export associations "for the sole purpose of engaging in export trade and actually engaged solely in export trade." The act provides, however, that such an association or its acts or agreements must not be in restraint of trade within the United States or in restraint of the export trade of any domestic competitor. Furthermore, the association must not do any act or make any agreement which "artificially or intentionally enhances or depresses prices" within the United States. Such an association is required to register with the Federal Trade Commission and furnish reports to it.

The exemptions provided in the Webb-Pomerene Act do not bestow upon associations the right to combine with foreign associations and companies for the purpose of dividing world markets, assigning international quotas, and fixing prices in certain territories. Such activities are not sanctioned by the Webb-Pomerene Act, since they are not legitimate activities "in the course of export trade." Associations also may not stabilize domestic prices by removing surplus products of its members from the domestic market in order to control the selling price in this country.

In general, a Webb-Pomerene Act association may act as the export sales agent of its members, arrange transportation for the goods of the members, agree upon prices and terms of trade for sale of the members' goods, and arrange for distribution of the goods abroad.

AMERICAN BUSINESSMEN sometimes have complained that they have suffered disadvantages abroad by virtue of the differences between foreign antitrust laws and our own, which follow them abroad insofar as conduct affecting our foreign commerce is involved.

They have therefore urged relaxation of our own antitrust laws, as they apply to American business abroad, so that practices permitted under foreign laws will be permitted under ours. In addition, the mere fact of having to deal with two sets of laws—or more, when they do business in more than one country—has been called an excessive burden.

In later years, however, there has been considerable movement abroad in the direction of historical American thinking about competition. This has been particularly true in Europe, notably in the antitrust rules adopted by the Coal and Steel Communities and the Common Market. Important differences nevertheless remain between foreign and our views and activities with respect to restrictive agreements and monopoly.

We are, however, seeking through various means to promote healthy competition throughout the world in the belief that this serves the purposes of economic growth, expanding international trade, and political freedom.

The Foreign Assistance Act of 1961 declares it to be the policy of the United States "to foster private initiative and competition" and "to discourage monopolistic practices." The Trade Expansion Act of 1962 authorizes the President to withhold or withdraw tariff concessions for "tolerance of international cartels . . . unjustifiedly restricting United States commerce."

Since the Second World War, the United States Government has had clauses relating to restrictive business practices included in a number of our friendship, commerce, and navigation treaties. These clauses normally provide for consultation when one party feels its trade is suffering harmful effects from practices of private or public commercial enterprises of the other party that restrain competition, limit access to markets, or foster monopolistic control. Under these clauses, each party agrees to take such measures as it deems appropriate to eliminate problems it causes to the other.

The Government also seeks to make sure that its lending and credit policy does not strengthen or extend business practices restraining competition, limiting access to markets, or fostering monopolistic control.

A relaxation of our own antitrust principles is not the answer to our international trade problems. If we are to have healthy competition, we must strive to eliminate existing private practices that hamper trade and try to prevent the erection of new private barriers to substitute for governmental barriers that we hope will be taken down.

Although we are limited in the extraterritorial antitrust protection we can give to American business in foreign countries, we have a number of laws that protect domestic commerce from unfair and monopolistic practices and restraints in connection with imports.

The Tariff Act of 1930 has provisions against "unfair methods of competition and unfair acts in the importation of articles—the tendency of which is to destroy or substantially injure an industry, efficiently and economically operated . . . or to restrain or monopolize trade and commerce in the United States."

The Revenue Act of 1916 authorizes the President to declare a retaliatory embargo against goods from countries that unfairly prohibit the importation of United States products. The act also provides against the "dumping" of foreign products in the United States. The act makes it unlawful to import articles at prices that are substantially less than the prices in the principal markets in the producing country, plus the costs of importing, if there is an intent to injure a domestic industry or to restrain domestic trade.

AN IMPORTANT CHALLENGE facing government today is the adjustment of trade practice regulations rapidly enough to satisfy contemporary needs in an era accelerating change.

Forcing difficult, and at times painful, adjustments upon agriculture, industry, and commerce are factors of cold war, growth of population, mass migrations, urbanization, expanding markets, technological progress, automation, electronics, new products, novel production methods, distribution innovations, accelerated obsolescence, and others like them.

Adjustments that arise from improved efficiencies due to technological progress are necessary. But dynamic change also offers opportunities to the unscrupulous. Regulatory policies that are not kept current can become a drag on economic progress, but in making changes we must be attentive to new regulatory needs. Otherwise, economic freedom may be eroded by spurious claims of efficiency.

Decisions in the field of trade practices have never been easy. They will become increasingly difficult. Fortunately, most of the antitrust and regulatory laws are couched in sufficiently broad language to provide the flexibility necessary for an adaptation to changing conditions.

Thus the burden is on the various regulatory agencies to accommodate the laws they administer to contemporary needs. This will require substantially improved methods of economic investigation and analysis and the more refined use of such economic indicators as changes in market structures, the behavior or conduct of the participants in a market, and the performance of the market.

CLARENCE H. GIRARD *became Deputy Administrator for Regulatory Programs, Agricultural Marketing Service, in 1962. Previously he was Director of the Packers and Stockyards Division of Agricultural Marketing Service, Department Hearing Examiner, and Chief of the Marketing Division, Office of General Counsel.*

Maintaining Quality of Farm Crops

by CALVIN GOLUMBIC

THE PRODUCE of one out of every 8 acres of fruit and vegetables is lost through waste and spoilage en route from the farm gate to consumer.

Even in an early stage of this journey, from shipping point to terminal market, losses of fresh produce average 1 to 5 percent. In retail stores the value of produce may diminish by 3 to 7 percent. Losses of similar magnitude can occur in the cereal grains and field crops from attack by fungi, insects, and rodents.

On a worldwide basis, this could amount to 55 million tons of grain alone—enough to feed a daily ration of about 1.5 pounds to 250 million people for a year.

Preventing waste, spoilage, and damage must begin at the time of harvest. The farmer's harvester must be properly designed and adjusted, or irreparable damage will be done to the quality of a crop. Bruising of produce and cracking of seedcoats of grain will provide entrance for decay and disease organisms. Contamination of bolls in mechanical picking of cotton can destroy the spinning quality of the fiber.

The maturity of most crops and the moisture content of some are equally of concern at harvesttime. For example, the choice of a picking date for a fruit depends on whether it will be held in storage for a short or long period, has good eating quality, can properly ripen in storage, and is to be transported to a nearby or distant market.

So important is maturity at harvest that mandatory maturity standards have been established. Florida citrus can be harvested only when the sugar-acid ratio of the juice has reached a specified level. California avocados must reach a specified oil content before harvest. The picking of apples in Washington begins only when indicated by a maturity committee set up by the State horticultural society.

The moisture content of a cereal crop or oilseed at harvest is of great moment. Unless the moisture level has diminished during the ripening on the plant to the so-called critical moisture content, it will be vulnerable to attack by fungi and insects that can induce heating and spoilage of the grain or seed. The critical moisture level is the moisture content of the seed when it is in equilibrium with an atmospheric relative humidity of 75 percent. For cereal grains, it falls in the range of 13.5 to 14.5 percent but is lower for oilseeds. Exact safe moisture levels have been determined for the principal cereal grains and seeds.

IN ANIMALS the preslaughter treatment, as well as the method of slaughter, is important, both from the aspects of quality and humane treatment.

Subjecting the animal to undue stress before slaughter can cause injuries, physiological disturbances, and such defects as dark-cutting beef or pale, soft, watery pork.

The mandatory procedures of the Packers and Stockyards Act of the United States does much to reduce the incidence of stress conditions in bringing meat animals to market.

Poultry is particularly subject to such downgrading defects as bruises, hemorrhages, and broken bones as a result of poor handling practices on the farm and during shipping, unloading, and shackling at the processing plant. Breast blisters, another common defect, show up in freshly slaughtered carcasses and may be caused by the rubbing of the skin covering the keel bone on some hard substances, such as packed litter or coop slats. These lesions must be trimmed, and trimmed carcasses are downgraded. Lowered incidence of these quality losses can result from a few commonsense precautions, such as catching birds at night, using less crowded coops, unloading coops with roller tracks, and shackling birds close together to induce calmness.

Immobilizing poultry in coops by exposure to carbon dioxide may be a feasible method to eliminate the injuries caused by removing live, fluttering birds through small coop openings. Electric stunning before slaughter is used by processors of turkeys to eliminate struggling by the large birds and to facilitate removal of feathers. It has replaced debraining for these purposes in the United States, but not in other countries.

Slaughter methods for meat animals in the United States are specified by the Humane Slaughter Act of 1958.

All methods except ritual slaughter require the use of approved mechanical, electrical, or chemical means of rendering animals unconscious quickly before dispatching them. These procedures also reduce struggling and consequent injury to carcasses.

The use of carbon dioxide to anesthetize hogs is the only approved chemical means of immobilization.

This treatment eliminates diffuse bleeding into the muscles. Hogs are conveyed through a trough of carbon dioxide and are immobilized in 20 seconds. The rate of killing in this method exceeds 500 an hour. Following slaughter, each carcass is dressed and divided in a continuous mechanized operation that reduces the time it takes the carcasses to reach the chilling rooms.

Carbon dioxide immobilization of hogs is employed in about 10 percent of the total slaughter in the United States. Electrical stunning is used in the remainder. In the Netherlands and Denmark some use is made of carbon dioxide immobilization, but generally electrical stunning is preferred both for hogs and cattle. England uses both electrical and mechanical methods for cattle.

Improvements in slaughtering procedures for poultry are needed to prevent such occurrences as the misbleed, the condition in which birds exhibit red or pink breasts and wing tips because of accumulation of blood in them. Blood coagulation and bruises also occur on the neck as a result of the common slaughter method of manually cutting across one side of the neck to sever blood vessels.

ONCE THE CROP is harvested or the animal is slaughtered, a number of procedures must go into effect if original quality is to be protected.

For the most perishable crops, the application of protective measures is a race against time. The field heat of the fruit or vegetable must be removed promptly, and steps must be taken to minimize attack by decay organisms and insects and to prevent other quality losses. For animal products, the body heat must be dissipated as soon after slaughter as possible. There is less urgency with the cereal grains and other field crops, but only if their moisture content is safe for storage.

Preparation for storage is the first postharvest protective measure that is taken with all farm crops. All the stages of marketing, including assembly at shipping points, transportation to terminal markets, and holding in bins, warehouses, or supermarkets, may be viewed as periods of storage. It is in this span from farm to supermarket or processing plant that most losses and spoilage occur.

There is no uniformity in the manner of preparing farm products for market in different parts of the world. In Europe, for example, slaughter methods for meat animals, evisceration, and chilling of fresh meat parallel in a general way the methods used in the United States, but wider variations exist in processing of poultry. The system of scalding, wet picking, and warm evisceration developed in the United States has been adopted widely in England and has been introduced in Denmark, Italy, Israel, and Australia.

Broilers are mainly ice packed in the United States, but the practice in other countries is to freeze the produce and deliver it frozen to the retail trade. In France and the Netherlands, wet scalding and picking followed by removal of viscera to give a "French dressed" product is a common practice. Dry plucking is still practiced in Greece. In Austria, one-half the poultry is sold by farmers to consumers.

The extensive application of washing, hydrocooling, and vacuum cooling procedures in preparing vegetables and some fruit for market is almost unique to the United States. Other countries rely to a far greater extent on careful hand picking, sorting, and packing, usually in one- or two-layer containers to reduce the amount of mechanical bruising and injury to fruit than does the United States, where automated mechanical handling methods must be used to compensate for higher labor costs. The use of water dumping and other means is being introduced into these mechanical methods to reduce bruising injury.

In the United States, washing and chilling (precooling) are generally the first protective procedures to be applied to perishable produce and animal products in preparing them for market. Chilling slows down the normal ripening and aging of fruit and vegetables. The growth of decay and spoilage organisms diminishes. Insect activity also is reduced sharply. Deteriorative chemical and enzymatic changes, such as rancidity in pork, loss of color in beef, thinning of egg white, and loss of sugar in sweet corn, diminish by one-half or more for each drop of $18°$ F.

Cold air, ice water, ice slush, crushed ice, and mechanical refrigeration are all used for precooling or chilling, depending on the commodity. Meat carcasses are chilled by cold air, but immersion in ice slush is the method of choice for cooling poultry after warm evisceration.

Milk is cooled on the farm in bulk tanks by direct contact with mechanical refrigeration coils or circulating ice water. Fresh produce may be cooled by any one of these means, depending on the characteristics of the particular fruit or vegetable.

Vacuum cooling is a type of cooling in which evaporation of moisture from the product takes place in a sealed chamber under reduced pressure. This method is suitable only for leafy vegetables and other produce that have a high surface-to-volume ratio. Almost all lettuce is now vacuum cooled. Celery, sweet corn, cauliflower, and artichokes are vacuum cooled less commonly.

Efficient continuous processes for cooling eviscerated poultry carcasses in ice water and ice slush have been developed. As many as 6 thousand birds an hour may be processed with mechanical cooling in a modern plant.

Hydrocooling is a corresponding method for fruit and vegetables.

Peaches, carrots, corn, asparagus, celery, and cantaloups are cooled in this manner. With corn, supplementary top icing in the refrigerator car or truck is needed to keep the husks fresh.

Chlorine in washes and dips containing 50 to 100 parts per million of chlorine is used widely as a sanitizing agent in the wash water during washing and hydrocooling of fresh produce. Sodium orthophenyl phenate is used to control decay in citrus, apples, pears, and sweetpotatoes.

Diphenyl-impregnated pads, box liners, and cartons are employed in the United States, Europe, Israel, and Africa to control green and blue molds and stem-end rot in shipment of citrus. Diphenylamine and ethoxyquin are used in the United States to control the physiological disorder of scald for apples going into storage.

Chloroisopropylcarbamate (C–IPC) and maleic hydrazide are used in the United States for retarding development of sprouting in stored potatoes.

In Great Britain and on the continent, nonyl alcohol serves a similar purpose.

Sulfur dioxide fumigation of table grapes is standard practice in the United States and other producing countries for controlling decay and retaining fresh color of the stems.

A high standard of sanitation during processing is the best safeguard against the spoilage of poultry and meat. The effect is to reduce bacterial loads on the surfaces.

A good sanitation program in a poultry plant would include careful washing of the premises and equipment at least twice a day, complete spray washing of dressed and eviscerated poultry, rapid and efficient removal of feathers and offal, copious overflow of water from scald tanks, and frequent washing of workers' hands.

An inplant chlorination program (10 to 20 parts per million of residual chlorine in all wash water) also helps reduce the low microbial load on processed poultry.

The antibiotic chlortetracycline at 10 parts per million in chill water can extend shelf life of poultry from 2 to 3 days to 1 to 3 weeks. The commercial use of this antibiotic is permitted, but it finds little application. It is no substitute for proper sanitation; resistant strains of bacteria develop, and growth of yeast and molds is stimulated.

Internal contents of freshly laid eggs usually are sterile, but contaminating organisms are present on the shell, particularly with moist, dirty eggs. Improper methods of handling and storage facilitate penetration of the spoilage bacteria, mostly of the *Pseudomonas* and *Proteus* species.

Eggs should be gathered two or three times a day, and held at temperatures of 50° to 60° F. and a relative humidity of about 70 percent. If they are to be placed in cold storage, the usual conditions are 31° to 33° and relative humidity of 80 to 85 percent.

Candling is universally used to sort eggs for internal quality (albumen thickness) and to detect defects, such as blood and meat spots. The mechanics of this operation have been speeded up in many countries by the use of multiple candling units. In the United States, research has been started on the development of a completely automated photoelectric system without human observers.

A common practice in this country and others is to clean shell eggs on the farm or in the packing plant. Cleaning may be dry or wet. Drycleaning uses an abrasive, such as emery paper, and is primarily for slightly soiled eggs.

Wet cleaning, or washing, of dirty eggs can be done by hand or by mechanical in-line washers in the plant.

Regardless of method, certain precautions must be followed rigorously; otherwise, more, rather than less, microbial spoilage will ensue. The eggs should be washed soon after laying with iron-free water, which is of proper temperature and contains a reliable detergent sanitizer, and air dried.

HEAT TREATMENTS are used also to preserve quality. They must be controlled precisely in order to maintain freshness and not give a heat-sterilized or "canned" product.

Pasteurization of milk is such a protective treatment. It eliminates all the pathogenic bacteria and improves keeping quality. Shell pasteurization (thermostabilization) of eggs, in which eggs are put in hot water at 145° for 3 minutes, reduces bacterial spoilage in cold storage of eggs.

The hot-water treatment appears promising in reducing the decay in peaches and cranberries. The fruit is dipped into water at 120°–130° for a brief exposure. The temperature and exposure period must be accurately controlled. The treatment apparently reaches and destroys decay organisms that cannot be eliminated by surface antiseptic washes.

The prime requisite in preparing cereal grains for storage is establishing a safe moisture content, which drops as seeds approach maturity. Grains and oilseeds are harvested more and more at a high content of moisture and then dried artificially in various forced-heated or unheated air systems.

Seeds, like other plant material, are living, respiring organisms. Their respiration continues after harvest but at a very low rate unless their moisture level is high.

An increase in moisture content above a certain critical value sets off a series of destructive events. The respiratory rate goes up, and the seed starts to germinate. Micro-organisms, chiefly the fungi, are always present on the surface and within the seedcoats of grain. They begin rapid growth under these conditions, nourished by the grain endosperm and embryo. Unchecked, these respiratory activities lead to heating and other types of damage to the grain. Insects also may contribute to the total respiration and heating.

Artificial drying is a way to maintain the quality of corn. It is necessary when corn is harvested and shelled in the field by picker-shellers, which harvest and shell corn at moisture contents of 25 to 28 percent. About one-half the 1963 corn crop in the Midwest was dried mechanically.

Mechanical drying introduces a number of problems if the interactions of the variables of drying temperature, airflow rates, and the moisture level at harvest are not controlled. Milling quality may be impaired. The kernel becomes friable and is easily shattered during handling and transit. Foreign buyers complain that the shipments they receive are of a lower grade than that shown in the export certificate. The wet miller cannot separate the protein and starch of the kernel completely or efficiently. Finally, damage may be so extensive that nutritive value of the grain may be impaired. Damage from mechanical drying usually cannot be detected by present methods of grading. A rapid test to indicate this kind of damage is needed.

The quality of farmers' stock peanuts is influenced by the manner of curing or drying after harvest. As with corn, the requirements of mechanized harvesting have made artificial drying of peanuts necessary and practical. Such drying provides a means of control over the curing environment that has never been possible with the stackpole method of curing.

Artificial drying can produce peanuts of high quality, but it can also cause off-flavor and a poor milling quality. The variables causing these difficulties are not completely understood, but research has been started to identify and control them. We have no objective means of detecting this kind of damage except by the difficult procedure of flavor testing.

Drying of seed cotton before ginning has been an accepted practice for many years. Trash and other plant debris in the harvested product are hard to remove otherwise.

Mechanical harvesting, which accounted for about 80 percent of cotton harvested in 1963, gives a product with a higher content of trash than hand-picking. Lint cleaners have been introduced as a supplementary means of removing the trash.

Problems of quality maintenance have arisen. Unless the drying stage is controlled carefully, fibers are damaged in ginning. Damaged fiber can have a disastrous effect on the operation of a spinning plant. Ends down per thousand hours, the usual measure of spinning performance, greatly increases. The production rate drops. Processing costs go up.

Yet so subtle are the deteriorative changes in the fiber that the present-day fiber tests and other methods of analysis cannot detect them. An increase in numbers of short fibers seems to be associated with this quality problem, but the only certain means of detection is by spinning tests.

Moisture must be controlled in preparing tobacco for storage because the moisture content required for proper handling of tobacco is higher than that considered safe for storage. The tobacco must contain enough moisture to prevent shattering of the leaves, but it must also be dry enough to minimize

molding during the short period it is on the warehouse floor. After auction, it is redried as a rule to a moisture content of 10 percent before it goes into hogsheads for aging.

CLEANING GRAIN and seeds is an important procedure in storage.

Dockage and other foreign matter, weed seeds, and other contaminants tend to have higher moisture content than the grain bulk. The way is thus open for development of foci of insect and fungal infestation. Dockage may have a great influence on the attractiveness of the grain to some insects and on the number of progeny that will develop. Seeds used for planting must be as free from unwanted and noxious seeds as possible.

Grain is cleaned after harvest, but artificial drying and aeration, the other main quality-control procedures, are used much less outside the United States. Some aeration and drying of grain is done in the Soviet Union. Some elevators in West Germany are equipped for aeration. Australia has introduced aeration in wheat storages.

In a few Asian countries, there is limited artificial drying of rice, but most producing countries depend on sun drying. All rice grown in the Southern States is artificially dried.

GRADING AND INSPECTION is an essential step in preparing a farm crop for market.

As soon after the crop leaves the farm as feasible, it should be inspected and graded. This may be at a shipping or assembly point, packing shed, or processing plant.

Even if growing conditions and cultural practices are ideal, the element of biological variation is always present. It becomes necessary then to grade the crop as to quality and sort the good from the bad. It is still true that one rotten apple will ruin the barrel.

Mechanical and electronic equipment is available to help in this sorting operation. Electronic sorters for dry seeds, like beans, peas, rice, and peanuts, are used for eliminating discolored and damaged seeds. An adaptation of this principle is used to sort wet products, such as soaked beans, olives, and diced carrots.

An advanced sorting system permits two workers to inspect and pack 7,200 eggs an hour. Eggs on a moving conveyor are inspected for dirty or cracked shell; moved to an electronic detector, which ejects eggs containing blood spots; automatically classed as to weight; and alined with small ends down. Finally, vacuum-transfer units place them six at a time in cartons.

Quality evaluation is a process that requires judgment and decision by trained inspectors. The number of mechanical and electronic aids available to them for increasing their efficiency and accuracy grows yearly.

An example is the grading system for farmers' stock peanuts that the Department of Agriculture developed and adopted in 1962. The inspector has mechanical equipment for sampling, subdividing, sizing, shelling, counting, cleaning, and splitting the sample he evaluates.

A new system of grading tomatoes for color and waste received its final test in 1962. Its key elements are a novel grading table and an electronic tomato colorimeter.

Under development by the Department in 1964 was an automatic recording system for quickly issuing grade certificates in cotton-classing offices and preparing classing information for data-processing systems.

Almost all farm products moving in interstate commerce are graded and inspected according to quality standards developed by the Department. New standards are set up almost every year. There are more than 120 wholesale grades for fruits and vegetables alone. Inspection and grading are authorized by various Federal statutes, including the Grain Standards Act, Federal Seed Act, Poultry Products Inspection Act, Meat Inspection Act, and the Research and Marketing Act.

Inspection and grading may be performed at a shipping point, packing shed, terminal market, or processing plant. Inspection of fruit and vegetables at the shipping point is conducted as a cooperative Federal-State service. At terminal markets it may be Federal or Federal-State. Grading and inspection of grain is done by inspectors licensed by the Department but employed by States or grain exchanges at the major markets. The inspectors are under Federal supervision. Federal inspection of poultry and meat for wholesomeness is mandatory for meat that moves across State lines.

Quality, condition, damage, and foreign matter are the principal attributes that the inspector evaluates and measures. The additional factor of moisture content is highly important in grain and oilseeds. By these means the obviously unfit, defective, deteriorated, contaminated, and decayed products are downgraded.

In theory, the remainder can be sorted into categories that will maintain quality for a particular use. Only the most sophisticated grading systems are approaching this refinement. Nevertheless, effective grading and inspection, coupled with a pricing system that rewards the farmer for good practices, is one of the best means of upgrading quality of crops.

In countries where grading systems do not exist, crops are likely to be sold on a weight or volume basis, and the farmer has no incentive to produce a better product.

Plants and packinghouses under Federal inspection get a close scrutiny for sanitation and cleanliness. Performance and sanitary requirements for processing equipment are specified. The preparation of meat and poultry products is supervised to assure their cleanliness and wholesomeness. These regulations assist greatly in reducing contamination of meat by psychrophilic bacteria, the major spoilage organisms of animal products.

The introduction of new processing techniques and equipment is mandatory when research shows they improve sanitation and help maintain quality. Research applications of this kind are the requirement for use of drainage lines to prevent excessive moisture pickup during chilling of eviscerated poultry and prohibition of the scalding operation until the bird ceases to breathe. The latter requirement prevents absorption of fecal bacteria and detergents into the air sacs of the bird.

INSPECTION AND GRADING practices differ widely among countries.

Most countries in western Europe pasteurize milk as is done in the United States, but in Switzerland the milk is delivered raw and the consumer boils it in the home. Sterilized milk is used in parts of England and some other European countries. Great Britain, Denmark, and the Netherlands test their milk for keeping quality, a test that is not used in the United States. The Netherlands uses protein content as well as fat in determining price of milk. In Europe, unlike the United States, no distinction is made between manufacturing-grade milk and milk intended for fluid consumption.

Routine meat inspection, including ante mortem and post mortem inspection and disposal of unfit meat, in most countries resembles that in the United States.

Inspection of eviscerated poultry for wholesomeness, however, varies from mandatory post mortem bird-by-bird inspection, as in the United States, to bird-by-bird inspection only for an exported product, to no inspection at all. Grading of poultry also is practiced less in other countries than in the United States. There is not this difference in grading of eggs, but the relative weight given to quality factors and the differences between grades of eggs differ markedly.

Maturity and marbling are important factors of quality in meat grading in the United States. Canada pays no attention to marbling and downgrades on the basis of excess fat, but excess fat is not a factor in United States grades.

In Europe, where generally leaner and more mature cattle are handled, the maturity factor is less important.

Superficial similarities in grades for fruit and vegetables among countries disappear upon examination of the quality factors and tolerances.

Working parties of the Economic Commission for Europe (ECE) have made progress in developing uniform standards for fruit and vegetables (18 in 1963), but difficulties arise with other perishable commodities, probably because of the wider divergent concepts of quality for these products.

The Organization for Economic Cooperation and Development (OECD), which includes the United States and Canada among its 21 member countries, has set about the task of refining the standards of the ECE.

The Common Market (EEC) has adopted 21 standards based in part on the findings of the two other organizations (ECE and OECD). The Codex Alimentarius Commission of the United Nations has also begun to influence the development of uniform standards.

No country employs as many quality factors in its standards for grain as does the United States. The systems in Australia, Argentina, and the Republic of South Africa are on a fair average quality (FAQ) basis determined anew each year. Essentially this is selling on a sample basis rather than by grade. Canadian standards exhibit characteristics of both American and FAQ systems. A step in the direction of uniformity has been taken by the Common Market, which has proposed a set of uniform grain standards.

Cotton from many countries is also sold on a sample or type basis. The United States system of grade and staple, however, is used for trading in American cotton.

PACKAGING foodstuffs in plastic films and other materials increases their sanitary quality by reducing contamination by organisms.

Proper designs of package can lower the amount of bruising, scuffing, and damage to fresh produce. Slowing up moisture loss prevents wilting.

The design of a package for fruit and vegetables must provide for means of ventilation; otherwise, their normal respiration will be changed to an anaerobic respiration, or fermentation, with consequent development of off-odors and off-flavors. Ventilation is provided by small perforations or incomplete closures in the plastic bags.

Despite these openings in the film, good moisture retention is still possible because the perforated area is small compared to the total surface of package. Topped carrots, for example, lose 29 percent in weight in 6 days at 70° and 50–55 percent relative humidity, but only 4 percent when packaged.

Because they contain only remnants of the respiratory enzymes present in the living animal, meat and poultry meat can be tightly sealed in plastic films. A good packaging material for poultry should be impermeable to oxygen and carbon dioxide, moisture-vapor proof, and nonabsorbing for blood, water, oil, or grease.

Films for fresh red meat should be permeable rather than impermeable to atmospheric oxygen, which is needed to maintain the desirable red color. Cellophane, polyethylene, polyvinylidene chloride, and rubber hydrochloride are the commonly used packaging materials for poultry and meat.

Dry foodstuffs, such as rice, beans, and peas, are protected from many kinds of insects by the use of paper packaging, transparent films, and laminated foils. Good mechanical construction and closure can prevent 75 percent of the infestation. Complete protection is gained by impregnating the exterior with an insecticide. Synergized pyrethrum is used in this way in packaging flour.

The produce goes into storage after cleaning, precooling, sorting, grading, and packaging, which may take place in a refrigerated truck or railroad car en route to market or in a warehouse or supermarket shelf until it reaches the consumer.

Temperatures in the range of 32° to 34° and relative humidities of 85–90 percent are suitable for storage of fresh meats, poultry, milk, and many kinds of vegetables and fruit. Fruit and vegetables of tropical origin usually have higher requirements in storage.

High humidity is needed to prevent excessive loss of moisture, but higher levels than that recommended would promote rapid growth of molds.

Inadequate air circulation also can produce a mold problem through formation of pockets of air with excessive humidity.

Weight loss of eggs under the recommended conditions may be less than 1 percent a month, but at room temperature and relative humidity of 60 percent, the weight loss could be as high as 7 percent.

Grain is stored safely under a wide range of temperature conditions, but a temperature of 50° is considered nearly ideal. Agricultural seeds are packaged in a variety of ways from paper packets to large bins. Expensive seeds may be stored in hermetically sealed cans to retain viability. Bulk storage using upright and flat structures is the method of choice for holding large volumes.

Maintenance of the safe moisture level becomes a problem in bulk storage of the grain. Moisture migration, which may occur as a result of seasonal changes in temperature, can lead to moisture buildup in limited areas of the storage and the development of a heating area, or hot spot. This is a self-propagating and sometimes an almost explosive event. Increasing amounts of metabolic water are produced from the increased activity of fungi and insects and set off a rapidly enlarging cone of biological activity, which penetrates the bulk.

Aeration systems have been developed to counteract the unfavorable distribution of moisture in bulk storage and to provide for additional cooling and drying of the grain mass. In the past, grain was turned periodically to maintain its quality. Now, instead of moving the grain through air, the practice is to move air through the grain. Circulation of air at proper conditions of temperature and humidity can prevent or minimize the buildup of moisture.

Automatic controls prevent the aeration system from operating when the humidity is too high. Aeration is particularly suitable to use in flat structures where it is impractical to turn the grain. The system can be used also to distribute fumigants efficiently throughout the bulk. By eliminating an extra step in handling, aeration saves wear and tear on the grain and thus reduces damage.

When the grain is destined for shipment domestically or abroad, malathion sprays are applied as protective treatments against insect infestation as the grain is loaded into the conveyance. Properly used, malathion has no effect on the odor or flavor of bread made from treated wheat, nor is germination impaired. The treatment is not permanent, however, and repeated applications are limited since a point is reached where the insecticide residue would exceed the permitted tolerance.

Holding some seeds in semiarid regions can lower quality. An increase in hard-seededness of clover, alfalfa, soybeans, and some varieties of beans may result on storage in a dry atmosphere. This condition is undesirable in most crop species because the percentage of seeds that produce plants within a given time is reduced. Under such climatic conditions, the seedcoat of cottonseed may shatter and introduce such difficulties in processing that a prior moisture-tempering treatment may be necessary.

Dormancy of seeds in storage is an unpredictable condition. The problem is greater some years than others and worse when seed is grown under some environmental conditions than others.

Dormancy lingers longer in some seed lots than others. Farmers who plant dormant seeds cannot expect a stand of plants within the usual time.

Dormancy in cereals frequently can be overcome by drying.

Hermetic storage of grain—that is, storage in airtight structures—is an age-old means of preserving grain. Storage in underground pits has been used throughout the Middle East and central Mediterranean regions for much more than 2 thousand years. Pit storage is common in Egypt and India.

In Argentina, partly underground structures have been designed that are economical and would be suitable for use in developing countries. Rectangular pits are scooped out of the ground. The walls and floor of the pit are lined with masonry and then waterproofed with asphalt. Finally, a tight moisture and airtight cover is mounted over the heaped mass of grain. The resulting structure resembles a swimming pool with a ramp on each end to facilitate filling and emptying.

In hermetically sealed structures, the respiration of molds, insects, and the grain itself consumes the oxygen in the spaces of the grain mass and increases the level of carbon dioxide. When the oxygen level reaches a critical value that coincides with the buildup of carbon dioxide, insects and molds become inactive or die, and respiration of grain becomes minimal. Insect mortality becomes 100 percent when the oxygen level drops to 2 percent, a level that can be reached in a few days if the moisture in stored grain is high. Even when stored at moisture levels of 23–24 percent, wheat remains bright and free flowing with no visible mold over a long period of storage, but off-odors and taste typical of fermentation develop and make the grain usable only for animal feed. At 18–19 percent moisture, these objectionable changes are much less evident and are absent in grain of 12–14 percent moisture.

Gastight structures also are used in cold storage of apples. The oxygen consumption here is mainly through the respiration of the fruit. The level of carbon dioxide is controlled by absorbers in order to prevent smothering and damaging the fruit. Genera-tors are available that burn most of the oxygen out of the atmosphere in the storage.

Such controlled-atmosphere storage is widely employed in the Pacific Northwest and to some extent in England, Denmark, and Germany.

Enclosing the fruit in plastic films of the right permeability is another way to provide storage in carbon dioxide modified atmospheres. Carbon dioxide accumulates from the respiration of the fruit. Polyethylene box liners are used in this way for pears, Golden Delicious apples, and sweet cherries.

Carbon dioxide can also prolong the refrigerated storage life of meat, poultry, and eggs. Concentrations up to 25 percent are effective in extending shelf life of poultry. Concentrations of 10 percent are used in chilled-beef shipments from Australia to England that last 6 weeks. Carbon dioxide from bacterial respiration builds up in the commonly used overwrapped tray package for poultry and meat and has the beneficial effect of slowing down further bacterial growth.

Both low (2.5 percent) and high (60 percent) concentrations of carbon dioxide are used in cold storage of eggs. Storage humidities of 90–95 percent can be used for gas storage of eggs if the carbon dioxide level is very high (60 percent). The use of these humidities is possible because of the inhibitory effect on molds and certain bacteria of high carbon dioxide concentrations. These high levels, however, induce a more rapid liquefaction of the thick white.

A type of storage in use in California for protecting stored alfalfa meal from deterioration by molds and insects involves the use of a gas generator for producing an inert atmosphere in large steel bins. Natural gas burned in the generator produces an atmosphere composed mainly of nitrogen (83–86 percent) and small amounts of carbon dioxide, carbon monoxide, hydrogen, and oxygen. One cubic foot of inert atmosphere protects 2 tons of pelleted alfalfa in a silo containing 1,300 tons.

THE BASIC PRINCIPLES of food preservation—drying, curing, and refrigeration—are the same today as they were 100 years ago, even though their application has been greatly refined.

Preservation of foodstuffs by irradiation may be a major development. Its use commercially was encouraged by a decision in 1963 by the Food and Drug Administration to permit unrestricted public consumption in the United States of fresh bacon radiosterilized by cobalt 60. Clearance for several additional foods, among them chicken, ham, and white potatoes, seemed likely in 1964.

The adverse effects of high radiation doses, specifically the changes in appearance, taste, texture, and nutritive value, can be minimized by keeping radiation doses to the 4.5 megarad (million rads) level. The rad, a measure of absorbed energy, equals 100 ergs of absorbed energy per gram of irradiated material.

In a lower energy range, about 200 thousand to 300 thousand rads, radiation has given promising results as an adjunct to refrigeration in increasing the market life of some fruit and vegetables, particularly those such as strawberries, citrus fruits, and peaches, where present practices do not provide sufficient protection. Research going on in 1964 suggests that such pasteurization doses may be beneficial in prolonging the shelf life of ice-packed poultry.

Light doses of 8 thousand rads prevent sprouting of stored potatoes. Potatoes protected in this way are approved for use in Canada and the Soviet Union. Doses in the range of 10 thousand rads sterilize insect pests of stored grain. By interrupting their life cycle, control may be possible.

The Food and Drug Administration took cognizance of this development in 1963 and approved the use of wheat and wheat products treated with gamma radiation for insect control. Scientists of the Department of Agriculture and the Atomic Energy Commission began to explore techniques and evaluating equipment that could make radiopasteurization an economical method to maintain the quality of grain.

QUALITY is an evanescent attribute. It can never be regenerated or improved beyond the initial quality of an individual fruit or vegetable or animal carcass.

It is true, however, that a few commodities benefit from a period of aging or conditioning to bring out one or more desirable quality traits. Aging of beef, veal, and lamb in cold storage to improve tenderness is an example.

Aging is also beneficial in developing tenderness in poultry meat. It begins during the chilling of the carcass after evisceration. Holding overnight (12–16 hours) in ice water before freezing is recommended for turkeys. For broilers, the elapsed time in chilling and transit to market is enough for tenderization.

Freshly harvested wheat is believed to make a "green flour." New-crop wheat therefore gradually is blended into the old crop over a period of several months.

Rice reaches optimum quality after storage for about 10 months.

Sweetpotatoes need to be cured for 6 to 8 days at 85° before subsequent storage at 55°.

Pears need to be harvested when they are mature but before they have softened appreciably. Ripening or softening must be done after harvest.

Cotton lint spins better after storage for several months. The textile mill never changes over immediately to the new crop.

The origin of these quality changes must reside in ' the chemical and enzymatic reactions of the constituents of the foodstuff and fiber, but little is known about their specific nature.

The origin of many undesirable quality changes and defects or means of preventing them also is unknown. A number of problems await solution: Bone darkening of broilers, appearing as a brown to black discoloration of the bones and adjacent muscles after cooking; breakdown of thick white of eggs; storage off-flavor of eggs; kernel breakage of rice; yellowing or loss of color of many commodities in storage, including rice, beans, cotton fiber, meat, and vegetables; dormancy of seeds; rind breakdown of citrus fruits; and russet spotting of lettuce.

It is possible that some of these difficulties arise through an interaction between a postharvest treatment with an undiscernible compositional change initiated by preharvest conditions.

Thus the age, maturity, breed, feed regime, and preslaughter activity may be involved in the success or failure of aging to tenderize meat.

In other instances, it is a matter of simply having no control for postharvest decays clearly of field origin, such as stem-end rot of citrus fruit, Botrytis neck rot of onions, leak of potatoes, Botrytis rot of grapes, bullseye rot of apples and pears, several rots of strawberries, and most rots of cranberries.

Many kinds of fruit and vegetables are susceptible to chilling injury because they cannot withstand low temperatures. Holding them at higher temperature speeds up aging and decay.

Thus even in so advanced a marketing system as exists in the United States, there are many opportunities for improvement in preserving the quality and nutrition of the Nation's food supply.

Research that combines the talents of the biological and physical scientists and engineers has been responsible for much of our progress. It can pave the way for the development of new principles of handling and preserving food.

CALVIN GOLUMBIC *joined the Department of Agriculture in 1953, serving first in the Utilization Research Service and later as Chief, Field Crops and Animal Products Branch, Agricultural Marketing Service. He is a graduate of The Pennsylvania State University and holds advanced degrees in biochemistry from Rutgers University.*

The Storage of Farm Crops

by A. LLOYD RYALL

A PART OF EACH season's crop must be stored to assure orderly marketing, a stable price, and uniform supply.

Most of the products of agriculture can be stored in fresh or in processed forms. Whether those supplies not needed immediately after harvest are stored depends on facilities and knowledge of specific requirements.

Dry storage, which is essentially the same as that devised by primitive man, is widely used for relatively stable commodities which require, for normal storage periods, no more than protection from sun and storm.

Except in the humid Tropics and the frigid Arctic, such facilities are satisfactory for heat-processed foods in sealed containers for most of the plant and animal fibers, and, if protection from insects is provided, for many seeds and cereal products. About the only requirements are a floor, walls, and a tight roof.

The need for forced air movement to prevent the accumulation of moisture, spontaneous heating, and microbiological spoilage in commodities like grain led to the development of structures with airtight walls. Modern grain bins or silos commonly are built of reinforced concrete. Outside air is drawn in through ducts or openings and forced upward or downward through the commodity. This type of construction also facilitates fumigation to control insects and rodents. Such storages are not insulated. Generally, no attempt is made to modify the environment with forced ventilation beyond the prevention of harmful increases in the temperature and moisture in the commodity.

This basic storage method is modified further by changes in building design and refinement of the ventilation system. Instead of the tall, slender bin or silo-type structure, which is desirable for flow-type commodities, such as cereals and other seeds, the need now is for a single-story, ground-level warehouse adapted to mechanized handling and "aircooled" storage of such commodities as fresh potatoes and onions, squash, carrots, and sweetpotatoes and sometimes apples. Since control of temperature and humidity is needed, the walls and ceiling must be insulated. An effective vapor barrier is placed on the warm side of the wall. There must also be provision for thermostatically controlled ventilation with outside air and for circulation of air within the structure.

This type of facility is used extensively in temperate regions that produce large crops of fall potatoes and onions. The best conditions for potatoes (38° to 40° F. and 85 to 90 percent relative humidity) usually are possible by mid-November with normal seasonal temperatures. Cooling of the tubers from September harvest is gradual, because night air temperatures are not low enough during the early fall for rapid cooling. Often some moisture must be added to the air, by means of atomizing nozzles, to maintain desirable humidity during the cooling and storage period.

Aboveground buildings are now favored over the older earthbank or below-grade, air-cooled storages in which temperature control by ventilation is more difficult to attain because of the input of ground heat during most of the storage season. Aboveground storages usually are of frame or cinderblock construction. They should have at least 2 inches of rock wool or equivalent in the walls and somewhat heavier insulation in the ceiling.

Equipment is available to control the intake of outside air thermostatically and mix it automatically with the recirculating air. In this way commodity temperature can be maintained in the optimum range without hazard of freezing or sacrifice of airflow through the stored commodity. A constant air flow rate of 0.8 cubic foot a minute per 100 pounds of stored potatoes has been recommended. That is enough to maintain uniform temperatures throughout the piles or stacks without causing an excessive loss of moisture from the potatoes.

Sweetpotatoes are stored in facilities like those used for potatoes and onions, but the storage requirements and the climate in the storage areas differ.

Most of our sweetpotatoes are produced in the Southeastern and Southern States, where the fall and winter weather is milder than in the sections where fall white potatoes and onions are grown. The best holding temperatures for sweetpotatoes are 55° to 60° F. In well-built, insulated storages, these temperatures can be maintained with controlled ventilation, but some heat is necessary in severe weather.

Curing of the roots (85° and 90 percent relative humidity for 8 to 10 days) to heal skinned areas, cuts, and broken ends is highly desirable before storage. The better sweetpotato storages are equipped to heat and humidify the entire storage area or special curing rooms during this prestorage period. Sustained storage at temperatures below 50° causes chilling injury to all sweetpotatoes. Some particularly sensitive varieties are injured by only a few days of exposure to temperatures of 50° or below.

COMMODITIES that require rapid cooling and sustained low temperature for successful storage are not adapted to holding in even the best air-cooled storages. One more refinement must be added to the storage facility—heat must be removed rapidly and con-

sistently. Cooling usually is done by mechanical refrigeration, although refrigeration may be supplied by ice or bottled compressed gases for limited applications.

The principle of mechanical refrigeration has not changed since its original application in 1834 by the inventor Jacob Perkins. Substantial developments and improvements have been made in equipment.

Ammonia, among the first refrigerants used, retains first rank for large industrial units, but some of the halide compounds, notably Freon 12 and 22, have replaced ammonia in small mechanical units and are displacing ammonia in the larger installations.

Refrigeration is produced mechanically by the evaporation of a compressed gas in a closed system. Heat is required to change any compound from the liquid to the vapor state. When this heat is taken from a space or commodity to be cooled, refrigeration is being applied.

The basic equipment for mechanical refrigeration consists of a compressor, condenser, expansion valve, and evaporator. The pressure of the refrigerant, in the gas phase, is increased by passage through the compressor. Heat is produced by this compression so that the hot, compressed gas now moves through a condenser, where heat is removed by the circulation of water or forced air over the coils in which the refrigerant is confined.

After most of the refrigerant is converted into the liquid form in the condenser, it is piped to the place where cooling is required. There the liquid refrigerant is released through a small orifice, usually an expansion valve. Expansion permits the refrigerant to return to the vapor state in the evaporator coils, during which process it absorbs heat from the surface of the coil. The cold coils then provide the refrigerating surface for removing heat from the space or commodity.

Refinements of this basic process include thermostats for the control of compressor operation and release of compressed refrigerant into the evaporators. Temperature of the evaporator also can be controlled by the use of a solenoid valve to regulate suction pressure on the return side of its coil.

The distribution of the refrigerating medium is as important as the source of refrigeration. Distribution is best accomplished in precooling or storage rooms by forced air circulation. The earliest mechanically refrigerated storages generally had the evaporating coils on room ceilings or sidewalls and depended on natural convection currents, created by temperature differential, to provide air circulation. A few of the older commercial plants retain the system, but forced air movement is generally used to distribute air rapidly and uniformly.

Some refrigerated storages have centrally located blower units, which move air over the refrigerating surface and then through ducts to the individual rooms. Return air ducts, usually on opposite walls, permit the air to recirculate through the central system. A more modern installation includes expansion coil units in the individual rooms with fans to move air over drycoil or brine-spray units and through the room. Many are relatively small blower-coil units, arranged in rows or banks and suspended from the ceiling.

PRECOOLING ROOMS for rapid cooling of perishable fresh foods and blast tunnels or chambers for quick-frozen foods require greater refrigeration capacity and more air volume than rooms designed for the storage of either product.

Abundant expansion coil surface is needed for rapid heat absorption. Air velocities of 1 thousand to 2 thousand linear feet a minute at the face of the containers are commonly used for quick freezing, and air volumes of 400 to 500 cubic feet a minute per ton of product for fresh produce. Heat transfer from the product to the coils is greatly accelerated in such facilities. Rapid freezing or cooling is important to retain quality of the product.

Frozen foods must be held at temperatures below the freezing point of the commodity. Sustained temperatures of zero or below are essential for maintenance of quality. Higher temperatures at any point during storage or distribution adversely affect quality; deterioration is related directly to the time at higher temperatures. Frozen food storages are now commonly maintained at or below —5°.

Optimum holding temperature for most kinds of deciduous tree fruit is 31°. Most tropical and subtropical fruit, such as lemons, limes, grapefruit, and avocados, must be stored above 50° to avoid chilling injury.

Optimum temperature for leafy vegetables, such as lettuce, endive, celery, and others, is 32°, but tomatoes, bell peppers, cucumbers, and certain varieties of squash must be held at higher temperatures.

Tree nuts store well at 32°, but for prolonged holding subfreezing temperatures are desirable.

Temperatures in the range of 30° to 35° are generally recommended for the limited holding of fresh and mild-cured meat and for fish, eggs, cheese, and butter. For long storage, butter, meat, fish, and eggs are generally held at 0° or below.

MOST FRESH FOODS are subject to loss of moisture during storage. The extent depends on the nature and area of the surface of the product, the storage container, air velocity at the product surface, and the difference in vapor pressure between the product and the storage air.

Relative humidity (the percentage of saturation of air with water vapor at a given temperature) of the storage air and the difference in temperature between the commodity and the room air are the main factors in vapor pressure differential.

If relative humidity is high and the difference in temperature is small, the vapor pressure differential will be small, and loss of moisture from the commodity will be minimum. Accordingly, for most refrigerated products, maintenance of a high relative humidity in the storage room is desirable. Some exceptions are dried fruit, nuts, dry onions, vegetable seeds, hops, and some cured meats.

THE CONSTRUCTION of refrigerated warehouses varies according to climate and the availability of materials.

Reinforced concrete and cinder blocks are widely used.

Prefabricated insulated panels for storage construction now are manufactured by several companies. They are generally sandwiches of three-fourths-inch plywood with an insulating core of fibrous, or cellular, glass or an expandable plastic insulator. Their exterior surface may be faced with aluminum, stainless steel, or vitreous porcelain enamel on steel.

The panels are usually 4 feet wide and are available in lengths to 24 feet. They include vapor seals and built-in locking devices for fastening and sealing the individual panels.

The panels are free standing and load bearing. Thicknesses vary according to use—8 to 10 inches of insulation for freezer use and 4 to 6 for conventional coolers.

Cork has been the standard with which insulating materials are compared, but it is being displaced in storage construction by fibrous, or cellular, mineral products and foamed plastics, such as polystyrene and polyurethane. The thermal properties of these materials are quite similar, but other factors that should be considered are structural properties and resistance to moisture, rot, fire, insects, and rodents.

The prevention of the movement of moisture from the warm side into insulated walls or ceilings is essential to the successful maintenance of refrigerated storages. It can be accomplished by the use of an approved barrier on the warm side of the insulation.

Vapor barriers may be of a structural (rigid metal), membrane (metal foil or plastic film), or coating (hot or solvent mastics) type, depending on cost and specific requirements. Any of these basic types provide satisfactory vapor seals when all joints are properly overlapped and sealed.

A modification of refrigerated storage involves control of the composition of the atmosphere besides the usual control of temperature and humidity.

Most of the controlled-atmosphere storages are essentially hermetically sealed rooms with conventional insulation, vapor seals, refrigeration, and air circulation. The distinguishing feature is the gastight seal on the inner surface of the room and on any doors or inspection ports. The sealing material may be light galvanized sheet iron, laminated metal foil and plastic sheets, plastic coated plywood, or asphalt emulsions applied over fiberglass mesh.

A tight seal is imperative for rooms in which the atmosphere is modified by the respiratory activity of the fruit (its use of oxygen and evolution of carbon dioxide). At best, several weeks are required to bring the oxygen down to the desired level, while the concentration of carbon dioxide is controlled by a suitable absorber. If the room is not gastight, optimum atmospheres are never attained.

A SYSTEM OF CONTROLLING atmospheres by continuous flow of tempered and modified combustion gases has entered limited commercial use. Hermetically sealed rooms are not necessary for this system, but for economical operation the rooms must be reasonably tight.

Advantages claimed over the older system are less expensive facilities, faster modification of atmosphere, and the possibility of opening and recharging rooms during storage.

Controlled-atmosphere storage was used commercially only for apples and pears in 1964. It is particularly advantageous for varieties like McIntosh, Jonathan, and Newtown, which may be injured by storage at 31°, the standard temperature for most varieties. The combination of low oxygen (1 to 3 percent) and controlled carbon dioxide (o to 8 percent) with temperatures of 36° to 40°, depending on variety, permits long storage of the sensitive varieties.

Substantial tonnages of Delicious, Golden Delicious, and Rome Beauty apples are stored in controlled-atmosphere storages at 31°. The marketing season thus is lengthened a month or two beyond that possible by the control of temperature alone.

Hermetically sealed storage for grain does not involve temperature control.

Research in England and France has shown that grain with a moisture content above 18 percent will rapidly modify the atmosphere within a sealed bin. Oxygen is used, and carbon dioxide is produced by the micro-organisms and insects in the grain and by the limited respiration of the grain itself. Within a few days, the oxygen is exhausted, and carbon dioxide has accumulated to 14 to 16 percent. In this atmosphere, insects, fungi, and bacteria die or become dormant. The respiratory activity of high-moisture grain, however, may pass from the aerobic to the anaerobic phase; undesirable flavors and odors may then develop in the grain.

The chief application of hermetically sealed storage has been for grain that has been combine harvested at high moisture content (up to 30 percent) and is to be used for animal feed. If it is held in conventional storage, it would have to be dried to avoid losses from fungal decay and insect infestation. In hermetically sealed storage, fungi and insects are controlled by depletion of oxygen and accumulation of carbon dioxide. The value for feed is not affected by the extreme atmosphere modification caused by anaerobic respiration. In fact, some feeding tests have shown better animal gains on wet grain stored in hermetically sealed bins than on dry grain from conventional storage. High-moisture grain stored in this way is not suitable for flour or other food products because of off-flavors. Neither is it usable for seed, because of a loss of viability.

Some interest has been shown in the use of hermetically sealed storage for low-moisture (14 to 16 percent) grain for food. Atmosphere modification is slow and usually is quite limited with such grain, but spoilage by micro-organisms is not a problem. If the grain is disinfested before storage, damage by insects can be kept low. The grain does not gain moisture in a sealed storage, reinfestation by insects is prevented, and rodents are excluded.

WASTAGE during storage is being reduced, but it remains a serious economic loss.

In the United States, storage losses from spoilage and insect damage in wheat, oats, barley, rye, and rice in 1954 amounted to the harvest of more than 5 million acres—6.9 percent of the total United States production that year.

If we applied the information we have, we could reduce greatly the wastage of the more stable commodities, such as cereal grains and products, oilseeds, and dehydrated foods.

Losses in more perishable items—fresh fruit, vegetables, dairy products, eggs, and meat—could be much reduced by a more judicious use of refrigeration and sanitation.

Much of the loss that occurs during and after storage is caused by fungi, bacteria, insects, mites, and rodents. Refrigeration designed to meet the needs of the more perishable commodities will prevent most of the wastage from decay and insects.

Chemical treatments, like fumigants and dip or spray solutions, are used sometimes to reduce fungal or bacterial spoilage of refrigerated products, such as fruit, vegetables, and poultry.

Among the materials approved and used for specific purposes are sulfur dioxide for fresh grapes and dried fruit; nitrogen trichloride for citrus fruit, tomatoes, and cantaloups; ethylene oxide for high-moisture dried fruit and spices; chlorine in wash or hydrocooling water for reduction of surface inoculum on fruit and vegetables; sodium orthophenylphenate as a dip treatment for citrus fruit, sweetpotatoes, and peaches; and an antibiotic, chlortetracycline, for dressed poultry.

Approved chemical treatments with fumigants or sprays also are used to reduce insect infestation and prevent reinfestation in commodities held in nonrefrigerated storage.

Other factors, such as tightness of bins or warehouses, a thorough cleaning of premises before use, suitable containers, and periodic inspections of the commodity, are essential to good management and can substantially reduce the need for chemicals.

Supplementary treatments for grains may be applied as a spray as the grain goes into storage (premium grade malathion or synergized pyrethrum), or as a fumigant within 6 weeks of harvest. The fumigants may be methyl bromide, cyanide, or mixtures of other volatile insecticides. The exact treatment depends entirely on the facilities and the specific problem.

Light traps are commonly used to detect the beginning of insect infestation in tobacco warehouses. When insects are detected, space sprays with synergized pyrethrum or dichlorvos (2,2-dichlorovinyl dimethyl phosphate) are effective. If infestation becomes established, stronger measures, such as fumigation with cyanide or methyl bromide, become necessary.

Packaged food—dried milk, cereal products, and dried fruit—usually are protected adequately by careful sanitation of the storage space and surrounding area and a residual coating of approved insecticide on walls and floor.

Insect-resistant packaging, improved package seals, and the use of repellants or insecticides on the outer layer of multiwall containers may be effective sometimes.

A problem peculiar to the storage of cheese is mite infestation. Even under the refrigerated storage conditions recommended for Cheddar cheese (30° to 34°), mites can cause serious damage. The first essential in their control is a rigorous sanitation schedule. If infestations develop, methyl bromide can be used as a fumigant.

Wastage in stored products occasionally occurs also from spontaneous heating, freezing, failure of containers, or accidental contamination. All can be avoided in well-designed, well-managed, and well-operated facilities.

Other storage disorders that sometimes develop in fresh fruit and vegetables are classed as the physiological diseases. They occur as a result of malfunction of the living cells or tissues—sometimes from exposure to incompatible temperatures or atmospheres. Sometimes they are related to immaturity or overmaturity at harvest, and sometimes injury results from toxins produced within the tissues themselves. Common examples are scald and internal browning in apples, core breakdown in pears, pitting in grapefruit, and black spot in potatoes.

Most of the predisposing factors for the disorders are known. The physiological and biochemical changes responsible are under study in the laboratories of many countries. As understanding of the basic changes increases, further gains will be possible in control.

Anywhere in the world where a storage facility is needed, the fundamentals of design and operating equipment are almost the same. The environmental requirements of the commodity to be stored are identical, and the information needed to operate the facility has been developed.

If and when adequate facilities are available in every country and the needed information is disseminated, the quality of food, feed, and fiber will be better, and the nutrition of people will be improved greatly without one more acre of land or one more bushel of production.   q

A. LLOYD RYALL *became Chief of the Horticultural Crops Branch in the Agricultural Marketing Service in 1960. He has conducted and administered research on commodity handling, transportation, and storage for more than 35 years in Washington, Texas, California, and Maryland.*

Processing
and Preservation

by ROBERT L. OLSON and
CLYDE L. RASMUSSEN

IF WE COULD NOT PRESERVE food in some stable form, people would forever be forced to live right where the food is produced, and there would be no agricultural trade.

Canning, freezing, dehydrating, refining, extracting, and salting all make foods stable and transportable. Even such fresh foods as fruit, vegetables, and meat can be shipped great distances because they are preserved by refrigeration. Meat is shipped from Australia to England, oranges from California to Germany, and apples from South Africa to Sweden.

A major part of the food in world export has only simple or primary preservation—for example, natural sun drying of cereals and preliminary separation of sugar and extraction of vegetable oils without final refinement.

At destination, those products require further processing. This practice lowers the cost of food in international trade; labor and other resources of the importing nation are used in the final processing.

New products and processes, however, have contributed greatly to the growth in trade and will be even more important in the future.

Processed food—canned, frozen, and dried fruit, frozen poultry, dairy products, and many more—are an important part of the annual commercial agricultural exports, worth 4 billion dollars in 1964, of the United States. The high quality of processed food from the United States places them on the preferred lists of many people.

The retention of markets for processed food will depend to a big extent on the ability of American processors to improve quality further, reduce costs, and develop new products for a growing market for luxury products that may accompany economic improvement in western Europe.

The long-range existence of markets for preserved foods is by no means assured, however.

Agricultural self-sufficiency is a declared policy of the European Economic Community and other countries whose resources permit it. The technologies of production and processing of foods are largely transmissible, and cost advantages that may exist in their application anywhere can be counterbalanced by protective tariffs. An example is a severalfold increase in tariff on frozen poultry in 1963 that severely reduced United States shipments to the Common Market countries.

The continuation of United States commercial export markets must fit into the pattern of a growing self-sufficiency in other countries.

Oilseeds, feed concentrates for livestock, and strong wheats for bread do not seem likely to be abundantly produced in Europe, but resources there are well adapted to the production of other commodities. Markets for such crops may well increase and help counterbalance the reduction in markets for canned fruit, softer wheats, and animal products, especially frozen poultry.

Many American food processors have established European bases for their operations to preserve hard-won markets for their brand-named products. Japan and the United Kingdom have been an expanding market for American food because the growth of population and resources of land and climate limit the possibility of agricultural self-sufficiency.

Special Government programs provided export markets for about 2 billion dollars' worth of agricultural goods in 1964, primarily wheat, rice and cereal products, vegetable oil, and dried milk. An improvement in the economic status of the developing countries, the recipients of the exports, may transform those markets eventually into commercial markets. If so, it follows that they also will develop a demand for processed food.

The use of processed food is greatest in countries that are most fully developed economically. For example, more than 90 percent of the food consumed in the United States is transported to markets away from the farm and processed, preserved, or packaged in some way before it is consumed. Even though factory wages, transportation rates, and other costs of manufacturing and distributing have increased, retail prices of food have remained relatively stable, thanks to the strides made in mechanization and the application of research to all aspects of growing and processing.

We spent less than one-fifth of our disposable income for food in 1964; it was one-fourth in 1950. A point even more startling is that only one-seventh of our disposable income today would be used for food if we ate diets identical to those of a generation ago and processed in the same manner. The reason for that is that we have many new foods and convenient ways to prepare them.

IN THE GENERAL division of the world between regions that have abundant food and those that do not, the former have well-developed food-processing technologies and also a high level of specialization in food production.

Processing for convenience has become perhaps more important than for preservation alone.

The less-developed regions generally have primitive processing facilities at best and are forced to a large degree to live where the food is produced.

Processing generally is only to keep food for consumption in the off seasons.

People are plentifully supplied with the perishable commodities (such as fruit and vegetables) only during harvest seasons.

Neither the production nor the preservation of food in those regions has achieved the efficiency of modern technology that is necessary to sustain the material wealth of urbanized civilization. The preservation of food in small factories yields expensive luxuries for the wealthy, in contrast to the mass-produced, low-cost foods for all classes in the urbanized countries. Processing tends to be minor and simple. The bulk of the food supply is made up of a few basic items.

THE LESS-DEVELOPED nations are expected to follow the patterns of food-processing advancement of the past two centuries in other parts of the world. Such an advancement will not be easy.

At the United Nations Conference on the Application of Science and Technology for the Benefit of the Less Developed Areas in Geneva in 1963, some of the difficulties were outlined in the *Summary of Proceedings on Agriculture*. It stated: "A lack of knowledge of good food habits and of satisfactory domestic preservation, processing, and storage of foodstuffs is the rule rather than the exception in less developed countries. Trained professional and auxiliary staff, with a sound scientific and practical knowledge of nutrition, working in the fields of health, agriculture, education, home economics, and social sciences is often lacking. The importance of the interministerial cooperation and action, which is necessary to plan and to execute programs for improving levels of nutrition, is frequently not understood. . . . Much fundamental and applied research remains to be done in order to determine how traditional domestic and village level methods of food processing, which are suited to the local environment and tastes, can be developed on a commercial scale. . . .

"The application of food technology not only helps to conserve and to make foods readily available to the people, but, by rendering them easier to prepare in the home, saves valuable time, and provides other indirect but important benefits; for instance, conservation of local fuel supplies, which is often a critical factor in the selection of foodstuffs."

Among the foods that merit special attention in the developing countries are those rich in protein and suitable for the prevention and treatment of protein- and calorie-deficiency diseases. Such processed concentrates would provide protein to supplement the limited supplies of milk available and to overcome shortages of the traditional protein-short diets.

Protein-rich concentrates can be made from grains, legumes, and leaf meal, any one of which is usually available in most agricultural areas, and from fish.

But even before a developing country can use its food supplies in the production of concentrates, agricultural production and efficiency must expand beyond present levels. Until that occurs, the extraction of protein concentrates probably will occur in surplus-producing countries for shipment to other countries.

FOODS ARE PRESERVED so they may be eaten at some other place or at some other time.

Foods are processed to make them more convenient for the consumer to use and to make them into a form that is different from the starting material.

Preservation and processing, however, are so closely related that they can hardly be considered separately. What is done to preserve an item may also include processing, and vice versa. Heat sterilization by canning, for example, preserves foods, but it also makes them more convenient for future use.

Food processing today ranges from the natural processing of foods to preservation by radiation, design of foods for space flights, and synthesis of food products.

But, as J. G. Thieme, of the Food and Agriculture Organization, said at the United Nations Conference on the Application of Science and Technology for the Benefit of the Less Developed Areas, "The processing of agricultural produce in rural industries is often a 'neglected child' in the framework of development of technical assistance to the less developed areas."

His was one of only a few presentations at that meeting that acknowledged food processing as an aspect of the application of science and technology for the benefit of the less-developed areas.

Yet, even when the savannas of Africa and South America are cultivated and when the deserts of the Near East and Asia are irrigated, the cereals, fruit, vegetables, and animal products that may be produced there cannot be utilized efficiently unless they are preserved so they can be eaten far from their place of origin and long after their harvest or slaughter.

WE DISCUSS now several methods of preservation.

Natural sun drying has always been a major method. Seeds and nuts do not spoil because they have been dried to moisture concentrations low enough that microbial life cannot go on.

From ancient times, many kinds of fruit and vegetables have been gathered and spread in the sun for the same reason—to reduce their moisture concentration so they would not spoil. So also have fish and meat products been sun dried.

Sun drying is slow, except in arid areas, and many kinds of fruit and most meats and fish are sliced thin to speed drying. Where climate is not ideal for sun drying because of high humidity or precipitation, man has invented dehydration equipment to dry his foods artificially.

It is convenient here to distinguish between the foods that are naturally preserved (for instance, cereal grains and nuts) and those that are preserved by man's devising (dried fruit and vegetables, eggs, and dairy products).

Now milk and eggs are dried to powder form in spray driers, the liquid being atomized and sprayed into a hot-air stream for almost instant drying.

Tunnel and truck dehydrators with hot air delivered by fans are used extensively to dehydrate certain types of vegetables and fruit.

Modern dehydrators also include those in which wet food is placed on a belt and conveyed through equipment with temperature, humidity, and air-flow carefully controlled in order to dry the products with minimum adverse change in color, flavor, or other qualities.

Some products can be reduced to small size and then blown through ducts by hot air, which both dries and conveys the product to the collecting station.

Highly complicated vacuum equipment is used to dry food products at temperatures well below room temperature even at freezing temperatures so as to reduce adverse quality changes and produce products as near as possible to the original foods.

All of these methods depend, just as does the sun drying of seeds and nuts, on a reduction of the moisture content to prevent food from spoiling.

ANCIENT MAN learned by chance that food could be preserved by certain chemicals long before his concepts of Nature allowed him to consider the existence of separate chemical compounds. Meat hung in smoke eventually took up enough of the smoke chemicals to preserve it from microbial spoilage.

Salt deposits and tidal basins were the source of another preservative chemical for man's foods. With a high salt concentration in foods, microbial growth cannot be supported.

Later, in the light of refined knowledge, benzoates, sorbic acid and its salts, and microbially produced antibiotics were found to prevent spoilage

even when only a very small amount of the chemical was added.

Another type of chemical preservative has been developed. An example is the prevention of rancidity, or fat oxidation—a chemical deterioration of food—by adding antioxidant compounds.

Exclusion of oxygen by vacuum pack or by surrounding the food with a liquid material is yet another way to prevent oxidative deterioration.

In still another use of chemicals, sulfur dioxide, the principal active ingredient in the fumes of burning sulfur, is a preservative. In high concentration, sulfur dioxide will prevent microbial growth. For this purpose, sulfur candles have been burned in wine barrels and casks to sweeten them, and sulfur dioxide is added to wine musts to prevent growth of wild yeast and other microbes.

Dehydrated fruit and vegetables sprayed by or dipped in a solution of sulfur dioxide can be protected against normal chemical deterioration during storage and loss of nutrients, color, and flavor.

A special type of preservation by chemicals results from the temporary growth of desirable micro-organisms in food to produce products that develop desired qualities and components, which, in high enough concentration, preserve the food for later use.

An example is fermentation to make wine, sauerkraut, and pickles. Similarly, acidophilus and lactic bacteria form acid to curdle the protein in milk as the first step of cheese manufacture. These and other micro-organisms are then involved in curing milk curd to produce the large number of specialized cheeses known throughout the world.

Acetic acid bacteria are used to further ferment yeast-originated alcohol into acetic acid during the production of vinegar. In all these instances, some product of the microbial fermentation is eventually produced in sufficient concentration to prevent growth of undesirable organisms, and indeed, in concentration enough to curtail the growth of the producing micro-organism itself. Another major use of yeast fermentation is in making bread.

Food can be preserved by keeping it so cold that spoilage organisms cannot grow.

Winter climate has been a major source of refrigeration. The deep ground and cold water springs or wells lose their heat in winter and never reach peak summer temperature. Pond and lake ice have been collected and stored in sawdust and insulated structures for summertime use.

In later years, heat removal by evaporation of water has been used extensively, and is still a major source of refrigeration in the cooling towers of processing plants.

Most recently, the controlled evaporation, expansion, and compression of refrigerants has become the basis for the mechanical refrigeration systems that preserve foods by keeping them cool or frozen.

Spoilage micro-organisms can be destroyed by heat. Heat sterilization of foods in containers that do not allow reinfection with spoilage organisms is one of the few preservation methods discovered by modern man, but it has become an important one.

The pasteurization procedures used for milk and other beverages make it possible to control the degree of contamination with micro-organisms and cause the destruction of certain disease-causing organisms.

Cooking and baking food imparts a high degree of preservation to many products by reducing chance contamination. Recontamination of heat preserved or pasteurized foods can cause food to spoil. Heat-sterilized foods are preserved only as they may be protected from recontamination.

Heat is also used to control certain chemical changes that are not related to spoilage micro-organisms. For example, when vegetables are preserved by freezing or dehydrating, they are first blanched (scalded) with boiling water or steam to destroy the biochemical compounds that cause certain flavor and color deteriorations in the preserved foods.

Some important foods are preserved by separating them in pure forms that will not spoil.

Sugar is obtained from sugarbeets and sugarcane. From sliced beets, sugar is diffused with hot water. Cane is crushed between rollers. The diffusate or the pressed juice is purified by chemical reactions and filtration and concentrated by boiling. Pure sugar is crystallized by cooling the supersaturated concentrate and separated by centrifugal filters from the remaining molasses. Partly refined sugar concentrate from cane is often exported for final refinement in the consuming country.

Vegetable and essential oils are also separated from seeds and other parts of plants in a pure form that is useful in food and industrial products. Oil from seeds of cotton, soybeans, peanuts, or other plants is recovered by pressing or by solvent extraction and clarified and purified by filtration, tempering, and so forth.

Essential oils are generally steam distilled from seeds, pods, stems, leaves, wood chips, blossoms, and so on. They are purified and stabilized by various treatments in a form useful to the consumers and preserved so they can be shipped.

Robert L. Olson *was appointed an Assistant Director of the Western Utilization Research and Development Division in 1963. Previously he was in charge of vegetable processing investigations and served in various research functions. Before joining the staff of the laboratory in 1948, he was a research associate at the University of California Experiment Station.*

Clyde L. Rasmussen *joined the Product and Process Evaluation Staff of Agricultural Research Service in 1961 as an industrial specialist, stationed in Albany, Calif. Previously he was in charge of industrial analysis investigations of the Western Regional Research Laboratory.*

WORLD TRADE:

Background of Trade

by CHARLES A. GIBBONS

INTERNATIONAL TRADE in agricultural products is ancient (Jacob sent his sons to Egypt to buy grain during a drought in Palestine) but was small until recent times.

A thousand years ago a local shortage of food more likely meant migration, starvation, or a raid on a richer community than an exchange of other goods for food. Explorers during the 16th century sought sea routes to bring Asian spices to Europe, and Europe had some commerce in wool, flax, wine, beeswax, and foodstuffs, but all that was nothing compared to the surge that came when the Industrial Revolution began to build up populations who needed to import food and were able to supply other goods in exchange. At first the needed food was to be had in Europe, and little trading was done in agricultural raw materials. American farm exports in the early 1700's, mostly tobacco, were less valuable than the products of the forests and the sea.

More agricultural products move in international trade now than at any time in the past, but the agricultural share in total world trade is only a fraction of what it was a century ago.

The 19th century was a golden age for agricultural trade, made so by several events. The invention of the steam engine and its application to manufacturing, mining, and transportation lowered the cost of manufactured goods in the industrial cities of Europe. The invention of the cotton gin, reaper, steel plow, and other machines and the development of railroads reduced the cost of farm products in many parts of the world.

Improved sailing ships and later steamships cut the cost of shipping so much that by 1900 freight on a long ton of wheat to Liverpool cost only about 2 dollars more from Chicago than from Yorkshire.

These inventions laid the technological base for the exchange of European manufactured goods for food and raw materials from other countries. After the Louisiana Purchase in this country, the wars of independence in South America, and the settlement of the Napoleonic Wars in Europe, the political climate was generally favorable to commerce and the emigration of people to farm newly opened lands.

INTERNATIONAL TRADE depends on the existence of a large enough difference in prices between the place of origin and the place of consumption to pay the cost of transporting the goods and to reward traders for their services and risks.

Furthermore, the traders must know that the difference exists. Of unusual importance therefore were the reduction in time and cost of communication achieved through the telegraph (1844), the transatlantic cable (1866), and the beginning of a regular flow of statistical information about production and prices.

International trade is better documented statistically than any other aspect of international economics.

Most governments print more pages of statistics about foreign trade than about any other field of statistics. The only significant economic statistics for some territories are the accounts of foreign trade.

This field of statistics is so well developed because the figures have many uses and because the methods of getting them may be simple. No more is needed than to make a continuous count of goods that cross the frontiers, record quantities and values, classify the commodities, and add figures.

Difficulties of administration arise, however, from the nature of the transactions across the frontiers, the laws and regulations of the customs administration, and the compromises necessary to meet the conflicting needs of different classes of users of the statistics.

Each of the older countries developed some accounts of its foreign trade as a means of informing the different agencies of government, business, and finance. Each, therefore, considered as "foreign" trade the transactions so defined by its customs laws and regulations, and it tabulated the valuations recorded for customs purposes, which often were much less than the real values. Classifications of statistics by commodities, if used at all, were simple and devised to meet national needs.

When the upsurge of international commerce in the 19th century led to demands for more information, to be used for new purposes as well as old, the national accounts of international trade became more detailed, especially after punched-card machinery began to be used. The need for greater international comparability in trade statistics was so obvious by 1913 that a conference in Brussels approved a list of 186 headings, in 5 broad classes, and 29 governments (not including the United States) signed an international convention providing for annual publication of their foreign trade statistics according to this scheme. More elaborate schemes were proposed by the League of Nations, and after the Second World War the United Nations developed the Standard International Trade Classification (SITC), which was adopted widely after 1951.

The original SITC was not compatible with the most-used classification of commodities that had been developed for customs administration, the Brussels Tariff Nomenclature (BTN). When the European Economic Community adopted the BTN as its common commodity classification for tariff purposes, most other countries in western Europe did likewise. The SITC therefore was revised in 1960 to make it compatible with the BTN, and the Bureau of the Census, beginning with the monthly statistics for January of 1963, has tabulated the foreign trade of the United States according to the three-digit positions of the revised SITC.

At least 96 percent of the free world trade was covered in 1962 by the SITC or the BTN, which can be converted to the SITC. This rapid progress toward standardization in commodity classification does not, however, remove all the difficulties in tabulating and using trade statistics.

One remaining difficulty is the differences among countries in the definition of foreign trade—more precisely, the transactions that are to be included in the statistics of foreign trade. The differences are hard to eradicate because they are rooted in differing national needs and the historical accidents of differing administrations of customs and statistics.

For example, the United Kingdom and many countries formerly under British administration use the general system of trade, and the United States uses the special system.

The general trade system records as imports all goods entering the country, and as exports or reexports all goods leaving the country. Reexports may also be called exports of foreign merchandise.

The special trade system considers as imports only the foreign goods that have been cleared through customs, and includes in exports domestic goods shipped out plus foreign goods shipped out after having been cleared previously through customs.

These latter often are called nationalized goods to distinguish them from national or domestic goods. When there is no import duty, goods may be imported into a country and cleared through customs rather than be entered in transit, since nationalizing the goods gives the owner more opportunities for sales than the transit procedures allow.

As an example, coffee and bananas are imported into the United States and later shipped to other countries. They are recorded in United States exports as exports of foreign merchandise. When there is an import duty, goods are not likely to be cleared through customs but will be entered for direct transit or for warehousing in bond under customs control.

Direct transit relates to goods passing through a country for purposes of transportation only. It is important on the continent of Europe, where most countries use the special system of trade, but it also is used in the United States for the transit of Mexican cotton, for example. Goods put in a bonded customs warehouse and later sent abroad are recorded as indirect transit trade by countries using the special trade system, but as imports and reexports by countries using the general system.

The use of the general trade system leads to some double counting.

An example is rubber that moves from Indonesia to the United States via Singapore and England. It may be counted three times: An export from Indonesia, an import into Singapore and a reexport thence, an import into the United Kingdom and a reexport thence, and finally an import into the United States.

Because special imports do not include goods entered into bonded storage warehouses and subsequently shipped out of the country—while general imports do include such a flow of goods—many analysts wish to adjust general imports to the special basis by subtracting reexports. The remainder is called retained imports. It is only approximately equivalent to special imports, however, because of differences in the timing of imports. For a period as short as a month, reexports may easily exceed general imports. The result is negative retained imports, while special imports can never be negative.

Furthermore, even if retained imports are not negative, the qualities of the imports and the reexports during a month may be so different as to result in absurdly high or low values per unit of retained imports.

No INTERNATIONAL AGREEMENT has been reached on a definition of agricultural trade, probably because different agencies and individuals have sharply divergent notions about what should be included.

Certainly the present United States definition contains several anomalies that would be hard to defend on an international basis. For example: A live silver fox is agricultural, but a skin of a silver fox is nonagricultural; a live kangaroo is nonagricultural, but a kangaroo skin is agricultural.

In this discussion, agricultural trade for other countries is defined as including approximately—but only approximately—the same commodities as for the United States. Forest products and fish are excluded (as in the United States definition), but fishmeal is included along with meat meal; fish and whale oils are included along with animal fats; distilled liquor is included along with beer, wine, and nonalcoholic beverages; and furskins are included along with hides.

I exclude essential oils, casein, gluten, and starch, because they are too hard to separate from chemicals in the classifications of most countries. Application of the definitions used for other countries would raise the figure for the United States by 1.6 percent.

The decline in relative importance of agricultural products in world trade is due partly to the decline in prices of most agricultural products relative to nonagricultural products since 1913, but mostly to the great increase in the volume of trade in petroleum, minerals, and manufactured goods.

Statistics on the estimated value of world exports of individual SITC commodities have been published by FAO for the years 1957 through 1961, along with continental, regional, and world totals (in metric tons) for im-

ports and exports of nearly all significant agricultural commodities. These are more detailed and comprehensive than the statistics published by anyone else, but unfortunately they cannot be up to date.

In value, the seven main commodities in 1961, each with exports valued at 1 billion dollars or more, were (in millions of dollars): Wheat, 2,655; raw cotton, 2,335; raw and refined sugar, 2,176; coffee, 1,841; wool, 1,741; natural rubber, 1,432; and raw tobacco, 1,100.

Wheat is also the leading commodity in weight. The world trade in each of the following commodities in 1961 exceeded 3 million metric tons (the international unit of weight—2,204.6 pounds avoirdupois) in millions of metric tons: Wheat, 40.5; raw and refined sugar, 20.4; corn, 13.8; barley, 7.3; rice, 6.1; oilseed cake and meal, 5.2; wheat flour, 4.5; bananas, 4.0; and cotton, 3.7.

Noteworthy shifts in the commodity composition of agricultural trade occurred in the quarter century between 1934–1938 and 1961. Trade in silk dropped five-sixths as the Second World War accelerated an already existing tendency to use substitutes.

Area and production of rice in Asia failed to keep pace with population, and trade in rice fell about one-third.

Exports of flaxseed, cottonseed, peanuts, castor beans, and palm kernels all fell, while trade in their oils went up, the chief reason being the encouragement in the producing countries of the crushing industry. Contrary to this trend, exports of copra increased, and those of coconut oil fell, largely as a consequence of war damage in the Philippines.

The declines in trade were exceptional. Most agricultural commodities participated in the general increase in international trade during the past quarter century. Trade in wheat, already large, nearly tripled. Exports of other small grains and of sugar doubled. Trade in powdered milk rose 20 times. Exports of canned milk doubled. Fresh meat, canned meat, cheese, sugar, coffee, cocoa beans, lard, soybeans, tobacco, sisal, and vegetable oils all gained in trade faster than the world population.

On the other hand, cured meat, eggs, corn, tea, wine, cotton, wool, flax, and oilseed cake all gained in total trade but lost per capita.

Big shifts in the geographic pattern of trade also occurred. During this quarter century, the volume of trade in agricultural products increased by about one-half, a bit faster than the rise in world population and agricultural output but only a fraction of the increase in nonagricultural trade.

As real incomes rise, the demand in every country for imported foods and agricultural raw materials also rises. It is not surprising, therefore, that all regions increased the overall quantity of agricultural products imported.

All regions also increased their agricultural exports, but in this analysis they are divided into four groups according to the relation between changes in exports, imports, and their population:

Those that increased their exports faster than their imports: North America (the United States and Canada) and western Europe.

Those with exports increasing faster than their population but not so fast as imports: Oceania, non-Arab Africa, and the Soviet bloc.

Net exporting regions whose exports failed to keep pace with population and imports: Latin America and northern Africa.

Regions which are now net importers because their exports failed to keep pace with population and imports: Asia (the Far East and western Asia).

Only the United States, Canada, and western Europe fall in the first group, which may be described as having superior agricultural trade performance during the period under review, even though western Europe is a net importer.

The physical volume of the United States exports nearly tripled between 1934–1938 and 1961. The rise was unusually large partly because the 1934–1938 period was one of droughts and depressed exports. On the other hand, the latter part of this quarter century was not a period of all-out efforts at increasing production and exports, as the period of the Second World War had been. Especially noteworthy was the great postwar boom in exports of soybeans and products, in recent years the greatest dollar earner of all agricultural exports.

While the volume of United States agricultural exports was nearly tripling, the volume of imports rose only one-fifth. Bigger imports of coffee, meat, animals, wool, tobacco, cocoa beans, and bananas more than offset decreases in silk, oilseeds and oils, grains, and hard fibers.

Canada's agricultural exports more than doubled in this quarter century, while imports rose only about 75 percent. Exports were about 4 percent of the world total in 1963, compared to 3 percent before the war. Imports were about 3 percent of the world total.

Agriculture recovered from its wartime disruptions faster in western Europe than in eastern Europe, the Soviet Union, or the Far East, a reflection of greater skill in formation of agricultural policy and administration as well as in farming. This region is the greatest market for agricultural products, but its share of world imports has fallen from about 60 percent before the war to about 50 percent. At the same time, agricultural exports have increased, largely to Europe.

Of the second group of regions—those that increased their per capita exports and increased their imports even faster—Oceania and non-Arab Africa depend largely on agricultural products for their export earnings. They can be considered successful in the development of agricultural trade in this quarter century. The Soviet bloc, on the other hand, is industrialized and need not rely on exports of farm products, as it can pay for its net imports of agricultural products with the products of industry.

What is now the Soviet bloc—Russia and eastern Europe—was the breadbasket of Europe before 1914. In 1909–1913, the annual exports of grain averaged 16 million metric tons, more than half the net imports of western Europe at that time, or more than the exports of North America, Latin America, and Australia put together. By 1934–1938, net exports of grain were less than one-third as large as before the First World War. Net exports of sugar, another important item, fell more than 60 percent.

From the reduced levels of 1934–1938, net exports of grain fell to zero sometime during the statistical blackout between 1939 and 1955. When reasonably complete statistics became available again, the Soviet bloc was a net importer of grain. It had also changed from a net export to a net import position for tobacco and in 1960 became a net importer of sugar.

Two other regions increased their exports per capita in this quarter century: Oceania and non-Arab Africa. The former has a high-technology agriculture similar to that in North America but subject to greater uncertainties of rainfall.

Before the Second World War, Oceania had great export surpluses of wool, meat, dairy products, cereals, sugar, fruit, copra, and animal fats. Net imports of agricultural commodities were few: Tea, tobacco, rubber, flaxseed and linseed oil, rice, cocoa beans, cotton, other vegetable fibers, and several edible vegetable oils. Twenty-five years later, rice had disappeared from the list, cotton and cocoa beans had risen in rank, and flaxseed and linseed oil had fallen.

Although Oceania had a high rate of population growth (in large part because of immigration), it also had a high rate of capital formation and considerable unexploited land. Both the area harvested and yields per acre rose, and the efficiency of livestock production and marketing was increased.

In this analysis, the six Arabic-speaking countries of northern Africa (Algeria, the United Arab Republic, Libya, Morocco, Sudan, and Tunisia) are discussed separately from the rest of Africa.

Non-Arab Africa is an important exporter of coffee, cocoa beans, peanuts, cotton, tobacco, oil palm products, sisal, and rubber. All these are cultivated for export; local consumption is negligible for all commodities named except peanuts and palm products, but even for them more than half the output in the region is exported.

Non-Arabic Africa is also a net exporter, though on a small scale, of bananas, tea, and sugar.

Alongside this sector producing for export is a larger sector growing subsistence crops—corn, sorghum, cassava, yams, plantains, and numerous other vegetables and fruit. Only in a few instances has this native subsistence sector produced any surplus for export.

Even in the climatically more suitable parts of the continent, production of subsistence crops by modern technology has been started only in the past few years. Investment funds are available for promoting the output of export crops but generally are not available (except through governments) for promoting other crops.

The vast herds of cattle in Africa contribute little to trade. Non-Arabic Africa has about one-half as many cattle as Latin America, but the value of net exports of their products is less than one-twentieth as great.

THE THIRD GROUP of regions consists of net exporters that are falling behind in the race with population and imports. They are Latin America and northern Africa. The volume of exports of the former is about six times as large as the volume of the six Arab countries in Africa.

Latin America was the second-ranking exporting region before the Second World War, a position it also held in 1961, but its share of the world exports fell from 23 percent to 18 during the quarter century. Exports of wheat from Argentina have fluctuated greatly, but the trend has been downward since the early thirties.

Meanwhile, imports of wheat and flour into tropical countries of Latin America have been mounting, and the region has become a large net importer of wheat. Exports of feed grains, meat, oilseeds and oils, and animal fats also fell. For all those commodities, Argentina is the chief exporter in Latin America, and the poor export performance of Latin America is due chiefly to Argentina's failure to maintain her preeminent position.

The tropical Latin American countries expanded output and exports of sugar, coffee, cotton, bananas, tobacco, and sisal nearly as fast as the population grew. By comparison with the Far East, this was a good performance, but it does not compare as favorably with the expansion of exports from non-Arabic Africa, which climatically is somewhat similar.

THE FOURTH GROUP of regions includes the Far East and western Asia (Afghanistan westward). Together they constitute all the continent of Asia south of the Soviet Union.

Western Asia is often separately considered in analysis because its climate, crops, and culture are more like those of northern Africa than like those of monsoon Asia. The total population of western Asia is perhaps 95 million, and only about half of the inhabitants live in countries that depend primarily on agricultural exports.

For the region as a whole, petroleum is the big export commodity. Agricultural exports amount to only 2 percent of the world total; cotton, tobacco, and a variety of fruit and vegetables are the chief commodities. Cereals account for nearly half the imports, although the region was a net exporter of cereals before the war.

The Far East was the leading exporter in 1934–1938 of agricultural products. It led the world in exports of rubber, tea, silk, rice, jute, peanuts, soybeans, palm products, and several minor commodities.

Wartime destruction, postwar instability, and the growth of domestic requirements have reduced net exports of all the products just named except rubber and tea. The overall volume of agricultural exports dropped one-fourth in a quarter century, while population grew about one-half, and import needs grew even more.

The most spectacular rise was in wheat and flour, from net imports of 16 million bushels in 1934–1938 to about 450 million bushels in 1962. Before the war, the Far East had export surpluses of sugar, soybeans and oil, corn, barley, cottonseed and oil, lard, potatoes, and sorghum. In 1961, the region was a net importer of all those products as well as wheat. Imports of grains, cotton, wool, tallow, and oilseeds and oils (except palm products) into the Far East in 1962 were exceeded only by those into western Europe.

The basic reason for the shift from being a big net exporter to being a substantial net importer is the scarcity of cropland and of capital in relation to a poor but growing population. The area of grain harvested rose only about one-fourth since 1936, while the population increased nearly one-half. The total of land cultivated has been increasing but not nearly so fast as the needs for food, feed, and fibers. Much land remains uncultivated because of lack of capital for developing it.

At the same time, yields on the cultivated land in most countries of the Far East could be raised if more capital were used for irrigation, drainage, fertilizers, and machinery.

CHARLES A. GIBBONS *joined the Economic Research Service as a statistician in the Regional Analysis Division in 1962. Previously he worked as a statistician for the Food and Agriculture Organization in Washington, Cairo, Addis Ababa, and Rome. He was editor of the FAO Trade Yearbook from 1956 to 1962.*

Monetary Problems and Trade

by WARRICK E. ELROD, JR.

THE LIMITED availability of foreign exchange has been the chief deterrent to the expansion of agricultural exports to the developing countries of Asia, Africa, the Near and Far East, southeastern Asia, and Latin America.

To conserve their limited supplies of foreign exchange, they may impose exchange controls (including quotas on the use of currency, multiple exchange rates, or other restrictive mechanisms); make bilateral trade agreements; and impose special administrative controls, such as advance deposits, against some or all imports.

Monetary problems have not determined the amount of agricultural trade among advanced nations. Major barriers to agricultural trade in those countries have been the desire of the governments to protect their own agriculture and the insensitivity of demand for agricultural products in response to any changes in prices and incomes.

Consumers' tastes in the developing countries may vary from region to region, but there generally has been an increase in demand for agricultural imports from the United States and other exporters as incomes have risen.

In many instances, foreign traders, if allowed to choose, would have spent more of their scarce foreign exchange for products from the United States if their governments had not implemented trade policies that resulted in the purchase of other or similar products from other suppliers.

Despite deficits in the United States balance of payments, underdeveloped countries have had a short supply of dollars and have sought to conserve their supplies.

They have also held small supplies of other convertible currencies, except in some instances in which a former colonial power with a convertible currency has made provision for the newly independent country or the country has had favorable earning capacity.

CURRENCY TIES with a former mother country can determine the direction of trade, both agricultural and industrial. The ties may lead to patterns of agricultural trade that are less advantageous to the importing country and a less efficient allocation of resources in both the supplying and receiving country.

Shortage of foreign exchange can affect agricultural trade in another way. Developing countries have tended to utilize their foreign exchange to import the capital goods that they believed — probably rightly — would advance economic development, which they almost always have associated with industrialization.

If the tendency operates without limits, however, the results can be adverse. Argentina, for example, neglected its agricultural sector to the extent that it failed to provide the 93–96 percent of export receipts it once did. The receipts could have financed the industrial development of the country. Argentina's external financial difficulties arose out of the imbalance of its economic development and the impairment of its foreign agricultural trade.

Yet developing governments invariably have sought to encourage the import of capital goods, such as machinery, hoping to keep to a minimum their imports of food, luxuries, and consumables, except when social or political reasons dictate otherwise.

Governments usually have tried to avoid increasing the number of discriminatory quota restrictions or exceptionally high tariffs against agricultural imports as being inconsistent with the objectives of the International Monetary Fund and the General Agreement on Tariffs and Trade. They have used restrictive practices—exchange controls, bilateral trade agreements, and selective advance deposit requirements on imports—however. All or any combination of those mechanisms may be used because a country suffers from a shortage of convertible foreign exchange.

MANY COUNTRIES have simply limited the amount of foreign exchange that they have made available for the importation of selected items. That is the easiest and most direct way to limit imports of any type to a given amount.

Many countries have utilized multiple exchange rates to limit such imports. Under a multiple exchange rate system, a country sets varying rates of exchange between its own currency and foreign currencies, depending on the classes of imports. For needed industrial imports, a rate may be set, making the price of the industrial goods in the foreign currency cheap in terms of the currency of the importer.

The rate for luxuries may be set to raise the price of such imports in terms of the importing country's currency. As authorities may change the rates at any time, multiple-rate systems interject an element of instability into international trade.

It is desirable that countries adopt a unified rate for their currencies. Progress is being made. About a dozen countries continued to have multiple-exchange rates in 1964. Five of them were in Latin America—Chile, Brazil, Colombia, Ecuador, and Venezuela. Multiple-currency practices existed, however, in other countries where unofficial or illegal rates prevailed.

There has been no evidence that the multiple-exchange rate systems have greatly hindered agricultural trade.

Generally direct controls, such as import quotas or highly protective tariffs, have been used by countries seeking to discourage agricultural imports.

Authorities in some countries have placed limits on the amounts of the local currency that can be converted into foreign currencies.

In the French franc zone of Africa, for instance, it has been possible to convert CFA (Communauté Financière Africaine) francs into French francs. But there has been a limit on the amounts that the African countries could convert into other foreign currencies. The result has been that imports that might have been sought elsewhere were taken from France.

All countries in the CFA zone, except the Republic of Ivory Coast, which was a net earner of foreign exchange, have fixed quotas for converting into foreign currencies. Should they seek more than their allotted amounts, they may or may not be permitted to purchase additional amounts from the French Equalization Fund.

These special arrangements have directed, between the former African colonies and France, agricultural trade, which may have moved into other areas. Obviously, to the extent that the 13 republics in the CFA zone in 1964 could more easily obtain French francs than dollars or other convertible currencies would they be influenced in taking agricultural and industrial products from France rather than from other countries.

Similarly, the east African monetary system—which includes Uganda, the Republic of Tanganyika, Kenya, and Zanzibar—functions as an extension of the British monetary system, with the result that the trade of the area has been directed within the sterling area.

A country may institute bilateral trade agreements to offset unfavorable trade balances with certain other countries or to obtain more advantageous terms of trade. Any country may be short of the exchange of those trading partners with whom the country incurs deficits in the payments accounts.

The number of bilateral agreements among the free nations has been progressively reduced. Such agreements do continue, even though they distort trade patterns and in the long run may prove harmful to the country entering into such agreements. There may be short-run benefits, such as establishing fixed outlets for a given quantity of exports, or opening markets for new products.

Bilateral agreements generally have provided for offsetting quantities of imports and exports between the two partners and thus have reduced their mutual needs for foreign exchange in settling their international accounts.

These agreements have been popular in Latin America, but Colombia, Ecuador, and Uruguay have terminated several such agreements; Uruguay ended three with Iron Curtain countries whose currencies were not acceptable internationally.

Ceylon, Afghanistan, and other Near East and African countries had bilateral agreements in 1964. Bilateral agreements have represented the normal method of carrying on trade among Soviet satellites.

GOVERNMENTS may require importers to make advance deposits when the importers apply for letters of credit to import certain goods.

Such requirements have worked a hardship on importers and may have dampened the incentive to import.

Advance deposits have tied up funds for unnecessarily long periods in capital-scarce economies. The depositor received no interest during the period his funds were held.

This has been a problem in Korea and in the Philippines also. Until the exchange reforms of 1962 in the Philippines, certain classes of goods ("nonessential consumer goods") required advance deposits of as much as 200 percent.

Importers in Taiwan had to make advance deposits equal to the tariff to be charged on the import of certain raw materials. If the finished product were later reexported, the tariff was refunded. This tying up of moneys may have been a hardship where short-term interest rates were 12 or 15 percent or higher, and this has been a major factor in several important private trade negotiations with Taiwan importers. Deposit requirements may be imposed selectively to restrict import of specific commodities, or they may be applied across the board as a means of reducing internal inflationary pressures.

Quantitative restrictions on imports and on transfers of capital often have been instituted by Latin American governments to meet adverse short-term capital movements and other balance-of-payment problems that severely limit the availability of foreign exchange.

An example is Chile, whose inability to increase exports and to control inflation has led her to impose many import restrictions, including surcharges and advance deposits.

Argentina introduced advance deposit requirements in 1962 and abolished them by the end of the year.

In Brazil, the period of retention of deposits was 5 months, and the use of these requirements covered payments for invisibles (travel, transportation, tourist receipts) as well as payments for most merchandise imports.

Some countries, among them Nicaragua and Surinam, were able to reduce advance deposit requirements and to eliminate some other deposit restrictions. Peru has avoided import restrictions by increasing exports, primarily cotton, and added around 18 million dollars to her reserves over the 2-year period 1962–1963.

SOME COUNTRIES have experienced balance-of-payment difficulties because they attempted to support an overvalued exchange rate which tended to discourage exports and encourage imports.

Maintenance of the overvalued exchange rate required the use of foreign exchange reserves or external assistance to provide such reserves, but this practice was adopted in the belief that confidence in the currency would be maintained and in time the overvalued rate justified.

An exchange reform in Colombia, which was initiated as part of a new stabilization program in 1962, resulted in the loss of valuable reserves when the authorities tried to support the overvalued currency rate. Such practices often have been continued even after a temporary crisis has abated.

Although the use of import and payments restrictions or depletion of foreign exchange reserves through questionable remedies may be necessary, other methods, such as compensatory financing—that is, provision of financial aid to countries suffering losses in their export receipts—or some other forms of international aid have been more appropriate when a country faced serious balance-of-payment difficulties.

Whether a developing country restricts agricultural trade by exchange controls or specific tariffs, bilateral agreements, and by import deposit requirements (or multiple exchange rates), it seems likely that the country will still use the total foreign exchange it considers to be available in a given period as its import needs are usually so large. The industrial component of imports will simply be greater.

The developing countries have had difficulty earning needed foreign exchange wherever there has been a decline in prices of their commodity exports. These countries often have been heavily dependent upon one or two commodities for the major portion of their foreign exchange.

A decline in export prices relative to prices for capital goods imports has meant a deterioration in the terms of trade—that is, in real terms, the volume of exports necessary to requite a given volume of imports, a higher volume of exports being necessary when export prices have fallen.

This persistent deterioration in the terms of trade for the developing countries, which reduces their import potential, has accounted in part for their tendency to industrialize and to diversify exports.

During the fifties, the ratio of prices of primary products to the prices of manufactured products in Latin America declined by more than 20 percent. The volume of exports of all the less-developed countries increased by 52 percent, but the importing power of exports increased by only 44 percent. The gap would have been larger, except that the less-developed countries have also had to import large quantities of primary commodities.

As the sixties have progressed, commodity prices have begun to strengthen modestly, and this has been of some assistance to developing countries. The strengthening in prices has been selective and in some cases began only in late 1963 and 1964.

The improvement in the prices of tropical commodities, such as cane sugar, cacao, coffee, and jute, has been significant when compared with levels before the Second World War but less impressive when compared with exceptional peaks in the postwar period.

Little evidence exists of any general long-term depression of prices of the agricultural exports of the tropical underdeveloped countries. There has been only a very slow postwar growth in the volume of these exports, however, their rate of growth being only about one-third that of such exports as grains, oilseeds, and meats. This slow growth may arise from the relatively slow population growth rate in the developed countries. Many tropical export commodities have experienced extreme fluctuations in export unit value; the variation above or below the trend line, in prices for coffee, cocoa, and rubber has been nearly three times the variability in the export prices of wheat and soybeans. Unit values of bananas, tea, and sugar, however, varied about the same as unit values for wheat and soybeans. Thus the problem of wide swings in export earnings in developing countries is in large part related to the type of agricultural commodities produced.

ANOTHER MONETARY PROBLEM in almost all the less-developed countries is an unsatisfactory rate of inflow of private long-term capital. The result is that less foreign exchange has become available for imports. Unfavorable climates for investment have deterred such inflows.

The deficit on goods and services was reduced in 1962 by about 300 million dollars in Latin America, but a reduced inflow of capital and an increased outflow of capital caused an overall deficit in the area's balance of payments of 800 million dollars. Curtailed inflows have reduced the amount of new foreign exchange available; outflows have reduced available reserves severely and forced the imposition of restrictions on imports to reduce the pressure on reserves.

Interest rates in the developing countries have been high, by relative or absolute standards, as a result of a demand for funds far in excess of the supply of funds. High commercial interest rates have been prevalent as lenders have sought protection against the sharply depreciating value of the currency.

An annual rate of inflation of 50 percent in Brazil obviously would mean an annual rate of interest of more than that magnitude on money lent for the same period of time if the lender is to protect himself against depreciation of the currency. Rising prices may warrant acceptance of high interest rates, but it is highly unlikely that agricultural trade will be financed to any significant extent by borrowed funds.

Banks throughout the Near East and Far East, being confined to a narrow supply of funds, cannot meet the demand for all loans. Interest rates have been 12 to 15 percent. In countries whose governments have set upper limits on interest rates, the banks have rationed the supply by other means.

Many banks have required large collateral, sometimes as high as 50 to 100 percent of the amount of the loan. Funds available for financing agricultural trade consequently have been limited and costly, even when immediate sale of the commodities insured rapid repayment of a loan.

Conditions vary from country to country. In some countries, the central banking authorities have kept maximum interest rates at reasonable levels. Iraq is one. In 1959, the Central Bank reduced the allowable maximum on commercial loans from 7 percent to 5.5 percent. The entire rate structure was reduced, the going rate of interest actually declining to below the allowable maximum.

In Israel and Turkey, rates rose to about 20 percent during years of inflation, and the real rate of return to the lender often approached zero as currency depreciation accelerated.

Thus no general level of interest rates has prevailed. The levels can vary among countries and within a country, depending on the time periods. Funds have been available for financing commercial transactions in agricultural commodities, but they have been costly and usually have resulted in a much higher price to the consumer.

High interest rates have presented serious problems in agricultural communities, since the rate has led to a shift of available funds from the agricultural sector of the economy to the commercial, where, profits being higher, the higher cost of the funds can be covered. Unless governments compensate for this deficiency by subsidy or low-cost loans to agriculture, development in the farm sector is impeded.

WARRICK E. ELROD, JR., was named Chief of the International Monetary Branch, Economic Research Service, in 1962. He formerly was an economist in the Division of International Finance of the Board of Governors of the Federal Reserve System, and for 10 years before that a Foreign Service officer with duty in Europe and the Department of State.

Economic Growth

and Trade

by ARTHUR B. MACKIE and
KENNETH L. BACHMAN

PROSPEROUS NATIONS trade much more
than less prosperous countries. Each
community in a backward country
tends to be self-sufficient, and trade
lags, even among regions. Each step
up in development steps up domestic
and international trade. Thus the
actual and potential level of trade
among countries depends on the level
of their economic development.

Growth in trade usually means more
imports of agricultural and industrial
products. Economic growth gives consumers more purchasing power and
appetites for foods not widely grown
in their country. Diversity of consumption leads to increased trade.

Postwar economic growth in Japan
and western Europe, for example, has
made them good customers for our
farm products. We can expect those
countries, which have highly developed agricultural and industrial sectors, to buy even more from us as they
achieve still higher levels of incomes.

Rapid economic growth in Japan
since the Second World War has expanded imports of all goods and services from all countries from 990 million
dollars in 1938 to 4.8 billion dollars in
1961, or 3.8 times. Her imports from
the United States increased 6.2 times—
from 240 million dollars to 1.7 billion.
Our agricultural exports to Japan increased from 44 million dollars in 1938

to 518 million in 1961–1962, or about
11 times. On a per capita basis, the
value of Japanese agricultural imports
from the United States increased from
63 cents to 5.48 dollars.

Trade with less-developed countries
also has increased since the Second
World War. How rapidly their markets
will continue to expand depends on
how rapidly they can achieve economic growth and increase export
earnings.

Income is a major factor in world
trade. There is much more trade between industrialized countries than
between nonindustrialized countries,
or between industrialized and nonindustrialized countries.

A comparison of income, exports,
and imports for developed and less-
developed countries in 1959–1960
illustrates the importance of the stage
of economic development on the actual
level of trade.

The developed countries, with an
annual average income of 655 dollars
per capita, exported 125 dollars' worth
and imported 127 dollars' worth of all
goods and services in 1959–1960. The
less-developed countries, whose average
annual income was 110 dollars per
capita, averaged about 20 dollars'
worth of exports and imports then.

The value of agricultural exports
was 32 dollars—only 25 percent—of
total exports for the developed countries and 11 dollars, or 55 percent, for
the less-developed countries. The developed countries imported about 48
dollars per capita of agricultural products. The less-developed countries
averaged about 5 dollars' worth of
agricultural imports per capita.

Income, exports, and imports per
capita of all products were six times
larger for the developed countries (excluding the United States) than they
were for less-developed countries in
1959–1960. Agricultural exports were
only three times larger, but agricultural imports were about nine times
larger in the developed countries than
they were for the less developed.

Those comparisons emphasize the

importance of agricultural exports in the total trade of less-developed countries whose agricultural exports in 1959–1960 were more than half their exports. Agricultural exports were only about one-fourth of all exports in the developed countries.

The high dependency of the less-developed countries on agricultural exports is indicated by the relatively high level of exports per capita at this low level of income. The relatively low level of agricultural imports per capita reflects the greater use of their foreign exchange earnings for capital imports needed to finance industrial and general economic development. These data suggest that especially in low-income countries agricultural imports would be increased with higher levels of income and economic development.

As a general rule, the countries that have developed most rapidly since 1938–1940 have increased their imports of agricultural products most rapidly—that is, the rate at which agricultural imports have been expanded has been closely related to the growth in income.

Although incomes increased more in the developed than in less-developed countries from 1938–1940 to 1959–1960, total agricultural imports increased more in the less-developed countries. The faster increase in agricultural imports in the less-developed countries was due to food-aid shipments, primarily from America.

If only commercial imports are considered, agricultural imports increased most rapidly in the developed countries as a result of a more rapid growth in income. In both groups of countries, however, agricultural imports (excluding noncommercial shipments) increased about 12 percent for each 10 percent increase in per capita incomes from 1938–1940 to 1959–1960.

Patterns of food consumption have changed with economic development in many countries. Rising consumer incomes in many countries in the postwar period have enabled individuals to improve their diets and to demand

more of what they could not previously afford. These changes are the result of higher incomes and a more diversified demand for food—a demand that must be satisfied with imports if a country's resources do not allow for enough flexibility in production to meet it.

The effect of higher incomes in the developed countries has been to open up new and enlarged markets for feed grains and high-protein feeds needed for larger numbers of livestock.

While economic growth in the developed countries has brought a greater demand for animal protein, the effect in others has been to increase total food consumption, especially wheat.

In rapidly developing countries, like Japan and Italy, the process of substituting wheat for other foods has raised wheat imports and the importance of wheat in the United States agricultural exports. In Japan, the substitution of wheat for rice has converted Japan into a major wheat importer since 1950, and the higher incomes also have increased the consumption and demand for meat and meat products.

In India, a country with an average income per capita of less than 100 dollars, the per capita consumption of wheat increased from 51 pounds a year in 1938–1939 to 61 pounds a year in 1959–1960. The consumption of rice, jowar, barley, maize, bojra, and other food grains generally has declined. India has experienced moderate economic growth and increased imports of agricultural products in the postwar years.

Economic growth and trade are complementary.

The relationship was mentioned in 1850 by Richard Hakluyt, an English historian and geographer, who told English merchants:

"If you find any island or maine land populous, and the same people hath need of cloth, then you are to advise what commodities they have to purchase the same withal. If they be poore, then you are to consider the soile and how by any possibilities the same may be made to enrich them, that hereafter they may have something to purchase the cloth withal."

Mercantilists in the 17th and 18th centuries emphasized the importance of expanding exports as a means for increasing national wealth through favorable balances of trade. Imports were thought to be bad and therefore were discouraged. The idea of mutually helpful trade eluded them.

Not until the 19th century was the beneficial relationship of both exports and imports emphasized. Even then, though, the doctrines of trade and development placed more emphasis on exports and the role of trade as an engine of growth that transmitted economic growth from the industrial center, England and western Europe, to newly settled lands overseas.

Although world economic conditions are greatly different from those of a century ago, the complementary relationship between trade and development still exists in the sixties.

Today, however, the importance of both exports and imports is emphasized as being essential for expansion of world trade and economic growth. Exports are still important. They provide the necessary foreign exchange to pay for imports. Imports are necessary to the growth process in less-developed countries. Capital and imports of capital goods are needed to finance economic growth, and imports of food are needed to meet the rapidly rising demand created by the growth process.

An example: Failure by developing countries to import food to fill the demands created by rising incomes can seriously affect a developing economy. Food prices are likely to rise sharply, and because food is the principal expenditure of consumers, there is a strong pressure of increasing wages in nonfarm industries. Rising wage rates soon lead to a cost-price inflation spiral and so reduce the rate of economic growth. Thus the changing nature of the demand for and supply of food associated with economic growth also affects the level and nature of actual and potential trade among countries.

The nature of supply and demand for food is related to the stage of economic growth. In countries well below the takeoff stage in economic development, growth in per capita incomes and agricultural production is slow, and production of food increases slowly because of the lack of capital, low educational levels, and a slow adoption of improved technologies.

Increases in the total demand for food are primarily a function of population growth. But since population growth is often rapid, food requirements increase faster than food supplies. Then the demand for food imports increases, and if the increased demand is not met through increased trade, inflation occurs and slows down the rate of economic growth.

On the other hand, countries experiencing a rapid rate of growth in per capita incomes and agricultural production are faced with an ever-increasing demand for food—a demand that outpaces the domestic supply. Food imports in consequence must continue to go up rapidly, either as trade or aid to keep the growth process going. Rapidly rising incomes per capita increase the total demand for food more rapidly than the supply of food. Once the takeoff of economic development is passed, the gap between food supplies and demand tends to widen with rapid and sustained economic growth. The effect then is to increase the demand for food and, thus, agricultural trade.

A STUDY made by the Department of Agriculture in 1963 to forecast world food demands in 1980 provides useful insights as to the prospective increases in food demands and the increases in domestic production and food aid that may be needed. Underdeveloped countries were divided into two groups— those with medium to rapid rates of economic growth and those with slow rates of economic growth.

Because of the high-income elasticity

of the demand for food in value terms in the less-developed countries, food demands may expand rapidly.

By 1980, potential food deficits will increase to a dollar value of 21 billion in the rapidly developing countries and to 4.5 billion dollars for the slow-growth countries—an increase of tenfold and nearly fourfold, respectively.

Population and national income were assumed to increase at the 1953–1960 rates of 2.2 and 5.3 percent, respectively, in the rapidly developing countries. In the slow-growth countries, population was projected at the 1953–1960 rate (2.4 percent), but it was assumed that the growth in income might be raised to the modest level of 3.9 percent a year.

In the rapidly developing countries, food production was projected to increase substantially to an annual rate of 3.3 percent, and in the slow-growth countries to an annual rate of 3 percent.

A large part of this expected food deficit would involve the meeting of demands of consumers for better foods, rather than simply an increase in calories consumed. It is a real deficit, however, in that if their demands are not met, the rate of economic growth assumed is not likely to be met.

The projected rates of growth seem likely to increase greatly the food deficits under the assumptions used with respect to rates of population and production growth. A part no doubt can be met by commercial imports.

Perhaps some further increase in food production in these countries would be possible, particularly if they give greater emphasis to agriculture and the technical assistance programs of developed countries are stepped up.

Besides, the extent of the deficits suggest a major role for food-aid programs in the future growth of the developing countries. Increased food-aid contributions by the developed countries will be needed to meet the increased demands associated with economic growth.

But one thing appears rather certain from postwar experience: Foreign economic growth will have a major influence on market potentials for United States agricultural products. Of course, United States exports also will be influenced by changes in demand for and production of agricultural products in importing countries, supplies made available for export by competing foreign countries, and the ability of the United States to supply agricultural products for export.

If the trends in postwar trade and development continue and real growth rates in income and imports achieved by the developed countries prevail for the next two decades, the total value of all United States exports would more than double. The value of agricultural exports would almost double.

American exports of all commodities to the less-developed countries would also double, but our agricultural exports to those countries may triple.

It appears likely that agricultural imports of the developed countries will account for a declining proportion of total imports. Most of the developed countries are experiencing rapid improvement in agricultural technology and production. Moreover, the proportion of income spent for food likely will drop as personal incomes rise.

But in the case of the less-developed countries, it is quite likely that imports of agricultural products will increase as rapidly as income. These countries are experiencing rapid growth of population and find it difficult to expand their agricultural production quickly.

ARTHUR B. MACKIE *joined the Development and Trade Analysis Division of the Economic Research Service as an international agricultural economist in charge of trade and development studies in 1961.*

KENNETH L. BACHMAN *became Director of the Development and Trade Analysis Division of the Economic Research Service in 1961. Previously he was assistant to the Deputy Administrator of the Agricultural Marketing Service; Assistant Director of Farm Economics Research Division; and Head of the Production, Income, and Costs Section of Farm Economics Research.*

Trading by Governments

by RICHARD H. ROBERTS

GOVERNMENTS do the foreign buying and selling of many farm products. They take ownership of exported or imported goods and so engage in state trading. The trading is not necessarily done by government agencies, but it must be for them. Sooner or later they furnish the money invested in the commodities.

The government need not itself perform the trading operations. It may use private firms as agents to do the buying or selling. In passing the goods through government accounts, the government can exercise full control as owner. It thereby can inject terms or conditions not applied by private business.

Nations take differing attitudes toward state trading, particularly in agricultural commodities. Much of their uncertainty comes from shifts to state trading in wartime, efforts to develop more trade with Communist countries, business and political pressures to gain more trading advantages, and attempts to minimize the costs of supporting the incomes of their own farmers.

The universal pressures to provide special advantages for farmers contribute to the tendency to have government agencies do their foreign marketing, whether purchases or sales.

Governments try to manipulate the terms of exports and imports to assist in bearing the costs. In this way, government actions beget more government in business. To handle exports and imports, governments give authority and funds to commodity boards and put them into the business of foreign trading.

Commodities that have a standard form and quality in international trade usually are the chief types traded by government agencies and dominate the types governments sell through export sales monopolies.

Wheat and butter are examples. When exporting countries use their government trading to maintain high standards, the reputation for quality aids in building and maintaining the market. The buyers of the standard commodities in the importing countries usually are private traders, who consider it an advantage to deal with government selling agencies that have a reputation for dependability as to standards of quality.

Importing follows a different course. Oil materials and tobacco exemplify the differences that may exist in standards of quality. They may be exported by private firms, but the import purchases may be carried out by government monopolies for several reasons. Tobacco in some countries is a direct source of government revenues, and government handling facilitates collections. Oilseeds and other sources of oils are handled through government largely to aid internal farm price supports or maintain stable supplies.

In most wool exports, countries let prices follow free market conditions to reflect its differences in form and standards of quality. The same countries traditionally use government agencies to export their standard commodities and only in war emergencies do they shift their exports of wool and the pricing suddenly and wholly to government sales operations.

State trading was a matter of concern in the drafting of the Havana Charter immediately after the Second World War to establish an international trade organization. The plan was not adopted, but the main expressions became article XVII of the General Agreement on Tariffs and Trade (GATT). Among its other rules for foreign trading is a requirement that state trading operations must be reported. Apparently it was assumed that foreign trade enterprises of governments are set up to exercise discriminatory treatment and secure special advantages. The provisions prescribed nondiscriminatory treatment and specified that purchases and sales be in accord with commercial considerations and give adequate opportunity for competition.

GOVERNMENTS answer differently the questions about their state trading.

The experts have not arrived at uniform interpretations, and variations in form, results, and effects on competitors are many.

Japan has been reporting to the GATT that licensing controls of operations actually performed by private importing companies consist of state trading. The United States has stated that export operations of the Commodity Credit Corporation did not come in the reporting category. Denmark has reported that no state trading prevailed in food and agricultural products. The Netherlands has reported it had none. Sweden has reported none except for tobacco and authority over sugar. The egg export and import association of Sweden has regulated the internal market, with variable levies on imports of feedstuffs to pay subsidies to producers, but the commodity marketing boards had lost their foreign trade monopoly positions in 1956.

The Organization for European Economic Cooperation attempted to separate trade from government enterprises, financial accounts, and other operations. Exporting countries are reluctant, however, to complain about such matters. Furthermore, the guilt of an offender could not be decided unless it was admitted because the member governments had to reach unanimous agreement on any decision.

Attempts to devise rules that monopolies must invite public tenders also were fruitless. The Organization for Economic Cooperation and Development, the successor, has turned attention more to the terms and conditions under which trading is permitted, whether private or state.

THE GROWTH of nontariff trade barriers has affected private trading, particularly imports into the European Economic Community. The new barriers have given the six Common Market countries increased problems in the relation between state and private trading, particularly in the farm products.

In drafting the 1957 Treaty of Rome to set up the Common Market, the countries adopted a requirement that state monopolies end discrimination on conditions of supply and the marketing of goods. Employment and the living standards of producers, however, were to be given equivalent weight in these decisions. A special provision permitted Italy to trade in wheat until July 1, 1963, when imports were put under control of the variable levy system plus an extra 20 dollars a ton on imported wheat of high quality.

In discussions of trading principles, people have mentioned particularly the expansion of trade with countries of the Soviet bloc. A big point has been Soviet enticements to developing countries to commit themselves to bilateral agreements. The aid that is offered has proved to be cheap credit and barter to the advantage of the Communists.

The discussions of nontariff barriers bring out, further, that "gentlemen's agreements" flourish with monopolies, semigovernmental agencies, and the special trading authorities. These informal understandings shut off trade in varying degrees among nations, particularly by excluding competitive forces and redirecting trade to less competitive suppliers.

The GATT, regional groups, and a

United Nations Trade and Development Conference have considered these problems and the trading needs of developing countries. A revision of principles and rules for state trading has become an issue. A desire to trade more with the Communist nations adds difficulties in reconciling with private market trading principles. In promoting growth in developing countries, conflicts with the goal of non-discriminatory trade also arise. Only when trade is based on relative efficiency in production and marketing can it take full advantage of consumers' free choices in price and quality.

A DESIRE to buy goods from special sources is typical of state trading.

Some noncommercial influences frequently are brought to bear when a government performs a commercial function. State trading may be used as the means of allocating short foreign exchange funds to buy imports. Political objectives therefore may be sought in the commercial operations. Negotiation of terms, rather than free and open bidding, furthers political aims without making it necessary for a government to disclose reasons or motives.

One example is the French Société Interprofessionelle des Oleagineaux Fluides Alimentaires. Exercising government powers, SIOFA has bought or authorized others to buy the country's entire imports of edible vegetable oils and oilseeds. French producers of oilseeds thereby have been protected against market competition of other countries. The agency has given preferential treatment to oilseed imports from areas that do their trading in French francs.

The agency has broad authority in its operating methods. It has furnished little information to anyone outside the agency about its procedures in buying and importing. It has been free to change its operations without prior notice, unhampered by any fear that details of its precedents are known outside.

In determining the amounts of oils and oilseeds to be imported and the countries from which to buy, the agency has given preferential treatment to peanuts from Africa over soybeans from the United States, although the soybeans yield a higher quality and amount of meal. Peanut oil has been given an artificial preference for about two-thirds of the total imports of oils and oilseeds. Otherwise, cottonseed and soybean oils could be substituted in most of the products.

To support the prices of most agricultural products, France has intervened directly in foreign trade. For cereals, sugar, dairy products, and vegetable oilseeds, state trading has been the rule. Some other products have been released from these operations, in amounts that vary according to the exporting country.

The French Government in 1960 merged various commodity funds and the mutual guarantee and production adjustment fund into Forma, which conducts extensive internal buying and storage operations, subsidizes exports, and controls imports. It is financed mainly by the government. Amounts needed to support the internal milk market and subsidize exports have increased over several years.

France has always been a high-priced market for meat, but new trading operations have enabled her to continue domestic prices at about double those in many other countries and to remove surpluses by exporting some meat to Spain and Portugal at prices as low as one-third the French internal prices.

METHODS of administering state trading embrace many techniques.

West Germany has required that importers of cereals, feed, sugar, milk, and livestock offer the commodities to its import offices. With the option of accepting or refusing the offers, the offices may arrange for sales on the home market and reserve the right of taking over the imports and retailing them.

In Austria, a government monopoly imports raw and manufactured tobacco, has sole authority to decide on purchases, and conducts its operations on a commercial basis without discrimination as to sources of supply. State trading in grains began in 1960, when some other European countries were releasing some of their imported farm products from state trading.

Ireland has made a government grain importers' group solely responsible for imports of wheat, barley, corn, and flour. The group has resold to distributors and millers at prices fixed to maintain a balance between home production and imports. Stable and uniform prices have been maintained to help livestock farmers and provide authorized profit margins for millers. Any losses have been covered by the government. The state monopolies also have been handling butter, sugar, potatoes, oils, and oilseeds.

The Federal Wheat Administration in Switzerland has operated within the Department of Finance and Customs. Centralized imports have been considered essential to control prices of bread and protect the milling industry. The legal basis was included in an addition to the Federal Constitution and was adopted by popular vote in 1952. For feedstuffs and grains, a cooperative company of firms engaged in international trade formed a syndicate and was given a legal import monopoly. The company has controlled prices and quantities of imports to prevent gluts in the market and avoid the overproduction of milk, dairy products, meat, and animal fats. A butter supply center has held a monopoly of butter imports as a government controlled cooperative of firms and organizations in the wholesale trade. The center, rather than its members, has bought butter from foreign suppliers for retail distribution. Fats and seed potatoes also have been state traded.

Finland has a state monopoly of food grains, but a pooling of imports of sugar, corn, bran, oilseed meal, and vegetable oils is voluntary. Coopera-

tives have engaged in processing and marketing, and importers have been shareholders; thus the benefits of bulk purchases have been achieved.

Poland has reported that 34 foreign trade enterprises operate within a system of state monopoly and that state trading has been the only foreign trade operation because state monopoly in foreign trade has always been a basic feature of the socialized economy, as in the Soviet bloc generally. Polcoop and Rolimpex were listed as exporters and importers of fertilizers, foodstuffs, and other agricultural products.

Yugoslavia has also followed a similar Communist pattern.

JAPAN HAS distinguished between food control and government monopoly as separate categories. Rice, barley, and wheat have been covered under food control to assure adequate supplies at reasonable prices and to effect stability of the national economy. A food management law of 1942 provided the authority to control prices and marketing of the three items. The food agency has issued permits to private traders, who are required to sell imports to it. No long-term contracts have been concluded, but overall bilateral agreements (as with Australia) have sometimes been used.

The Japan Monopoly Corporation has handled tobacco to obtain revenue and salt to secure a stable supply. Its operations have included monopoly of imports, production, manufacture, and any exports of manufactured tobacco. Salt has not been exported because of comparatively high costs.

Canada has reported that its Wheat Board monopoly of wheat, oats, and barley is its only state trading enterprise. It has covered only designated western areas where the exportable surpluses are produced. The Board has not owned or operated facilities of any kind for storage and handling, but has directed the movement in domestic and export markets through the private trade.

Sales to mainland China and to the

Soviet Union in 1963 by the Canadian and Australian Wheat Boards have taken most of their surpluses. The credit terms given the Chinese and other Communist importers have not been offered to traditional non-Communist customers. This distinction between customers is quite the reverse of United States terms under Public Law 480 as between types of governments. Sales of wheat by Canada in 1963 carried Canadian commitments to take substantial quantities of Chinese goods, especially cotton textiles, in lieu of payments entirely in dollar exchange.

The Commodity Credit Corporation, carrying out United States operations as part of the Department of Agriculture, has protected itself with United States or foreign bank guarantees, which resulted in extra costs to the borrower. On the other hand, the Canadian Wheat Board's higher interest charges were offset largely by the Canadian Government's furnishing the guarantee to the effect that the Board would be paid by the foreign buyer.

Although the Commodity Credit Corporation charged interest rates as high as those the United States Treasury paid in borrowing from private banks, the higher interest rates in Canada tended to be offset by the Canadian Government's assumption of credit risk, a function kept in the private sphere by the United States.

Nearly all of Canada's other exports and imports have been privately traded, but the government offered considerable assistance to the traders.

MANY OF THE developing countries in Africa have given monopoly power over imports or exports of individual commodities to cooperatives, marketing boards, or other agents of the state.

In some, this has facilitated continuation of trade relationships with former mother countries and receipt of aid from them. In others, the establishment of new state monopolies has been part of the step to break away to bilateral relationships with other countries that offer aid, such as Russia.

The Republic of South Africa has continued operations in effect when the Union was a part of the British Commonwealth. A number of commodity boards control trade, especially in support of farmers' cooperatives. Wool has continued to be freely marketed through private auctions, but a government board has bought wool to support prices. Other commodities depend on the country's import or export position. Each board has conducted or controlled the trade in the interest of the producers and the internal economy. The imports have been directed to countries giving the most favorable terms, including returns from barter and export sales.

Australia and New Zealand have offered their butter, cheese, and dried milk at different prices in importing countries. Most of their dairy products have moved to the United Kingdom. The United Kingdom imposed quotas to keep out subsidized sales from nearby countries that became exporters in 1960 or later. Since then, the Commonwealth exporters have enjoyed special protection in the large United Kingdom market. The small quantities they have marketed at higher prices in small importing markets have resulted in problems of consultation, when United States firms obtained limited exportable supplies from Commodity Credit Corporation and offered them at foreign market price levels.

The United Kingdom shifted out of wartime state trading and has kept most of its markets open to competitively priced, unsubsidized imports from all sources. Direct subsidies were paid farmers, and goods were bought from Communist countries. Preferential tariff rates for some commodities have favored Commonwealth countries. Pressures from these countries against subsidized butter from other countries that were not previously exporters of butter led to the quota restrictions in favor of the Commonwealth shippers. Old ties have led to understandings that have achieved advantages of state trading without most of its troubles—at least, competitors have received that impression from the demand among large Commonwealth companies for Rhodesian tobacco.

The ties with large United Kingdom grain importers, flour millers, and cooperatives have facilitated bulk forward sales at fixed prices by state trading monopolies of exporting countries. When the Canadian Wheat Board completed its 1963 bulk sales to Russia at a fixed forward price below levels prevailing earlier in the year, market levels again started rising. The Board offered the Japanese importing monopoly a year's supply at the cheaper price. The small number of large firms in the United Kingdom was able to obtain a similar year's commitment with private bank credit and coordinated contracting based on informal understandings.

Argentina's I.A.P.I. was a well-known state trading agency under the Perón regime. Its announced objectives were to obtain the most advantageous possible terms on the country's imports and exports. After the Second World War, its high prices for exports of flaxseed to the United States led American officials to fix a high price-support level and set high production goals to reduce dependence on imports. The United States has since been a substantial exporter of flaxseed. After many years of selling agricultural commodities and food products and importing many supplies and manufactured goods, the agency was abolished when the administration changed. Trade shifted largely to private firms, and rigid controls of foreign exchange were relaxed.

Brazil's imports of wheat are conducted by the government. Thus the way was open for various purchases from the United States and also for bilateral agreements with the Soviet Union to obtain wheat, chiefly for coffee. Up to 500 thousand tons of wheat a year have been obtained from the Soviet Union. In earlier years, Brazil had signed 3-year commitments with Argentina for 1 million tons annually and with Uruguay for 300 thousand tons. The exportable supplies of these two countries fell off, however, and Brazil was not able to fill the quantities held open in Public Law 480 agreements with the United States. Brazil obtained large quantities for cruzeiros under Public Law 480 and filled United States usual marketing requirements largely by barter of manganese for deposit into Commodity Credit Corporation's supplemental stockpile.

Government agencies in Mexico deal in agricultural imports, but private trading is done in nonagricultural imports and in nearly all exports.

India has had differences over her domestic and international state trading. Problems of supplies and prices of food, especially rice and wheat, led to strong pressures to have the state take over internal supplies. Private dealers have continued to operate internally and to trade without price fixing but with the benefit of other controls. Transportation across the 14 state lines has been restricted. The national food ministry has made large purchases in the United States and has made delivery to the regional food directors in India. The imports have moved to consumers and millers without differentials in transportation rates in the regions. The lower priced imports have held down the market prices of domestic supplies. Whenever prices have sagged too much, importations have been reduced, and state agencies have started purchases to support domestic prices.

To trade with Soviet countries, India set up the separate State Trading Corporation. Soviet aid thus could be had while the flow of individual items of import and export were controlled.

In Burma, operations of the State Agricultural Marketing Board in the early fifties brought about problems in connection with exports of rice. The board held large quantities for better prices, but storage was inadequate and deterioration was extensive. Barter agreements were negotiated with Communist countries, but several were unsatisfactory and were allowed to expire ahead of schedule. The Soviet Union resold part of the rice to India, which normally is a Burmese market. The rice was unsatisfactory when it was received, and a drop in prices added to the difficulties. Some of the bartered items were unusable. The Burmese refused to accept Soviet textiles equal to 10 million dollars.

Indonesia does heavy state trading but contrasts with methods of other "socialist" nations. Its export commodities—tea, coffee, copra, rubber, and tin—are traded freely in the markets throughout the world. As a result, Indonesia would lose good profits when demand is strong if her commodity exports were tied up in bilateral contracts. Furthermore, in a weak market period, Sino-Soviet trade would not be offered as a temporary opportunity. Thus the maintenance of openings in world markets for the best prices has kept her from entering long-term governmental agreements.

EXPORTERS, officials, and others encounter a thorny question when they talk about shifting from private to state trading: How can one do business with state trading countries without being outtraded?

When private firms compete among themselves, the national monopolies they do business with apparently have some advantages.

A national monopoly that represents all the producers of a country can shade the price or other terms without risk of financial insolubility. Private firms that trade internationally, however, may handle the monopoly's commodities plus goods from market-economy nations. The firms compete for supplies and outlets. The producers in the nongovernment trading nations have to depend on what the market will bid, plus any subsidies they obtain. Quality competition among export-ing countries has provided a particular problem. The state trading monopoly can offer top quality consistently, but private firms may barely meet certain government grades and standards. The state monopoly may even raise the qualities delivered; the competing trade firms may mix in some parts from lower grades to reduce their costs. In making a mixture of grades, they may barely keep the delivered lots above minimum standards.

In the development of Public Law 480, the question was often raised: What would the private trade contribute? Why would it not be more efficient to use state trading for all surplus disposals?

The legislative decision was to require the use of private trade channels to the maximum extent practicable.

The competition of private owners brings greater efficiencies, especially over the long run. The flexibilities in marketing forced by the new investor insure against perpetuation of outmoded techniques. Duplication of domestic private channels or setting up parallel services was avoided. Also, the freezing of services within commission fees and government assumption of all risks were prevented in adopting full use of the private trade.

THE COMMODITY CREDIT CORPORATION, a part of the United States Department of Agriculture, has virtually full state trading authority, but it does not claim exclusive monopoly power.

The United States Government generally avoids using the authority fully under most circumstances. The authorizations for sales passed by the Board of Directors require everything to move through private firms, and any government-to-government transactions have to be considered separately as specific proposals to the Board. Few of these proposals are presented, and they are mostly for special low prices for cash dollar sales restricted to particular uses, such as lunches for schoolchildren.

The private firms are not generally employed merely as agents. They usually have full breadth of operation in pricing and other terms and conditions of sale, considerably beyond the margin of fixed fees or commissions for mere contracted services. The firms can take a profit or loss for themselves. They are expected to exercise full ownership and responsibility as traders, and their latitude of trading is much wider than under state trading conditions.

They have to take broad financial risks on making final deliveries under their contracts. Government decisions change many trading conditions. Sales of wheat by private firms to Russia and European-bloc countries have been affected by requirements to use American vessels and set high export payment rates by accepting offers on durum wheat, which was in exceptional oversupply.

MANY other concessional terms are available under separate United States authorities. Most of these have some aspects of state trading but not wholly and are not considered a basis for reporting under this heading to the GATT. Most of them are surplus disposals and are reported to the GATT fully under that heading, as well as to FAO, notably the Consultative Subcommittee on Surplus Disposal, which has been meeting in Washington monthly since early 1954.

The concessional terms furnished by Government authority make it necessary to have government-to-government consultations with other exporting countries. The other countries insist on these consultations, fearing that the United States may use its financial power to offer terms which might take their markets. They are anxious to be able to report to their own people that they have had a look in advance at the special terms and that the United States is not doing anything unfair.

The United States is committed in the GATT, like other member countries, not to take an unfair share of the export market. However, the United States has never insisted on prior consultations from others in all of their state trading transactions, export subsidies, or bilateral barters. The United States could meet others' terms once they were known to have been used, at least unless its opposition in principle against going the whole way to state trading should interfere in a particular case with its desire to be fully competitive.

The United States has used grants, donations, barters, sales for foreign currencies, foreign aid financing, credit sales, reduced prices, and other special terms to move surplus products. The only government-to-government transactions have been commodity grants, a few instances of special pricing for special uses, and some sugar exchanges over a short period.

Negotiation of terms on a government-to-government basis has been an essential characteristic of the large volumes moved under foreign currency sales, some of the barters, and the longer term dollar credit sales. The individual sales under these programs, however, have been made within publicly announced terms by private owners to foreign purchasers. The buyers have often been state trading import agencies, but the United States sellers have been private firms.

The private trade agreements under title IV of Public Law 480 will raise new questions in the area of state trading as they do in the areas of consultations between governments over terms and conditions.

The Consultative Subcommittee on Surplus Disposal of the Food and Agriculture Organization is more concerned over terms of trade between countries than mechanics through which terms are reached, except for one point: If concessional terms are substantial, consultations are essential with exporting countries.

The subcommittee is moving its chief attention from the changing attitudes toward surplus disposals into the gray area of transactions where there is difficulty in distinguishing between true commercial terms and concessional terms. At the urging of the United States, the analyses of actual cases of commodity transactions are not confined to surplus disposals. Instead, the case studies include other concessional terms given through such techniques as bilateral agreements and state trading.

A heightened interest in trade questions is stemming from the use of subsidies and state trading enterprises.

The growing issue of trade between market economy and state trading countries is considered one of the major unresolved problems in the international trade field. This issue is sharpened by the efforts to rationalize markets for agricultural products with new proposals for market sharing through international commodity arrangements.

THE GREATER FACILITY of state trading mechanisms to accommodate with changing situations heightens their attraction to many who are faced with new conflicts. The contrast of expanding supplies from the wealthier countries and less per capita in the developing countries emphasizes the market sharing problem. As a result, there is an increasing need for extensive international negotiation on these mechanics and terms of trade. This may bring a basic revision of GATT article XVII, which deals with state trading enterprises.

RICHARD H. ROBERTS *joined the Department of Agriculture in 1937. He supervised several livestock and wool programs and import and export programs of the Foreign Agricultural Service. A native of Iowa and the holder of three degrees from the State University of Iowa, he held a research fellowship in the Brookings Institution before he joined the former Agricultural Adjustment Administration in 1937. He was appointed Deputy Assistant Administrator for Export Programs, Foreign Agricultural Service, in 1954.*

East-West Agricultural Trade

by THEODORA MILLS

FOREIGN TRADE is a government monopoly in the Communist countries.

It is programed by government economic plans and usually is fitted into bilateral agreements negotiated or renegotiated annually.

The currencies of the Eastern countries are not convertible, not even with one another, so that trade between pairs of countries must balance. Imbalances must be settled in some convertible currency or gold or through the extension of credit.

The inconvertibility of bloc currencies also puts a premium on desired Western industrial goods and raw materials, like natural rubber, not to be found in the bloc, since these must be paid for in hard currencies—dollars, pounds, sterling, or others.

The prices at which international trade takes place are negotiated by the trade organizations of the bloc governments from the base point of average free world prices. The resulting prices remain separated from other government-fixed prices in all of the Eastern countries.

Thus the regulatory effect that foreign competition in trade may have on demand and supply in the Eastern countries is bypassed, and the problem of determining levels of productivity is made difficult.

A political motive always is present in state trading. This does not mean that political justification always or necessarily precludes economic justification. The program of bloc aid to developing countries, for example, is largely motivated by political considerations, but the program includes economic advantages to the bloc as well.

EAST AND WEST are geographic terms that I use here in their political sense.

East includes the two Communist giants, the Soviet Union and mainland China, and their respective satellites, Mongolia, Poland, East ˙Germany, Hungary, Czechoslovakia, Rumania, and Bulgaria for the Soviet Union, and Albania, North Korea, and North Vietnam for China.

Cuba should be included in the East, but as Cuba joined the East at the end of the period (1955–1962) for which data on agricultural trade were available for analysis, I leave Cuban trade in the free world category and merely footnote data for 1961 and 1962.

Yugoslavia, an independent Communist country, and all other countries are placed in the West.

The East-West subdivision of the world leaves on each side of the dividing line industrially developed countries and developing countries and mixtures of small and giant countries.

Because of the peculiarities that size and degree of development can exert on the foreign trade of countries, the trade of the developed and developing countries has been tabulated separately in order to show these effects, although it was not possible to do so for the seven East European-bloc countries, which include industrial East Germany and Czechoslovakia with such developing countries as Bulgaria, Rumania, and Albania.

Data for the Soviet Union and mainland China can be obtained separately. Agricultural trade data for certain industrial Western countries were compiled separately for 1959, 1960, 1961, and 1962.

These countries included the six of the European Economic Community (EEC or Common Market), the seven of the European Free Trade Association (EFTA), and Canada, Australia, Japan, and the United States. All these countries together have been designated as the industrial West. The remaining countries that trade with the Sino-Soviet bloc have been called developing countries.

Agricultural commodities for analytical purposes have been grouped into foods and feeds and inedible commodities, such as fibers, tobacco, and other things.

The foods have been subdivided into grain and six general categories: Fats, oils, and oilseeds, including butter and margarine; livestock and the livestock products for food; fruit and vegetables; sugar and its preparations; coffee; and all other food and feed. Soybeans have been listed separately among the free world imports because of the unique position they occupy in the trade with mainland China. Synthetic rubber, probably in very small amounts, has been mixed in with the natural rubber exported by the free world to the bloc, and no effort was made to exclude tobacco manufactures from raw tobacco. These unavoidable complications may have led to a somewhat too generous definition of agricultural trade.

East-West agricultural trade has been summarized in value terms because the commodity breakdown included only a few items for which volume figures might have been obtained. The values have been taken from the official trade data of the various free world countries and have been converted to dollars at the official exchange rates.

AGRICULTURAL COMMODITY EXPORTS during the 8 years 1955–1962 averaged 1.5 billion dollars a year, or 40.2 percent of total free world exports to the Sino-Soviet bloc. Agricultural imports from the Sino-Soviet bloc averaged 1 billion dollars annually, or 28.4 percent of total free world imports from the bloc.

Many deviations from these average

proportions of agricultural to total trade appear when agricultural trade is broken down into commodity groups and the countries of East and West are broken down into smaller groups.

The free world agricultural exports to the Sino-Soviet bloc over the years 1955–1962 were composed on the average of 17.7 percent cotton, 15.6 percent rubber, 13.6 percent grains, and 12 percent wool.

Sugar and its products and the category "other" inedibles came next in value with the three categories, fats, oils and oilseeds, other food and feed, and fruit and vegetables, each close to 5 percent. Livestock and livestock products for food and tobacco and its products were less than 4 percent.

Agricultural exports showed an increase of 78 percent from 1955 to 1960 and 123 percent from 1955 to 1962, but only 88 percent if Cuban sugar is omitted from the 1962 trade.

The commodity composition of the free world exports to the three major subdivisions of the Sino-Soviet bloc reflected the different requirements of these areas. Raw rubber accounted for 24 percent on the average of free world agricultural exports to the Soviet Union. Sugar and cotton were each in excess of 15 percent, and wool, 10 percent. All other commodity groups were around or under 5 percent. The developing countries have been the principal sources of supply of these commodities partly because some of them have special growing requirements.

EXPORTS OF GRAIN to the Soviet Union have fluctuated with the size of the Soviet crop but, until 1963, they were small.

The maximum export of wheat and wheat flour in any year was in 1956, and it came to only 24 million dollars, a trifle as compared to the Canadian sale in September of 1963, which amounted to about 500 million dollars.

Exports of fats, oils, and oilseeds to the Soviet Union have fluctuated, with a drop in 1962. An unusually large increase in 1961 probably was an attempt to obtain from the free world substitutes for the soybeans and similar commodities that were virtually unobtainable in 1961 from mainland China. The Soviet Union obtained no oilseeds from mainland China in 1962, but apparently did not seek supplies in unusual quantities from the free world.

A great increase in sugar exports during 1960–1962 illustrated an economic response to a political situation. Cuban sugar exports to the Soviet Union rose tremendously in 1960, nearly tripled the next year, reaching a peak of 293.7 million dollars, and fell off to 186.0 million dollars in 1962 with a decline in Cuban sugar production. These increases were so great that they distorted the pattern of agricultural exports to the Soviet Union.

Total agricultural exports of the free world (including Cuba) rose from 226 million dollars in 1955 to 457 million in 1958, and then hit 813 million dollars in 1961 and 725 million dollars in 1962.

An upward trend in fruit and vegetables and coffee over the years suggests (unless the rise was due solely to a rise in prices) that the Soviet Union has considered it desirable to purchase increasing amounts of these commodities, most of which come from developing countries.

Free world exports of rubber, cotton, and tobacco, although small in 1955, increased sharply in 1956 and 1957. Rubber exports continued to rise until 1962. Tobacco exports rose steeply in 1962, most likely reflecting temporary difficulties with supplies from bloc countries.

Exports of livestock and products for food were the only commodities showing a definite decline, which began in 1958, but was sharply reversed in 1962, when a record 32.0 million dollars' worth were exported.

The commodity composition of free world exports to the countries of Eastern Europe was not strongly dominated by any one commodity, although on the average cotton accounted for 19.2 percent of these exports and the next largest groups, grain and wool, accounted for 14 and 13 percent, respectively.

Miscellaneous other inedible products averaged nearly 12 percent of agricultural exports.

Proportionately, coffee, sugar, and rice were the smallest categories. Rubber averaged 6.4 percent of agricultural exports. The relative uniformity of the commodity pattern, the modest proportion of subtropical crops, and particularly the nearness of the industrial countries of the West explained why as much as 40 percent of the agricultural commodities came from those countries, even though the developing countries accounted for the remaining larger share.

FLUCTUATIONS IN THE trade pattern during the course of the 8 years were less pronounced for agricultural exports to the European-bloc countries than for trade with other bloc areas. The maximum increase in all agricultural exports to Eastern Europe took place between 1955 and 1962 and amounted to 48.5 percent, while exports of all commodities doubled.

Despite the increase in Cuban exports of sugar in 1961 and 1962, the value of all agricultural exports was not significantly affected. Fluctuations in the value of other commodity groups outweighed the increase in sugar. Wheat exports ranged from a mere 20 million dollars in 1958 to more than 88 million dollars in 1960. The value of cotton exports doubled between 1955 and 1960 and then declined. Livestock products and other foods and feeds fluctuated considerably, rising to peaks in 1962.

Agricultural exports from the free world to mainland China amounted to 36 percent of the value of total exports before 1961. In 1961 and 1962, they accounted for 76 percent of total exports, largely because of the Chinese need for grain.

Exports of grain, principally wheat, to China in 1961 and 1962 were just over 300 million dollars each year, or more than total agricultural exports in previous years.

There also were phenomenally large exports of sugar from Cuba, 91 million dollars' worth in 1961 and 82.6 million in 1962.

The average commodity distribution for the 8 years reflected the change in the trade pattern in 1961 and 1962. Because of the large exports of grains, primarily wheat, in these later years, grains accounted for 28.4 percent of the total value of agricultural exports to China. Rubber exports, which declined after the peak year of 1959, accounted for 23.3 percent of agricultural exports. The commodities following in importance—cotton, 17 percent, and wool, 14 percent—also showed increases followed by declines in 1961 and 1962. Cuban sugar exports, however, rose phenomenally in 1961 and dropped slightly in 1962, bringing the average value to 11 percent of total agricultural exports.

The developing countries were the larger suppliers of agricultural exports to China until 1961, when grain from the industrial countries dominated. This trade pattern has continued and may well continue.

The free world agricultural imports from the Sino-Soviet bloc during 1955–1962 averaged 24.6 percent livestock and livestock products for food and 21.8 percent grain. Fats, oils, and oilseeds totaled 10.4 percent; soybeans alone averaged 3.8 percent. Fruit and vegetables followed closely.

Tobacco and its manufactures, the least valuable import, accounted for 1.3 percent of the average. Total agricultural imports increased 59 percent from 1955 to 1962, and slightly more from 1955 to 1960. The rate of increase of agricultural imports was much less than for exports. The same was true for total imports as compared with total exports, although both total imports and total exports increased more rapidly than agricultural imports and exports.

REGIONAL PECULIARITIES stood out when free world agricultural imports from the Soviet Union were considered separately. Grain dominated; 47.8 percent of the agricultural imports was grain. Wheat accounted for just over one-third of the average value of all agricultural imports. Cotton accounted for 18 percent; other food and feed for 13 percent; and sugar and its preparations for 9 percent of average agricultural imports from the Soviet Union.

The industrial countries of the West during 1959–1962 obtained 67 percent of the agricultural imports from the Soviet Union. The developing countries took the rest. Furthermore, the total imports of the industrial countries from the Soviet Union included a larger share of agricultural commodities than did the imports into developing countries.

These facts suggest that the Soviet Union attached even greater importance to its Western industrial markets than it did to its markets in developing countries.

Fluctuations from year to year in the size of the West's agricultural imports from the Soviet Union were particularly pronounced for grain. They reflected the size and availability of grain crops in the Soviet Union and the demand for grain in the Western countries.

Western imports of grain from the Soviet Union were valued at only 50 million dollars in 1955 but reached 100 million dollars and more in other years, averaging 110 million dollars for the 8 years. In terms of value, 1961 was the record year for grain; 1959 was the record year for wheat alone.

Free world imports of cotton declined steadily until 1958, rose sharply in 1959 and 1960, and then dropped, chiefly because the Common Market countries imported less. The earlier downturn was a result of a prolonged drop in imports by the United Kingdom. It was followed by a sharp rise in 1959.

Total agricultural imports from the Soviet Union nearly doubled in value from 1955 to 1960 and remained about the same in 1961 and 1962, when total imports of all kinds continued their more rapid increase.

The commodity composition of free world imports from the European-bloc countries was quite different from the bloc as a whole and from the Soviet Union, reflecting as it did the more intensive as well as diversified agriculture of Poland, Hungary, and Bulgaria.

Livestock and products for food accounted on the average for 43 percent of the agricultural imports from Eastern Europe.

Despite this concentration of imports, a number of other commodity groups reached sizable proportions of the total. Grain, chiefly coarse grain (barley, oats, corn, and millet), sugar, and fruit and vegetables each totaled more than 10 percent of the total value. Textile fibers were small-scale imports. Tobacco and its manufactures accounted for 2 percent, but showed a steady if slow rise with a spurt in 1962 despite the difficulties experienced with blue mold in the crop in 1960 and 1961.

Fluctuations in the size of agricultural imports from Eastern Europe during the 8 years have not been noticeable, with the exception of the erratic behavior of sugar and coarse grain.

Free world imports of sugar declined through 1957, then shot up to a high level for 3 years, and spurted again in 1961 and 1962. The strong demand for feed grain in Western European markets in 1960–1962 invited the sharp rise in free world imports of them, despite the probability that the bloc as a whole, and even the actual exporting countries, could have fed the grain to their own livestock more economically.

Industrial Western countries, most of them Eastern Europe's neighbors, imported more than 80 percent of all the agricultural commodities imported by the free world from Eastern Europe.

The United States has also imported

annually about 30 million dollars' worth of agricultural commodities, mainly from Poland. To Poland we export much larger amounts of grain under the Public Law 480 program.

Total agricultural imports of the free world countries from Eastern Europe more than doubled in value from 1955 to 1962. Total imports, agricultural and nonagricultural, did not double in value during these years.

FREE WORLD IMPORTS from mainland China were composed largely of agricultural commodities, especially in 1955. The proportion dropped when China's agricultural difficulties began. The trade decline started with rice in 1960, but the real drop in agricultural trade did not come until 1961, and it was nowhere near as severe as the drop in Sino-Soviet trade that began in 1960. A slight increase in agricultural imports from mainland China was noticeable in 1962.

The commodity composition of agricultural imports from mainland China showed uniformity. Livestock and products for food topped the list with 17.6 percent. All kinds of grains came next, with 15.5 percent, mostly rice. Fruit and vegetables were 13 percent. Soybeans accounted for 10.9 percent of the average value of agricultural imports, and other fats, oils, and oilseeds, for 9.2 percent.

The miscellaneous category in the inedible products averaged nearly 14 percent. Textiles other than cotton (mainly silk) and the category of other food and feed were each nearly 9 percent of the total.

The drop in imports from mainland China in 1961 and 1962 reduced the value of imports of all food and feed from a little more than 300 million dollars, a level maintained for 4 out of the preceding 6 years, to 170 to 200 million dollars. The much less important inedible agricultural commodities fell modestly. Imports of silk actually increased in value in 1961.

THE DETAILS of free world exports and imports can be summarized by balancing the values of one against the other.

Free world exports of agricultural commodities to the Soviet Union exceeded the value of such imports by an annual average of 260 million dollars. Exports were greater than imports for every commodity category except grain, the major export crop of the Soviet Union.

In some instances, such as rubber and coffee, there were only free world exports. In others, such as cotton, wool, sugar, tobacco, fats and oils, and livestock products, the trade went both ways.

Actually, the free world began as a net importer of Soviet cotton in 1955 and 1956 before becoming a net cotton exporter to the Soviet Union. The Soviet demand for Egyptian cotton, coupled with the Egyptian need to maintain exports to the Soviet Union to pay for Soviet loans, may explain much of this shift in the cotton trade of the Soviet Union.

The large accumulation of total agricultural export excesses over imports came mainly during 1960–1962 and will diminish with the transferal of Cuba to the bloc, since this will switch the sugar trade from exports to imports.

The poor Soviet grain harvest in 1963, resulting in huge Western exports of wheat to the Soviet Union, meant net agricultural exports in 1963 and 1964 despite the inclusion of Cuba in the bloc.

FREE WORLD agricultural exports to the countries of Eastern Europe have exceeded imports by large amounts every year. The maximum excess of exports over imports was 360 million dollars in 1957. The minimum of 177 million dollars was in 1962.

The free world was a net exporter to Eastern Europe of most agricultural commodities except livestock and livestock products for food and other commodities in certain years. The inedible commodities, especially cotton, were the largest agricultural net exports to

Eastern Europe, and the balance for grain was obtained from large export surpluses of wheat and rice, because the free world was a net importer of coarse grain from Eastern Europe.

The free world exports of fats, oils, and oilseeds were not far in excess of the amounts of these commodities imported from Eastern Europe. The West was a net importer every year of Eastern European livestock and products for food and at an increasing rate until 1962. Also, in the later years of the period, the free world was a net importer of fruit and vegetables, a trend that Bulgaria has fostered.

The free world was a net importer of all foods and feeds from mainland China from 1955 through 1960, and a net exporter of rubber and fibers, except silk. For agricultural commodities as a whole, the free world has been an annual net importer for never less than 145 million dollars from 1955 through 1960. The free world was a large net exporter of agricultural commodities to mainland China in 1961 and 1962.

The switch in 1961–1962 to an agricultural net export position was due not only to the tremendous exports of grain by a few Western countries but also to the sharp decline in imports of foods and feeds from China.

THE ANALYSIS so far has concentrated on commodity breakdowns and the subdivisions of the Sino-Soviet bloc, rather than the peculiarities of agricultural trade between the bloc and the major Western countries. Tabulations of agricultural trade between the Sino-Soviet bloc and the industrial countries have been distorted from the mean by including the atypical years 1961 and 1962.

This distortion is important with respect to the peculiar situation in the sugar trade, but the deviation in Chinese trade with the West may continue for a few years, thus describing a trade trend, not a trade freak.

The Common Market countries have been net agricultural importers from the Sino-Soviet bloc by amounts fluctuating around 300 million dollars.

Net imports from the Soviet Union averaged annually a little less than 80 million dollars; that is less than from either the European- or Asian-bloc countries, with the exception of the Asian bloc in 1961 and 1962.

Net imports from the Asian bloc fell in 1961 to 25 million dollars, a quarter of their former level, and virtually disappeared in 1962.

COUNTRIES OF THE European Free Trade Association also were net agricultural importers from the Sino-Soviet bloc by amounts averaging 250 million dollars. Net imports increased each year from the Soviet Union and especially from the European bloc until 1962 when there was a decline. Net imports from the Asian bloc rose in 1960 and were half this amount in 1961–1962.

Canada and Australia already were net exporters of agricultural commodities to the Sino-Soviet bloc in 1959 and 1960 before agricultural difficulties in China required tremendous grain purchases from these Western countries. The range of agricultural commodities they exported to the Sino-Soviet bloc was limited and concentrated mainly on grain and wool.

Japan, despite—or maybe because of—its nearness to the Sino-Soviet bloc, has traded little with it for many years, although the size of this trade rose sharply in later years.

Japan has exported few agricultural items to the bloc and has imported cotton, grain, legumes, feedstuffs, oilseeds, and other commodities. Agricultural imports from the Soviet Union increased tremendously in 1960 and fell off in 1961 and again in 1962, but the rise in imports from Eastern Europe continued through 1961. Imports from China remained quite stable until 1962 when they doubled, reaching 30 million dollars.

UNITED STATES AGRICULTURAL exports to the East have been less than 100 million dollars in a peak year. Imports have been much smaller.

Exports to the Asian bloc have been embargoed, and imports licensed by the United States since about 1950 and exports to the Soviet Union and Eastern Europe have been controlled by license requirements since mid-1954.

A less restrictive policy has been pursued with respect to Poland since 1957, when Public Law 480 agreements were initiated. It is not surprising, therefore, to find that United States agricultural trade with Poland accounted for 87 percent of agricultural exports to the Sino-Soviet bloc in the 4 years 1959–1962 and 77 percent of agricultural imports from the bloc.

Our agricultural exports to the bloc have averaged 98 million dollars. They were low in 1959 and high in 1960, but close to the average in 1961 and 1962. Imports from the bloc have remained close to the average of 39 million dollars each year.

Grain largely dominated United States exports in 1960, accounting for 74 percent of the total agricultural exports to the Sino-Soviet bloc, but it accounted for less than 50 percent in the other years. The proportion of grain in 1961 was less than 40 percent, because exports to the Soviet Union, which did not include grain, were unusually large. Virtually all of the grain exports have gone to Poland under Public Law 480.

Exports of cotton, the next largest item, averaged about 17 million dollars but varied in its proportion to the total. The cotton was sent to Poland. An important category, especially in 1961, was the other inedibles, chiefly hides, inedible crude soybean oil, and tallow. Tallow, exported principally to the Soviet Union, was the largest of these in 1961 and 1962.

The major import from the bloc has been canned meat, which comes almost entirely from Poland. Other commodities, largely limited to inedibles, have included hides and skins, bristles, feathers, and a relatively large amount of cashmere from Outer Mongolia.

Countries of the West, even those that are agriculturally self-sufficient, tend to concentrate their exports on commodities in which they are relatively more efficient producers and import goods in which they are relatively less efficient producers. Their trade is multilateral as contrasted with bilateral. This means that trade between any two Western countries is not restricted to an even balance between exports and imports. Trading this way is facilitated by currency convertibility.

THE BLOC countries do not trade in this way. For them, foreign trade is a government monopoly and is responsive, therefore, to political policy. Their trade is on a bilateral, rather than a multilateral, basis. Their currencies are not convertible. The ability to maneuver politically thus is put before economic efficiency.

Agricultural trade in the East, which has not increased as much as nonagricultural trade, has been hampered by the low priority given to the agricultural sector of the economy by the state. The government plans for agricultural production usually have been grandiose, but these plans often have not been met.

Furthermore, efforts of agricultural producers to meet these plans have been hampered by weather and the various difficulties and inertia that accompany collectivized agriculture. As a result, agricultural foreign trade often has included exports that could ill be spared and imports that were long postponed.

The future course, like the past practice, of East-West agricultural trade will depend not only upon economic, but also upon political, factors and factors of weather.

THEODORA MILLS *became an analyst in the East European Branch of the Regional Analysis Division in 1961. Previously she was in a similar position in the Department of State. She served 2 years with our Embassy in Moscow during 1949–1950. She is a graduate of the University of Chicago.*

Cooperatives

in World Trade

by JOHN H. HECKMAN

AGRICULTURAL COOPERATIVES are relative newcomers in domestic and world trade, but they are important and their influence is growing.

Some local associations were organized more than 100 years ago. They joined the regional cooperatives, and their services expanded during the economic advances since the thirties.

Their greatest participation in foreign and domestic trade is in Europe and North America. They bulk large in the trade of the Orient and Latin America, and they have taken hold in Africa.

The pioneers of Rochdale in England are credited with sparking the successful consumer movement in the 1840's, but local farmer cooperatives were forming in many countries wholly independent of the pioneers.

One group may have had motives different from those of another group, but all had a common motive—to improve the farmer's economic position. Activities varied, but they were chiefly those of obtaining supplies to better advantage, assembling or processing for better marketing, or improving practices. The general aim was to obtain goods and services at cost.

That motive prevailed in most countries. The beginnings, too, were with local groups, who succeeded or failed according to their own initiative and ability. As rural people are tradition-

ally conservative, so, in general, have been their cooperatives.

Farmers in New England sought a market for dairy products. Several cooperatives were organized before 1860 for selling butter and cheese. Soon the number was more than 400. They began to purchase farm production supplies later.

Farmers in the Middle West organized cooperative grain elevators in the fifties to strengthen their position in marketing grain. Livestock marketing associations, including an auction in Illinois, were organized. Buying clubs were formed to obtain farm supplies.

The early organizations did not have the benefit of cooperative laws. They had to be organized under the general corporation laws. The first cooperative law was adopted in Michigan in 1865.

FARMERS in other countries also felt a need for mutual economic assistance.

Dairy farmers in the Jura Mountains in Switzerland were among the first to organize formal cooperatives to improve marketing methods during the early 1800's. The small herdsmen formalized into cooperatives the community associations for making butter and cheese that began in the 13th century.

The need of small farmers in Germany for credit in the 1840's gave rise to a system of cooperatives that had a far-reaching influence in many countries. Concerned with the inability of the small farmers to obtain credit at livable rates, Friedrich Wilhelm Raiffeisen, a German financier and philanthropist, developed the unlimited liability association scheme that still bears the name.

The Raiffeisen Credit Society Plan caught the attention of the hard-pressed Danish farmers. The shift from grain production to dairying required more cash. It was hard to get, and they thought the moneylenders took advantage of them. In 1851 they formed the first credit cooperative. It was followed in 1863 by the first dairy cooperative

COOPERATIVES IN WORLD TRADE

and in 1866 by the first purchasing association.

The farmers of Sweden, keeping pace with their Danish neighbors, organized the first farm supply cooperative in 1849. It grew out of the county agricultural society. Its major activity was importing seed, breeding stock, and machinery. Cooperative creameries and bacon processing plants came along in the 1880's.

Norwegian farmers were responding to the need for credit at the same time. A law in 1851 authorized the setting up of cooperative credit societies. The first dairy cooperative followed in 1855. The need for farm supplies led to the first purchasing cooperative in the early 1880's.

English farmers trailed their urban cooperative counterparts by 24 years in establishing their first cooperative. They profited from their early experiences and developed leadership. The first association was organized in 1868 to provide unadulterated feeds and fertilizers. The first society to spring from strictly agricultural leadership came 2 years later. Its purpose was the same.

The need for reliable farm supplies prompted the farmers of the Netherlands to set up their first cooperative in 1876. Its purpose was to provide fertilizer, feeds, and other supplies

Cooperatives in other countries of Europe developed along similar patterns. By the beginning of the century, local cooperatives had been formed in nearly all countries, and federations were being established.

THE RAIFFEISEN PLAN had an effect on the early cooperatives in Latin America. Immigrants after the Franco-Prussian War brought the idea with them. The first societies were formed in Brazil early in the present century. These cooperatives and those organized until about 1920 were set up by the rural people. Soon after that, governments became prominent in cooperative programs.

Agricultural cooperatives in the Ori-

ent generally came later than in the United States and Europe. Governments had a more positive role in their formation.

In India, the need for adapted credit under livable conditions inspired the first cooperative societies. The first cooperative act and resulting societies were in 1904. A study team sent to Germany a few years later brought back details of the Raiffeisen pattern. The early programs were sponsored by the government.

Agricultural cooperatives in Japan date from the 19th century. They performed many services of marketing, providing farm supplies, processing, and credit. They were sponsored and closely directed by the government.

GOVERNMENTS have had varying roles in the development of cooperatives.

In Europe, especially in the central and northern parts, governments have been neutral regarding agricultural cooperatives. They consider cooperatives a part of the economic system and can stand or fall by themselves.

In some countries, however, notably in Switzerland and Scandinavia, cooperative segments are such high proportions of certain agricultural activities that they are commissioned by governments to implement government programs. Examples are price supports and export controls.

Government relations with cooperatives have been much more positive in the Orient, Latin America, and Africa than in other areas. In view of the urgency for progress and the dearth of rural leadership, this role is justified if the government role is guiding, sustaining, developing, and temporary and not usurping and permanent.

Early farmer cooperatives in the United States received sympathetic and friendly assistance from National and State Governments. Official policy endorsement came later, but the extension services, National and State departments of markets, and land-grant colleges gave educational assistance in developing cooperatives.

Agricultural cooperatives in the United States maintained a steady growth into the forties. Since then, expansion has been more rapid. Development has been by both expanding the organization structure and by adding services. Cooperatives have formed federations of local and special federations among the federations. Expansion also has been achieved by the addition of new services. Larger units and more services have meant a smaller number of cooperatives.

EARLY, SYMPATHETIC ASSISTANCE by Government agencies in the United States began to be supplemented by enabling laws in the twenties.

Six major laws are enabling and assisting and not regulating.

The Capper-Volstead Act in 1922 clarified the rights of cooperatives in relation to the antitrust laws.

The Cooperative Marketing Act of 1926 formalized earlier assistance of the United States Department of Agriculture into a policy "to promote the knowledge of cooperatives and cooperative practices." This act and the ensuing programs have become known internationally as a pattern for non-regulatory government assistance.

The Federal Farm Loan Act of 1916 provided for long-term farm loans.

The Farm Credit Act of 1933 provided for short and intermediate production credit to farmers and authorized the banks for cooperatives.

The Federal Credit Union Act of 1934 authorized the organization of Federal credit unions and assistance in their development.

The Rural Electrification Act of 1936 strengthened the Executive order of the President that in 1935 created the Rural Electrification Administration, which makes loans to rural electric and telephone cooperatives.

These laws and the Executive order laid the foundation for the development of the so-called service types of cooperatives and the stabilization and expansion of cooperatives already in operation. The ones already operating were chiefly for marketing farm products and purchasing farm supplies.

COOPERATIVES have made striking adjustments to serve the expanding needs of their members and keep pace with changing economic conditions. The greatest adjustments have been made by the marketing and farm supply cooperatives. The changes involve numbers, size, and scope.

There were about 9 thousand marketing and supply cooperatives in the country in 1964—about one-fifth fewer than in 1930. Improved roads, trucks, and other means of transportation and the expanding economy encouraged mergers. The number of members in 1964 was more than that of a generation earlier. The point is especially significant from the standpoint of servicing the farmers, as there were a little more than half as many American farmers in 1964 as in 1930. At that time, fewer than one-half of the farmers belonged to a marketing or a purchasing cooperative; now, a farmer very likely belongs to a marketing and a purchasing cooperative and to one or more service cooperatives—almost a fourfold increase in coverage.

Farm supply cooperatives, because of mechanization and the greater use of fertilizers and the other requisites, expanded faster than did marketing cooperatives. For example, about 90 percent of the combined business was done by the marketing group in 1930; the proportion was less than 80 percent in 1964.

The added services I mentioned have applied to both marketing and purchasing cooperatives. These have changed the conventional pattern of local associations with single services, which formed federations to extend their activities. The development resulted in regional marketing or purchasing federations.

Most of the conventional marketing or purchasing federations have expanded to include the services of the other. Many local cooperatives organized to provide farm supplies therefore have added marketing services. To support them, the federations have developed marketing and even processing services. In like manner the marketing cooperatives have added farm supplies.

Frequently the original name of the cooperative, which designates its first service, is retained. For example, a cooperative with "consumer" in its name is now deep in marketing farm products, including processing for marketing. Another with a single commodity marketing title has added a complete supply department and also commodity after commodity to its marketing services, including a completely integrated broiler program from the hatching egg to the processed bird. The farmer cooperatives of the United States have gone further than those of any other country in the integration of functions.

Cooperatives necessarily have become larger to provide the increased volume of needed services and to fit into the generally expanding economy. Thus they are sometimes classed with big business. While the total volume is naturally large, few individual cooperatives are large comparatively.

Three cooperatives were classed in 1963 among the 500 leading manufacturers in the United States, and they are not near the top. One of them, Land O' Lakes Creameries, Inc., Minneapolis, Minn., is a dairy cooperative. Cooperative Grange League Federation, Inc. (GLF), Ithaca, N.Y., began primarily as a supplier of feeds. Consumer Cooperative Association (CCA), Kansas City, Mo., was organized to provide petroleum products.

THE PROPORTION of various goods or services handled by agricultural cooperatives varies among commodities and services. The estimated value of the total marketing and supply services provided by cooperatives approximated 30 percent of the value of the total agricultural production of farmers in 1964.

Cooperatives have long had an important part in the distribution of milk and the processing of dairy products. The latest summarized material is for 1957, when dairy cooperatives performed one or more functions in the marketing of almost 60 percent of the whole milk delivered to plants and dealers. The cooperatives processed almost 75 percent of the total production of dry skim milk, 70 percent of the dry buttermilk, almost 60 percent of the creamery butter, 23 percent of the Cheddar cheese, and 14 percent of the condensed milk.

Cooperatives handle about 90 percent of the lemons, 85 percent of the cranberries, 70 percent of the almonds, more than 50 percent of the fresh oranges, and 15 percent or less of the vegetables.

Cooperatives store or market an estimated 40 percent of the grain. They handle 50 percent of the rice in the major rice-growing States and 40 percent for the United States as a whole.

Other commodities handled in substantial proportions by agricultural cooperatives are wool, about 20 percent; livestock, 13 percent; turkeys, 17 percent; and eggs, 10 percent. They also handle about 20 percent of the lint cotton and the cottonseed that are crushed at mills.

PRACTICALLY ALL FARMERS in the United States are members of a purchasing association that handles farm production supplies. To obtain special supplies, some farmers belong to more than one purchasing association.

Farmers obtain through their cooperatives about 15 percent of all their supplies and equipment. Among the higher proportions handled by cooperatives are fertilizers and petroleum, 23 percent each; seed and insecticides, 19 percent each; and feed, 18 percent.

It is estimated that farmers' mutual fire insurance companies handle more than 50 percent of the farmers' business. In like manner, rural electric cooperatives serve about 50 percent of all farms. Cooperative or mutual irrigation companies supply water for about 25 percent of the irrigated land. In cooperative credit, banks for cooperatives supply about 60 percent of the credit to agricultural cooperatives; Federal land banks, about 20 percent of the land mortgage credit; and production credit associations, about 15 percent of the short and intermediate credit used by farmers.

AGRICULTURAL COOPERATIVES in other countries generally have expanded vertically, like American cooperatives.

There has been less tendency, however, for the marketing federations to add purchasing services, or vice versa. Exceptions to this general pattern are the Consorzi Agrari of Italy and the Boerenbond Belge of Belgium. Both were organized to provide multiple services and continue to do so.

The cooperatives of Japan exemplify the integrated services. A village multipurpose cooperative serves the farmers of the community. Generally it has credit, marketing, and farm supply departments. It also operates a consumer store. The various departments of the village cooperative are serviced by specialized state federations, which in turn are federated nationally.

The agricultural cooperatives of other countries handle substantial proportions of the total volume of certain commodities in their countries. In some, the proportions are higher than they are in the United States. In fact, as I mentioned, in some European countries, cooperatives handle such a high proportion of the total volume of certain commodities that they have been given the responsibility of administering government programs that involve those commodities.

It is estimated that the cooperatives of France handle about 80 percent of the grain, 45 percent of the fertilizers, 42 percent of the commercial dairy products, 23 percent of the wine and feedstuff, 20 percent of the fruit and vegetables, and 15 percent of the sugarbeets.

In Sweden, the cooperatives handle about 80 percent of all agricultural

products, 65 percent of the fertilizer and feeds, and 60 percent of the cereal grains. The national dairy cooperative, SMR, handles the entire wholesale trade in milk, cream, and butter.

In Norway, the cooperatives market about 55 percent of the farm products sold. They supply about 60 percent of the feed concentrates and 45 percent of the commercial fertilizer used. They handle about 72 percent of the dairy production, 75 percent of the meat, 60 percent of the meat animals, 70 percent of the eggs, and 45 percent of the garden products.

In Denmark, cooperatives handle about 91 percent of the dairy products, 53 percent of the feed, 45 percent of dressed poultry and seeds, 40 percent of the fertilizers, and 37 percent of the cattle sales.

In Finland, the cooperatives handle 98 percent of the milk received by dairies and 90 percent of the meat processed at slaughterhouses.

The cooperatives of Australia and New Zealand handle about 85 percent and those of the Netherlands about 70 percent of the dairy products of their respective countries.

The cooperatives in Canada handle about 60 percent, those in Australia about 50 percent, and the ones in Germany 37 percent of the grain.

AGRICULTURAL COOPERATIVES in the United States turned to foreign markets as their programs expanded. Some began in the twenties. Others began during the depression years. Cooperatives marketing cotton and citrus and dried fruit were among the pioneers.

I give some examples.

STAPLE COTTON COOPERATIVE ASSOCIATION, Greenwood, Miss., began exporting cotton soon after its organization in 1921. Its export program, a supplement to its domestic program, accounts for about 15 percent of total volume. Major outlets are in western Europe. Sales also are made in Japan, India, Australia, and other Far Eastern countries.

Cotton Producers' Association, Atlanta, Ga., is an example of horizontal integration in its foreign and domestic programs. Organized to market cotton, its program has expanded to include farm supplies, storage, more cotton services, and the marketing of livestock, poultry, and nuts. The poultry program is integrated from hatching eggs to broilers processed for retail selling. It operates export programs for cotton, poultry, peanuts, and pecans.

The fact that the per capita income of its members was 72 dollars a year spurred the association to action, and it began exporting cotton in 1933. The program has continued and expanded. Exports approximate 150 thousand bales each year. Distribution is wide and includes practically all countries of Europe, the Middle and Far East, and some in Africa. Sales are made by salaried officers and through brokers.

The integrated broiler program soon led to the exportation of poultry. Cotton Producers' Association is the largest United States exporter of broilers—about 20 percent of the total. The volume has expanded to approximately 35 million pounds a year, which is about 25 percent of total volume of the association. Approximately three-fourths of its shipments are to western Europe; about two-thirds of them to Common Market countries. Other important receiving areas are Asia and Africa.

Calcot, Ltd., Bakersfield, Calif., began in 1927 as a local cotton marketing cooperative. It has expanded to cover the cotton districts of California and Arizona. Its services include receiving, warehousing, and compressing.

The distance of its location from domestic markets encouraged exporting, which began in 1948. Sales are made in 9 Asian countries, in 13 countries of Europe, and in the Middle East and Africa. Indeed, the sales cover the cotton importing world. An average of about 40 percent of its 800-thousand-bale volume is exported.

Texas Cotton Growers Cooperative Association, Dallas, Tex., organized in 1940, exports about 20 percent of its volume of about 150 thousand bales. Its sales follow the general cotton foreign trade pattern of western Europe and the Far East.

The Plains Cotton Cooperative Association, Lubbock, Tex., began exporting cotton in 1957. About 20 percent of its total volume is exported. The cotton produced by its members is in heavy export demand, and it is estimated that an additional 45 percent of its total production is sold in foreign markets. It has outlets in 22 countries, mostly in western Europe and the Orient. It maintains sales offices in Japan and Korea.

FRUIT COOPERATIVES began exporting in the thirties. Associations handling citrus and dried fruit were among the first. Those marketing apples, pears, grapes, and nuts soon followed. The exports of processed citrus have become important lately.

On an ocean trip, I had an experience that proved to me how much people like fruit from our cooperatives. Earlier, the tables had been decked with mangoes, papayas, bananas, and oriental melons, all popular and delicious. The ship stopped at Hong Kong. A cargo of fruit from the west coast had just arrived there. The first evening out, the fruit served was California oranges and Northwestern apples, both of cooperatives' brands. The international set common to ship dining rooms acclaimed the fruit from the West.

Sunkist Growers, Inc., Los Angeles, is the pioneer cooperative in exporting citrus. It is also the largest citrus marketing federation in the country. It has more than 10 thousand member growers in California and Arizona.

Expanding production and the depression prompted Sunkist to enter foreign markets. Now Sunkist is a well-known brand around the world. The sales program was supplemented by advertisements in foreign papers and posters. The trade development program is supported by material prepared in 12 languages.

Sunkist exported about 7 million cartons of fruit in 1963, about a half million more than in 1962. The leading commodity is lemons, followed by Valencia and navel oranges and grapefruit. The foreign sales program is correlated with domestic sales by exporting the most plentiful sizes.

Pure Gold, Inc., Redlands, Calif., exports about a million cartons of citrus a year. Major commodities are oranges, lemons, and grapefruit. That is about 20 percent of total sales.

Major markets are western Europe and England, and about 10 percent is sold in the Far East.

Florida Citrus Exchange, Tampa, has been an exporter of citrus for a long time. Its program was strengthened by the organization of an export or international division in the fifties. The cooperative exports about 650 thousand boxes a year, not counting fruit shipped to Canada. The shipments account for about 6 percent of the volume. Major foreign outlets have included Germany, France, and the Netherlands.

Plymouth Citrus Products Cooperative, Plymouth, Fla., exports large amounts of single-strength citrus juices and frozen concentrates. About 1 million cases of plain juices, blends, sections, and salads are sold outside the United States. More than one-half is sold in Canada; most of the remainder goes to Germany, France, and Switzerland.

Sunsweet Growers', Inc., San Jose, Calif., exports about one-fourth of its dried prunes, apricots, peaches, and pears. About 90 percent of the fruit goes to Europe; 3 percent each to Asia, South America, and North America; and the remainder to South Pacific. Sales are made in practically all the major markets of Europe and the Far East.

Sun-Maid Raisin Growers of California, Fresno, was one of the early exporters among United States cooperatives. The brand name is well known in all raisin-importing countries. Sun-Maid maintains sales offices

overseas and also sells abroad through brokers.

California Almond Growers' Exchange, Sacramento, handles about 70 percent of the almonds produced in California, about 15 percent of which is exported. The quantity, however, varies widely according to the domestic crop. Sales are made in 54 countries. The greatest volume goes to Europe, Canada, Japan, and Australia.

Diamond Walnut Growers, Inc., Stockton, Calif., exports about 2 percent of its volume. Canada is the greatest receiver. Some sales are made in Europe and South America.

Apple Growers' Association, Hood River, Oreg., and its merged predecessors cover the span of the Hood River apple industry. The association began exporting many years ago, and it sells a higher proportion in foreign markets than any other deciduous fruit cooperative. Approximately 35 percent of its apples and 20 percent of its pears are sold in foreign markets. The United Kingdom is the largest individual receiver; heavy shipments go to most countries of western Europe. Sales are also made to many markets of the Orient, Latin America, and Canada. The export outlets are especially valuable, as the greatest demand is for sizes that are not particularly popular in the United States.

Blue Ribbon Growers, Yakima, Wash., organized in 1902, has grown up with the fruit industry of the Yakima Valley. Pears and apples are their major export items, normally being about 20 and 6 percent, respectively. The United Kingdom, Sweden, Finland, and Canada are the chief importing countries.

Wenatchee-Okanogan Cooperative Federation, Wenatchee, Wash., was set up in 1922. It is a federation serving local associations in the Wenatchee-Okanogan area. Wenoka has been exporting apples and pears for many years. Normally the exports account for about 2.5 percent of total volume. Sales follow the common export pattern of apples and pears; most go to the United Kingdom and Scandinavia.

The California Fruit Exchange, Sacramento, began its foreign trade program during the depression under a tree near Visalia. The sales manager and a member were discussing ways to improve the market. The idea of foreign outlets sounded good; it was tried; and the exchange is still in it. Winter pears and Emperor grapes are the leaders, although a number of fruits are exported, including apples. In addition to balancing the sales program, the export business is important, as many growers of special varieties depend almost wholly on the export market.

The United Kingdom is the heaviest receiver. Shipments go also to Scandinavia and other European markets. Hong Kong, Singapore, New Zealand, and India are among the markets. Some shipments are made also to Latin America.

Skookum Packers' Association, Inc., Wenatchee, Wash., has exported apples and pears for many years. In 1962 about 14 percent of their pears and 8 percent of their apples were exported to Great Britain, Europe, the Far East, the Caribbean, and South America.

A NUMBER OF DAIRY products are exported by cooperatives. Well over half the total volume is powdered nonfat milk.

Land O' Lakes Creameries, Inc., Minneapolis, Minn., the largest cooperative merchandising federation for dairy products, began exporting before the Second World War. Their greatest expansion, however, has been since 1946. Foreign sales now approximate 8 percent of the total trade. Distribution includes the Far East, Latin America, and Europe. Three-fourths of the volume is powdered skim milk, followed by butter, butter oil, and powdered whole milk. Sales are made directly and through brokers.

Maryland and Virginia Milk Producers' Association, Laurel, Md., sells primarily fluid milk. It has a manufacturing division to divert excess supplies from the fluid milk market. The division entered foreign markets in 1959 and in 1964 exported about 15 percent of its production. More than 60 percent of the volume exported is skim milk powder.

The Dairymen's League Cooperative Association, New York, illustrates the rising importance to cooperatives of foreign outlets for nonfat dry milk and dry whole milk. Its manufacturing division began exporting these products in 1962. Now foreign markets take about one-third of its total dry milk. Major outlets are in the European, Mediterranean, and Caribbean regions.

O-At-Ka Milk Products Cooperative, Inc., Batavia, N.Y., is one of the newest as well as one of the largest producers of evaporated milk in the Nation. It began manufacturing evaporated milk in 1962, and by the end of the year had sold nearly 4.5 million pounds. A substantial volume went to markets in Germany, France, England, and the Congo. A contract between O-At-Ka and the Government of India called for a shipment of about 260 thousand cases of evaporated milk.

GRAIN AND OILSEEDS are relatively new items exported by cooperatives.

Producers Export Company, New York, is owned by 22 of the 30 regional grain cooperatives of the country. Organized in September 1958, it opened for business October 15, and sold a full cargo of grain sorghum 2 days later. The company has the use of port elevators in Baltimore, Toledo, Chicago, Kalama, Wash., and Houston. The one in Baltimore is operated by the company. The others are made available by regional members.

This port service and the 220-million-bushel terminal and subterminal capacity at 131 locations put the company in position to service all outlets.

The major sales area is western Europe, but the Far East, especially Japan, the Near East, and Africa also are important outlets. Sales are made through representatives in the various markets.

Major trade items are wheat, corn, soybeans, and grain sorghum. The company goes beyond the transfer of commodities and titles in its foreign marketing. Six of its members have laboratories and bakeries, at which blends of various grain types for required bakery mixtures are determined, a work that is helpful to consumer cooperatives that operate bakeries. One is the Consumer Cooperative Wholesale Society of England. The society purchases special types of wheat to mix with the native grain.

Mid-States Terminals, Inc., Toledo, Ohio, organized in 1959 by five regional cooperatives in Ohio, Indiana, and Michigan, is a member of Producers Export and operates a port elevator. The volume of Mid-States for the year ending June 30, 1960, was 7 percent of the Toledo port, 9 percent in 1961, 17 percent in 1962, and 20.2 percent in 1963.

Some members of Producers Export Co. independently have developed foreign outlets for special products. These are chiefly vegetable oil and meal and some beans.

Arkansas Grain Corp., Stuttgart, a member of the company, has exported soybeans, crude and refined soybean oil, and meal since 1958. Major sales areas are western Europe and Mexico.

The cooperative devised a solution to its problem of disposing of surplus rice hulls and the problem of European dairymen of making the correct mixture from meal concentrate. The solution is in using the surplus hulls with the meal to prepare mixtures that contain specified proportions of protein.

Michigan Elevator Exchange, Lansing, exports approximately 10 percent of its grain and beans. Grain is handled through the Producers Export Co. and beans by the exchange. Major outlets for beans are in Europe and sales are made through brokers.

Two processing plants, members of the Grain Terminal Association, Minneapolis, export vegetable oils and meals. Honeymead Products Co., Mankato, Minn., organized in 1960, a large soybean processing plant, exports soybean oil and meal, mainly to western Europe. The Minnesota Linseed Oil Co. of Minneapolis exports linseed oil and meal, chiefly to Europe.

Organization of Soy-Cot Sales, Inc., Chicago, reflects the rising importance of cooperatives in foreign trade and the introduction of new commodities. It was set up in 1962 and began operations on the 1963 crop. Eleven cooperative cottonseed processors in the Mississippi Delta, Texas, Oklahoma, and Arizona, and eight cooperative soybean processors in the Midwest are members. The aim is to market the products of its members; primary emphasis is on exports.

Ranchers Cotton Oil, Fresno, Calif., began selling linters in Japan in 1952. Germany was added a year later. In 1960 Japan became a customer for refined cottonseed salad oil. The export business accounts for about 16 percent of total sales.

Rice Growers' Association, Sacramento, Calif., sells about 75 thousand tons of brown and milled rice for export. Sales for export account for about 30 percent of its volume of milled rice. Major outlets are in the Orient and Canada.

The Arkansas Rice Growers Cooperative Association, Stuttgart, formerly exported rice to Cuba. Outlets have been established in South Africa, Nigeria, and Ghana. Sales are made through brokers. About 40 percent of the volume is exported.

Inland Empire Pea Growers Association, Spokane, Wash., exports more than 60 percent of its volume. All of one variety, Marrowfat, is exported; more than 90 percent of the Whole Green variety is sold abroad. These export varieties round out the total production program of growers. England and West Germany are the largest receivers. Substantial amounts go to Canada, France, and other European countries. Sales are made to exporters for resale in Latin America.

Sioux Honey Association, Sioux City, Iowa, began exporting honey in 1952. Major outlets are in Germany, Belgium, and France. Export sales have been made as a part of general sales, but business and trade opportunities increased to the extent that an export division was established.

EXPORTS BY POULTRY cooperatives reflect a great increase in broiler production. Some eggs are exported, but they are negligible compared to broilers and turkeys.

Rockingham Poultry Marketing Cooperative, Inc., Broadway, Va., entered the foreign markets with broilers and turkeys in the early fifties. Their first sales to Europe have been extended to include Africa and Asia. Of the export volume of about 10 million pounds, about 80 percent is still to European markets. Some of its first customers were consumer cooperatives. Foreign sales have accounted for about 12 percent of total volume.

North American Poultry Cooperative Association, New York, is a marketing federation owned by poultry cooperatives in the Northeast, South, and Midwest. Its primary function is to market eggs in New York City. Some eggs are exported. The expansion of the broiler production, though, put them in the export business, and more than 2 million pounds a year are sold in European markets. These sales represent about 30 percent of their total broiler volume.

Norbest Turkey Growers' Association, Salt Lake City, Utah, a federation of 13 associations, is a substantial exporter of dressed turkeys. Foreign shipments total about 4 million pounds a year and approximate 3 percent of total volume. Slightly more than half is sold in Europe, about one-fourth in Canada, and the rest in Asia and South America.

THE TWO-WAY PROCESS of foreign trade involves both exports and imports. Most of the early trading was exporting by the marketing cooperatives. The purchasing cooperatives, however, entered the field with substantial imports of farm supplies. Some have begun to export supplies.

Its widespread program of providing supplies to the many members in the Northeastern States prompted the Cooperative Grange League Federation Exchange, Inc., in 1920 to seek some foreign sources. Such imports have expanded greatly. As the quantity of products manufactured by GLF increased, beginning in 1948, some supplies were exported. Since then, GLF has had an expanding two-way international trade program. Much of its trading in foreign countries is cooperative to cooperative. Major cooperatives involved are those in Canada, the Netherlands, England, and Costa Rica.

The first products imported by GLF were grass, clover, and feed-grain seeds. Twelve types are now imported.

GLF expanded its foreign buying in 1948 to include twine; 40 percent of its supplies now come from Mexico and Europe. Later additions were wire, nails, fertilizers, fishmeal, burlap, molasses, and sunflower seed. The proportion of products imported range from small amounts to 100 percent, in the case of sunflower seed and some fertilizers. About 75 percent of the wire and nails are imported.

GLF began exporting canned beans in 1948. This added a source of income to its members, as 95 percent of one variety of canned beans is exported. Other commodities include dairy and poultry feed, processed grain, and dog and fish food.

GLF's foreign trade area covers much of the world. Major areas are Europe and Canada, but important sales and purchases are made in the Near East, Far East, South America, Central America, the Caribbean, and Africa.

GLF and Eastern States Farmers' Exchange announced their merger and new name, Agway, effective July 1, 1964. Headquarters are Syracuse, N.Y.

United Cooperatives, Inc., Alliance, Ohio, a federation of large farm supply cooperatives, began importing certain farm supplies in the early fifties. The first items were binder and bailer twine, followed by wire and nails. The annual volume approximates 25 thousand tons of wire and 415 thousand bales of twine. The wire and nails are chiefly imported from West Germany and Belgium; smaller amounts come from the Netherlands and Japan. Major sources of twine are Canada, Mexico, and Denmark. Small amounts are bought from Africa, Portugal, and Haiti. The Danish trade is cooperative to cooperative, as purchases are made through the Danish Cooperative Wholesale Society.

National Cooperatives, Inc., Albert Lea, Minn., primarily provides general farm supplies and dairy equipment to its members, which are chiefly large regional United States supply cooperatives. It began to export milking machines and accessories to Canada in 1944. The trade area has expanded to include Europe, South Africa, the Caribbean, Central America, and the Near East. It exports about 12 percent of its milking machines and related equipment. The commodities exported have also expanded to include pumps, appliances, tires, and batteries. National sells as much as possible through the cooperatives of the importing countries. Business is done with the cooperatives of Canada, Puerto Rico, and the Netherlands.

Western Farmers Association, Seattle, has expanded its early poultry and egg marketing activities to a comprehensive, combined program. It exports some seeds, mainly to England and South America, but imports are the more important part of its international business. Wire and twine are obtained through United Cooperatives, of which it is a member, but a number of commodities are imported directly. About 75 percent of the fishmeal it uses is imported from Canada and Peru. About 90 percent of its urea,

ammonium nitrate, phosphate, and sulfate for fertilizers is imported. White clover seed are imported from New Zealand.

Eastern States Farmers' Exchange, West Springfield, Mass., a new member of the cooperative export family, shipped broiler feed and lay feed to Lebanon in 1963.

The International Cooperative Petroleum Association, New York, is a federation of cooperatives in many countries who use fuel oils and lubricating oils and greases. It began operation in 1950 and has done substantial business with member cooperatives in nine countries in western Europe, in Egypt, India, Pakistan, and Ceylon.

THE FOREIGN TRADE programs of agricultural cooperatives in other countries have followed the same general pattern of relative importance as their domestic programs. Some cooperatives in western Europe do more foreign business proportionally than any in the United States. Foreign trading is being done to an increasing extent by cooperatives in the Orient, Latin America, and Africa.

Canadian cooperatives carry on extensive two-way trade with United States customers. Feed grains, soybeans and meal, clover and grass seeds, honey, citrus fruit and juices, dried fruit, and nuts are purchased in the United States. In reverse, the cooperatives of Canada sell a wide variety of grass and clover seed, potatoes, honey, and fishmeal in the United States. Nonfat milk powder is a major item exported by Canadian cooperatives.

Agricultural cooperatives of the Netherlands are prominent in both exporting and importing. They export approximately 60 percent of the butter, 50 percent of the cheese and condensed milk, 30 percent of the potatoes and eggs, and 25 percent of the grains and feeds. They also handle 50 percent of the imported grain.

Cooperatives in Denmark export 90 percent of the bacon, 65 percent of the butter, and 36 percent of the eggs.

Swedish agricultural cooperatives handle the exports of all dairy products except dried and condensed milk, 60 percent of the eggs, and most of the hay.

Cooperatives of Norway handle 100 percent of meat and butter, 92 percent of the furs, 90 percent of the cheese, 65 percent of the wool, and 50 percent of the hides that are exported.

Cooperatives in Finland handle 100 percent of the butter and about 98 percent of the milk powder, 96 percent of the cheese, 90 percent of the meat, 75 percent of the eggs, and 50 percent of the furs exported from their country. They also handle the major part of the seasonal imports of meat and cheese.

In the Orient, the agricultural cooperatives of some countries engage in international trade.

Cooperatives in Japan export fresh and processed fruit, canned mushrooms, fishmeal, and vitamin oils.

The newly organized National Cooperative Marketing Federation in India has developed export and import programs.

Cooperatives in Latin America and Africa in international trade include some in Uruguay, wool and wheat; Mexico, fish; Brazil, fruit, sugar, and wine; Argentina, cotton, fruit, wheat, vegetable oils, beef, and leather; Tunisia, wine; and Kenya, dairy products and peanuts.

The cooperatives in several countries of Africa assemble and prepare products for handling by central marketing boards. Among these are Republic of the Congo (Léopoldville) and Tanganyika, coffee; Zambia and Southern Rhodesia, tobacco; Ghana, cocoa and rubber; and Nigeria, cocoa, palm oil and kernels, and rubber.

THE PAST CENTURY has seen great development in the agricultural cooperatives of the world. They have traveled far from the struggling locals formed in the United States, and Europe and later in the Orient, Latin America, and Africa. During the journey they have developed into substantial factors in the economies of their own countries and of others abroad.

The cooperatives of several countries of Europe handle more than half of the exports of certain commodities from their countries. In the United States, cooperatives are heavy exporters of cotton, fruit, nuts, dairy products, grain, beans, oilseeds, and poultry. These shipments relieve the pressure on domestic markets and supply outlets for products for which there is limited demand in this country.

The foreign trade of United States cooperatives also includes imports. Farm supply associations are importing wire, nails, fertilizer, seed, twine, burlap, and fishmeal.

This two-way foreign trade enables the cooperatives of the United States and other countries to balance supplies with demand more adequately and obtain supplies at the most favorable rates. The improved market outlets and lower costs of supplies benefit both producers and consumers of the world.

JOHN H. HECKMAN *has spent most of his professional life working with agricultural cooperatives. He began as county agent and later was extension marketing specialist in Arkansas. In the Farmer Cooperative Service, Department of Agriculture, he did research and service work with fruit and vegetable cooperatives and made market surveys and conducted and directed research and service programs in membership relations and prepared numerous educational and teaching aids. On detail to the Foreign Agricultural Service, he made studies of cooperatives as outlets for United States agricultural products in western Europe, Japan, and Canada and prepared a series of publications on them and on the agricultural cooperatives of western Europe.*

Representing the Agency for International Development, he served as cooperative member education adviser to the All India Cooperative Union, New Delhi, assisting the union in developing a cooperative education program, a training program for leaders, developing training and educational material in the organization and operation of a national training center.

Our Agricultural Trade Policies

by RAYMOND A. IOANES

THE UNITED STATES has become a leader in sponsoring liberal trade in farm products. We have dismantled barriers to imports of many foreign-produced commodities that compete with our own production. At the same time we have obtained increased access to foreign dollar markets for our own agricultural commodities.

We have gained much in terms of dollars from following liberal, orderly, trade-expansive policies.

In 1944–1953, for instance, our commercial exports of food and fibers totaled 17.3 billion dollars. Our competitive imports amounted to 15 billion dollars. In 1954–1963, our farm exports were as high as 28.3 billion dollars, and our imports of competitive farm products had a value of 19.4 billion dollars.

OUR POLICIES OF LIBERAL trade in agricultural products have roots deep in history. We shifted in 1921, however, to a policy of protectionism. We raised agricultural tariffs sharply several times, in keeping with a trend toward more restrictions on all imports.

The change was triggered by sharp breaks in agricultural prices, which began in 1920. Prices farmers received had reached a peak of 236 percent of the 1910–1914 level. By June of 1921, the price index had fallen to 112 percent of the 1910–1914 average.

Agricultural prices stayed at depressed levels throughout the twenties.

The country groped for farm relief measures. One was increased duties. The reasoning was: American farmers are getting ruinous prices; if we keep out foreign-produced commodities, we will ease the pressure on prices and they should rise—or at least not go any lower.

Special measures to increase exports instead of curtailing imports might have been successful, but the die had been cast. Tariffs were increased by the Emergency Tariff Act of 1921; more by the Tariff Act of 1922, the Fordney-McCumber Act; and still more by the Tariff Act of 1930, the Smoot-Hawley Tariff Act.

Many observers were alarmed at the swing to protectionism. B. H. Hibbard, an economist at the University of Wisconsin, said in 1933:

"We have used our tariff acts to break down friendly relationships a century old, e.g., with our best customer, Canada. The crowning act of salvation of the country through the increase in tariff rates came in 1930 with the passage of the Smoot-Hawley Act. The most learned of the Senators when asked, during debate on this bill, whether or not there might be danger of retaliation against the provisions of the pending measure, replied, 'That is an old cry. It will be time enough to be afraid of retaliation after it happens.' It has happened. The battlements of the European fortresses make our tariff embankments look like the work of schoolboys on a holiday afternoon."

In 1931–1934, when the Smoot-Hawley Act was in effect, our agricultural exports dropped to an average of about 800 million dollars, as compared with shipments worth 1.8 billion dollars in the preceding 4 years.

THE RECIPROCAL TRADE Agreements Act of 1934—an amendment to the Tariff Act of 1930—authorized the negotiation of trade agreements between the United States and individual countries, and concessions, chiefly in the form of reductions in our import duties on foreign products, to the extent of 50 percent below those then in effect.

The United States moved promptly to use its new authority. By the end of 1934, the average equivalent ad valorem duty rate on dutiable farm products had been reduced to 55 percent—considerably below the average of 85 percent in effect in 1932.

The General Agreement on Tariffs and Trade, which became effective in 1948, accelerated the trend toward freer trade in farm products. The GATT set up trade rules for many industrialized countries and made it possible for the United States to use the authority of the Reciprocal Trade Agreements Act to reduce tariffs at general negotiating sessions, instead of on a piecemeal basis with individual countries.

Thus in 1948 the United States reduced the average equivalent ad valorem duty rate on farm products to 18 percent. By 1962, when the Reciprocal Trade Agreements Act was replaced by the Trade Expansion Act, the average duty rate had been cut to about 11 percent.

If the agricultural products given duty-free treatment are included, the overall duty rate on farm products in 1962 averaged 6 percent. Although general price inflation has accentuated the rate of decrease on dutiable farm products—about 75 percent of which are subject to specific duties—the actual reduction has been substantial.

The United States has not been able to go all the way back to the liberal trade of the period before the First World War. A number of Government programs to bolster farmers' incomes have been necessary. Substantial imports of some products, which would adversely affect programs established for them, are restricted under section 22 of the Agricultural Adjustment Act, as amended—among them, in 1964, wheat and wheat flour, cotton, peanuts, and certain dairy products.

Sugar imports are regulated under the Sugar Act of 1948, as amended.

Only 26 percent of United States agricultural production, however, is covered by nontariff restrictions—a far smaller proportion than in any other major country.

BECAUSE WE ARE liberal traders ourselves, it is United States trade policy to seek for our farm products the same liberal access to foreign markets that foreign-produced commodities have in the United States market.

Our first point of attack in our efforts to gain access to markets is on tariffs.

The Trade Expansion Act of 1962 is an expression of our intention to attack high duties boldly. We are hopeful that flexible provisions of the act will lead to mutually advantageous trade concessions. The act authorizes tariff cuts up to 50 percent on most imported goods, industrial and agricultural, in exchange for concessions that foreign countries give us. We can cut tariffs to zero on some commodities in return for similar cuts abroad. The act also strengthens the hand of the United States in dealing with nontariff restrictions put on American products by foreign countries.

The United States proposes to use the Trade Expansion Act to negotiate agricultural and industrial tariffs and trade restrictions as a single package in the GATT negotiations. The United States will not conclude tariff negotiations unless access is provided for agricultural exports comparable to those provided for industrial shipments.

Industrialized countries, though financially able to buy from us, have been reluctant to throw their doors open wide to such United States products as wheat, wheat flour, rice, poultry, and others we are eager to sell.

Some governments unquestionably would like to exclude agriculture completely from tariff-cutting negotiations. Other governments would include agriculture but under rules that would give little or no promise of trade liberalization.

Foreign officials, notably those of Western Europe, tell us that they must reserve domestic markets for their own producers because of certain economic and political dilemmas.

They say, for example, that their relatively inefficient agricultures must be restructured—a process that would be hampered by strong competition from imported farm products.

They say that their farmers, who have not shared fully in the prosperity that nonfarmers enjoy, are therefore deserving of special protection.

They say that their farmers, who make up a substantial percentage of the voting population, will not permit any substantial increase in imports of competing farm products.

To make sure that imported farm products will not offer competition to industrial consumers, most foreign governments protect their farmers with nontariff barriers, and they—not tariffs—constitute our biggest access problem. Nontariff barriers can completely deny market access for our poultry, wheat, wheat flour, or canned orange juice even if duty rates on them were set at reasonable levels.

Many kinds of nontariff devices are in use. They include the variable import levy, minimum import or gate prices, quantitative restrictions, conditional imports, mixing regulations, state trading and monopolies, import surcharges, import discriminations, and preferential treatment.

Whatever their form, economic trade barriers can insulate the producers of a country from price competition as effectively as if literal walls were erected at the frontiers.

Because of the special problems introduced by nontariff trade barriers, it is United States policy to work for market sharing when effective tariff cuts cannot be made.

Market sharing is a special arrangement that would give the United States or any exporting nation continued access to markets in countries or customs unions that protect their agricultures with nontariff barriers.

The market-sharing principle would not guarantee access to any exporter.

It would offer the opportunity of access.

For example, if exporters have been supplying 15 percent of a country's annual consumption of a product in a representative period, exporters may ask that country not to limit imports below that percentage during the period covered by the agreement. The various exporting countries would compete among themselves for the available share of the market.

Market-sharing arrangements should provide an opportunity for exporting countries to compete for larger trade volumes in future years because market demand for many products is growing.

If the market-sharing arrangement involves a percentage share of the market, the growth factor is included automatically. If the arrangement is based on a fixed volume of trade, definite provision for growth would need to be incorporated.

The market could be shared in any one of several ways. Sharing could be based on quantitative assurances, ceilings on variable import levies, restrictions on the use of minimum prices, ceilings on internal price supports and deficiency payments, or a combination of these.

Much would depend on the commodity involved and the participants. For many products, the agreements would not need to be complicated or elaborate.

Fairly complicated arrangements, however, may be required for some products. A start has been made in working out rather formal commodity arrangements for cereals, meal, and dairy products.

International commodity agreements, like those in effect for wheat, sugar, and coffee, are more formalized intergovernmental understandings, which could be used to improve market access. The considerable time required to negotiate such agreements, however, plus difficulties of administering them, limit their extensive use.

It is United States policy to press for moderate internal pricing of farm commodities by importing countries.

High internal prices in importing countries encourage uneconomic production. When high prices are protected by high trade walls, comparative advantage cannot function, with generally adverse effects for both importing and exporting countries.

Uneconomic production works hardships on the nonagricultural sectors of importing countries. Higher prices for food and clothing reduce the real incomes of industrial workers and lead eventually to demands for higher wages. High wages, in turn, increase manufacturing costs, which impair the competitive position of the country's manufactured goods in the world's market.

Uneconomic agricultural production in importing countries also damages America's agricultural trade, of course. As the protected, price-supported production of importing countries rises, they need to import less and less of our food and fiber.

Other countries occasionally look askance at our farm programs. The United States is eager to talk over the entire spectrum of agriculture—import restrictions, export payments, price supports, supply management, and related operations—with officials of other countries.

Out of free interchanges of ideas may come understanding and reciprocal modification of internal agricultural policies and fewer restrictions on trade.

As it is, we have had considerable success in gaining access to foreign markets for our farm products. The agricultural exports we sold for dollars rose from an average annual value of 800 million dollars in 1930–1933, when the Smoot-Hawley Tariff Act was in effect, to an average of 3.4 billion dollars in 1960–1962, under the Reciprocal Trade Agreements Act. Even if allowance is made for an inflation in prices, the gain was more than 50 percent.

But an access to foreign markets is somewhat like a businessman's license to operate. Access, like the license, is an essential first step, but it does not in itself guarantee a substantial volume of sales.

IT HAS BECOME United States policy, therefore, to back up access to markets with activities to develop markets.

At one time our role in agricultural exports markets was passive. We waited for foreign customers to knock on the door. We came to the conclusion in the midfifties that we had to play an active role in export markets. We have been pursuing that policy vigorously.

We have become eager salesmen, actively promoting United States farm products in some 50 countries by means of market development with trade groups, exhibits of our farm products overseas, trade centers, visits of foreign businessmen and other groups to the United States, demonstrations, seminars, publications, radio and television programs, point-of-sale promotion, and advertising in newspapers.

IT IS United States policy to price export commodities at levels that will meet the competition of the foreign producers.

Other things being equal, customers will always buy the lowest priced product. Competitive pricing, therefore, is necessary. Our efficient production assures our competitive position on many farm commodities.

When United States internal prices are above world levels, however, as is the case with wheat, cotton, and a few other products, we must make export payments to hold a fair share—and no more than a fair share—of the world market.

IT IS United States policy to pay increasing attention to preferences of foreign buyers.

The customer may not always be right, but generally he thinks he is

right. To sell to him, we must understand his point of view and adapt our practices to it as far as we can.

We are learning more and more, through research and experience, about customers' tastes and habits—about foreign legal requirements with respect to weights and measures, packaging, dyes, bleaches, grades and standards, and quality control.

Many of our competitors, from long experience in the export market, know what buyers want. We, too, can produce and deliver the kind of products our foreign customers want, and that is what we must do.

IT IS United States policy to stimulate export sales for dollars through the use of short- and long-term credit.

Credit helps us make dollar sales to countries that are not yet ready to buy for cash but hope sometime to become cash buyers.

Short-term credit—up to 3 years—is extended on foreign commercial sales of products owned by the Commodity Credit Corporation and on tobacco under CCC price-support loan.

Long-term credit, authorized by Public Law 480, title IV, may be extended up to 20 years on sales of United States farm products to foreign governments and to individuals, commercial firms, agricultural cooperatives, or other organizations of the United States or friendly foreign countries.

Both short- and long-term credit programs provide for repayment of principal and interest in dollars.

IT IS United States policy to seek orderly agricultural trade.

The United States does not throw large quantities of food and fiber on world markets, because such an action would disrupt foreign agricultural prices and lead to other economic dislocations.

The United States, for the same reasons, opposes unduly heavy or uneven imports of farm products.

Our efforts to promote orderly trade begin with the production phase. We seek, as the first step in market regulation, to prevent the production of supplies that may be a burden to us and to world commerce.

Unlike some other countries, we have placed on our farmers a big part of the market regulation load by asking them to cooperate in programs to control production.

The record shows that we have acted responsibly in the agricultural production area. Our efforts to keep farm output in line with domestic and export needs are unparalleled.

That we have not succeeded entirely is due more to our enormous agricultural capability than to our intentions. We reduced total cropland harvested by more than 50 million acres between 1953 and 1963. Much of the reduction came in important export crops. For example, during that period we cut wheat acreage 33 percent; rice, 18 percent; tobacco, 28 percent; and cotton, 42 percent. Some of the reduction in acreage, however, was offset by high acreage yields.

We have matched responsible production policies with equally responsible stockpiling practices.

We have maintained in the United States, at great expense, great stocks of food and fiber. Early in 1964, the Commodity Credit Corporation had in storage almost 950 million bushels of wheat, 825 million bushels of corn, about 5.6 million bales of cotton, and substantial quantities of other agricultural products.

The total inventory had a cost value to the United States of 4.8 billion dollars. The storage cost alone amounted to 1 million dollars a day.

Our restraint in keeping surplus products off world markets has helped to maintain stable world prices. Our stocks have been available at all times to meet critical world needs.

During the Second World War we shipped large amounts of agricultural products to our Allies. We dug deeply into our supplies in 1946 and 1947 to meet urgent food requirements of Europe and Asia.

Our food and fiber were available when the Korean war greatly stimulated world demand, when the Suez crisis developed in 1957, and when unfavorable weather in eastern and western Europe in 1963 severely cut harvest of wheat and other grains.

The United States feels, however, that the burden of supply adjustment should be borne by all free countries.

Orderly trade does not depend solely on production and distribution policies of the United States. Other exporting countries contribute to the overall volume of commodities moving in international trade. Importing countries also add to the volume. United States farmers often are puzzled at being asked to curtail their production when they see other exporting countries taking no steps to check output or even employing extraordinary measures to expand production.

In other ways we have respected our responsibilities to our partners.

The United States has been particularly careful that shipments under Public Law 480 have not disturbed commercial markets. We emphasize the movement of Food for Peace to the less-developed countries, which are not large cash customers for farm products. We make sure that our agreements under Public Law 480 take into account usual commercial purchases from the United States, usual commercial purchases from other free world sources, or a combination of these commercial movements.

We regularly consult with free world competitor countries when we develop the programs. We also participate in the work of the FAO Consultative Sub-Committee on Surplus Disposal, organized "to insure that the disposal of surpluses is made without harmful interference with normal patterns of production and international trade."

We set export payments at rates no higher than are needed to help us meet world prices for cotton, wheat, and rice, but not to undercut world prices on these products.

From the standpoint of our own interests, the export payment rates must be set carefully. For example, if the export payment rates on United States cotton are set at levels that do not assure normal United States cotton marketings, other producing countries step up their production and take part of our fair share of the market.

Consultation among major exporting countries with respect to prices on commercial exports is highly desirable. Price wars always are disturbing, whether they involve the occasional price cutting of gasoline service stations in United States communities or the price cutting by countries exporting farm products.

Price cutting may give a country a temporarily increased share of the world market, but it can lead to disturbing retaliation which can mean market instability and uncertainty.

The United States desires that importing also be orderly. Orderly importing depends to a considerable extent on the trade policies of other countries.

Heavy imports of beef by the United States in 1963 underscored the need for orderly importing. The 1963 beef imports, estimated at a record 1.8 billion pounds, represented more than 10 percent of American production. Imports increased because United States prices were attractive; the United States duty of 3 cents a pound was low, and there were no other import restrictions; and other beef-importing countries, notably the United Kingdom and countries of the European Economic Community, were restricting their imports.

The United States became the target for much of the beef exported by Australia, New Zealand, Ireland, Mexico, Argentina, and other countries. We could not, of course, remain the only country in the world accepting beef imports on an unlimited basis.

Talks began in 1964 with representatives of the beef-exporting countries to work out arrangements that would permit sharing of the United States beef market on a fair and equitable basis and yet avoid undue disturbance in the long-run to our cattle and meat industries.

OUR TRADE POLICIES must never become static. They must be adapted rapidly to changing world economic and political conditions.

Two examples in one year showed us that we are able to meet developments by rapid adaptation.

The French veto in 1963 of the British bid to enter the Common Market introduced a new set of trade variables and a reappraisal of our trade policies as they involve the United Kingdom, the Common Market, and other importers of our farm products.

Short grain crops in the Soviet-bloc countries in 1963 led to a decision by the United States to sell to the Soviet Union and other eastern European countries such price-supported United States products as wheat, feed grains, and cotton.

Longer range policies must be adapted to the trends that we now see developing.

The importance of agriculture in the fabric of world economic relations has not been diminished by science and technology. Actually, agriculture has become a more powerful force as less-developed countries grow economically, as the tendency toward international division of labor becomes more pronounced, as populations increase, and as those populations strive for an improved standard of living.

In the kind of world that is taking shape, restrictive trade will be an anachronism. Nations have no choice, therefore; they must lower their restrictive barriers. Only through liberal trade can the good things of our civilization be made available to all.

RAYMOND A. IOANES *became Administrator of the Foreign Agricultural Service in 1962. Previously he was Deputy Administrator for 6 years. He joined the Department of Agriculture in 1940. His work since 1949 has concerned many aspects of agricultural trade policies.*

Our Agricultural Exports

by ROBERT L. TONTZ and
DEWAIN H. RAHE

AGRICULTURAL EXPORTS account for about 15 percent of the farm marketings of United States farmers. The export market absorbs the production from one out of every five acres on which a harvested crop is grown.

The foreign market is of major importance as an outlet for many products, particularly those in greatest abundance. It takes half of the wheat American farmers grow and a fourth of their sales of cotton and feed grains.

Exports as a percentage of yearly production in fiscal year 1963 equaled more than half of the rice crop, about two-fifths of the soybeans, including oil, and inedible tallow, one-fourth of the tobacco, and one-fifth of the output of cottonseed oils and lard.

The United States, the world's leading exporter of agricultural products, accounts for one-sixth of the world's total.

Many Americans employed in related industries, like financing, storing, shipping, and trading of agricultural commodities, contribute materially to moving this large volume of farm products abroad. An example of that contribution is that about one-fourth of the cost of a bushel of wheat to the oversea customer is the cost of freight and loading.

Exports of farm products aid in maintaining the well-being of the United States economy. Many dollars come back to the United States from our sales of farm products to other countries, and thereby compensate partly for the outflow of dollars for economic, technical, philanthropic, and military aid.

In fiscal 1963, exports over imports of United States farm products contributed a favorable agricultural trade balance of more than 1 billion dollars. Otherwise, the balance-of-payment deficit would have been 30 percent greater than the 3.3 billion dollars actually incurred.

Farm exports have been running well ahead of farm imports since the midfifties, largely because of the rapid expansion of exports to new record highs. Exports during the 7 years that ended June 30, 1963, averaged 4.6 billion dollars annually and exceeded their previous 7-year average by almost 40 percent.

On the other hand, American agricultural imports for the 7 years to June 30, 1963, of 3.9 billion dollars annually were 8 percent less than for the previous years.

The achievement of the peak export levels came through the development of export programs by people in agriculture, trade, and Government and increased purchasing power in other countries, partly through the stimulus of our generous economic aid.

The implementation in 1955 of the Agricultural Trade Development and Assistance Act—Public Law 480— also was designed to expand our agricultural exports. This act supplemented exports under Government programs, principally under the Mutual Security Act (Public Law 665) and was designed mainly to enable developing countries to buy our goods.

Of the 5.1 billion dollars' worth of farm products sent abroad in 1963, commercial sales for dollars totaled 3.6 billion dollars, or 70 percent of the total. The value of dollar sales rose 58 million dollars over the previous fiscal year and set an alltime record.

The sales for dollars, by which and

through which the bulk of United States farm products is distributed, are given top priority in helping expand exports.

The leading commodities sold for dollars included cotton, wheat and flour, tobacco, soybeans, corn, and also fresh, frozen, and canned fruit and juices. Most dollar sales were made to Canada, Japan, the United Kingdom, West Germany, and the Netherlands.

Exports to friendly but dollar-short countries under Government-financed programs—Public Law 480, the Agricultural Trade Development and Assistance Act of 1954, and Public Law 87–195, the Act for International Development—totaled 1.5 billion dollars, or 30 percent of our total agricultural exports.

Leading commodities among the Government-program exports were wheat and flour, cotton, vegetable oils, corn, rice, and dairy products.

Principal countries taking exports under Government programs were the economically developing countries, among them India, the United Arab Republic, Turkey, Yugoslavia, and Brazil.

The special Government export programs use four major approaches: Foreign currency sales, famine relief and donations, barter, and long-term credit.

Sales for foreign currency represent by far the largest of the special export programs. These sales enable friendly countries that are short of dollars to buy with their own currencies the commodities that we have in large supply.

Much of the foreign currency that is received in payment is loaned back to the purchasing country for use in its development programs. In 1963, title I of Public Law 480 accounted for 21 percent of the total United States agricultural exports.

Grants of food to friendly countries from Commodity Credit Corporation stocks for emergency assistance and the promotion of economic development in newly developed areas are author-ized under title II of Public Law 480. Title III makes food supplies available for distribution abroad through voluntary agencies and international organizations.

Although these two kinds of programs in 1963 accounted for only 7 percent of the total farm exports, their usefulness is much greater than the statistics may indicate. These are special-purpose programs, designed to meet the particular needs or emergency circumstances or to feed people not reached by the commercial marketing system.

The barter program also under title III of Public Law 480 and other legislation enable the United States to exchange surplus agricultural commodities for strategic and other materials less expensive to store and less subject to deterioration than farm products. Exports under barter represented a small share of United States agricultural exports in 1963, equaling 1 percent of the United States total.

A relatively new feature in the special export programs is title IV of Public Law 480, which authorizes sales of commodities for dollars at moderate rates of interest, with up to 20 years to make payments. This program has been underway since the last quarter of 1961.

A new credit plan to encourage foreign countries to increase purchases of United States farm products was inaugurated in July 1963. The plan, previously restricted to foreign government agencies, was broadened to provide credit also to private firms to finance sales of American commodities.

WHILE PROGRESS has been made in increasing exports under Government programs, just as for commercial sales for dollars, limitations exist that make expansion difficult.

Underdeveloped countries, the principal recipient of United States Government-program shipments, often lack transportation, storage, and handling facilities to distribute imported food to their needy people. It is a major problem for the exporter and importer alike.

Work is going ahead so that over time the lack of physical facilities will become less and less a factor. In many countries and in large parts of other countries, there are no relief or welfare organizations of the type required to donate food through noncommercial channels. In many areas, customary eating habits are such as to keep people from making use of the foods that the United States has in greatest supply.

Then, too, the role of the United States in the export market is so large that it must be watched carefully so that it will not disrupt the world market. United States programs must not only protect the commercial market for the United States and allied countries; they must also help, rather than hinder, the agricultural development of the less prosperous countries.

One example of market development activity undertaken by the United States which applies both to commercial sales and Government-program exports is the export payment assistance program. This form of assistance is necessary because the selling of agricultural commodities in the world market is a highly competitive business.

About three-fourths of foreign agricultural products entering world trade compete directly with United States agricultural exports. The abundant production of American farms enables the United States to offer a wide range of agricultural products on the world market. But domestic prices in some instances are higher than prices of competing foreign products, especially for certain price-supported commodities. Then the Government may assist both commercial sales for dollars and sales under Government-financed export programs (Public Laws 480 and 87–195) by means of export payments in cash or in kind or by the sale of Government-owned stocks below domestic market prices. Export payment assistance since 1958 has consisted largely of payments in cash and in kind.

When an export payment program is in effect for an agricultural commodity, all exports of the commodity, except donations, generally are eligible for export payments (or differentials equivalent to export payments).

Export payment assistance was provided for 1,694 million dollars of the 5,084 million dollars of United States agricultural exports in 1962–1963.

Exports outside of Government programs (commercial sales for dollars) that benefited from export payment assistance equaled 721 million dollars, while exports under specified Government-financed programs that received assistance totaled 973 million dollars.

Total export payment assistance on United States agricultural exports in 1962–1963 equaled 628 million dollars, which is excluded from the total value of agricultural exports.

Although a number of farm commodities benefited from export payment assistance in the year ended June 30, 1963, two major surplus commodities—wheat (including flour) and cotton—were the principal commodities assisted.

Exports of these two, assisted by export payments, totaled 1,483 million dollars and made up 88 percent of the 1,694 million dollars of exports receiving export payment assistance.

The export payment rate for wheat (including flour) was 67 cents a bushel and for cotton, 8.5 cents a pound.

Other commodities benefiting from export payment assistance were rice, nonfat dry milk, butter, butter oil, cheese, tobacco, and peanuts.

OF THE PROGRAMS designed to build agricultural exports, a basic one is trade liberalization. Export markets cannot be maintained or expanded in countries that deny or limit access for United States products.

Our trade policy is based on the proposition that the way to build world trade is to conduct it on a multilateral, nondiscriminatory basis, at moderate levels of fixed tariffs, and so thereby give consumers ready access to products from the most efficient producers.

To that end, the United States has joined with some 60 other similarly minded nations in the General Agreement on Tariffs and Trade (GATT). These nations account for about 80 percent of the world's international trade.

The United States also is working through other formal diplomatic representations, meetings, and contacts to gain fair competitive access to foreign markets for American farm products.

The Trade Expansion Act of 1962 provides increased authorities—not contained in the Reciprocal Trade Agreements Act of 1934—for the President to grant broad tariff concessions and, if necessary, to retaliate against unfair treatment by removal of concessions to our trading partners abroad.

The act permits the President to negotiate reductions of up to 50 percent on duties that were in effect July 1, 1962. Tariffs may be eliminated on items on which the duty is 5 percent or less. A special provision affecting the European Economic Community allows us to cut tariffs to zero on industrial products on which the United States and the Common Market jointly account for at least 80 percent of the aggregate world export value.

In an agreement with the Common Market for tariff reductions, the President is also given authority to reduce tariffs to zero on any agricultural product on which it is determined that such action would help to maintain or expand United States exports of the same product.

The emergence of trade blocs, such as the European Economic Community (EEC), the European Free Trade Association (EFTA), the Latin American Free Trade Area (LAFTA), and the Central American Common Market (CACM) of the free world, along with the Russian-led Council for Mutual Economic Assistance (Comecon) of the Communist world, represent the beginning of a significant grouping of what are for the most part our traditional foreign customers.

These trade groups, particularly those of western Europe, are among the principal customers for United States farm products. Overall, the free world trade blocs took approximately 2 billion dollars, or 40 percent of total United States agricultural exports, in 1963. The Soviet bloc took little.

The European Economic Community is the No. 1 market in the world for United States farm exports. In 1963, the United States shipped about 1.1 billion dollars' worth of farm products to the six members of the European Economic Community out of total farm product exports to all areas of the world amounting to 5.1 billion dollars. Exports to them equaled 21 percent of all United States farm product exports and about 30 percent of United States exports of farm products sold for dollars in 1963. Exports to Greece, an associate of the European Economic Community, were mainly shipments under Government programs and were relatively small, equaling only 2 percent of total United States agricultural exports to the European Economic Community.

Of major trade significance in the European Economic Community's Common Agricultural Policy is its system of variable import levies. The variable import levies are designed to offset the difference between world prices of commodities and the desired price in the Common Market. This system promotes a policy of protection, self-sufficiency, and price equalization in the Common Market countries. Wheat, including flour and feed grains, accounted for about 90 percent of the 1961–1962 value of the United States commodities on which the EEC imposed variable levies on July 30, 1962. In addition to wheat, variable import levies also have been placed on imports of poultry and eggs and certain other products from third countries.

The United States also is a major importer of products from the Common Market. We imported 2.4 billion dollars' worth of commodities from the Common Market in 1963, but had a net balance of 1.1 billion dollars.

Agricultural shipments to the six members and Greece totaled 1.1 billion dollars in 1963 and were more than four times the value of agricultural imports from these countries. The value of agricultural imports from the Common Market was less than 300 million dollars yearly since 1958. Many of the imported products were specialty items.

In the first year of the 7 years in which the Common Market is to develop fully, United States agricultural exports to the EEC under the variable levy system declined 10 percent, following imposition of the levies on July 30, 1962. Exports of commodities affected most by the variable import levies were broilers and fryers and wheat flour.

Exports of broilers and fryers, the most important meat products shipped to the European Economic Community, declined 70 percent in 1962–1963 from a year earlier.

The variable import levy for wheat flour nearly eliminated United States flour from the Netherlands market, hitherto an important dollar outlet. Most shipments of wheat flour in 1962–1963 reflected Public Law 480 title II and title III flour for Italy's school lunch program and other projects.

Exports of wheat declined 63 percent in 1962–1963 from a year earlier, mainly because of record EEC production. Also, it should be noted, Italy imported an unusually large quantity of United States wheat in 1961–1962 because of its poor crop.

Exports of feed grains dropped only 4 percent, compared with a year earlier. The rapid expansion of the livestock industry in the Common Market area has been the main reason for the continued large exports of feed grains to the EEC.

Exports of commodities not subject to the variable levy system were about the same in August–July 1962–1963 as a year earlier. Sharp increases in exports of fruit, vegetables, soybeans, protein meal, and rye offset declines in cotton, tallow, pork, rice, tobacco, and edible vegetable oils.

Exports of cotton fell 45 percent from a year earlier, mainly because of a 2-million-bale rise in cotton production in the foreign free world and some decline in the use of cotton in Common Market countries.

Soybean exports increased 10 percent in response to further increases in demand for protein meal in the Common Market livestock industry. Exports of protein meal also were larger.

Tobacco exports declined 10 percent mainly because of substantial stockpiling of United States leaf before the increase in duties for tobacco when the Common Agricultural Policy became effective on July 30, 1962. In addition, the United States has encountered increased competition in the European Economic Community market from other producers—especially Southern Rhodesia, Zambia, and Malawi. Other export declines were in lard and tallow, pork, variety meats, rice, and oils.

THE OUTLOOK for United States agricultural exports is favorable for a continued expansion.

Overall projections of our agricultural exports to all market areas, which take into consideration population increases, economic growth rates, technological changes, historical trends, and related factors, show that United States farm exports for 1968 will be at a level nearly 20 percent above the level of 5.1 billion dollars in 1962.

Projected exports would account for more than half of the United States output of food grains; around a third of the cotton, soybeans, and vegetable oils; and substantial quantities of feed grains, tobacco, and other goods.

ROBERT L. TONTZ *is Chief of the Trade Statistics and Analysis Branch, Development and Trade Analysis Division, Economic Research Service, Washington, D.C.*

DEWAIN H. RAHE *is Agricultural Economist in the same Branch.*

Our Agricultural

Imports

by ALEX D. ANGELIDIS

THE UNITED STATES is the second largest importer of agricultural products. The United Kingdom is first.

We imported 3.9 billion dollars' worth of agricultural products in 1962.

At their peak in 1952, during the Korean war, the imports totaled 5.2 billion dollars.

Our agricultural exports were worth 5 billion dollars, and we were the largest exporter.

Agricultural commodities consist of nonmarine food products and other products of agriculture (such as raw hides and skins, fats and oils, and wine) that have not passed through complex processes of manufacture.

Agricultural imports accounted for one-fourth of United States imports of all commodities (16.2 billion dollars) in 1962. Imports of agricultural products were equivalent to 11 percent of domestic cash receipts from farm marketings—35.9 billion dollars. (Exports were equivalent to 14 percent.)

About 55 percent of agricultural imports were partly competitive with United States products. The rest, 45 percent, were chiefly coffee, rubber, cocoa beans, carpet wool, bananas, tea, spices, and silk, none of which, except bananas and coffee in Hawaii, the United States produces in commercial volume.

Only the most ardent protectionists advocate doing away with the com-plementary imports. Not only are they not produced in commercial volume; they can be produced only at such high unit costs that retail prices would be prohibitively high. Americans want them and will pay reasonable prices for them. They are, in fact, considered so essential to a high standard of living that nearly all are allowed to enter the country free of duty.

There is less agreement among United States producers on the national policy toward the supplementary, or partly competitive, commodities, although they are becoming less important relative to exports.

Supplementary imports were equivalent to two-fifths of agricultural exports in 1962, compared with three-fifths in 1950–1954 and four-fifths in 1935–1939. These imports are equivalent to the production on 20 million acres in the United States. (The figure for exports was 63 million.)

Supplementary imports are not so competitive as they may appear to be. United States commercial exports of farm products sold for dollars (that is, not Food for Peace shipments) came to 3.5 billion dollars, whereas our imports of competitive agricultural products came to 2.1 billion dollars, a plus export balance of 1.4 billion dollars. These competitive imports were equivalent to 6 percent of cash receipts from farm marketings.

Imports pay for exports. American purchases from abroad are paid for in dollars, which enable other countries to buy American products. Because of our willingness to import foreign products, we have been able to obtain from other countries increasingly liberal treatment of our exports.

American farmers carry out their production operations with less protection from competitive imports than do farmers of practically all other countries. Average import duties are relatively low for our agricultural imports. About half of agricultural imports—including nearly all of the complementary commodities—in 1962 were free of duty.

For the dutiable commodities—mostly supplementary—the ad valorem equivalent of all duties averaged 11 percent, compared with 88 percent in 1932. For all agricultural imports—both free and dutiable—the ad valorem equivalent averaged 6 percent in 1962.

The United States has steadily been reducing its tariff rates on agricultural imports for 30 years, beginning with the Reciprocal Trade Agreements Act in the thirties. The average duty imposed on United States agricultural imports is lower than that imposed on United States nonagricultural imports. Further reductions are in prospect under the Trade Expansion Act of 1962.

THE UNITED STATES imports agricultural commodities from more than 125 countries, but more than half comes from 10—Brazil, Mexico, the Philippines, Colombia, Australia, Canada, Dominican Republic, New Zealand, Malaysia, and Argentina.

Many suppliers are newly developing countries, whose predominantly one-crop agricultural economies depend heavily on their sales in the American market.

Legislative authority exists to regulate imports of agricultural commodities under specific conditions. For example, whenever imports interfere materially with the marketing quota, price support, or other programs conducted by the Department of Agriculture, the law provides for regulation of such imports under section 22 of the Agricultural Adjustment Act, as amended.

Commodities controlled under section 22 are wheat and wheat products; cotton, certain cotton waste, and cotton produced in any stage preceding spinning into yarn (picker lap); certain manufactured dairy products; and peanuts.

Sugar imports are regulated by quotas under the Sugar Act of 1948, as amended, to provide a stable market for domestic sugar. Amendments in 1962 gave a larger share of the United States market to domestic producers. Agricultural imports must meet United States requirements as to health, sanitation, and quarantine.

In order to satisfy the concern that imports of some dairy products might increase to much higher levels, the supplying countries in October 1963 declared their intention to restrict voluntarily shipments of Colby cheese, Junex, and frozen cream to the United States. Junex is a butterfat-sugar product containing not more than 44 percent butterfat.

Likewise, agreements were signed in February 1964 between the United States and Australia, New Zealand, and Ireland to limit shipments of beef, veal, and mutton to the United States through 1966.

SUPPLEMENTARY IMPORTS include sugar, meat, oilbearing materials and oils, apparel wool, cattle, tobacco, fruit, vegetables, hides and skins, grain and feeds, dairy products, and cotton.

The United States in 1962 imported some 4.6 million tons (509 million dollars) of cane and beet sugar, about half of domestic consumption and almost a fifth of the amount imported by all countries.

Three-fourths of the import tonnage came from the Philippines, the Dominican Republic, Peru, Mexico, and Brazil. Foreign cane sugar producers can deliver sugar more cheaply than we can produce beet sugar ourselves. The Sugar Act of 1948, as amended, stabilizes the domestic market by limiting imports and controlling domestic production. Fees are levied on imports to bring foreign prices up to the domestic level.

Product weight of all the red meat and poultry imported in 1962 was 1.3 billion pounds (466 million dollars).

More than 800 million pounds consisted of boneless beef needed to satisfy demand for frankfurters, prepared hamburgers, and luncheon meats. When farmers hold back old cows, prices for low-grade beef rise and encourage such imports from Australia,

New Zealand, and Ireland. The duty on this beef is 3 cents a pound.

Imports of canned cooked hams and shoulders, which come from Denmark, the Netherlands, and Poland, are high priced and satisfy a special demand, which continues to exist even though consumers may choose cheaper United States hams.

The American appetite is also satisfied in part by canned beef from Argentina and refrigerated pork from Canada.

Altogether, red meat imports accounted for 6 percent of United States consumption of meat in 1962.

Imports of oilbearing materials and vegetable oils amounted to 151 million dollars in 1962 (half of them copra and coconut oil). They accounted for 9 percent of the vegetable oil used in the United States and included copra from the Philippines, castor beans from Ecuador, castor oil from Brazil, tung oil from Argentina, olive oil from Spain and Italy, palm oil from Indonesia and the Congo, and palm kernel oil from the Congo. Some imported oils have special characteristics for various industrial uses in the United States. Coconut oil is used chiefly to make soap and to prepare bakery products.

The apparel—clothing—wool imports amounted to 191 million pounds (120 million dollars). Most of it came from Australia, South Africa, Uruguay, and New Zealand. Imports made up about two-fifths of United States consumption; they were about half in 1950.

The National Wool Act of 1954 supported prices to encourage domestic production. The output has been rising slightly, but smaller use of wool and greater use of synthetic fibers have done more than the act to reduce dependence on imports. High production costs have priced wool out of the apparel market, and the trend toward lighter weight clothing has been felt in the wool industry.

Import duties on raw wool are 11 cents to 27.75 cents a pound, according to kind and quality.

Imports of cattle, mainly in the 200-700-pound weight class, totaled 1.2 million head (110 million dollars), not including breeding animals. Imports have been high because drought conditions in Canada and Mexico forced shipments to the United States market at attractive prices. Cheap United States feeds also encouraged stocker and feeder movements into our feedlots for finishing. Imports of cattle were equivalent to about 4 percent of United States slaughter.

Imports of cattle in specified weight classes are subject to duties of 1.5 and 2.5 cents a pound. In some instances, after imports exceed certain stated amounts in a given year, the 1.5 cents duty advances to 2.5 cents a pound.

The United States imported 164 million pounds of tobacco (101 million dollars) in 1962, principally oriental cigarette leaf from Turkey and Greece to blend with domestic leaf to satisfy the varied preferences of American smokers. Oriental varieties are not produced in the United States or not in large enough volume to meet domestic demand. The equivalent of two cigarettes in each pack is foreign tobacco. Practically all imports of cigarette leaf had a duty of 12.75 cents a pound.

The United States imports many kinds of fruit and fruit preparations. The largest single import is olives from Spain, followed by canned pineapples from Taiwan. The bulk of the 88 million dollars' worth of imports in 1962, however, came from Canada and Mexico and consisted mostly of specialty items supplementing our production in winter and early spring, when our production is not plentiful. Altogether, imports amounted to about 6 percent of cash receipts from fruit marketings in 1962.

Imports are dutiable, but for some items the rate is reduced during seasons when United States production is low.

Imports of vegetables and preparations were worth 83 million dollars in 1962. The array included fresh tomatoes from Mexico; canned tomatoes and tomato sauce and paste from Italy; and tapioca, tapioca flour, and cassava from Thailand. Other items included carrots, cucumbers, garlic, mushrooms, onions, peppers, potatoes, turnips, and rutabagas. About half of the vegetable imports comes in winter and spring, principally from Mexico.

Imports amounted to 4 percent of cash receipts from vegetable marketings in 1962. Duty rates are lowered during stated periods each year to encourage imports when our output is low.

Imports of hides and skins amounted to 63 million dollars, principally sheep and lamb skins, goat and kid skins, and kip skins, which are not produced in sufficient volume in the United States. The United States produces chiefly cattle hides and maintains a thriving export business, because they are plentiful and inexpensive.

Except for hides and skins of cattle of the bovine species, imports of hides and skins are free of duty.

Imports of grain and feeds cost 58 million dollars in 1962. Grain—three-fourths of the total—included wheat (principally feed wheat), barley, barley malt, corn, oats, and broken rice. Feeds included processed items like bran, shorts, byproduct feeds, malt sprouts and brewers grain, cottonseed oilcake and meal, and dog food.

Grain—about 1 percent of cash receipts from grain marketings—comes mostly from Canada. Imports of Canadian barley malt help make up deficiencies in the United States supply of high-grade malting barley. Exports of grain to Canada for use there are many times the imports from that country.

Considerable amounts of grain are imported into Puerto Rico, which purchases most of its grains from nearby Latin American producers because of lower transportation costs.

Imports of wheat and wheat products are regulated by section 22 import quotas. Import duties on the principal grains range from 4 cents a bushel for oats to 25 cents for corn.

Imports of dairy products, totaling 54 million dollars in 1962, consisted chiefly of cheese and casein. Imports included foreign specialty cheeses like Swiss; Blue-mold from Denmark; Edam and Gouda from the Netherlands; Pecorino, Provolone, and Provolette from Italy; and Roquefort from France. Certain products are controlled by section 22 import quotas.

American producers are making inroads on imports as they improve and design their products to satisfy American consumers. Imported cheese made up 5 percent of United States consumption in 1962. Casein is imported mainly from Argentina, Canada, Australia, and New Zealand. Cheese imports are dutiable at 12 percent to 25 percent ad valorem.

Imports of cotton and cotton linters amounted to 30 million dollars, mainly long staple for use in shirts and other fabrics that require long-staple fiber. Except for short, harsh, Asiatic cotton, imports are regulated by section 22 quotas.

Long-staple imports ($1\frac{1}{8}$ inches and longer) are limited to 95 thousand bales on an August 1–July 30 year. Imports of upland type (less than $1\frac{1}{8}$ inches) are limited to 30 thousand bales on a September 19–September 18 year. Imports, amounting to about 1 percent of United States consumption, come mainly from United Arab Republic, Peru, and Mexico.

The import duty on long-staple cotton is 3.5 cents a pound; extra-long-staple ($1\frac{11}{16}$ inches or more), 1.75 cents a pound. Short-staple cotton (under $1\frac{1}{8}$ inches) and cotton linter imports are free of duty.

COMPLEMENTARY IMPORTS include coffee, rubber, cocoa beans, carpet wool, bananas, and tea.

Imports of coffee, the chief complementary commodity, amounted to 3.2 billion pounds in 1962 (990 million dollars)—three-fourths from Latin America, mainly Brazil and Colombia. The United States buys about half of the world's imports of green coffee beans. Per capita United States consumption was approximately 16 pounds in 1964.

Imports of crude natural rubber totaled 944 million pounds (228 million dollars). Practically all came from Asia, especially Malaya, Indonesia, Thailand, and Singapore. Some came from Liberia.

Synthetic rubber has limited the imports of the natural product, and natural rubber accounted for only about one-fourth of total rubber used in the United States in 1962, compared with nearly two-fifths in the early fifties. The United States buys about one-sixth of world exports.

Imports of cocoa beans totaled 639 million pounds (131 million dollars). Seventy percent came from three countries—Ghana, the Republic of Ivory Coast, and Nigeria.

The United States buys about one-third of the world's bean imports. The United States also imports prepared chocolate and cocoa from the Netherlands, the Dominican Republic, and Switzerland.

Imports of carpet wool amounted to 181 million pounds, actual weight (89 million dollars). Most came from Argentina, New Zealand, and Pakistan. The fiber in carpet wool is shorter and coarser than that in apparel wool. Because of a greater use of manmade fibers, wool accounts for about half of the surface fiber content of carpets.

Bananas come mainly from Ecuador, Honduras, Costa Rica, and Panama. Imports totaled 77 million dollars in 1962, nearly one-half of the world's exports.

Imports of tea were 130 million pounds (60 million dollars), mostly from India, Ceylon, and Indonesia.

ALEX D. ANGELIDIS *became International Economist in the Trade Statistics and Analysis Branch, Development and Trade Analysis Division, Economic Research Service, in 1961. Previously, he was employed in the Foreign Agricultural Service and Office of Foreign Agricultural Relations, Department of Agriculture, and Bureau of the Census, Department of Commerce.*

Controls of Imports

by TERRENCE W. McCABE

THE UNITED STATES and most other countries have exercised control of imports to keep out animal and plant pests and diseases, weeds, and adulterated foodstuffs and to achieve other aims.

The first prohibition of imports of cattle was enacted in 1865. The authority, delegated to the Secretary of the Treasury, was seldom used. An epidemic of a contagious bovine pleuropneumonia of foreign origin in the United States in the 1880's led to the adoption by the Congress in 1884 of the first Federal animal quarantine law and granted the necessary authority to the Secretary of Agriculture.

The Federal Plant Quarantine Act of 1912 was the basis of the protective system against the entry of plant pests from abroad. The Federal Plant Pest Act of 1947 strengthened the system.

The Agricultural Research Service of the Department of Agriculture is responsible for the quarantine work. About a hundred persons—veterinarians and trained nonprofessional inspectors—have been engaged in the animal quarantine work. About 400 inspectors are required to administer the plant quarantine. The solicited cooperation of American travelers overseas has been of great help to them.

TO KEEP OUT foreign pests and diseases, the Department of Agriculture has long required a permit to import most kinds of animals, nursery stock, most kinds of fruit and vegetables and other plant products, animals for fairs and zoos, materials or plant pests for research and museums, animal biologicals for veterinary and medical use or research, and foreign soil for research or any other use.

Weed control is exercised under the Federal Seed Act of 1939, as amended. The Bureau of Customs assists the Department of Agriculture in the administration of the act by collecting samples of each seed importation.

Investigations and activities of the former Bureau of Chemistry of the Department of Agriculture brought to light a flood of adulterated and fraudulent foodstuffs and led to the enactment of the Food and Drug Act of 1906. Enforcement of the act was vested in the Bureau of Chemistry until the Food, Drug, and Insecticide Administration was established in 1927 as a separate unit in the Department. It was redesignated the Food and Drug Administration in 1930 and was transferred in 1940 to the Federal Security Agency, which in 1953 became the Department of Health, Education, and Welfare.

A more inclusive act, the Federal Food, Drug, and Cosmetic Act, was enacted in 1938. One of its purposes was to prevent the importation of adulterated, misbranded, poisonous, and deleterious foods. Section 801 required that the Bureau of Customs of the Treasury Department submit to the Food and Drug Administration samples of foods that were being imported or offered for importation. The Tea Importation Act also is administered by the Food and Drug Administration.

The importation of fluid milk and cream was regulated in the Federal Import Milk Act. This act, administered by the Food and Drug Administration, required that imported milk and cream must come from healthy cows that have had a physical examination each year, have passed a tuberculin test applied by a duly authorized

official veterinarian of the United States, and the milk must have been processed under sanitary conditions in dairy farm and plant. The Food and Drug Administration may not issue import permits under this act unless all these conditions have been fulfilled.

ALL COUNTRIES maintain varying degrees of controls of imports through quotas, import licensing, import fees, or surtaxes. The nontariff control of agricultural imports in the United States was authorized by section 22 of the Agricultural Adjustment Act, as amended.

The collapse of farm prices in the United States in the postwar period of 1920–1921 brought a continuing demand for Government legislation for relief and assistance to agriculture. Import restrictions were proposed in legislation on equalization fees and export debenture plans. The bills were not enacted, but in 1921 the Congress passed the Emergency Tariff Act of 1921 to "make the tariff effective for agriculture" by increasing considerably the duties on agricultural items in the Underwood tariff.

In the meantime, the Congress was writing the Fordney-McCumber tariff bill, which became law in 1922 and incorporated general increases in agricultural duties.

Hearings were begun in the spring of 1929 on the Smoot-Hawley Tariff Act. Originally, additional protection was sought only for agriculture, which had not shared in the prosperity of the late twenties. Since the Smoot-Hawley tariff schedule approved in 1930 carried many specific duties, as distinguished from ad valorem, the fall in prices after 1930 was a leverage factor for further controls on agricultural imports.

FARM PRICES reached new lows in 1933, and the Congress quickly passed the Agricultural Adjustment Act. The act sought to raise agricultural prices and to increase farm purchasing power through control of acreage, voluntary marketing agreements, and the licensing of processors and handlers in order to eliminate unfair trade practices and charges, levy such processor's taxes, and use such taxes in appropriate funds for the expansion of markets and the removal of agricultural surpluses.

There was no specific mention of import controls in the Agricultural Adjustment Act, but the broad powers granted to the Secretary of Agriculture did allow him to exercise some authority on imports. One method was through the imposition of the compensatory taxes on imported articles that were processed or manufactured wholly or in chief value from a commodity on which a domestic processing tax was in effect. The purpose of the tax was to maintain the previously competitive relationship between domestic and imported articles. The import compensation tax receipts of 540 thousand dollars in 1933 were less than 1 percent of the total of the processing taxes collected.

The Secretary of Agriculture could also control imports through the broad powers granted him in making marketing agreements. During the first 2 years of the act, however, provisions for import control were included in only one agreement. Drawn up at the time of the repeal of the Volstead Act, it provided for the institution of import quotas on wine and liquors at the average annual level during the 5 years before the First World War. The quotas were found to be unnecessary, however.

The sugar program authorized by the Jones-Costigan Act of 1934 was the first adjustment program applied to a product that was heavily imported. The act provided a framework for setting up a system of quotas for both domestic areas and foreign countries. Quota provisions under later sugar laws were not much different from those established by the Secretary of Agriculture under the Jones-Costigan Act.

Acreage reduction was augmented by severe drought conditions in 1934, and large drops occurred in crops in 1934–1935, particularly feed and cereal grains. Their prices rose to the top of the high tariff wall and stimulated large increases in imports.

The Congress recognized that some import control feature would be required, because, as noted by the House Committee on Agriculture in Report No. 1241 of June 15, 1935, "Efforts to restore agricultural prices in this country will not be wholly successful if competitive foreign imported articles are allowed to take the domestic market away from the domestic products."

THE FIRST LEGISLATION for the general regulation of agricultural imports was enacted as section 22 of the amended Agricultural Adjustment Act of 1935. It has been amended several times and was revised in its entirety by section 3 of the Agricultural Act of 1948 and again by section 3 of the Agricultural Act of 1950. It was further amended by sections 8(b) and 104 of the Trade Agreement Extension Acts of 1951 and 1953, respectively. These amendments stipulated that no trade agreement or other international agreement entered into by the United States may be applied in a manner inconsistent with the requirements of section 22 and provided for emergency procedures.

The amended section 22 directed the Secretary of Agriculture to advise the President whenever he has reason to believe that any article or articles are being imported under such conditions and in such amounts so as to render or tend to render ineffective or materially interfere with any price support or other program, relating to agricultural commodities, undertaken by the Department of Agriculture, or to reduce substantially the amount of any product processed in the United States from any agricultural commodity or product thereof with respect to which any such program or operation is being undertaken.

If the President agrees there is a reason for such belief, he directs the Tariff Commission to conduct an investigation, including a public hearing, and to submit a report to him of its findings and recommendations. The President is authorized, on the basis of such findings, to impose quotas or such fees in addition to the basic duty as he shall determine necessary.

The additional fees may not exceed 50 percent ad valorem and the quotas proclaimed may not be less than 50 percent of the quantity imported during a previous representative period, as determined by the President. Furthermore, the President may designate the affected article or articles by physical qualities, value, use, or upon such other basis as he shall determine.

Whenever the Secretary of Agriculture reports to the President that a condition exists requiring emergency treatment, the President may take action without awaiting the report of the Tariff Commission. Any such action by the President shall continue in effect pending the report and recommendations of the Tariff Commission and action thereon by the President.

The first action under section 22 was taken on July 26, 1939, when the President requested a review of the material interference of cotton imports with the domestic cotton program.

Presidential Proclamation No. 2351 of September 5, 1939, contained the acceptance by the President of the recommendation of the Tariff Commission for the establishment of an annual quota to be allocated by country of origin, of 14,516,882 pounds for imports of cotton having a staple length of less than 1⅛ inches (other than harsh or rough cotton of less than three-fourths inch in staple length and chiefly used in the manufacture of blankets and blanketing, and other than linters); of 45,656,420 pounds for imports of cotton having a staple length of 1⅛ inches to, but not including, 1¹¹⁄₁₆ inches; and of 5,482,509 pounds for imports of cotton card strips made from cotton having a staple length of less than 1³⁄₁₆ inches, comber waste, lap waste, sliver waste, and roving waste, whether or not manufactured or advanced in value.

Quotas on wheat and wheat flour were established by Presidential Proclamation No. 2489 of May 8, 1941. The proclamation established country quotas totaling 800 thousand bushels on imports of wheat and 4 million pounds of wheat flour, semolina, and other wheat products.

DURING the Second World War, the matter of import controls became a part of the solution to the larger problem of the supply and allocation of food and fiber among the Allies. With wartime food and fiber shortages, the controls were not to protect domestic production, but rather to assist in the planning of maximum use of limited Allied shipping.

Under the authority of the Second War Powers Act, the import controls were maintained, through War Food Order No. 63, during the Second World War and the early postwar period for a large number of agricultural commodities.

Authority for import controls was later extended under Public Law 155 until July 1, 1950. It was further extended through June 30, 1951, by Public Law 590. With the expiration of Public Law 590, import controls on agricultural products were continued by Defense Food Order No. 3, issued on June 29, 1951, under the authority of section 104 of the Defense Production Act of 1950.

Except for supplementary action that modified the cotton quotas, only one action was instituted under section 22 while Food Orders No. 63 and 3 were in effect. This action on edible tree nuts, under Presidential Proclamation 2955 of December 10, 1951, established a fee of 10 cents a pound (but not more than 50 percent ad valorem) on imports of shelled and blanched almonds in excess of 4.5 million pounds.

With the imminent expiration of section 104 of the Defense Production Act, the President accepted the Tariff Commission's report of June 8, 1953, and issued Presidential Proclamation

No. 3019, effective July 1, 1953. The proclamation transferred import controls in effect immediately before that date under section 104, except for butter oil, which had not been offered for entry since 1942, to section 22 authority.

Country quotas on an annual basis were instituted under the order for butter, 707 thousand pounds; dried whole milk, 7 thousand pounds; dried buttermilk, 496 thousand pounds; dried cream, 500 pounds; dried skimmed milk, 1,807,000 pounds; malted milk and compounds or mixtures of or substitutes for milk or cream (the aggregate quantity), 6 thousand pounds; Cheddar cheese, and cheese and substitutes for cheese containing or processed from Cheddar cheese (the aggregate quantity), 2,780,000 pounds; Edam and Gouda cheese (aggregate quantity), 4,600,200 pounds; Blue-mold (except Stilton) cheese, and cheese and substitutes for cheese containing, or processed from, Blue-mold cheese (aggregate quantity), 4,167,000 pounds; and Italian-type cheese made from cow's milk, in original loaves, 9,200,100 pounds.

A global quota was placed on peanuts of 1,709,000 pounds, shelled basis, annually and a fee of 25 percent ad valorem was added to imports of peanut oil in excess of 80 million pounds annually. Flaxseed and linseed oil imports had levied against them a 50-percent ad valorem fee.

Twenty-five primary investigations had been conducted by the Tariff Commission under section 22 by 1964. Besides the quotas on cotton, wheat, tree nuts, certain dairy products, flaxseed and linseed oil, and peanut oil, section 22 quotas or fees have been placed and subsequently removed on shelled filberts, tung nuts, tung oil, rye, rye flour and meal, hulled or unhulled barley, hulled or unhulled oats, and unhulled ground oats.

SEVERAL section 22 import controls were in effect in 1964.

They were: Those placed on cotton and cotton products on September 5, 1939, with the modification that the country quota on long-staple cotton was modified to a global quota basis. The quotas on harsh or rough cotton less than three-fourths inch and card strips made from cotton of 1 3/16 inches or more in length have been removed;

the quotas on wheat and wheat flour established May 1941, except ex-quota importations of certified or registered seed wheat and wheat and wheat flour for experimental purposes in small quantities made without clearance and in larger quantities with the written approval of the Secretary of Agriculture or his representative;

the quotas on specified dairy products established on July 1, 1953, except that the quota on Edam and Gouda cheese was raised to 9,200,400 pounds, Italian-type cow's milk cheese to 11,500,100 pounds, and Blue-mold cheese 5,016,999 pounds annually. Further global imports of 1.2 million pounds of butter oil are now allowed annually, but all other articles, except those under quota (containing 45 percent or more butterfat), are embargoed;

and the control on peanuts, whether shelled or unshelled, of July 1, 1953.

OTHER INSTRUMENTS may be used.

Section 7 of the Trade Agreement Extension Act of 1951, replaced by section 351 of the Trade Expansion Act of 1962, provided for the readjustment of a negotiated duty or an imposition of a fee at no more than 50 percent ad valorem where no duty exists where it is found that items entered under the lowered negotiated duty are presumably causing injury to agriculture or industry.

The Trade Expansion Act also provided under section 252 for the establishment of import restrictions whenever unjustifiable foreign import restrictions impair the value of tariff commitments made to the United States, oppress the commerce of the United States, or prevent the expansion of trade on a mutually advantageous basis.

The Agricultural Act of 1956 provided in section 204 for import limitation on agricultural products through negotiation with exporting countries. The President was given authority in a 1962 amendment to control imports from countries which were not parties to any agreements.

The Tariff Act of 1930 itself provided under section 337 for the exclusion from entry whenever the existence of an unfair trade practice has been established. Section 303 of the Tariff Act provided for the levying of countervailing duties when it has been found that any subsidy has been granted directly or indirectly upon the manufacture or production or export of an article being imported.

The Antidumping Act of 1921, as amended, provided for the levying of antidumping duties whenever it has been determined by the Tariff Commission that the class or kind of foreign merchandise is being or likely to be sold in the United States at less than its fair value.

In October 1963, a form of import control was provided through voluntary limitation by Australia, Ireland, and New Zealand on their exports to the United States of certain nonquota dairy products in 1964. The products, the imports of which were limited, were Colby cheese, fluid cream, and Junex, a 44-percent butterfat and 56-percent sugar product. In acknowledging these arrangements, the Secretary of Agriculture noted that if imports from all sources substantially exceeded the shipments of these three major suppliers, the United States would have to proceed to section 22 action.

This 1963 arrangement was the model later used in 1964 to control imports of meat products.

TERRENCE W. McCABE *became Chief of the Foreign Agricultural Service's Import Branch, which is concerned with the control of imports of agricultural products, in 1962. His career with the Department of Agriculture began in 1937, when he joined the Crop Reporting Service.*

The Trade Expansion Act

by IRWIN R. HEDGES

THE TRADE EXPANSION Act of 1962 gave the President authority to enter into trade agreements until June 30, 1967—a period of 5 years.

The heart of the act was section 201, which granted the President the authority to reduce the rate of duties existing on July 1, 1962, by not more than 50 percent. Based on 1961 imports, the value of agricultural imports subject to the 50-percent rule was about 1 billion dollars.

Under certain conditions, the President was authorized to go beyond a 50-percent reduction and eliminate duties entirely.

Section 202 gave him authority to do so on any article for which the duty existing on July 1, 1962, was 5 percent or less. Based on the value of agricultural imports for 1961, goods worth about 309 million dollars, or 651 million dollars including certain forest and naval stores, were imported at a duty of 5 percent or less.

Section 211 pertained to any article in which the United States and the European Economic Community together accounted for 80 percent or more of the free world exports. Agricultural products were specifically excluded from this provision, however.

In the trade agreements with the European Economic Community on agricultural items, the President under section 212 was given authority to eliminate the duty if he determined that such action would tend to maintain or expand United States exports of like items.

Under section 213, duties could be eliminated entirely on tropical, agricultural, and forestry commodities if more than half of the world production was between 20° north latitude and 20° south latitude, if they were not produced in the United States in significant quantities, and if the European Economic Community made a commitment on a substantially nondiscriminatory basis with respect to import treatment of the commodity that was likely to assure access to its markets comparable to our market.

The value of United States imports in 1961 of products subject to this provision amounted to 167 million dollars.

With the exception of the tropical, agricultural, and forestry products provision, in general, all tariff concessions granted had to be staged in five annual installments.

Section 225 provided for the reservation of certain items from negotiations: Those included in proclamations under the national security provision; those included in proclamations under the escape clause provision and in cases under the escape clause provision where the Tariff Commission by majority vote found injury or threat of injury from imports; and those included in the proclamation of the President's authority to negotiate international agreements limiting the exports from foreign countries and our imports.

Section 252 of the act was also of special interest to agricultural trade. It directed the President to do everything feasible within his power to obtain the removal of unjustifiable foreign import restrictions that impair the value of tariff commitments made to the United States, oppress the commerce of the United States or prevent the expansion of mutually beneficial trade; to refrain from negotiating further concessions in order to obtain the reduction or elimination

of such restrictions; and to the extent deemed necessary impose duties or other import restrictions on the imports from any country that imposed such unjustifiable restrictions against United States agricultural products.

The act did not change basically the procedure required before the President can enter into a trade agreement.

The act called for the President to publish a list of items that were being considered for tariff reductions. The list had to specify the pertinent statutory authority if more than a 50-percent reduction were offered.

Under the act, the Tariff Commission was required to make a study of and hold public hearings on the items appearing on the list. The Commission was required to make findings known to the President as to the probable effects of the proposed offers on the domestic producers.

The President was required to seek advice from the various departments of the Government with respect to the proposed trade agreement. The act also required the President to have public hearings by an agency or interagency committee concerning any proposed trade agreements.

The act provided for the appointment by the President of a Special Representative for Trade Negotiations to exercise direction over the negotiations and other activities authorized under the act. In effect, this created an officer, reporting directly to the President at Cabinet level, to be in charge of the negotiations. Formerly this function was assigned to the Department of State.

THE ACT was the most important piece of trade legislation since the passage of the original Reciprocal Trade Agreements Act of 1934.

That act, passed in 1934, threw back the tide of protectionism that reached its high water mark with the passage of the Smoot-Hawley Tariff Act of 1930 and committed the United States to a policy of trade liberalization. Under the authorities of the original Reciprocal Trade Agreements Act and successive amendments, United States tariffs were significantly reduced.

The principle of most-favored-nation treatment provided for in this act has been incorporated in all agreements negotiated under the General Agreement on Tariffs and Trade. This principle requires that any tariff reduction negotiated bilaterally with any one country automatically is extended to all other friendly countries. In practice, it has multiplied manyfold the benefits of the tariff reductions that have been negotiated.

Since 1947 the United States negotiations, utilizing the authorities of the Reciprocal Trade Agreements Act, have been carried out within the framework of the General Agreement on Tariffs and Trade (GATT), an international organization established to work out rules of international trade and to police trade agreements.

The fifth round of tariff negotiations conducted under the auspices of the GATT, which was concluded in March 1962, was primarily with the European Economic Community (EEC). The purpose was to substitute the tariff bindings, which the six individual member countries of the EEC had with other countries, for one common external tariff (CXT) on imports from all non-EEC countries.

In the course of the negotiations, the European Economic Community offered to make a general across-the-board cut of 20 percent in individual tariffs in exchange for a similar cut by other countries.

The United States, under its legislation, could negotiate only on an item-by-item basis and hence could not accept this offer. It was partly in response to this situation that President Kennedy sought and obtained from the Congress the broad tariff-cutting authorities contained in the Trade Expansion Act of 1962.

The Congress, in enacting the Trade Expansion Act of 1962, and the executive branch of the Government subsequently made it clear that the negotiations had to include trade in agricultural products. In part, this reflected a feeling that the GATT negotiations in the past had not adequately dealt with agricultural trade.

The GATT negotiations before 1964 for the most part had focused on reductions in barriers maintained at the frontiers and hence had largely been concerned with tariffs. In agriculture, tariffs maintained against imports were frequently not the most significant factor restricting trade. Virtually all major trading nations had domestic farm programs that interfered with the free movement of goods internationally.

These programs were basically the agricultural counterpart of minimum wage laws, social security, labor legislation, postal and transport subsidies, and a host of other types of special-interest legislation. In addition, agricultural programs were frequently inspired by reasons of national security and the desire for social and political reasons to maintain a strong and independent farm population.

For whatever reasons they had developed, the existence of national agricultural programs seriously compromised the willingness of most nations to negotiate agricultural trade liberalization. By one means or another, ways had been devised to exempt from the rules of the GATT measures considered essential for the carrying out of national agricultural policies.

The United States was no exception, although it had followed a relatively liberal policy toward competing agricultural imports. Most competitive imports entered the United States over moderate fixed duties and no other barriers.

The United States did seek and obtain from the GATT a waiver of section 22 of the Agricultural Adjustment Act of 1933. This section directs the Secretary of Agriculture to recommend to the President the establishment of quotas on imports if he has reason to believe that imports are interfering or threaten to interfere with the operation of domestic price support or production control programs. The waiver granted the United States simply provides GATT authorization in advance for invoking section 22 whenever required.

IN ACTUAL PRACTICE, the United States has received little advantage from its special waiver.

Article XI of the GATT permits any GATT member to impose restrictions on imports when necessary to the enforcement of governmental measures restricting domestic production or marketing of the like article. Only imports of cotton, wheat, peanuts, and certain dairy products were subject to section 22 restrictions in 1964. Of these, only dairy products were not subject to production and marketing restrictions and hence very likely could not be justified under article XI.

In practice, also, it has been customary for the GATT to approve members' requests to impose import restrictions under special circumstances such as to make effective domestic price-support programs.

Throughout Western Europe following the Second World War, agricultural protectionism gained ascendancy as an aftermath of the food shortages and privations suffered during the war. The United Kingdom, by means of a deficiency-payments program that guaranteed her farmers returns far above prices of competing imports, substantially increased domestic production at the expense of imports. She decreased the proportion imports represent of total consumption from 1939–1940 to 1961 as follows: Wheat from 77 percent to 62 percent; feed grain from 59 percent to 40 percent; meat from 52 percent to 36 percent.

The emerging Common Agricultural Policy (CAP) of the EEC loomed as the greatest obstacle to progress in liberalizing agricultural trade. In the last round of GATT negotiations, the European Economic Community refused to offer fixed tariff bindings on most agricultural imports that competed with its own domestic production. The products affected included wheat, feed grain, rice, poultry, meats, and dairy products. Instead, it was announced that these products would be subjected to a system of variable levies and minimum import prices to be set later.

The variable levy system of the EEC, like the British system of deficiency payments, guaranteed its own producers an opportunity to supply the domestic market up to 100 percent of its requirements. The levy was simply the difference between the offering price on imports at the frontier and the domestic support or target price.

If prices at which imports were offered fell, the variable levy increased; the more efficient exporter could not improve his access to the EEC market by lowering his prices. This was in marked contrast to the situation in which a fixed duty was the sole or main protection against imports.

When fixed duties are the form of protection used, the efficient exporter can freely compete with domestic producers in supplying the market after paying the import duty.

THE POSTWAR TREND toward greater agricultural protectionism must be halted and reversed if we are to have more liberal international trade rules for agricultural products.

The negotiations that take place under the Trade Expansion Act, to have significance for trade in agricultural products, will have to deal with features of domestic agricultural policies, such as variable levies, deficiency payments, and price supports, that affect international prices and the quantity of products that move in world trade.

That would represent a new approach to trade negotiations, as was pointed out by Sicco Mansholt, Vice President of the Commission of the EEC at the GATT Ministers Meeting in Geneva in May 1963.

National agricultural policies, he said, are decisive for world trade, and the negotiations must deal with the critical elements of those policies.

Dr. Mansholt made it clear that in his judgment all participants, both importing and exporting nations, must be willing to include critical elements of domestic agricultural policies in the negotiations. The United States indicated it was willing to do so on a reciprocal basis.

The attitude of other industrialized countries toward the inclusion of critical elements of domestic agricultural policies in the negotiations will be crucial.

The European Economic Community, the United Kingdom, Canada, and Japan account for nearly 75 percent of United States commercial exports. If the other countries of western Europe are included, the percentage rises to almost 85 percent.

In industrialized countries, it is a fact that agricultural production under the influence of technology and scientific advancement is tending to increase more rapidly than consumption.

Where farm returns are maintained at artificially high levels, this is dramatically so—as indicated in the statistics on imports and production for the United Kingdom I cited. Japan is perhaps an exception, since her agricultural resources are meager in relation to her population and economy. Japanese demand for agricultural raw materials, and hence imports, may continue to increase.

We already have a very favorable trade in agricultural products with Canada. This is not expected to change significantly. The agricultural phase of the negotiations under the new Trade Expansion Act will focus on western Europe. Primarily that means the European Economic Community and the United Kingdom. In each instance, positive results will depend on the extent to which limits can be negotiated on the trade restrictive effects of domestic policies. With respect to the United Kingdom, that would involve limitations on the British system of deficiency payments; with respect to the European Economic Community, it would involve limitations on the trade restrictive effects of variable levies and minimum import prices.

Under the variable levy system of the European Economic Community, the most crucial element of interest to exporting nations is the level of internal prices, since the variable levy is simply the difference between prices of imported goods at the frontier and the level of prices maintained on the domestic market. The higher domestic price levels, the higher the variable levies on imports, assuming no change in world prices. Efforts to negotiate maximums in variable levies, to be meaningful to exporting nations, must therefore focus on internal prices.

Under the CAP regulations of the EEC, the level of grain prices is crucial. Not only are grains the most significant commodity group, from a trade standpoint; the level of grain prices likewise affects directly the prices of all meats, dairy and poultry products, and hence the import levies on these products as well. This results from the fact that the largest single element in the levies on livestock and poultry products is likely to be a feed equalization fee, representing the difference in cost between EEC domestic and world prices of the quantity of feed required to produce a unit of livestock or poultry products. This is the procedure that has been adopted for the poultry regulation, and the same principle likely will be applied to the meat and dairy regulations.

Recognizing the difficulties inherent in negotiating rules of trade in major agricultural commodities and the inadequacy of conventional tariff bindings as a mechanism for this purpose, the GATT ministers at their meeting in May 1963 directed that special groups be established for the cereals, meats, and dairy products so as to develop international commodity arrangements for these products.

The United States first took the position that to the maximum extent possible agricultural products should be subject to the across-the-board linear reduction formula adopted. The Trade Expansion Act permits the United States to negotiate reductions in tariffs up to 50 percent, and the policy is to use this authority to the maximum. The United States has indicated a willingness, however, to cooperate in working out the rules of trade for cereals, meats, and dairy products in special groups.

The success of these groups in executing their task may well influence the outcome of the entire negotiations under the Trade Expansion Act.

The United States has said that it cannot conclude another round of trade negotiations unless its major agricultural commodities moving into export markets are included in a meaningful way.

Countries that depend heavily on agricultural products for their export earnings, such as Australia, New Zealand, Argentina, and Canada, likewise would have difficulty in participating in a general round of tariff negotiations, unless they were assured improved outlets for their agricultural exports.

As a minimum, the United States and other agricultural exporting nations will be seeking maintenance of access to major commercial markets comparable to that which existed in a recent representative period of years.

If this is not attainable, it is difficult to see how the hopes for an era of more liberal and expanding international trade generated by the passage of the Trade Expansion Act can be realized.

With imagination and ingenuity, it should be possible to reconcile the legitimate objectives of national agricultural policies with the equally desirable objectives of freer trade. The United States intends to use the powers the Congress has provided under the Trade Expansion Act of 1962 to that end.

IRWIN R. HEDGES *is agricultural trade specialist in the Office of the Special Representative for Trade Negotiations, Executive Office of the President.*

The Requirements of Buyers

by JAMES O. HOWARD

WHETHER THEY are selling corn to consumers in England, cotton to spinners in Japan, or soybean oil to processors in Spain, American exporters must know the requirements of their customers. What works in the United States may not work in London, Hong Kong, or Accra. In some markets, it may be a matter of education. In others, it may be necessary to change the product.

The American food production and processing industry starts out with certain advantages in selling overseas. It is among the world's largest and has many years of experience in meeting the various needs of American consumers. Our well-developed canning industry has some excellent controls for flavor, color, sanitation, uniformity of pack, and packaging. Our system for marketing bulk commodities enables us to move products like grain and cotton over long distances at far less cost than most competing countries. Our large stocks, variety of types, and dependable sources of supply give us an important advantage over many countries. Our sanitary regulations and standards enhance the export of our agricultural products. Our market research, market testing, and market promotion have been watched with considerable interest overseas.

With all these advantages, one may well wonder that there should be any problems. But there are. Even with agricultural exports of 5 billion dollars and more a year, five-sixths of our agricultural market is still here at home. Much of the thinking in the trade thus is pointed toward the domestic market. Some firms have been unwilling to take on the additional problems of selling overseas. Others have looked at foreign markets as a place to sell the supplies they could not market in the United States.

Domestic buyers, being closer to the production areas and better informed about them, sometimes acquire the choicest qualities and leave to foreign buyers the less desirable ones, although in some of the more specialized exporting countries the best often is reserved for export and the balance is retained for consumption at home.

Part of this lack of proper respect for the needs of foreign customers is the result of the food shortages of the Second World War and the years that followed, when an American exporter could easily sell almost anything.

After the Korean conflict, our competition from some other countries has grown measurably keener each year.

The United States agricultural industry has been adjusting itself to this realization. The program to develop foreign markets for agricultural products is part of that reaction.

A NECESSARY PRELIMINARY step for exporters of agricultural products is to develop a marketing plan.

A food processor thinking of entering the foreign market may employ a firm to take over the entire job.

Another establishment may want to handle its own exporting. It would need to become familiar with the needs of its potential customers before making any marketing plans. It would need to know where to start and how to proceed in that market. Only after an exporter has become familiar with all the problems and possible avenues of approach will he be ready to engage in a full-fledged selling operation.

After determining the market, research—a thorough investigation—will show what changes to make in the product and its merchandising

The importance of such research was emphasized in an article by Albert Stridsberg in Advertising Age. He stated that the rate of failures of new products of United States companies in Europe is high and includes little-known companies as well as substantial numbers of our largest advertisers.

Even a small country may have diverse marketing situations. It is not enough to test only the major market in a foreign country. Belgium, for example, is not just one market. It has three distinct areas: Flanders, the Brussels-Antwerp metropolitan axis, and the Walloon sections of southern Belgium.

TASTES, HABITS, AND PREJUDICES in food and clothing differ from country to country.

Consumers in Thailand, for example, favor highly spiced foods and, like consumers everywhere, generally are suspicious of foods they do not know. Orange must not be used on a package because the color is associated with the saffron robes of Buddhist priests. White stands for mourning in some countries, as black does in this country. In others, purple is reserved for royalty.

Customs and tastes may be deep rooted. For example, the Boston market prefers and gets eggs with brown shells. People in New York City insist on white eggs. Italians prefer a yellow-pigmented chicken, believing that the yellow denotes fat and a more healthful product. Consumers in the Netherlands prefer a white-fleshed bird. The color of the poultry is due largely to the feed the birds get. Flint corn, such as that from Argentina, produces a yellower bird than does dent corn from the United States.

United States exporters of feed grain meet the Italians' preference for yellow-pigmented birds in several ways. They encourage Italians to use dehydrated alfalfa meal in mixed feeds to give an extra yellow to the birds.

American poultry breeders have begun to breed birds that tend to have more yellow pigment regardless of the feeds. At the same time, Italian consumers are advised that white-pigmented birds are as healthy as the yellow ones. For the Netherlands and some other European countries, United States poultry breeders have been attempting to breed white-fleshed birds.

I give another example: Right after the Second World War, the United States sent an emergency relief shipment of rice to a country in the Far East. It was a glutinous rice, a type that normally is unacceptable to the people of that country. They were hungry and ate the rice, but the experience has been remembered and has made it more difficult for American rice to move to that country. Similarly, Germans during the war ate a meat substitute made of soybeans. The product was nourishing, but was so alien to German tastes that it left a prejudice in the German mind against anything made of soybeans.

LABELING REQUIREMENTS and weights and measures also differ.

Pounds and pints mean little to people who think in terms of kilograms and liters. Continental Europe, much of Latin America, and several countries in Asia, including Japan, use the metric system.

England and Commonwealth countries use measures different from ours, although the names are the same. The English bushel is 3 percent larger than ours, and their gallon is 20 percent larger.

The Japanese insist that only the metric system be used. American exporters therefore have to print a special label or overprint the unit measurements in the metric system.

Some countries require that the label show the date canned goods were packed. In the United States, the date is stamped into the can.

Our laws permit the marking of the country of origin any place on the package as long as it is legible. France insists that it be embossed on the end of the can. That means additional expense and a separate group of cans.

In the Philippines, a private brand name has to be secondary to that of NAMARCO, the National Marketing Corporation in the Philippines.

Some of the differences are a matter of custom. American housewives measure dry ingredients and want recipes stated in tablespoons and cups. Many countries want the measures expressed in terms of dry ingredients, but insist that the recipes on the package be in terms of weights.

Brand names may mean different things in the different countries. One brand name, when translated into another language, turned out to be a vulgar word. One promoter used the flags of the world on its emblem and found that the products could not get into certain Arab countries, since the flag of Israel was included.

PACKAGING, package size, and adaptation to climate are important. As one voice of experience put it, "One of the tremendous mistakes being made is the assumption that because your package has been successful here it will be successful overseas."

Crackers and cookies packed in the typical American paper envelopes and pasteboard boxes would soon become soggy in the high humidity of the Tropics. Once I saw crackers being vacuum sealed in tin boxes in the Philippines. The cost of the packaging was probably several times more than the value of the crackers, but the additional expense was considered necessary in that country.

The exporter of canned food faces such packaging questions as size and fill of containers and damage to cans. In one country, 22 sizes of cans of fruit were being imported from several competing countries. Some of the sizes varied little from those common in that country. Some varied a great deal. Pity the poor foreign consumer who tries to shop and compare values, particularly if the volume of the con-

THE REQUIREMENTS OF BUYERS

tents is stated in many different ways!

Dented cans are a problem for importers. In a Department of Agriculture study, *Fresh Fruits on the London Market*, by H. L. Harrington, the author concluded: "The matter of dents came up almost every time canned foods were discussed. The survey team was shown numerous piles of dented cans which were discarded and other lots which were for sale at salvage prices. . . . It was suggested repeatedly that the use of lighter gauge steel in can-making was the principal cause. Others blamed poor case or can design. . . . One consoling factor was that [cans from] the United States compared favorably with other countries."

Some years ago the United States was losing a valuable market for high-quality eggs in Venezuela. Breakage was a special problem, and the eggs were not arriving in the condition required. Men from industry and the Government designed a special export container, which solved the breakage problem. Although the market later was lost when Venezuela began to produce its own eggs, the same type of containers has been used to ship eggs from the United States to the Congo.

American exporters are trying to cut down breakage and bruises to food packaged in fiber containers by reducing the number of times the containers are handled. The piggyback refrigerated trailer system, designed for domestic truck and train combination hauls, is being used between ship and truck. Citrus fruit has been loaded into such trailers in Lakeland, Fla., trucked to Jacksonville, shipped by boat to the west coast of France, and trucked across Europe to the warehouse of a grocery chain in Switzerland. Poultry is moved in the same way to Caribbean markets. Tropical fruit is shipped in the refrigerated trailers on the return.

The sizes of packages and products must be considered carefully. Our cake mixes make bigger cakes than consumers in some countries want. Many of our choice turkeys are too large for European ovens. An Italian importer of American poultry found that our broilers were not selling well. On investigation he discovered the reason: The birds weighed more than 2.5 pounds. The Italian restaurants served poultry in half-chicken or quarter-chicken portions. Since the Italian Government did not permit them to raise the price of their meals, they needed fully matured birds of about 2 pounds that could produce some profit.

FOOD HEALTH LAWS of foreign countries create problems. They differ from country to country.

Since the war, interest overseas in legislation as to pure food has increased, especially in the use of additives to food and feed and preharvest and postharvest chemical treatments. West Germany and other Common Market countries have adopted a number of laws pertaining to food. When foreign laws differ from those of the United States, the American exporter has a problem.

Some examples of the effect of regulations on trade:

Fresh citrus fruit, treated with decay-inhibiting chemicals and waxes that are acceptable in the United States, must be labeled at retail in Germany to indicate that the peel should not be eaten. The requirement tends to create an unfavorable reaction to the fruit, but actually the consumer's health is not endangered. German scientists generally admit this, but efforts to change the law have been slow.

Citrus Red No. 2, a harmless dye approved by the United States Food and Drug Administration, has not been approved for use in any European country except Sweden. Early Florida oranges therefore are not admitted in most of western Europe. The dye is used on the skin of certain Florida oranges that do not have the bright orange color many consumers expect.

France promulgated a directive barring imports of poultry from countries that use certain growth factors in the feed, apparently in the belief that the chemicals make the poultry unfit for human consumption.

West Germany and several other countries prohibit the use of bleaching, maturing, and oxidizing agents in the milling of flour. The substances are required in the United States to obtain the proper baking qualities. Hard winter wheat, of which the United States is a major supplier, requires this treatment more than hard spring wheat. Our hard winter wheat therefore is at a competitive disadvantage in some countries.

The European Economic Community, which takes more than 30 percent of the total dollar exports of United States agricultural items, has undertaken to unify food regulations of member countries. The major areas of work are food additives, wine, meat and meat preparations, eggs, and various types of seeds. United States exporters are anxious to see EEC regulations written that are not in conflict with United States regulations and will not put United States firms at a competitive disadvantage in EEC.

UNIVERSALLY ACCEPTED international standards would eliminate many of the difficulties caused by conflicting food laws and regulations.

Some help in that end may come from a joint program of food standards of the Food and Agriculture Organization and the World Health Organization, with which the United States is actively cooperating. These organizations have set up a Food Code Commission (Codex Alimentarius Commission), whose purpose is to simplify and harmonize food standards.

The Commission has established committees of experts to coordinate and supplement the work of other bodies in this field. Draft standards developed in this way and approved by the governments are published in a consolidated international code. The ambitious project covers a large number of food products, many types of processing for which standards must be developed, and such diverse sub-jects as food additives, pesticides and residues, and labeling.

The United States Department of Agriculture meanwhile has taken steps to inform European scientists about our food laws. Several food scientists recommended by the National Academy of Sciences and similar bodies went to Europe in 1963 to discuss the problems with their foreign counterparts. A scientist of the Department is stationed in Europe to carry on this exchange of information on a continuing basis. European scientists visit the United States to consult with our scientists and see our inspection operations. Technical information on these subjects is sent regularly to technical and popular publications. American trade groups, which are cooperating with the Department in the development of oversea markets, have participated in these activities.

THE NEED for a common language of price quotations must be faced when a United States firm begins export selling. It finds that the foreign buyer normally does not pay with dollars, but with his own currency, and wants the price quoted in that currency.

Some American merchants prefer to quote in United States units rather than foreign measures. Others quote prices at the United States port, rather than adding the shipping and insurance and telling the importer what the goods will cost in his own country. Shippers who are serious about the export business generally make adjustments in these matters, however.

For bulk commodities and some processed foods there must be a grade, a basis for judging the quality of the merchandise. There are physical samples of some grades, like cotton, but most are only written descriptions. A foreign buyer who handles a wide range of our products may regard the nomenclature of our grades as a jungle.

The Agricultural Marketing Service of the Department of Agriculture has developed 365 grade standards for farm products. Some States have their own grades. The Federal grades are applied by Federal and licensed Federal-State inspectors, who issue Federal or Federal-State certificates, which are used in varying degrees.

Because of the wide variety of agricultural commodities for which grades have been developed and the variations in usage of grade terms in trading, it has not been feasible to establish uniform grade terminology. Thus, "U.S. No. 1" will be the top grade for one commodity and the second grade for another. The nomenclature runs through such terms as U.S. Grade A, Prime, 90 score, Middling, Fancy, Colossal, and Class I Flue Cured.

About 150 grades pertain to fresh fruit and vegetables, and an equal number to processed fruit and vegetables. No foreign importer deals with more than a small percentage of the commodities involved in these grades, but the problem still is complex.

Standards and related questions on quality of deliveries are being studied by the Department of Agriculture and trade associations.

United States standards are compared with foreign standards, tables of equivalents are prepared, and samples that accompany shipments to oversea destinations are examined periodically to determine whether any changes have occurred during transit under varying physical conditions.

The Food Code Commission is working on uniform standards. A number of Americans are members of its technical groups. The Organization for Economic Cooperation and Development has begun to coordinate its efforts to develop uniform grades with those of the Commission.

FOR GRAIN EXPORTS, United States Government standards are especially important, because practically all sales are made "U.S. Certificates Final"— that is, if the seller furnishes a Department of Agriculture certificate showing that the grade is for the quality specified in the contract, the buyer must accept it.

The United States standards for grades of wheat have been tightened as a means of increasing dollar sales of American wheat in oversea markets.

New standards, which became effective June 1, 1964, are based on smaller ranges of tolerance for grades. That means less dirt, foreign matter, and dockage in American wheat than in earlier years. Previous standards had too great a tolerance within grades to provide a reliable basis for judging soundness or cleanliness.

Foreign buyers attach considerable importance to the physical characteristics and grade tolerances for wheat, but they also want information on the baking quality and other performance qualities. A test for protein content was established some years ago on an optional or permissive basis for wheat exports. It is used to some extent to measure the quantity of protein, but because it does not allow for the wide variation in the quality of protein, a second test—the sedimentation test— was added in 1961 to measure this factor. Although less precise than some tests used in the domestic trade, it is quick and inexpensive and is being accepted as a useful measure.

Beginning with the 1962 crop, the sedimentation test was made part of the Government loan program. Farmers are thus paid partly on the basis of the baking quality of their wheat.

The Commodity Credit Corporation in 1963 launched an experimental program whereby 6 million bushels of wheat of known sedimentation and protein were segregated for sales to the trade.

In the program, the Commodity Credit Corporation took the risk of any deterioration of these factors in storage and stood ready to make the necessary guarantees when the wheat was loaded aboard ship. Officials have expressed the hope that the system, known as Identity Preserved (I.P.), would open new markets for the types of quality wheat the United States can supply.

QUALITY OF THE PRODUCT is an important and widely debated aspect of agricultural exporting.

Most American exporters guard jealously the reputation of their products in foreign markets. A study of canned and dried fruit in the London market by Department workers disclosed that our canned fruit was so highly regarded in that market before the war that it was used by British buyers as type samples of what they wanted from other countries.

Exporters agree generally that selling low-quality products abroad without clearly representing them for what they are is bad.

Speaking of the period immediately after the war, a specialist in European marketing noted that the "dumping" of substantial quantities of poor processed foods in Europe probably set back the introduction of modern convenience foods by 10 years.

The debate hinges around what to do with a product which is healthful but which some consider to be of low quality—wheat with a high percentage of broken kernels, dressed chicken with a wing missing, or the off-color apple, for instance.

The problem is acute in grain, of which we produce many varieties in many places of different climates and soil conditions. That and our system of grain handling give us many qualities.

An experienced American exporter of grain said: "We have qualities to fit every need and every pocketbook. Never make the mistake of being an apologist for United States quality or let anyone persuade you to talk about quality without talking about price, for they are inseparable."

There are others in the United States who believe that we should not allow low-quality products to be exported. They point to a country like Denmark, which has strict controls of quality on most exports of food. The word "Denmark" is displayed on labels along with the brand name. Their advertising slogan is: "It's good. It's from Denmark." Denmark also has done much to standardize its exports. Danish poultry and ham are exported under a common brand. Other countries permit only one or two grades to enter foreign markets.

Such controls among our competitors frequently are exercised through governmental or quasi-governmental boards, which have power to regulate and promote exports. They have some advantages over private United States trade. Denmark has nine government boards for such commodities as butter, cheese, bacon, and poultry. Australia has seven.

The Deciduous Fruit Board of South Africa goes a step further. It selects a few British importers to handle all their exports of fruit to the United Kingdom. The importers agree to use resources of their own to promote the use of South African fruit.

The United States has had some experiences in mandatory export quality control. Special export grade requirements have been set up for apples, pears, and Emperor grapes under two specific Federal laws. The regulations prohibit exports of these fruits (with minor exceptions) that do not meet a specified grade. Emperor grapes must have a specified degree of ripeness. For apples and pears, factors of condition are not mandatory but have been written into "Condition Standards for Export," which may be specified in contracts by buyers.

As to products that receive further processing abroad, such as cotton, soybeans, and grain, the problems differ from consumer products, such as frozen poultry, canned goods, and fresh fruit. For most commodities, however, competition in quality has been increasing in foreign markets.

Selling abroad, then, is more complex than selling at home. In some aspects, notably food health laws, the complexity has been increasing.

On the other hand, American exporters have advantages in research, merchandising, quality control, and mass production and distribution developed in the domestic and foreign market.

In DEPICTING the complexities of foreign marketing, I have described more complex situations than those of a firm that is interested in only one or two foreign markets. That firm may be able to solve all the exporting problems itself. When many markets are involved, however, and the problems seem beyond the scope of the exporting firm, help may be needed.

Combination export managers may be willing to take over the whole job. They handle a variety of products (hence the term "combination") and one or more of them may be represented in most port towns. They vary in size. A large one working in the Pacific area, for example, may have offices in a number of port cities of the countries being served and may work with importers in other cities.

Such a firm would study the products of a client and perhaps suggest a contract to undertake research in certain areas. Test selling may follow. If results are favorable, they may sign a contract with the exporter to become his foreign sales representative. Their charge is a percentage of the gross sales—perhaps 10 to 15 percent of gross sales, or more if they render unusual services, such as the hiring of extra employees to specialize in the firm's products and the development of advertising campaigns.

The United States Departments of Commerce and Agriculture have a wealth of materials for exporters—general background studies, lists of importers, and descriptions of import regulations. Steamship lines and American banks operating overseas have collected similar information and are willing to discuss export problems with customers. They handle details of shipping and international banking.

Overseas, American embassies, with their agricultural and commercial attachés, and representatives of American banks and shipping companies offer help with information and contacts. There are importers in most countries who may be interested in representing United States firms.

At a WHITE HOUSE CONFERENCE on Export Expansion in 1963, a goal was set of bringing 10 thousand additional firms into the export business.

It is to be expected that most of the firms that respond will turn much of the work over to others. All, though, should approach the possibility of oversea trade with the intention of finding out what the foreign consumer wants and meeting or changing those wants.

If he runs into problems on which governmental help is needed, he should seek that help. For example, if Japanese buyers want soybeans for food products that have a low oil content and beans for oil with a high oil content, both needs should possibly be reflected in the breeding programs of our experiment stations.

If there are alternative systems of farm income supports and one system gives more opportunity to meeting foreign price competition than the other, perhaps this can be given more consideration in determining policy for the products that depend on exports.

It may be that research stations should be working on other aspects of foreign marketing, such as the processing and packaging of exports.

Even the setting of domestic freight rates is important, as was shown when reduced freight rates for wheat moving to the west coast enabled the United States to compete on more favorable terms with Canadian wheat in the Japanese market.

There are many problems in international trade, but they are not insurmountable. Many exporters already have found the answers, and success is possible for others who are ready to meet the needs of foreign buyers.

JAMES O. HOWARD *became Director of the Trade Projects Division of the Foreign Agricultural Service in 1958. He has particular responsibility for assisting in the coordinating of special programs to stimulate American agricultural exports. The programs are carried out in cooperation with 44 agricultural and trade groups. He joined the Department of Agriculture in 1939.*

Cooperative

Programs

by DAVID L. HUME

THAT EXPORTS of agricultural products are a fourth of the value of all exports of the United States is largely the result of several programs that create, maintain, and expand our market.

Most foreign programs in a broad sense influence in some measure the building of foreign markets for United States agricultural products: Programs for economic development, defense assistance, banking and credit, donations of surplus foods and other commodities, educational exchange and research, and other foreign activities.

Directly related to increasing agricultural exports are the programs of the Department of Agriculture for barter, sales based on the extension of both short-term and long-term credit, price assistance, and international trade fairs and centers and exhibitions.

Most directly and specifically designed for building export markets for American agricultural goods are the foreign market development programs of the Foreign Agricultural Service. In them, individual projects are operated for the purpose of developing and maintaining commercial export markets for specific commodities.

The projects are carried out under the authority and impetus of the Agricultural Trade Development and Assistance Act of 1954—Public Law 480. Section 104(a) of the law provides for the use of foreign currencies "to help

develop new markets for United States agricultural commodities on a mutually benefiting basis."

Among other things, Public Law 480 (title I) provides for the sale of surplus United States agricultural commodities for shipment to and consumption in selected friendly countries.

Factors considered in qualifying countries for title I sales are as follows: The participating country's needs, economic status, and foreign exchange position; effect on dollar sales and other export programs; effect on export markets of other supplying countries; the relationship of the program to foreign aid programs and overall foreign policies of the United States. Title I sales are made by American firms to foreign buyers—sometimes a foreign government and sometimes a commercial importer.

At the completion of a properly consummated sale under title I of Public Law 480, the United States exporter receives United States dollars from the United States Government in payment for the goods sold. In turn, the United States Government receives as its compensation an equivalent amount in the currency of the country to which the surplus agricultural commodities are shipped.

Foreign currencies paid to the United States under the law are deposited to a United States account in the foreign country, thus becoming United States property. The law requires that 5 percent of the foreign currencies generated under title I be set aside for market development uses and that 2 percent be authorized for conversion to currencies other than those of the country to which the goods have been sold.

Foreign currencies, through conversion, therefore are used to support market development in countries where there is no Public Law 480 program as well as in countries where there is one.

There are 20 specific uses to which foreign currency may be put. One of these is for "104(a) market development," to which I referred.

The major part of the market development program is the part that is carried out in cooperation with a number of trade organizations, which represent United States agricultural producers, processors, and distributors. They contribute United States money, personnel, supervision, and program management and experience.

The Foreign Agricultural Service contributes foreign money and supports the market development program otherwise in many ways. Marketing specialists are available to work with industry organizations. Trade statistics are furnished. The agricultural attachés may be program advisers and channels between the program and American embassies.

The trade organization sometimes is referred to as a cooperator and the program itself as a cooperative program.

I GIVE an example of the steps in which 104(a) foreign currencies may be used to develop markets.

Assume that the producers and processors of agricultural Commodity X, organized in a trade organization, see an opportunity to increase exports through promotional activities. The following outline depicts a typical sequence of steps that may be taken by the Commodity X group to set up a cooperative program.

The group confers with commodity specialists of the Foreign Agricultural Service. They jointly conclude, on the basis of facts at hand, that a cooperative foreign market development program could reasonably be expected to increase commercial exports of Commodity X.

A survey team is organized. It comprises qualified members of the Commodity X industry and Commodity X marketing specialists of the Foreign Agricultural Service. The team travels to the countries selected as targets for increasing foreign sales of Commodity X, conferring, as appropriate, with United States agricultural attachés; foreign government officials; importers, processors, distributors, retailers, and others familiar with the markets for Commodity X in the particular foreign country. A report is made of findings.

Assume that the survey team has now determined and reported the scope of the existing market for Commodity X in the selected countries; the existing United States share in this market; the nature and importance of the competition both from local producers and other importers; the kind and influence of import tariffs and the types of barriers to trade, if any; and a great many other factors, upon which it has based the conclusion that a permanent increase in United States exports can be effected by properly oriented and planned promotion.

At this point, the Commodity X trade group and the Foreign Agricultural Service decide to engage in a cooperative program. This decision is formalized by a program agreement signed by both parties. It becomes the basic document pursuant to which the Service and the Commodity X cooperator enter into specific projects.

The survey team may have recommended promotion activities in as many as five or six countries; specific promotion activities would then be authorized by a project for each country.

For ease of administration, one project may authorize the same promotion activities for a group of selected countries, but promotional activities in any given country are authorized only after they have been approved in a formal project.

Assume that FAS and the cooperator decide to write a project authorizing the various types of promotional activities. Projects are in the nature of contracts in that they are signed by both parties (the Service and the cooperator).

They specify, among other things, the period the activity is to cover; limit the total amount and rate of expenditure for the money authorized; show a breakdown of the money to be provided by the Service and the cooperator; and specify reporting requirements.

The project defines the activities the cooperator may engage in.

They may include:

Public relations, designed to improve the acceptance for market development of a new commodity by foreign importers, wholesalers, retailers, and consumers.

Educational affairs, including conferences, seminars, and commodity classing and grading, which are aimed at increasing sales through the diffusion of knowledge about the commodity.

The point of sale, such as designing, printing, and distributing placards, banners, handbills, and similar items, usually for posting at retail counters.

Mobile exhibits, designed for mobility in bringing a sales message to a number of different markets. These may combine the techniques of education, point of sale, public relations, and other types of promotion. Mobile exhibits have visited many countries and hundreds of cities that otherwise would have been inaccessible to other promotion activities.

Demonstrations, in which technicians show how to prepare or use United States agricultural commodities. This technique is particularly effective at trade fairs, where large crowds congregate in short spans of time.

Advertising, designed to increase the United States share of the total market and frequently to promote foreign brands of goods consisting entirely or largely of United States farm products.

Contests or devices, designed to attract interest in a commodity and thereby increase sales through such devices as writing slogans, answering relatively simple questions, or submitting a coupon, which usually requests a free sample of the item.

Free samples may be distributed to target groups, such as schoolchildren or housewives, with the idea that a taste or test will stimulate a desire to buy the item for consumption on a repeating basis.

Special promotions, an acceleration of a number of promotional activities, pointed toward a big increase in sales for a particular holiday or season. Special promotions also include foreign tours by "queens" in American-made textiles; by winners of cooking contests; and other activities.

Surveys and evaluations, designed to assess existing programs so that promotion emphasis is directed toward the kind of activities potentially most fruitful and to find new areas of demand.

Visits by foreigners to the United States. These are designed to increase sales by introducing actual and potential foreign buyers to United States commodities in United States settings, and by bringing them into contact with various sellers. Leading opinionmakers, such as government officials, representatives of trade associations and chambers of commerce, and scientists, are invited to the United States to observe our marketing systems and production and processing.

Visits by United States representatives to foreign countries may be planned to increase agricultural exports by broadening the interest in foreign marketing among United States businessmen themselves; widening the lists of potential foreign customers of exporters; bringing to bear on potential customers the special sales impact that only the "man with the order book" can make.

The visits to America by foreigners and by Americans to foreign countries are among the most important of all market-development activities. It is difficult to assess the value in terms of dollars and cents of a two-way relationship, which develops on an increasingly friendly, and even personal, basis, between United States sellers and foreign buyers, but it is a key in successful market development.

Motion pictures and visual aids are used to inform foreign buyers in a number of different ways concerning a commodity, a group of commodities, or an industry. This technique also is used to raise the level of interest in foreign trade among United States sellers.

Next, a cooperator is expected to develop an overall marketing plan by which the promotional activities considered effective in a particular country are organized into a program.

Such a plan is formulated for each commodity and country. It takes into account the findings of the survey previously referred to and is based on the coordinated judgment of the cooperator, commodity specialists, and the agricultural attachés as to what the objectives should be and how they can be achieved.

The plan sets forth in detail the promotion program needed to fulfill specific marketing objectives, such as:

Increasing the United States share of the market for Commodity X from, say, 20 percent to 25 percent in a given country, or

slowing down the average rate of loss of the market by the United States in a given country for Commodity X from, say, 20 percent a year to 10 percent, or

introducing Commodity X on a relatively broad scale for purposes of testing the mass marketing for the commodity in a country where consumers have little knowledge of or familiarity with it, or

servicing the potential market in a given country that greatly needs Commodity X but cannot afford to import it as a usual commercial item. In so doing, the United States may expect to be a principal supplier when economic conditions permit commercial imports, or

maintaining the United States position in free markets for Commodity X by assuring the United States share in the future growth of such markets.

THE MARKETING PLAN indicates the actual activities authorized by the project and relates these activities to the fulfillment of its objectives.

Marketing plans are changed and amended on a trial-and-error basis, or as changing conditions dictate.

Finally comes the execution of the plan.

The cooperator now begins to engage in the activities, as indicated by the marketing plan, that appear likeliest to effect the desired objectives.

He obtains the support and assistance of marketing groups and institutions in the foreign country.

He may engage the services of public relations and advertising firms to assist in carrying out special promotions.

He establishes appropriate working relationships with local trade organizations; with governmental or quasi-governmental commodity boards; and with importers, processors, wholesalers, distributors, and retailers.

It is at this point in the execution of the plan that the pooled resources of foreign currency—provided under Public Law 480; United States dollars provided by the industry cooperator; and funds provided by the foreign industry—and the coordinated effort of all FAS and industry management functions come into focus in the form of a development program.

The plan calls for annual reports of activities by the cooperator and semiannual fiscal reports. The cooperative work is audited by independent auditing firms, Government agencies, and the cooperator himself.

Periodically, the agricultural attaché and his staff evaluate the activities and consult with the cooperator and otherwise engage in exchanges of information with him.

When the project has run its term, it is given a final evaluation. The results are assessed in terms of how successfully it has met the objectives.

The leadership for carrying out the development programs is provided by a coordinated relationship among four groups: The United States commodity group or trade organization; the commodity division of the Foreign Agricultural Service; the oversea office or representative of the United States commodity group; and the United States agricultural attaché in the country where the program is operated.

Since the foreign market development program began in 1955, the Foreign Agricultural Service has engaged in cooperative promotion with

44 industry organizations and groups, which have carried out more than 750 market projects in 67 countries.

Aggregate resources committed to foreign market development by these industry organizations and groups since the inception of the program— over and above the foreign currency resources they have received through the Service—reached an equivalent of more than 25 million dollars in 1964.

Trade cooperators have established 58 offices outside the United States and have more than 300 employees who work on market development.

The commodity divisions of the Foreign Agricultural Service are the basic organizational units in the Department of Agriculture through which cooperative foreign market development programs are operated. There are seven: Cotton; Dairy and Poultry; Fats and Oils; Fruit and Vegetable; Grain and Feed; Livestock and Meat Products; and Tobacco.

The Trade Projects Division provides the direct administrative support for the entire program. It works with all commodity divisions in obtaining the preparation and approval of program agreements and projects, budget and fiscal affairs, and other service-type activities.

The Trade Projects Division also operates the market development evaluation program and supports foreign market development in a number of ways by operating activities that do not lend themselves to a commodity-by-commodity approach.

The agricultural attaché is the principal Government official working outside the United States in foreign agricultural market development. He participates in the creation and approval of projects for the country in which he is located. He is a key official in approving the transfer of foreign currency from the account of the Government to the cooperator. He coordinates the foreign market development programs with the policies of the United States Ambassador in the country to which he is accredited.

He evaluates the value of the programs and reports on them.

The total authorization for the program in 1963 from all sources was about 22.7 million dollars. That is less than one-half of 1 percent of the total value—5 billion dollars—of all agricultural exports in 1963.

It is interesting to note that percentages relating to advertising by manufacturers for selected industries in the United States are indicated to be: For drugs and cosmetics, 15.4 percent; automobiles, 1.3; food, 4.3; soap and cleaners, 12.1 percent; and tobacco, 4.6 percent.

WORLD TRADE in agricultural products in 1962 has been estimated at a total value of 30.1 billion dollars (based on 1957–1959 prices). Although we have no estimate of the proportion of this trade that can be attributed to market development and promotion, we know that the friendly competitors of the United States have been engaged in extensive and varied activities to develop and expand foreign markets for their agricultural products.

I give brief reports on some of them.

Australia has participated in 40 major international fairs in more than 20 countries in Asia, Europe, New Zealand, and North America since 1949. Since 1954, she has sent overseas 12 major trade missions; 3 trade ships; and 4 trade survey missions. She issues several trade promotion periodicals, one of which is printed in Spanish, Arabic, Japanese, German, French, and English. It is estimated that the Australian Government provides in the order of 10 million dollars (United States equivalent) annually for foreign promotion of agricultural products.

Denmark carries out foreign promotion activities through market analyses, fairs and exhibitions, oversea offices, and commodity-by-commodity promotion. The total program has cost the equivalent of more than 10 million dollars annually and is supported by farmers and the Danish Government.

Activities are carried on in West

Germany, the United Kingdom, the United States, Thailand, Syria, Greece, Kuwait, Japan, and other countries. Denmark makes extensive use of direct advertising and in-store promotions. For example, during 1962 and 1963, Denmark employed 170 specialists to promote Danish foods at retail stores in the United Kingdom.

In the Netherlands, promotion and research are carried out essentially by six products boards—poultry and eggs, dairy products, flower and ornamental products, fruit and vegetables, potatoes, and seeds. The Ministry of Agriculture does not itself conduct promotional campaigns. Through such activities as providing information services and coordinating agricultural exhibits, however, it complements the work of the boards. Funds for promotion are provided by the government and by the products boards through levies assessed against sales transactions. The Netherlands Dairy Products Board in 1959, for example, budgeted the equivalent of about 3.8 million dollars for all promotion and research for dairy products alone.

The principal export promotion programs of New Zealand are carried on by producers' boards with substantial cooperation from the government and its trade commissioners overseas. The main exports of New Zealand are meat, dairy products, and wool. Promotion efforts are centered on them. The meat board in 1962 carried out activities in Canada, the United States, Japan, Pacific Islands, Malaya, and Singapore. It is estimated New Zealand annually invests more than 10 million dollars in trade promotion.

ALTHOUGH the foreign market development program was in its 10th year in 1964, it was still considered to be a relatively new effort.

Interesting examples can be cited of the fruitage of the program for practically every agricultural commodity that has been involved.

I quote some examples from reports received by commodity divisions.

"Cash markets for soybean oil in Iran have been successfully developed. During 1962, the soybean oil cooperator sent several soybean oil processing technicians to Iran to provide vegetable oil processors with United States technical know-how on refining and hydrogenating soybean oil. As a result of this training, Iranian technicians have greatly improved their ability to handle soybean oil and the major vegetable oil processors have started buying oil for dollars. Most of the soybean oil is now being used in shortening, but, since the country's refining capacity is in excess of their hydrogenation capacity, marketing of a liquid soybean oil is needed. The soybean oil cooperator has been successful in obtaining an agreement from one of the country's largest plants to put liquid soybean oil on the market. Success of these promotion efforts is shown by United States exports of soybean oil to Iran, which rose from 2.2 million pounds in 1960–1961 to 27 million pounds in 1961–1962 and during the 1962–1963 period, October–March, exports have nearly reached the level of the entire previous marketing year.

"One of the major objectives of the cotton market development program has been to stimulate greater expenditures on cotton promotion by interested groups overseas. A significant achievement in this direction came about during 1963 in the largest export market for United States cotton. Japan's cotton spinners began a new domestic cotton promotion campaign in February. The All Japan Cotton Spinners Association (AJCSA) has allocated the equivalent of 830 thousand dollars annually for the new 'self-help' program. This is more than twice the amount provided for promotion under the existing program carried out by AJCSA in cooperation with the United States cotton cooperator and the Foreign Agricultural Service. Counting the new program, the Japanese industry is investing more than 1 million dollars in 1963 to promote the development of new and expanded uses of cotton in Japan. This is more than five times the amount of FAS funds being spent in Japan on cotton promotion.

"In 1959, prior to leather promotion in Japan, cattle and hide prices on the west coast and in the intermountain area of the United States were about 15 percent below high market prices in the eastern half of the United States. This price disadvantage reflected the eastern location of a majority of our tanneries and the limited outlets and extra freight costs for western hides accordingly. Now in 1963 hide prices in the West are equal to or command a premium over those in the rest of the United States, and cattle prices in the western area have increased by a dollar and a half up to 3 dollars per head. United States hide sales to Japan increased from 12 million dollars in 1959 to over 27 million dollars in 1962.

"The first substantial sale of United States frozen poultry to western Europe moved under Public Law 480 in 1956.

"It consisted of approximately 1.5 million dollars' worth of chickens, turkeys, and included also a few ducks. At the same time the cooperative FAS/poultry industry market development program was activated in this area. After the initial introductory sale under Public Law 480, and with the inception of the market development program, United States frozen poultry products commenced to move commercially into the West German market. By 1962, the commercial demand for United States frozen poultry had spread to other western European countries. Within a period of 6 years, aided by the cooperative market development program, sales of frozen poultry to the western European area were returning in excess of 50 million dollars annually to the United States."

DAVID L. HUME *became Assistant Administrator for Export Programs of the Foreign Agricultural Service in 1962. He is a native of South Dakota and has worked in the fields of agriculture and food in both industry and Government for over 25 years.*

Bartering Farm Products

by ROBERT O. LINK

THE BARTER SYSTEM is a device used by the Department of Agriculture to help build foreign markets for farm products.

The name "barter" is derived from the statutory authority for the program, but it may be misleading by implying that what is involved is a direct exchange of United States commodities with another country for products of that country.

Our barters are contractual agreements by United States business firms to accept and export to restricted destinations commodities owned by the Commodity Credit Corporation.

In exchange, the barter contractor (or a supplier who has agreed to accept payment from the barter contractor instead of directly from the Government) provides the United States Government with specified materials, goods, or services.

Barter transactions may be bilateral and come close to the traditional concept of barter, as when a strategic material from India is accepted by the Commodity Credit Corporation in exchange for wheat or cotton to be exported to India.

On the other hand, they may be open end—that is, they may consist of separate purchase and sale transactions with no direct tie-in between countries receiving our agricultural products and the country supplying the materials or services. Of course, to the Government they are still "barters" in the sense that an agricultural commodity in Government inventory is traded for another asset.

The barter program began when we were still actively procuring from abroad many strategic materials for stockpiling in wartime.

The notion of barter at that time was to use our agricultural surpluses to pay for needed strategic materials instead of spending dollars for them.

About 493 million dollars' worth of strategic materials were acquired through barter against unfilled strategic stockpile objectives during the early years of the program. Largely because of the defense need for the materials that were being acquired, no restrictions were imposed then on the countries to which bartered agricultural commodities could be exported.

As the need for strategic materials diminished, it became clear that additional trades of agricultural commodities for such materials were desirable only if we could be reasonably satisfied that the agricultural exports under barter would be additional to export sales for dollars.

That principle was recognized in amendments that the Congress enacted to the legislation authorizing barter transactions and has resulted in the establishment of commodity-country export classifications designed to channel barter exports into new markets and markets where the United States has not been able to maintain a fair share of the import potential.

A later development in the barter program was a shift in emphasis away from barters for strategic materials toward more transactions in which our agricultural products can be used to pay for goods and services which Government agencies, especially the Department of Defense and the Agency for International Development, would otherwise buy abroad for dollars.

The major reason for the shift was the need to take every reasonable measure that provided an opportunity for improving the critical United States balance-of-payment position.

SOME EXAMPLES of the way barter has been used to build foreign markets for agricultural products are: Development of a market in Japan for United States grain sorghums; restoration of a substantial share of the Japanese corn market for the United States, pending freight and pricing adjustments to permit our corn to compete on a cash basis in the Japanese market; arresting the decline in the United States share of the tobacco market in the United Kingdom; bolstering cotton sales to major markets for American cotton in a period when our cotton exports were sagging; and preservation of a market for wheat in Peru at a time of declining foreign exchange reserves in that country.

Through December 31, 1963, barter had accounted for agricultural exports worth roughly 1.75 billion dollars.

The barter program has been a controversial matter.

Some have said it has displaced cash sales that would otherwise have been made.

Others have contended that it has displaced exports of friendly foreign countries through unfair competition.

Administrators of the program therefore must steer a careful course. They must give due regard to the effect the transactions may have on United States foreign policy, balance of payments, and dollar sales. They must also consider the interests of other members of the International Wheat Agreement and other international commodity agreements to which the United States is a party.

Barter provides a way to meet the spot problems that develop in agricultural export markets. It is an incentive to private traders to open new markets.

ROBERT O. LINK *joined the Department of Agriculture in 1933. His career in the Department included work in fiscal, information, and administration offices and in the barter program.*

Sales Programs

for Dollars

by CHARLES E. RAEDER

THE DEPARTMENT OF AGRICULTURE for some years has been striving diligently to expand and facilitate exports of agricultural commodities for dollars and has developed programs to that end.

Recognizing the need of foreign importers for credit facilities, the Commodity Credit Corporation (CCC), an entity within the Department, developed in 1956 an export credit sales program to extend deferred payments for CCC-owned commodities to United States exporters, who in turn could accommodate foreign importers by an extension of credit.

Under authority of its charter act, sales of its commodities and tobacco under loan to it may be made under the export credit sales program on a deferred-payment basis for periods up to 3 years.

Interest is charged at a rate it announces each month and runs from the time of delivery of the commodities to the United States exporter until the end of the deferred-payment period.

All sales under the program are made to United States exporters.

In applying for credit, the exporter is required to state the extent to which he will pass on the credit to foreign buyers.

From the beginning of the program on March 30, 1956, to September of 1963, sales of surplus agricultural commodities through this program

amounted to about 206 million dollars.

Title IV of the Agricultural Trade Development and Assistance Act (Public Law 480), approved September 21, 1959, authorized the President of the United States to enter into agreements with governments of friendly nations under which the United States undertakes to provide for delivery annually of quantities of surplus agricultural commodities for periods not to exceed 10 years, if those commodities are in surplus at the time of delivery.

This legislation provided for repayment in dollars, with interest at a rate not in excess of the cost of the funds to the United States Treasury. Repayment may be made in approximately equal annual amounts over periods of not more than 20 years from the date of the last delivery of commodities in each calendar year.

In the 2 years since the first agreement was entered into in August 1961 through July 1963, title IV agreements have been made with 14 countries. They involved a total of 133 million dollars (estimated export market value, excluding ocean transportation costs) of United States surplus agricultural commodities.

All but approximately 4 million dollars of the total was composed of price-supported commodities of Commodity Credit Corporation. About one-tenth of the value of commodities exported under the title IV program through July 1963 came out of its stocks.

In amending title IV of the Agricultural Trade Development and Assistance Act, the Congress in 1962 broadened the legislative authority of this title by providing that long-term supply and dollar credit sales agreements may be entered into with United States and foreign private trade, as well as with friendly governments.

The legislative purpose of the amendment, which authorized the Secretary of Agriculture to enter into agreements with the private trade, is to stimulate and increase the sale of surplus agricultural commodities for dollars through long-term supply agreements and through the extension of credit that will increase dollar exports of surplus agricultural commodities, develop foreign markets for our farm commodities, and assist in the development of their economies.

The program provides the private trade a greater role in expanding dollar exports of surplus agricultural commodities and in developing future commercial export markets.

The emphasis is on the use of the credit extended in connection with the sale of surplus products to finance food processing and distribution and other supporting facilities and services essential to efficient and economical marketing of commodities.

Payment periods, up to 20 years, are set on the basis of the particular project or purpose for which the credit is to be utilized. Interest rates are based on the cost of funds to the Treasury for comparable maturities.

ALTHOUGH the legislation provided that commodities may be supplied over periods up to 10 years, as a general policy, supply periods are limited to 3 years.

Eligible commodities include those under price supports of Commodity Credit Corporation and other surplus commodities eligible for export financing under Public Law 480.

Emphasis is placed on programing commodities in most burdensome supply. The agreements require that cash dollar exports be safeguarded and assurances that sales thereunder will not unduly disrupt world prices of agricultural commodities or normal patterns of trade.

Title IV of Public Law 480 is intended basically to be used in countries that can undertake long-term dollar obligations.

A principle in the merchandising of any product is that the sales price must be competitive.

Certain American products influenced by our price-support programs are domestically priced above world market prices of comparable type and quality and therefore must receive the benefit of an export allowance. To enable them to compete in world trade, the Department has devised export allowance techniques, termed payment-in-kind programs.

Until May 12, 1958, Commodity Credit Corporation sold most of its commodities for export on competitive bid. Since then, it has developed payment-in-kind programs for corn (May 12, 1958); barley, oats, grain sorghums, and rye (July 1, 1958); rice (December 15, 1958); and nonfat dry milk (June 27, 1962); butter and butterfat (November 1, 1963).

The payment-in-kind program for wheat and wheat flour went into effect September 4, 1956; cotton (May 5, 1958); and its products (August 1, 1956).

These programs were designed to encourage exports from commercial supplies instead of from CCC inventories, thus placing the merchandising functions in private trade.

Certificates at the applicable export allowance rates redeemable in commodities from CCC stocks are issued to United States exporters upon proof of export of commodities obtained mainly from private stocks. The wheat flour and cotton textile export allowances are paid in cash.

Exporters thus move commodities from the farm into export through commercial trade channels rather than through the CCC.

Export allowance rates determined by the Department reflect the amounts necessary to make these commodities competitive in foreign markets with crops produced in other countries.

The rates are kept under constant review so as not to exceed the gap between higher domestic prices and lower prices of the crops of competing nations.

Other than through redemption of payment-in-kind certificates and sales applicable to the CCC export credit program, barter program, and unusual circumstances as specifically authorized, CCC sales for export only of commodities (except cotton) covered by payment-in-kind programs are generally no longer made. CCC sales of these commodities for export only have been reduced markedly.

This was expected, and the shift from CCC export sales to payment-in-kind programs is viewed as largely offsetting since the latter reduce CCC acquisitions from the larger amounts the Corporation would have acquired if these programs had not been inaugurated.

The cotton payment-in-kind program differs from the one for grains, as exports of cotton may include cotton that had previously been purchased for unrestricted use from the Corporation or redeemed through farmers from its loan program either for cash or by using its certificates earned by export of cotton at a predetermined export payment rate.

The export payment rate for the market year 1962–1963 and for the marketing year beginning October 1, 1963, was 8.5 cents a pound, but was subject to change without prior notice.

Although the major commodities in CCC inventory in 1963 were covered by payment-in-kind programs, CCC sold for export a number of commodities on either a fixed or competitive bid price.

Those commodities included peanuts, soybeans, flaxseed, honey, rosin, turpentine, and dry edible beans. The prices at which the commodities were sold reflected the world price. Commodities so acquired from the Corporation generally must be exported and cannot be sold in the domestic market without penalty.

A program of long standing, authorized in section 32 of Public Law 320, as amended, was approved August 24, 1935. This act appropriates an amount equal to 30 percent of gross customs receipts for each calendar year for use to the succeeding fiscal year to encourage the exportation and domestic consumption of agricultural commodities and for other purposes.

Section 205 of the Agricultural Act of 1956 authorized the appropriation for each fiscal year beginning with the fiscal year ending June 30, 1957, of 500 million dollars to enable the Secretary of Agriculture to carry out the provisions of section 32, subject to all provisions of law relating to the expenditure of funds appropriated by such section, except that up to 50 percent of the 500 million dollars may be devoted during any fiscal year to any one agricultural commodity or the products thereof.

Since January 1, 1950, a carryover of up to 300 million dollars of unexpended funds has been authorized. The Agricultural Act of 1949 directed that section 32 funds be used principally for perishable nonbasic commodities other than those designated to receive mandatory support under the 1949 act.

Export programs under section 32 are announced after the Secretary of Agriculture finds that a surplus exists.

Export allowances are paid to commercial exporters following the export of privately owned commodities pursuant to programs announced by the Secretary. Only a small part of the available section 32 funds has been used for export allowances in recent years. Section 32 funds were being utilized in 1964 to encourage the export of tobacco of certain crops.

Under the authority of the Commodity Credit Corporation charter and specific case-by-case approval by its board of directors, sales of its stocks are made directly to foreign governments or quasi-governmental organizations for certain restricted uses, such as school lunch feeding program or other public institutional programs.

These sales are made at concessional prices but do return dollars to the United States Treasury and at the same time introduce American products into the diets of schoolchildren and others.

CHARLES E. RAEDER *became Assistant General Sales Manager, Foreign Agricultural Service, in 1961, with responsibility for grain export sales and pricing programs.*

The Trade

Fairs Program

by KENNETH K. KROGH

DISPLAYS at international trade fairs, food fairs, and similar events abroad are one of the means the Department of Agriculture uses to develop broader foreign markets for American agricultural products.

The exhibits, designed to acquaint potential customers with the availability, quality, and uses of our commodities, give millions of persons throughout the world their first opportunity to see, taste, and feel the products.

Responsibility for the program is assigned to the International Trade Fairs Division of the Foreign Agricultural Service. The Division works closely with the commodity divisions of the Service and the agricultural attachés.

In organizing its trade promotion exhibits at trade fairs, the Foreign Agricultural Service works with other Government agencies, chiefly the Department of Commerce and the United States Information Agency, and with private agricultural trade groups. In general, the industries concerned provide exhibit ideas, technicians, display materials, and sometimes commodities for sampling or sale.

The Service organizes and manages the exhibits; arranges for their design, construction, and operation; and provides travel expenses of industry technicians and commodity specialists participating in the joint efforts.

The Service also organizes and arranges for special trade promotion activities in connection with the exhibits. Costs are met through the use of foreign currencies accruing to the Government under Public Law 480.

Between 1955 and 1964, 135 agricultural trade promotion exhibits were sponsored in 32 countries. The total attendance at international trade fairs and other special events approximated 51 million. The displays ranged from small portable exhibits to a large exhibition in Amsterdam in November 1963, which covered some 165 thousand square feet.

The exhibition in Amsterdam, known as the United States Food and Agricultural Exhibition and Symposium for Western Europe, was the largest undertaking of its kind sponsored by the Department.

Included in it were a large special exhibits area to tell the story of United States agriculture, food quality, and the advantages of two-way trade; a complete American-type, self-service store with a full range of commodities on display and for sale to visitors; a commercial booth area where American firms sold, took orders, demonstrated, and promoted their products; a theater featuring an original film; a large cookout and barbecue patio; a leather and cotton fashion show; a kiddie kitchen; a "food in space" exhibit, with the capsule used by Walter Schirra in orbiting the earth; and other special displays and demonstrations.

A 5-day European-American symposium on agricultural trade in Amsterdam brought together leaders from agriculture, industry, the food trade, labor, consumers, universities, and governments in Europe and the United States for a people-to-people conference on food and trade policies.

Among the European cities and countries where fairs have been held since 1955 are London, Paris, Cologne, Munich, Rome, Vienna, Madrid, Brussels, Amsterdam, Stockholm, Copenhagen, Poznan, Zagreb, and Athens. In Asia, fairs were held in Tokyo, Osaka, Djakarta, New Delhi, Karachi,

Bombay, and Colombo. Sites in the Middle East were Tel Aviv and Cairo; in Africa, Lagos and Accra; in Australia, Sydney; and in Latin America, Lima, Bogotá, Valencia, and São Paulo.

The commodities displayed, distributed in sample form, or sold at the exhibits included the feed grains and meals, lard and meat products, citrus fruit and juices, dried fruit, canned fruit and vegetables, dry peas and beans, honey, walnuts, beverage bases and concentrates, tobacco, cotton fabrics, recombined milk, ice cream, wheat and wheat products, soybeans, cheese, poultry, and many other processed and frozen foods.

How EFFECTIVE are the trade fairs in developing oversea markets for farm commodities?

Trade fairs bring together larger concentrations of buyers and sellers at one place and one time than are to be found on any other occasion.

Trade fairs abroad are an important economic institution. A large share of all the business transactions that take place in many countries is transacted at trade fairs.

It is traditional in many countries that any seller seriously interested in a market will appear in the trade fair for that market. Buyers thus expect to find all of their alternative purchase possibilities at a trade fair.

Trade fairs provide unique focal points of activity around which broad market development programs for farm products can be organized.

Individual commodity groups make their most important sales contacts of the year at trade fairs and schedule their followup calls for the periods immediately following the fairs. American trade groups thus schedule oversea trips for their representatives to coincide with major trade fairs.

United States products exert greater sales impact when a number of them are exhibited collectively in a major exhibit than when they are shown separately. The exhibits thus are organized and designed by the Department of Agriculture for maximum effectiveness through consultation with private trade groups.

The Department operates the exhibits, but representatives of private trade groups man them, present their commodities, and carry out various market promotion activities.

Newspapers, trade papers, radio, and television cover trade fairs and provide space for information on American products.

Trade fairs provide a means of promoting the sale of commodities that are relatively small in the United States market but which have potentially large sales possibilities abroad. The United States rice trade credits participation in oversea trade fairs with boosting its European exports manyfold since the midfifties. Honey and other processed foods, although not major commodities in the United States, are highly desirable items in many markets abroad.

Exhibits at trade fairs provide opportunities for organizing promotional teamwork between various products that complement each other and gain greater sales possibilities through cooperative promotion. Thus demonstrations of fried chicken at trade fairs include rice, and rice demonstrations include chicken gravy.

Participation in international trade fair exhibits is one of the best means by which beginners in oversea market promotion gain experience in foreign marketing and become acquainted with oversea markets.

The trade fairs program thus has served as a training ground for the new trade groups participating in the overall market development program and for the new members of the more established organizations.

Test-sales activities carried out through the device of operational self-service markets instituted and managed as a part of an overall exhibit activity form a practical and inexpensive way to test oversea markets for a wide variety of processed foods.

As IN ALL MARKET promotion, the trade fairs program adapts itself to changing conditions as well as to the circumstances of the country or region in which the exhibition is held.

The fundamental objective, however, remains as it was in the beginning: To help establish a favorable image of United States food and agriculture products in the minds of foreign buyers and consumers, thereby expanding the demands for them.

In the formative years of the overall market development program, food and agriculture exhibits in international trade fairs provided trade development groups with a quick means of gaining experience in active oversea market promotion.

Now that private trade development groups have become better established, the emphasis has been changing somewhat. While retaining interest in the traditional type of fair, the Department is giving increasing attention to special promotion programs of a multi-commodity nature and to established trade center activities in London, Tokyo, and elsewhere.

A larger proportion of the resources of the promotional exhibit program is also being directed toward large solo-type exhibits. Such an exhibit can accommodate the full range of agricultural interests desiring to exhibit abroad as well as addressing itself to a large economic entity, such as the European Common Market, rather than to one specific country.

The full scale of trade fair activity, consequently, includes agricultural exhibits at the traditional type of international trade fairs, large solo-type exhibitions, trade centers at which exhibitions and collateral promotions take place, and portable exhibits.

KENNETH K. KROGH *was named Deputy Assistant Administrator of Export Programs for the Foreign Agricultural Service in 1963. He was formerly Director of the International Trade Fairs Division, a position he held from the inception of the Trade Fairs Program in 1955 through 1962.*

Our Agricultural Attachés

by DOUGLAS M. CRAWFORD

NINETY-ONE AMERICANS with farm backgrounds represent American agriculture in more than 100 countries as reporters of worldwide developments of importance to our trade, as the spearheads of efforts to widen markets for our products, and as representatives of the Secretary of Agriculture.

The attachés report on agricultural conditions in every major agricultural producing nation. They forward a constant flow of basic data on production, prices, exports, and special situations to Washington. Some cover only the country in which they are stationed. Some cover a region. Nearly all countries, except mainland China and some Iron Curtain countries, are visited by the attachés. When direct contact is impossible, as with China, they follow developments from indirect sources.

In 40 countries, one attaché is stationed. Eleven have an attaché and an assistant. In such larger posts and important producing, supplying, or buying countries as Mexico, Brazil, France, the Netherlands, Germany, Italy, and India, each staff consists of three Americans. In the two ranking dollar markets, Japan and England, four officers are posted; the fourth officer devotes all his time to activities connected with a trade center, an undertaking to encourage trade that the Department of Agriculture and the Department of Commerce jointly sponsor.

The attaché is a direct representative of the Secretary of Agriculture, but his function overseas is not an independent operation. He is assigned to a United States Embassy or consulate, whose overall responsible official is the American Ambassador or the ranking officer of the Department of State. The Ambassador is the personal representative of the President and therefore has prime responsibility for carrying out the foreign policy and program aims of the United States.

Many of the attachés' activities pertain to the preparation of evaluation reports on agricultural developments, problems, and trade matters. Material on them is sent directly to Washington for reproduction and distribution to the United States trade by the Foreign Agricultural Service. In other matters that are more closely related to United States policy and objectives, the agricultural officer coordinates his activities directly with other members of the Embassy staff and, as required, the principal officers of the mission.

In his oversea career, an attaché may participate in a wide range of activities and events pertaining to agricultural matters. Most of his time is devoted to reporting, market development, and representation.

Since 1919, when the first attachés were sent overseas, the single function that has remained the most consistent and has continued to expand is reporting. All of the worldwide reporting activities are based upon a master schedule that is developed in Washington. Central coordination is necessary so that all current developments that affect a given commodity are assembled and written and sent to Washington at fixed dates.

For example, all changes overseas on the production of wheat are sent to the home office on a specified date so that full, worldwide analysis can be carried out at one time. Reports on cotton, feed grains, tobacco, fats and oils, and fruits are scheduled to arrive when data are most needed. Less frequent reports are required for some of the minor commodities. The total number of scheduled required reports assigned to agricultural attaché offices was 1,700 in July 1964.

The schedule of required reports is the heart of the global factfinding and analysis system. Attachés submit many more unscheduled reports each year— as many as 4,800 altogether. Most of them concern spot analysis, changed prospects of crop production, weather damage, insect infestation, new tariff decisions, major policy changes, and similar occurrences.

Specifically, the effects of a continued drought, say in Argentina, Australia, or Canada, must be followed continuously and closely. The severity of dry weather bears directly on the amount of grain and livestock products that are available for export and therefore may mean a different competitive situation for the United States. Likewise, a blowdown of bananas in one country in Central America could affect the availability of bananas in the United States.

Most of the reports are sent by fast mail, but sometimes urgently needed figures, such as a late crop estimate to complete an analysis, are sent by cable.

An international telex communication operation between Washington and several posts quickly transmits grain prices and market news. It is possible to have market prices from Hamburg, Rotterdam, and Tokyo available in Washington within a few hours. A differential of 6 hours between European and United States time permits the transmission and receipt of closing hour information in Washington by early afternoon.

ATTACHÉS FOLLOW no set pattern in gathering basic material needed for a report.

The availability of reliable data varies. In some countries, which long ago developed agricultural and statistical services, much of the needed data can be obtained from government sources. In other countries, whose statistical services are incomplete, information may be scanty or lacking or subject to evaluation, and therefore cross-checking is not possible.

Depending upon the commodity on which information is desired, the attaché interviews businessmen, importers, exporters, processing organizations, shipping lines, and other sources. Even when reasonably complete material is available, there is always need to travel and observe the crop or livestock condition in the field or factory or processing plant.

Rarely is any crop concentrated in one locality. Usually an attaché has to visit numerous scattered plantings to ascertain the actual conditions and approximate volume of output. At first it may be difficult to arrive at a fair basis for an estimate, but the job becomes easier as the attaché is able to make more frequent visual comparisons of the same crop over a wider area. Despite problems of language, poor roads, and lack of reliable previous data, the attaché usually can make a reasonable forecast.

Data on international trade can be obtained even if official figures are late or not published. Information can be derived from shipping manifests, officials of steamship conferences that haul international cargo, and export associations, such as those for coffee and sugar.

Once received in Washington, reports are processed immediately and sent to the appropriate individuals or commodity or trade division. The reports are analyzed, and a summary appears as an individual release, part of a regional or worldwide digest, or in a regular publication, such as Foreign Agriculture, a timely, informative weekly magazine prepared in the Foreign Agricultural Service. Certain commodity reports are distributed directly to the trade.

Cotton reports, as prepared by the attachés, are available to interested persons and firms through the Agricultural Stabilization and Conservation Service and the Agricultural Marketing Service in New Orleans and Galveston. Grain reports move directly to users in Kansas City and Chicago. The whole reporting activity is a service function to the United States public.

This reporting activity gives the United States as complete, current knowledge of world agriculture as any in existence for conducting private and Government trade programs.

IN ANOTHER MAJOR responsibility, market development, the attaché is associated with individuals and groups in a strong market-promotion effort that involves more than 40 agricultural and trade groups working in association with the Foreign Agricultural Service. These trade cooperators represent nearly all United States commodities that move to foreign markets. Mostly they are nonprofit, national organizations.

As the permanent agricultural representative abroad, the attaché is in frequent contact with the oversea representatives of American commodity associations. He consults with them in annual work plans and special projects. When cooperators begin operations in a new country, the attachés help them establish contacts with government officials and the trade.

An example is the effort to enlarge our exports of American rice to South Africa. The exports in 1959 amounted to 5 thousand tons, of a total 34 thousand tons the Republic of South Africa imported. The United States share rose to 41 thousand tons, or 40 percent of total arrivals, by 1962. The United States Rice Export Association, working with the attaché, launched a successful promotional program. Prospects of an even larger share of this market led the association to establish a rice marketing center in Johannesburg.

IN THE INTERNATIONAL trade fairs program, the resident attaché collaborates with staff members sent from Washington to carry out the activity. From the planning stage to the time of the opening of a fair, many questions and problems arise which can best be settled with help from foreign government officials already known by the attaché. His role becomes one of an expediter—a most helpful one because of prior residence and firsthand knowledge of the agricultural and other conditions within the country.

A member of the attaché's staff is assigned to London and Tokyo to supervise operations of trade centers, which are conducted in partnership with the Department of Commerce. Display areas of the centers are available to the Department of Agriculture for a particular type of exhibition. For example, in a feed grain show held in Tokyo during May 1963, both American and Japanese producers and traders were represented. In addition to the regular displays, charts, and samples, a symposium was conducted to explain better and more efficient ways of utilizing imported feedstuffs, the value of balanced rations in live-stock feeding, and efficiency in meat production.

IN NUMEROUS OTHER ways, an attaché can inform prospective buyers about American products and livestock. Many foreign nationals visit our oversea offices and call to ask such questions as, "Where can I buy vegetable seeds from the United States?" and "Because of humid conditions, will the seeds have to be packed in a particular way?" The attaché, from reference sources, can furnish the prospective buyer with the names of several suppliers.

The attaché may be asked to suggest an itinerary for an Argentine milk producer who wants to inspect herds of dairy cattle in the United States. An importer in Guatemala tells the attaché he wants to import certain varieties of United States apples for sale during the Christmas holidays. He asks for prices and suppliers and time and condition of delivery. The attaché may not have a ready answer, but a cable to Washington will give him the necessary information.

A THIRD MAJOR PHASE of the attaché's work is representation—in its broadest sense the utilization of every opportunity to explain American agricultural policies, programs, and trading practices. Since the attaché is an employee of the United States Department of Agriculture, he functions as the key oversea representative of the Secretary of Agriculture.

As a member of the Embassy staff, the attaché may be called on to explain many different problems and developments that affect the United States in dealing with foreign people. In essence, the attaché has to convey the American farm story to others in its largest sense.

This representation is in two categories: One is the function the attaché can carry out by himself. The second embraces broader responsibilities, which can best be carried out in cooperation with the mission staff and the Ambassador. In either, support and advice and consultation come from Washington and also go to Washington. The attaché is not a free agent.

As any person on foreign assignment may expect, questions are asked relating to all sorts of agricultural situations in the United States. Most of them concern the attaché's daily business. In Manila, a sugar exporter may ask about the quota import system. An importer representing an American firm will ask help in obtaining a license to bring in a commodity that is unnecessarily protected.

Representation at this level tends to run in two directions. One concerns what we do in America. The other is a request to remove undue foreign import restrictions that hinder the normal flow of trade.

In the larger, more complicated issues that affect trade and the imposition of undue and unfair restrictions, there is need to seek additional assistance and support.

At times, issues can be resolved by telling the story to a larger audience through the aid of the United States

Information Agency. As trade matters become increasingly more involved, the Ambassador and other members of the Embassy lend a hand.

Finally, if a whole regional trading community becomes involved in unresolved questions, other agencies, the Congress, and at times the President of the United States become spokesmen of American policy.

As more integrated and multilateral trade systems come into being, continued joint endeavors will be required to liberalize trading practices.

THE ATTACHÉS have a hand in a multitude of other tasks.

Some examples:

Selection of the site for the International Institute of Agriculture, which was finally located at Turrialba, Costa Rica, after surveys were carried out in Mexico, Guatemala, and elsewhere in the Western Hemisphere;

the handling of Hevea budwood for wartime rubber plantings in Mexico;

functioning as official buyers for copra in the Philippines in the immediate postwar era;

joining other Department workers in a survey of the amount of sugar stock available in Java in the late forties;

a review of possible damage claims to agricultural crops in Lebanon following the landing of United States Marines in 1958;

working out details for International Farm Youth Exchange programs between the United States and foreign countries;

helping an agricultural school obtain disease-resistant tomato seeds for trial plantings;

determining the disease that killed chickens in a flock maintained by an official of a foreign ministry of agriculture.

EVER SINCE the formation in 1930 of the predecessor bureau of the Foreign Agricultural Service, which employs and supervises the attachés abroad, the type and role of personnel stationed overseas have changed.

Many of the attachés in the thirties were from the crop estimating service of the Department. Others had a more technical agricultural background. A few were agricultural economists.

Activities in 1930 were concentrated primarily in London, Berlin, Marseilles, and Belgrade. There was representation also in Shanghai, Buenos Aires, Pretoria, and Sydney. Depression and lower appropriations led to the closing of the posts in Australia and South Africa. Assistants in Marseilles, Belgrade, and Buenos Aires returned to the United States.

Work in the thirties dealt mainly with commodities. The emphasis was placed on competition and demand studies. Individual posts made commodity reports of regions. For example, all information on wheat was sent to Berlin by the European-based attachés, and the man in Berlin prepared a master report for Washington. London compiled all European data on fresh fruit and tobacco. Paris was responsible for dried fruit and nuts.

A well-established market news system on imports of fresh fruit into Europe was a development of the thirties. Every Thursday a special cable was sent to fruitgrowers in the Western States outlining market conditions in the principal markets. When surpluses and depressed prices occurred in one outlet, ships afloat could be diverted for unloading in ports having more promise of sale.

Two major events in June 1939 reshaped the activities of the domestic and foreign parts of the Foreign Agricultural Service. The Foreign Agricultural Service was renamed the Office of Foreign Agricultural Relations, and the nine attachés on oversea rolls were transferred to the Foreign Service of the Department of State, along with representatives of the Department of Commerce. This latter step was taken in the belief that the United States should have only one Foreign Service—the single point of direction and authority in foreign affairs would be the Department of State. Other Federal departments would participate in a combined Foreign Service.

With international tensions mounting and the approach of the Second World War, trade promotion had less meaning than previously. Although the agricultural attaché's function was different from that of the commercial attaché, and more concerned with commodity than country coverage, in the interest of a combined service, the agricultural officers were moved to the unified Foreign Service.

The functions of attachés were altered accordingly. Continuous information was still needed, but instead of being concerned primarily with market outlets and competition, the job was to find the location of exportable supplies of foodstuffs. Efforts of attachés were closely linked with temporary Government agencies whose representatives assisted foreign governments to produce various types of crops needed in the war.

I give some examples of the activities of the attachés in Mexico in wartime. The Board of Economic Warfare had on its rolls several rubber experts who had to leave Malaya and the Netherlands Indies. They had technical knowledge of how rubber should be produced but were unaccustomed to Government procurement programs. To help unify the effort, the agricultural attaché was asked to lead this part of a wartime rubber project.

Ships were in use elsewhere, but bananas could be moved from Mexico to the United States by rail, and many inquiries about supplies and prices were received from United States buyers. Supplies of castor beans were located in Oaxaca. Quantities of a wild oilseed, cacahuanache, the source of a drying oil, were sought out in Chiapas. Help was given to start the commercial production of pyrethrum, an insecticide base, which was difficult to move from Kenya in east Africa because of wartime ship sinkings. While not engaged directly in purchase operations, the attachés helped select grades and locate sources of agricultural materials.

AT THE END of the war, the agricultural attaché's role changed again.

Food supplies were still short of requirements, and a great deal of attention was paid to reporting the progress of recovery in the major European agricultural producing areas.

Attachés in a number of countries participated in efforts of the United Nations Relief and Rehabilitation Administration and in agricultural projects carried out under the Marshall plan.

OFFICES OVERSEAS expanded. Full-fledged attaché operations were started in many of the Latin American countries. Brazil in the late forties had the largest number of personnel assigned; an attaché office was in Rio de Janeiro, and supporting staffs were at the consulates of Porto Alegre, São Paulo, Belem, and for a time at Manaus.

Expansion continued until 1951, when 78 representatives carried out the foreign agricultural work.

By 1950, after an association of 11 years with the Department of State, some congressional spokesmen and others began to question the desirability of continuing the existing arrangement. The principal issue involved differences between a "one voice" concept of a unified oversea service and how the Secretary of Agriculture should exercise his responsibility in carrying out functions directly related to policies and programs of his Department.

After a number of discussions, a joint statement was released in February 1951, in which Charles F. Brannan, Secretary of Agriculture, and Acting Secretary of State James E. Webb agreed to cooperate more closely in the general field of foreign agricultural relations.

The agreement provided for more voice in drawing up the annual budget, faster communications, direct correspondence to and from agricultural attachés by the Secretary of Agriculture, the selection and promotion policies relating to attachés, and wider use of information sent by attachés.

The Agriculture Committee of the House of Representatives took an active interest in the activities of attachés. Foreign inspection trips were undertaken by committee members. An interim report on findings in March 1951 stressed the need for a closer contact between the Secretary of Agriculture and his representatives overseas.

Expressions about the desirability of returning the attachés to the Department of Agriculture continued. The first step was the re-creation of the Foreign Agricultural Service in March 1953. One year later, hearings were conducted by the Congress on the desirability of having the agricultural attachés directly responsible to the Foreign Agricultural Service and the Secretary of Agriculture.

The approval, on July 10, 1954, of the Agricultural Trade Development and Assistance Act, better known as Public Law 480, was another step in the process of reuniting attachés with the home organization.

Finally, in the Agricultural Act of 1954, jurisdiction over the attachés was shifted from the Department of State back to the Department of Agriculture. In a statement made at the time of the signing of the act, the President said the move was made "in order to sharpen the effort to find new world markets for our agricultural products."

Of the 55 agricultural officers who were serving with the Department of State at the time of the passage of Public Law 690, 39 transferred to the Department of Agriculture. After a careful analysis of the agricultural intelligence and marketing needs, it was determined that the number of posts should be increased from 40 to 58. For the first time, improved coverage was provided for Africa, and eight new posts were established in the Near East and Asia. A few additional officers were assigned to Latin America and Europe.

In the recruitment of new personnel for overseas, primary stress was placed upon backgrounds in agricultural economics and marketing. At the same time, a junior professional program was established to bring into the Foreign Agricultural Service young graduates of the land-grant colleges for training and service overseas. A program of language training was begun. By 1956, staffing was completed for the oversea operation, and the new attaché service was a functioning entity.

IN SERVING the United States overseas, the family of the attaché becomes involved in many ways with his official life. On numerous occasions, his wife will be with him during representational functions. Many times she will have direct responsibility when women visitors arrive at the post. She participates in the women's activities of an Embassy and the welfare and charity programs that are a part of Embassy life. In carrying out a number of activities, the home of the attaché is an extension of his office.

Agricultural attachés are employed directly by the Foreign Agricultural Service and have general service ratings established under the regulations of the Civil Service Commission. Young professional employees are not sent directly to foreign posts; they spend several years in Washington working and learning about the home organization. By the time they are assigned overseas, they have reached at least a GS–9 grade and more likely GS–11. The salary scale for those grades in 1964 was 7,030 to 10,650 dollars a year.

These younger professional employees are about 30 years old when they have their first foreign assignments. They have strong educational backgrounds in agricultural economics or agricultural marketing. If they are to be sent to posts where foreign languages are required, arrangements are made for intensive training, usually in Spanish, French, or German, before they go overseas.

The attaché is granted home leave in the United States after the completion of a 2-year tour of duty. Home leave provides an opportunity to the attaché to become reacquainted with various facets of American agriculture and also a chance to talk over things at firsthand with his colleagues in Washington. While there is no set number of years an attaché will be on duty overseas, he generally returns to the United States for service after spending two or three tours of duty abroad. Assignments in Washington generally are for 2 or 3 years.

One of the important supports an attaché receives at his post is the assistance given him by the local national employees on his staff. There is a tendency to think of the attaché activity as being exclusively one operated solely by American personnel. This is to overlook the great and continuous contribution made by both professional and other foreign employees. No office can carry out all its purposes without the valuable services these foreign nationals render.

Working for the Foreign Agricultural Service are some 150 foreign nationals. Several have been educated in the United States. A few hold higher degrees from our land-grant institutions. As collectors of basic data in foreign government offices, report writers, interpreters, and translators, they make invaluable contributions. They also provide continuity between one attaché and his predecessor.

MANY OF THE foreign employees remain for long periods with oversea operations. Since a number are very well trained, there are other opportunities which open for them. Two have joined the foreign agricultural service of their own country. One represents Switzerland in Brussels on European Common Market agricultural developments. Another was appointed agricultural attaché for Denmark in Ottawa. Several have joined the ministries of agriculture of their own countries and hold important positions as agricultural economists and department heads and with crop reporting services. Others are now working for one or more of the 40 market cooperator groups, working hand in hand with the Foreign Agricultural Service on the expansion of export trade.

The diverse nature of the work brings the attaché into contact with all sections of the United States mission, particularly the economic section because of many parallel and complementary interests in trade and other matters; the political section, for some of his actions involve matters of policy and public relations; and the United States Information Agency. Administrative details abroad relating to the operation of attaché offices are handled by the appropriate State Department personnel.

SEVERAL OTHER agencies of the Federal Government send employees overseas on a permanent basis.

The Department of Commerce, the Department of Labor, and the Department of the Interior participate in oversea programs as part of the State Department Foreign Service. Others, such as the Department of the Treasury, maintain an independent oversea staff of attachés directly responsible to the home department.

The Foreign Service included 149 commercial officers in 1963. They were stationed at 94 posts in 68 countries. They serve particularly the needs and requirements of the Department of Commerce. In addition to this group, which is primarily concerned with trade promotion, the Department of State maintains a worldwide corps of more than 300 economic officers.

The Department of the Interior is represented abroad by 17 minerals attachés and reporting officers, 6 petroleum attachés, and 4 fisheries attachés. They mostly are assigned on a regional basis, so that there is coverage of major areas of the world.

The Department of Labor has 73 attachés and reporting officers in 61

Embassies. Some are Foreign Service officers. A number come from the Department of Labor, and others have been selected from the trade union movement in the United States.

The Treasury Department has about 15 officers serving as financial advisers or attachés in 9 of the key posts. The Department of State has 21 scientific officer positions.

AT LEAST 25 countries have agricultural representation in various parts of the world.

Probably more agricultural counselors and attachés are on duty in Washington, D.C., than in any other major capital. They represent Argentina, Australia, Belgium, Canada, Denmark, El Salvador, France, Germany, Great Britain, Hungary, Ireland, Italy, Japan, United Arab Republic, Mexico, the Netherlands, the Republic of South Africa, Spain, and the Soviet Union.

Their work varies according to the agricultural conditions of the countries they represent. Ministries of agriculture in other countries tend to be primarily technical institutions and to have less to do with economic affairs than the United States Department of Agriculture. A number of countries handle details of importing through food purchase missions rather than through representatives of the ministry of agriculture.

The attachés of some countries perform double functions. For example, the agriculture representatives of the Netherlands in Washington and elsewhere directly participate in programs to establish the Dutch agricultural colonies or work out the means of having individual citizens of the Netherlands emigrate to new countries. Many foreign attachés have to collect data on improvements in crop and livestock production. Others arrange for university and other advanced training for foreign students in land-grant institutions.

Such countries as Denmark and Canada have been represented continuously since the early part of this century.

An increase in the number of foreign attachés or agricultural counselors in Washington has occurred since 1950. Some countries, such as Germany, have an agricultural secretary and a forestry secretary. The United Kingdom designates its Washington representative in the agricultural field as agricultural and food attaché. The Italian agricultural officer has the title, Director of Food and Agriculture of the Italian Technical Delegation.

MANY OTHER foreign capitals have a well-established agricultural representation.

In Rome, for example, there are attachés who serve their countries on trade and technical matters and are liaison officers with the Food and Agriculture Organization of the United Nations.

Several of the attachés assigned to Buenos Aires have direct responsibility in the acquiring of food supplies for their countries. Great Britain has veterinary officers on the attaché staff who work with Argentine officials in meat inspection prior to shipment.

A number of agricultural attachés are assigned to missions connected with the European Common Market in Brussels. Various European countries have assigned agricultural representatives to the Organization for Economic Cooperation and Development in Paris.

MOST OF THE foreign representatives are assigned to embassies from the home ministry of agriculture. The assignments are carried out in various ways. For example, the representative from Great Britain usually serves one term of 3 years abroad. Thereafter he returns to the home ministry for domestic duty. The agricultural attachés of Denmark tend to spend an entire career in one foreign capital. Some attachés serve as agricultural officers in a system of trade commissioners. Others are members of the regular diplomatic service of foreign countries.

It is customary for agricultural attachés assigned to foreign capitals to gather for informal meetings and luncheons. All of the attachés in Buenos Aires, including the American representative, meet once a month to discuss agricultural problems and developments of mutual interest. A similar type of informal association is carried out in London, Bonn, and Paris.

In Washington, the Department of Agriculture arranges for bimonthly luncheons with the foreign attachés and other diplomatic representatives. Employees of the Department address the gathering and talk about their various activities at home and abroad. Fifty or more foreign agricultural and diplomatic officers attend the meetings.

SEVERAL DEVELOPMENTS may affect the work of American agricultural attachés.

An agricultural attaché was assigned to the United States mission in Brussels to observe activities of the European Common Market as they relate to United States agricultural trade.

An officer was assigned to the United States mission to the European office of the United Nations and Other International Organizations in Geneva. The assignment is associated with the developments and decisions of the General Agreement on Tariffs and Trade.

Other regional arrangements for trade are coming into being in Central America, Latin America, Malaysia, and Africa. Their trading arrangements have a direct bearing on usual third-country importers and exporters of agricultural commodities.

As formal operating councils and commissions are created and a need arises to assign agricultural representation to the United States mission accredited to the particular community, new types of assignments of attachés may be needed.

Several studies have been made of the functions and responsibilities of American representatives overseas. One was made by the Committee on Foreign Affairs Personnel, headed by Christian A. Herter. The committee proposed three parallel services, consisting of the State Department, the United States Information Agency, and the Agency for International Development, to perform and carry out the oversea tasks. It suggested that the attachés of Foreign Agricultural Service be reunited with a single Foreign Service.

Another development that may have a bearing on the work of our agricultural attachés is the International Agricultural Development Service, whose function is to coordinate the technical assistance programs of the United States Department of Agriculture in line with provisions of the Act for International Development of 1961. If a larger number of departmental technical personnel is involved in oversea assignments, the agricultural attaché may well become a member of the foreign-country group associated with the programs. The attaché would continue to be the personal representative of the Secretary and continue to devote major attention to policies and trade programs.

Because of the growing complexity of trade in agricultural products, rising regionalism, reorganizations in government departments, greater interest in the conduct of foreign affairs, and the establishment of several independent countries, the position and responsibilities of the American agricultural attaché no doubt will likewise grow and become more complex. His effectiveness and accomplishment, though, will continue.

DOUGLAS M. CRAWFORD *became Assistant Administrator for Agricultural Attachés, Foreign Agricultural Service, in August 1961. Previously he served as agricultural attaché in Argentina, Guatemala, the Philippines, and Mexico and as special representative of the Production and Marketing Administration in Indonesia. He took his college work at Stanford, the University of California, and the National University of Mexico.*

Getting and Using Statistics

by CLARENCE M. PURVES

To OPERATE their farms successfully, farmers must know the conditions of future demand for their products, the prices they may expect before deciding the crops to grow, and the supplies available to decide the best time to market their produce.

Some farmers need only local facts to determine what to produce. Others may need much more information.

The continued improvement in transportation, the increasing commercialization of production, and the widening of competition for markets continually intensify the need for information on production, utilization, trade, and prices.

So also a government needs facts about the agriculture of its country if it is to see to it that people have enough food and other farm products.

Governments also need information about the agriculture of other countries to help their producers find foreign markets for their commodities and determine which products to produce domestically and which to import. Higher efficiency of agriculture has magnified competition in world markets. The prices of products have ebbed. Prices for the items used in agricultural production have gone up. To aid producers in meeting these conflicting trends, governments need statistics to study the past and look into the future.

A primary objective of the United States Department of Agriculture when it was established in 1862 was to collect, arrange, and publish statistical and other useful information on agriculture. Its first crop estimates were published in 1863. Its regular monthly reports on crop conditions and annual reports on acreage, average yield, and production of important crops and on the numbers of livestock on farms became one of its major functions.

Its statistical reports gained a worldwide reputation for value to producers and traders. When David Lubin conceived the idea of a world statistical service, his aim was to provide estimates on world agricultural activities as similar as possible to those being provided for the United States by its Department of Agriculture.

DAVID LUBIN was a merchant from Sacramento, Calif., who tried his hand at farming. After several failures, he became convinced that farmers needed more information about developments in different regions to aid them in deciding what to produce and to judge whether traders were paying them fair prices for their products.

To provide this information, he proposed the creation of a World Chamber of Agriculture. He attempted to interest the heads of various governments in his idea. Finally in 1905 he impressed the King of Italy sufficiently that he called an International Conference of Nations to consider the establishment of an International Institute of Agriculture.

Representatives to the Conference agreed that such an institution would be of value to agriculture, and a treaty was signed in 1905. Ratification of the treaty, arrangements for quarters, and the organization of a permanent committee to administer the Institute were completed by 1908.

The Institute began as soon as possible to fulfill one of its major responsibilities—to collect, compile, and disseminate worldwide information on acreage sown, crop conditions and yields, and production of farm products. It believed such information would help stabilize world prices and benefit producers and consumers.

It soon learned, however, that it was not easy to collect statistics. Only a few countries had facilities for collecting statistics on current crop conditions and production. Definitions of area and production and ways of reporting crop conditions were not uniform. Units of measurement varied. Different languages were used. Some countries reported sown acreages; others, harvested acreages; and some, total production. Others reported only the production for sale or export. Some reported crop conditions as a percentage of normal; others, as "very good," "good," "passable," and "poor" or in numbers from 1 to 6 to show conditions from poor to excellent.

When the Institute began to publish its statistics in 1910, it was able to report inadequately on only seven commodities. The first reports on the wheat crop covered less than one-third of the world's production.

The Institute found that its limited budget made it impossible to set up a system for collecting statistics and that it must depend on information furnished by its member governments. Production estimates in many countries were not available for a year or more after the harvest. Some countries sent the Institute any figures they had handy.

The Institute decided its greatest service would be to help its members improve their statistical services and to work out more uniform definitions of crop conditions, area, and production and the numbers of livestock on farms.

In its first few years, the Institute engaged primarily in bringing together and summarizing such statistics as were available, determining crop years for world summaries, and standardizing their publications, but it was unable to carry out fully the hopes of its founders of providing current and complete statistics.

Differences of opinion among the permanent committee as to policies, lack of funds, the failure of several members to pay their dues, and the beginning of the First World War demoralized the organization, and the collection of statistics was sharply reduced.

But the urgencies of war, a spiraling of prices in the early postwar years, and the subsequent collapse in agricultural prices showed the need for more and better statistics on production and trade. More countries were willing to support the Institute, and reports on agricultural production and trade were available for more countries and on more commodities.

The 1921 Yearbook of the Institute brought together statistics on wartime production. Data on land use by countries were published in 1923 for the first time.

Thereafter annual reports contained the statistics by countries on total area and population; land use; agricultural area, yield, and production of crops (25 crops in 1923); numbers of livestock; imports and exports of agricultural products; stocks of grains in major exporting countries; prices of leading agricultural commodities in world markets; and ocean freight rates and exchange rates.

Shortly after the First World War, the Institute began publishing monthly reports on crop conditions in major agricultural countries, but they were largely descriptive, rather than quantitative, estimates.

The Institute was urged during the twenties to accompany the statistical summaries with an analysis of their economic significance on the world supply and demand conditions for farm products. It issued its first agricultural situation report in 1930. It described by countries the production situation and the potential market for farm products, government measures for farm relief, action taken by voluntary organizations in the interest of producers, and the economic situation and its relation to world agriculture.

Since one of the first essentials of a crop reporting system is a periodic census of agriculture to provide a benchmark from which to measure annual changes, the Institute began planning for a worldwide agricultural census to be taken about 1930.

In making arrangements to conduct the census, representatives of the Institute visited every cooperating country and instructed them in the problems of census taking, tabulation, and analysis. Special emphasis was placed on making the enumeration as complete as possible, avoiding duplication due to multiple cropping or multiple ownership, training enumerators on methods of making estimates from incomplete data, and adjusting estimates for interplanted crops.

Fewer than one-third of the countries of the world had ever taken an agricultural census before 1930, but 63 countries participated in 1930.

Several of the countries found the problems of obtaining a complete enumeration more difficult than had been anticipated, and the problems of tabulating and preparing the data for publication in some countries was so great that only part of the data collected was analyzed and published.

The census, however, did add greatly to the statistical knowledge available on world agriculture and was instrumental in increasing the interest in agricultural statistics and pointing out the value of statistics in assessing the significance of agricultural resources.

During the Second World War, the activities of the Institute were again sharply curtailed. Agricultural production and trade in a large part of the world were disrupted. Food supplies of nearly all of the allied countries were pooled and allocated among nations to provide adequate food for the fighting forces and to ration supplies among the civilian populations as equitably as possible. This endeavor emphasized the glaring inequities in living standards between groups and countries and an alliance was formed to fight hunger, disease, inequality, and illiteracy.

In an international conference in 1943 in Hot Springs, Va., 44 countries took steps to offset hunger by producing more food and providing markets to absorb it. An interim committee was set up to draft a constitution for an International Food and Agricultural Organization. In 1945, the constitution was adopted, and the Food and Agriculture Organization of the United Nations became the international forum for world agriculture.

STATISTICAL PROGRAMS and publications of the International Institute of Agriculture were taken over and expanded by FAO. From its beginning, FAO realized that reliable and adequate statistical information was indispensable to all concerned in planning and promoting agricultural development, in improving the distribution of food and other products, and in raising the general standard of living.

FAO took the lead in organizing the program for the 1950 world agricultural census and giving assistance to member countries in carrying out its program. Experts were sent to various countries to assist their governments in setting up statistical organizations and in improving their methods of collection, analysis, and presentation of agricultural facts. This assistance to foreign governments has been continued. Even more aid was given to member countries to conduct and tabulate the 1960 census.

FAO has been able to expand its statistical coverage of world production and trade in agricultural products through its larger membership. By 1964, 112 countries had joined FAO as full, or associate, members, and all major agricultural countries were members, except the Soviet Union and mainland China.

Each member is requested to report its production and trade of agricultural products. Attention has been given to providing statistical instructions to member countries and in standardizing reports on production and trade.

The regular statistical reports of FAO

now include yearbooks on production and on trade and a monthly bulletin on agricultural economics and statistics. The contents of the yearbooks are an elaboration of those published by the International Institute and contain data for nearly every agricultural commodity in international commerce.

When reports from member countries are unusually late, FAO uses private sources or includes unpublished estimates in its continental or world totals in order to make them comparable with earlier years.

In most cases, FAO does not adjust the production and trade reports of member countries for incompleteness or other inaccuracies in the estimates, but rather depends upon improving its statistics through working with the member countries and helping them to improve their estimates.

Another limitation of the FAO statistical yearbooks, as a source for agricultural statistics, is their delay in publication. Because of the mass of data involved and frequent delays in reports from member countries, estimates on production for a given harvest are not available in yearbooks until 1 to 2 years after the actual harvest. The lag in publication of trade data is about as great. The monthly bulletin of agricultural economics and statistics is the major referent for updating statistical data. This publication presents the latest data on production and trade for the major agricultural products and monthly prices in major world markets for the preceding 12 months.

One of the first research projects conducted by FAO after its organization was to prepare food balances for as many countries as possible. These were based upon data from many sources and contained many unsupported guesses. They indicated the source of supplies and the utilization of food products and provided a basis for appraising the completeness and reliability of statistics for different countries. Although they were incomplete for many countries, they were an important source of information for the Freedom From Hunger campaign of the Food and Agriculture Organization. Research in food balances has been continued.

Training centers have been set up in Latin America, Africa, Asia, and Europe to assist governments in their statistical problems. These training centers have enabled FAO to provide closer supervision of technical statistical programs in each area, to meet the needs of training for statisticians, and to service the various regional statistical bodies and meetings of experts. Assistance in conducting sample surveys and agricultural censuses have been an important part of the work of these regional offices.

The annual reports of FAO on the state of food and agriculture have become important in presenting analyses of world and regional production, consumption, stocks, trade, and price changes of agricultural products and for summarizing special statistical research projects.

Index numbers are prepared to measure the world's total agricultural production, as well as food, and are shown by regions. These index numbers have been useful in comparing the trends in production in different areas of the world and for measuring the relationship between the increases in food production and the growth in population.

Index numbers also are presented for the major individual countries in each region, thus facilitating further comparison. These data provide a background for the accompanying analysis of the world agricultural situation outlining major problems existing in agricultural production and distribution and the steps taken by individual countries and international organizations in an effort to solve them.

Many of the smaller and lesser developed countries with limited statistical services depend largely on the Food and Agriculture Organization for their statistics on world agriculture. Most of the larger exporters and importers of agricultural products, however, have built up their own system for collecting world agricultural statistics and have adapted their sources to meet their own requirements.

THE UNITED STATES Department of Agriculture began collecting and compiling statistics on foreign agricultural production, trade, and prices in 1921 with the establishment of the Bureau of Agricultural Economics. The statistics were needed to provide exporters with current information on possible export markets and on supplies likely to be available from competing countries.

It also collected statistics on some important imported commodities, such as wool, sugar, and tropical products, to provide information on available supplies, and to aid the Government in making policy decisions on tariffs and other international trade problems.

The Department collects information on foreign agricultural production and trade from many sources. At first it made widespread use of foreign publications and trade sources in foreign markets, but it soon found that it would have to set up a corps of trained representatives in foreign countries if it were to bring together dependable and timely information.

These representatives—agricultural attachés—could observe crop conditions abroad, talk with representatives of foreign governments and importers to determine demand conditions, and report promptly to the Department for general release. Only a few agricultural attachés were sent at first to larger exporting and importing countries. The information obtained by them proved to be so useful to exporters and Government departments that their number has been increased.

In countries not covered by the service, periodic reports are received through the Current Economic Reporting Program of the Foreign Service, Department of State. Through this system, current agricultural statistics are obtained for every country in the world except those not recognized by the United States.

Most of the world summaries are published in the Department of Agriculture's annual release, *Agricultural Statistics*. The 1963 issue contained 114 tables on world livestock numbers and world production and trade of the major agricultural products.

Supervision of the program introduced in 1954 to export agricultural products in exchange for local currencies under Public Law 480 and other relief and economic development programs has greatly increased the need for current information on agricultural production and trade activities in underdeveloped countries.

An accurate measure of the food supply situation is necessary to determine the amount of food imports needed to carry out effectively their economic development programs.

Public Law 480 requires that the commodities received under these programs shall be utilized within the country receiving them and that they be in addition to the usual imports of the country. To check compliance accurately requires current statistics on production and trade.

Another advantage of a worldwide network of agricultural attachés, in addition to timeliness of data, is their ability to appraise the reliability of official estimates and recommend adjustments where they feel the official estimates of a country may be low because of incompleteness in reporting or to an unusual method of estimating production. Some countries are also known to overestimate production for political or economic reasons. When estimates are known to be too low or too high, the Foreign Agricultural Service adjusts them to be in line with the estimates for other countries.

THE REGIONAL ANALYSIS Division of the Economic Research Service of the Department analyzes the statistics collected in regular commodity reports on commercial crops and brings together any data available on crops grown primarily for local consumption. It prepares index numbers and food balances by countries for use in determining trends in agricultural development. These are used to show levels of food consumption by countries in the administration of Agency for International Development programs and in the analysis of probable foreign demand for United States agricultural products.

Economic Research Service, in cooperation with Foreign Agricultural Service, also issues an annual Outlook Situation report about midway in the fiscal year. It projects production for the year and analyzes market conditions, country by country. Their index numbers and food balances, based largely on the foreign statistics collected by Foreign Agricultural Service, provide an important background for appraising the outlook for exports summarized in the Agricultural Situation report.

The two agencies also conduct long-term supply-and-demand projections by countries to determine the trends of such factors as changes in population, economic development, per capita income, and agricultural programs that are likely to affect the long-term supply-and-demand situation for agricultural products in those countries.

The studies are done under contract with colleges and research institutes within the countries under study and are financed by foreign currencies that become available for market development under Public Law 480.

COLLECTING agricultural statistics is not easy in any country. The extensive area covered by agricultural activities and the variations of soil, climate, and topography increase the dispersion in any facts collected and may lead to errors unless a large sample is taken. To avoid these errors, most countries prefer a complete periodic counting.

Several personal and social factors also make the collection of statistics difficult. Few farmers have records or accurate measurement of the acres planted or amounts produced. Livestock range over wide areas, often in community flocks. Their products are sold in small amounts and in many forms. Some farmers can only guess. Many hesitate to tell their true output because they are suspicious of the use that will be made of the data. Illiteracy, ignorance, a lack of interest, and superstitions are other factors. The expense and time involved limits the amount of data many countries can collect.

STATISTICIANS have been working for years on ways to overcome these handicaps, to obtain true objective estimates with only random errors.

Sampling is a widely used technique in collecting data. A sample of a small number of observations properly chosen at random tends to have the characteristics of the universe from which it is taken. Some error exists, of course, and facts can be determined only approximately. Sampling restricts precise information for small areas, but it cuts the cost, reduces the time of tabulation and analysis, and often makes possible the obtaining of information when a complete enumeration is impossible.

The United States, a pioneer in statistical sampling, has used it to measure intercensal year-to-year changes in crop production and livestock numbers. The high level of literacy of its farmers and the fact that the area planted to each crop by each farmer generally is fairly accurately known have been major factors in the success of the Department's crop reporting system.

By continual research in sampling techniques and ways of measuring bias and by checking against periodic censuses, the errors in estimates have been reduced greatly, but there are still occasional changes in conditions that result in significant errors in sample data based upon opinions.

The success of the United States with sampling agricultural activities has induced some other countries to try it. The Food and Agriculture Organization has advocated it through publications and instructions and has assisted several countries in the use of sampling in taking censuses as well as in making annual estimates.

Two general types of sampling are followed. One is to choose representative areas and study thoroughly the agriculture of each area. A total for the country or region studied is obtained by multiplying the totals of the sampled areas by their inverse relationship to the total of area they represent.

The second is to choose a sample of holdings, study them thoroughly, and multiply their tally by inverse ratio to the total number of holdings in the universe.

The first does not provide reliable information on the characteristics of the holdings, such as size of farm and tenure. The second is more subject to underenumeration because of fragmentation and the amount of urban holdings.

Neither provides accurate estimates for minor civil areas, but both can give fairly reliable estimates for a universe if the size of the sample is adjusted to the precision required and ways can be found to overcome the personal and social bias of the persons enumerated.

This second problem—bias—has proved to be the more difficult to solve. Publicizing the uses and needs of accurate data, assuring the informants that their answers will be kept confidential and used only in totals and averages, and helping the informant determine correct answers all help to improve reporting, but they cannot overcome the natural conservativeness of most farmers and their lack of accurate records.

Experiments have been made with taking strictly objective samples of areas and yields. It is possible to make precise acreage estimates from aerial photographs of agricultural areas. Cultivated land, native pasture, woodland, and so on are easy to identify. Many crops, like corn, soybeans, cotton, and tobacco, also are distinguished easily. Recent technical developments indicate it may soon be possible to identify separately areas in wheat, oats, and other grains.

In the aerial sampling, enumerators are given photographs of definite segments that delineate the boundaries of each field. Then by personal enumeration they obtain a record of the name and acreage of the crop in each field and check it against the aerial measurements. From these samples, an estimate for the universe—the total area surveyed—is made by increasing the acreage in the sample to equal that in the universe. If the sample is 1 percent of the total area, the results would be multiplied by 100.

After the first survey of acreage has been verified, future enumerated changes in the identical sample can be used to estimate total changes from year to year. This method, restricted to small, compact areas, gives lower sampling errors than random sampling and is well adapted for measuring things fixed to a specific area, such as numbers of farms, crop acreages, and storage facilities.

Variation in yields, which usually are the cause of greatest fluctuations in production, have traditionally been based on the judgment of farmers and therefore have been subject to bias and errors of judgment. Through research and development, methods have been found to use sample data for estimating yields per acre by weighing, measuring, or counting growth factors on small measured plots and relating them to final yields.

OBJECTIVE surveys of yield based upon sampling involve three stages.

First, a sample of fields is chosen, located at random for each crop. The samples for defined areas are chosen in proportion to the acreage of the crop in each area—thus providing a self-weighted sample.

Secondly, plots to be measured within each sample field are located by random numbers, so that all areas of a chosen field have an equal probability of selection.

Thirdly, the enumerator marks off an area of uniform size and makes prescribed observations of growth factors that are later compared with measured yields. These relationships can be used in future years for forecasting yields through observing growth factors before harvest. Such surveys take time and must be done accurately by highly trained observers, but a relatively small sample so obtained is a valuable check on data obtained by other methods and provides information on the quality of the crop, such as protein content or weight per bushel, in addition to yield measurement. While objective yield surveys have been used in only a few countries, their use is expanding.

The Food and Agriculture Organization has devoted much of its resources to conducting training centers, preparing statistical instructions in census taking, and sampling and gathering data on crop yields.

It has helped countries conduct sample censuses and set up crop reporting systems and standardize units of reporting area and production.

It has also cooperated with the United Nations in working out standard statistical classifications for recording trade, measuring the value of trade, and grouping commodities.

Finally, it has given some scholarships to students specializing in statistical methods and in the solution of statistical problems, helped countries prepare their census data for electric data processing, and arranged for a few countries to have their data tabulated in processing centers.

United States aid programs also have helped several countries to set up crop estimating systems and train their workers in statistics. A large number of promising students from foreign countries have been sent to the United States to attend colleges and to receive training in crop estimating and other types of statistical collection and analysis. Nearly 300 foreign visitors from 59 different countries have been trained in agricultural statistics since 1942.

Several other countries have also given training courses for students from countries lacking college facilities. While many of these students take up positions in industry and trade rather than government after returning to their home countries, they are adding to the statistical knowledge and to the use and appreciation of statistics in their countries.

International commodity groups also help countries to improve their statistics and make them more comparable and to acquaint them in the methods of analyzing production and marketing problems.

WHILE STATISTICS for many countries are still little more than guesses, rapid strides have been made in bringing together data on world agriculture so that farmers and governments everywhere can now get information on supplies and market conditions for their products and for alternative products, providing them a sounder basis for their decisions.

More and more countries that were hesitant about publishing their facts on their agriculture now make them available, and the number of countries that change their statistics for political purposes or in the hope of getting a better price for their products is steadily diminishing.

While David Lubin's goal of making accurate and current statistics available on world production, trade outlets, and prices for all major agricultural products is still far from achievement, it now appears possible. Their need no longer is questioned.

CLARENCE M. PURVES *joined the Department of Agriculture in 1925 as an agricultural economist in the former Bureau of Agricultural Economics. Since 1943 he has served in various capacities in the Foreign Agricultural Service and in 1958 was named Director of Statistics and Assistant to the Administrator. He acts as coordinator of statistics with other Government agencies and as consultant on statistical presentation and compilation.*

International Organizations

by RALPH W. PHILLIPS

GOVERNMENTS everywhere have formed many organizations in this century to deal with international problems, including those of agriculture. Some, like the League of Nations and the International Institute of Agriculture, have passed from the scene and have been replaced by others.

It would be idle to pretend that the many organizations that now exist reflect a new and strongly developed sense of community among nations. Why, then, have they been brought into being? What purposes do they serve for their member nations? How do they achieve these purposes? Do they contribute enough to the solution of the complex problems of a modern world to justify their continuation? Without them, how could the present and ever-increasing needs for intercourse among nations be met?

The first question can be answered best in relation to man's history, for the emergence of these organizations as important mechanisms for the conduct of international affairs is but a modern expression of a trend that is as old as man himself.

Man can store up and use knowledge. Each generation adds to the store. Each new generation has at its disposal all the knowledge that has been acquired and passed on by those that have gone before. A generation does not live out its life instinctively

423

according to a pattern followed by the generations before it; it adds something new and develops a pattern of its own. Life therefore grows ever more complex, more highly organized.

When man first emerged long ago as *Homo habilis*, a being with the intelligence to fashion and use tools, his pattern of life was simple. It changed little from generation to generation.

Over the long period of prehistory, bits were added—tools, clothes, better shelters, fire, some knowledge of the stars, the lever. Even so, progress was slow, compared with the rate achieved after organized agriculture began, and slow, indeed, compared with the rate at which knowledge has been accumulating during the 20th century.

In order to cope with the application of his increasing store of knowledge, man has had to develop increasingly complex organizational arrangements at the community, provincial, and national levels, and, in relatively recent times, at the international level. Agriculture has shared fully in this trend and has been a major contributor to it.

Organized agriculture had its beginnings only about 10 thousand years ago in the development of cereal agriculture on the flanks of the Near East mountain ranges. If all man's existence could be telescoped into a single year, the time during which cereal agriculture has been practiced would occupy only about 2 days.

The practice of growing cereals provided the basis for the formation of the Near Eastern village-farming communities, which, in turn, provided the social and economic conditions wherein the meat-producing animals were domesticated.

As organized agriculture spread over the world, as cities developed and farmers grew food for city dwellers as well as themselves, as sailing ships and then modern vessels moved around the world, and airplanes speeded the movements of people and products among nations, the need for mechanisms for consultation among countries arose and increased.

This need was accentuated by the rapid development of knowledge of agricultural science and technology during the past 50 years and by the surplus production of some products in some countries resulting from the application of that knowledge. International organizations emerged in response to the need for better mechanisms for consultation among nations about agriculture and the many other affairs of people.

AGRICULTURAL SCIENTISTS began to organize for the international exchange of information only about a century ago. For example, the first International Veterinary Congress was held in Hamburg, Germany, in 1863, and this group has met at regular intervals ever since. At about the same time, the problems of sugar producers resulted in the signing in 1864 of what was perhaps the first intergovernmental commodity agreement.

Many nongovernmental groups that were interested in various phases of agriculture had begun to meet on an international basis before 1900, particularly in Europe.

The International Commission on Agriculture was formed in 1889. It was the result of efforts by private individuals and groups in Europe who felt the need for organization to offset the inherent weaknesses of the industry and to deal with common problems of agriculture on a worldwide basis. They were stimulated to form it largely by the severe agricultural depression of the 1880's and 1890's. It was probably the first formal international group established to deal with the general interests of agriculture.

The first international intergovernmental body formed to deal with the general problems of agriculture also had its roots in that depression. It was the International Institute of Agriculture (IIA), with headquarters in Rome. It owed its existence almost entirely to the vision and energies of David Lubin, an American, who had seen the misery among farmers during the depression and set out to try to help farmers through some international mechanism.

The IIA convened international meetings in many fields, assembled and published statistics on world agriculture, organized the first world census of agriculture in 1930, and issued many technical publications.

Its work was brought nearly to a standstill by the Second World War. Then, following the establishment of the Food and Agriculture Organization of the United Nations in 1945, the IIA was dissolved, and its assets were absorbed by FAO. Thus, within the first half of the 20th century, the first international intergovernmental agricultural organization had been set up and had lived out a useful existence and had been replaced by an organization with broader duties.

Although international agricultural organizations are new, governments have set up a considerable number that deal directly with agriculture or with some matters related to agriculture.

These organizations fall into four broad categories: Those that deal with agricultural problems as a whole; those that deal with trade in agricultural products; those that are concerned with overall economic problems and consequently with agriculture as a part of the total economy; and scientific and technical organizations whose activities touch upon agriculture.

TWO INTERGOVERNMENTAL organizations deal with agricultural problems as a whole and are limited to work in this field.

One is the Food and Agriculture Organization of the United Nations (FAO), is international in scope.

The other, the Inter-American Institute of Agricultural Sciences (IAIAS), is an arm of the Organization of American States and is regional in scope.

FAO was established in October 1945 and grew out of a conference held in Hot Springs, Va., in May and June of 1943. Its headquarters are in Rome. It had 106 member nations and 6 associate member nations at the close of the Twelfth Session of the FAO Conference in December 1963.

FAO deals with a broad sweep of agricultural problems, including human nutrition, the use of land and water, production and protection of plants, production and health of animals, fisheries, forestry, rural institutions and services, the use of atomic energy in agriculture, agricultural commodities, analysis of agricultural economic problems, and world statistics.

IAIAS was created in accord with a resolution of the Eighth American Scientific Congress in Washington in 1940, following a recommendation of the Governing Board of the Pan American Union. The convention under which it was formed did not enter into force until November 30, 1944.

Its objectives are to encourage and advance the development of the agricultural sciences in the American Republics through research, teaching, and extension. For many years its activities were centered at Turrialba, Costa Rica, where attention was given primarily to research and the training of graduate students. Some training and other technical assistance activities were carried out in member countries, and the Institute cooperated with FAO in a number of inter-American meetings on technical problems.

In recent years, the IAIAS has been undergoing a reorganization. The main training and research center remains at Turrialba, but administrative headquarters have been established in San José, Costa Rica, and subregional institutes have been developed at La Molina, Lima, Peru, for agricultural engineering and at La Estanzuela, Uruguay, for work in Temperate Zone grassland and animal husbandry.

ORGANIZATIONS that deal with problems of trade in agricultural products are the International Wheat Council, the International Sugar Council, the International Coffee Organization, the International Olive Oil Council, the International Cotton Advisory

Committee, the International Wool Study Group, and the International Seed Testing Association.

The first four administer international marketing agreements. The others deal with problems related to trade, but they are not directly involved in trade itself.

The General Agreement on Tariffs and Trade also must be considered in this group, even though its functions extend much beyond agricultural commodities that move in international trade. In addition, a number of regional bodies, including the European Economic Community, are concerned with trade.

The International Wheat Council was established in April 1942 to administer the first International Wheat Agreement. It replaced the International Wheat Advisory Committee, which had been set up in 1933. Its headquarters are in London.

The International Sugar Council was established to administer the International Sugar Agreement that first came into force in September 1937. Its seat is London.

The first International Coffee Agreement was signed in September 1962, and came into provisional force in July 1963. The headquarters of the International Coffee Organization, which administers it, are in London.

There is also an International Olive Oil Agreement, operated by an International Olive Oil Council, with headquarters in Madrid. The United States is a member of the three commodity groups I mentioned but not of this agreement.

The International Cotton Advisory Committee, established in September 1939, assembles and analyzes data on world cotton production, consumption, trade stocks, and prices; observes developments in the world cotton market; and suggests measures considered suitable and practicable for the achievement of better international collaboration. Its headquarters are in Washington.

The International Wool Study Group provides information regarding the supply-and-demand position and probable trends. It gives attention to measures designed to stimulate world consumption of wool and to problems that arise in world trade in wool. Headquarters are in London. Its first meeting was held in 1947.

The International Seed Testing Association is concerned with the adoption of uniform methods of testing and with uniform terminology that, in turn, facilitate trade in seeds. It sponsors comparative testing and research to improve techniques and holds congresses for an exchange of information. The headquarters are in Copenhagen. It came into existence in 1924 as an outgrowth of the European Seed Testing Association, which was formed in 1921.

The General Agreement on Tariffs and Trade (GATT) came into force on January 1, 1948. It grew out of proposals by the United States for a multilateral approach to the solution of international trade problems—high tariffs, quota restrictions, and other artificial barriers, which had grown up almost everywhere during the economic depression years of the thirties and which became even more widespread after the Second World War.

The agreement was intended as an interim arrangement under which negotiations could be conducted, pending the formation of an International Trade Organization (ITO). Even though a charter for ITO was completed in March 1948, however, that organization has not come into existence, and GATT has provided an umbrella for the conduct of tariff and trade negotiations. Its basic objectives are to promote cooperation in international trade, to reduce tariffs, and to eliminate other government-imposed barriers to international trade.

Descriptions of organizations I have mentioned and of regional trade agreements are given at greater length in other chapters. One regional organization, which gives primary attention to trade and related matters, the European Economic Community (EEC), also is treated in another chapter because of its particular importance to the United States economy. I describe it briefly, as an example of a regional organization, to round out the picture of organizations dealing with trade.

EEC was established by France, the Federal Republic of Germany, Italy, Belgium, the Netherlands, and Luxembourg in 1957. It has headquarters in Brussels. It is often referred to as the Common Market. Its primary objective is the taking down of trade walls so that, eventually, commerce within the combined area may be carried on freely, much as it is among the States of the United States. Although the member countries of EEC are highly industrialized, agriculture is also of major concern to the Community. United States' interest in the EEC stems both from its overall concern with the economic strength of the free world and from the fact that trade with these countries is a major factor in United States imports and exports.

A NUMBER of organizations deal with the broad problems of international politics, economic development, and finance and at the same time touch on agriculture. These include the United Nations (U.N.), the International Bank for Reconstruction and Development (IBRD), International Monetary Fund (IMF), International Finance Corporation (IFC), International Development Association (IDA), the Organization for Economic Cooperation and Development (OECD), the Organization of American States (OAS), the Caribbean Organization, and the South Pacific Commission.

The United Nations, in addition to its major concern with international political problems, gives much attention to economic problems and economic development. This is done primarily through two arms, the Expanded Program of Technical Assistance (EPTA) and the United Nations Special Fund, both of which include large segments devoted to agriculture, and also through the United Nations Children's Fund (UNICEF).

Some things also are done under the United Nations' regular program. For example, the World Food Program is a joint FAO and United Nations effort to test, for an experimental period of 3 years, the use of agricultural surpluses through multilateral channels for economic development. Also, through its Commission on International Commodity Trade (CICT), the United Nations gives continuing attention to commodity problems.

Although the review of agricultural commodity problems is a matter for the FAO Council's Committee on Commodity Problems, the CICT does take agricultural aspects of trade into account in its overall reviews.

In addition, through the Economic Commission for Africa (ECA), the Economic Commission for Asia and the Far East (ECAFE), the Economic Commission for Europe (ECE), and the Economic Commission for Latin America (ECLA), the United Nations gives overall attention to the economic problems of those regions, including economic problems of agriculture.

FAO and the United Nations cooperate in the agricultural economic work of these Commissions.

The Expanded Program of Technical Assistance (EPTA) was authorized by the United Nations General Assembly in 1949 and began operations in July 1950. The United Nations and most of the other organizations in the United Nations family participate by giving technical assistance to the less-developed countries.

Moneys paid into the central fund on a voluntary basis by member countries of any of the participating organizations are divided among the organizations in accord with the amounts of assistance requested in their respective fields by recipient countries. The participating organizations coordinate their activities through a Technical Assistance Board in which each organization has a seat.

The assistance is given through the sending of experts, provision of fellowships, holding of training and development centers, often on a regional basis, and supplying limited amounts of specialized equipment needed to facilitate projects upon which experts are tendering advice. FAO, as the primary organization in the agricultural field, carries out about one-quarter of the EPTA-financed work.

The United Nations Special Fund was authorized by the United Nations General Assembly in October 1958 to provide systematic and sustained assistance in fields essential to the integrated technical, economic, and social development of the less-developed countries. Like EPTA, its funds are contributed to a central fund by governments, on a voluntary basis, and in turn most of these funds are expended through the various organizations in the United Nations family. Unlike EPTA, the work is developed on a project-by-project basis, rather than on the basis of country programs consisting of numbers of projects, and the average project is substantially larger than those under EPTA. Late in 1963, more than 100 million dollars had been assigned by the Special Fund to FAO for the execution of agricultural projects.

The United Nations Children's Fund retains the initials, UNICEF, from its earlier name, United Nations International Children's Emergency Fund.

UNICEF was established by the United Nations General Assembly in December 1946. Its funds, like those of EPTA and the Special Fund, are contributed by governments on a voluntary basis.

Among its many activities, considerable support is given to projects aimed at improving the nutrition of children and pregnant and nursing women. It also gives support to projects aimed at providing better food supplies—milk production and conservation projects, for example—and at better utilization of protein supplies, particularly from plant sources.

The International Bank for Reconstruction and Development, popularly known as the World Bank, was founded in July 1944 and began operations in December 1945. It lends funds or guarantees loans for reconstruction of industry and development of economic facilities. It also provides some assistance to countries by sending missions to advise on investment and development problems. Its activities, which range over the whole of economic development, include loans in support of agricultural projects and industries that serve agriculture.

The International Monetary Fund was developed as a companion of IBRD. Both were formed at the Bretton Woods (New Hampshire) Conference in July 1944, and both began operations in December 1945. Before becoming a member of IBRD, a government must be a member of IMF.

The IMF promotes monetary cooperation and expansion of international trade by providing procedures for orderly adjustment of foreign exchange rates, by consultation on major changes in exchange practices before they are put into effect, and by promoting common efforts among its members to remove restrictions on exchange transactions. Its actions contribute to stabilization of currencies, economic development, and the encouragement of international trade. Hence, as an important segment of the overall economy, agriculture benefits from the activities of IMF.

The International Finance Corporation (IFC), like the IMF, is linked closely with the IBRD. It is a separate legal entity, however, and its funds are separate from those of the IBRD. The IFC was established in July 1956. Its purpose is to encourage the growth of private enterprise in its member countries, and particularly in less-developed areas, by providing (in association with private investors) risk capital for the establishment, improvement, and expansion of productive private enterprises when other sources of funds at reasonable terms are not available.

The International Development Association (IDA) is associated with IBRD but is not a part of it. IDA helps to finance development projects that have been carefully selected and prepared, but it provides capital to less-developed countries on more liberal terms and over a wider range of projects than does IBRD.

The Organization for Economic Cooperation and Development evolved from the Organization for European Economic Cooperation. OEEC was formed in April 1948 as the European counterpart of the United States agency established to administer the Marshall plan. It was transformed into OECD in September of 1961, with altered terms of reference and expanded membership, including the United States, Canada, and Japan.

The basic aims of the new organization, OECD, are to achieve the highest sustainable economic growth in member countries while maintaining financial stability and thus to contribute to the development of the world economy, to contribute to sound economic expansion in both member and non-member countries, and to contribute to the expansion of world trade on a multilateral, nondiscriminatory basis in accord with international obligations. Its areas of work include coordination of economic policy, aid to developing countries, and trade and payments. Attention is given to agriculture, industry and energy, science, technology and education, manpower and social affairs, and nuclear energy.

THE ORGANIZATION of American States dates from April 1948, but its origins trace back to 1826, when Simón Bolívar called the Congress of Panama in an attempt to organize an American league of states. Although the treaty signed by the participants was ratified by only one country, and so never came into effect, the Congress of Panama established a precedent for several congresses that followed during the 19th century.

Thus, over the 138 years since the Congress of Panama, the OAS has gradually emerged as a cohesive, coordinating force in the Western Hemisphere. The main agricultural arm of OAS is the Inter-American Institute of Agricultural Sciences.

Another regional body in the Western Hemisphere is the Caribbean Organization. It was formed originally as the Caribbean Commission in October 1946 and was then composed of the Governments of France, the Netherlands, the United Kingdom, and the United States. Before that, however, there had been an Anglo-American Caribbean Commission, consisting of the United Kingdom and the United States, which had existed from March 1942. Both the earlier bodies were set up as intergovernmental advisory and consultative bodies on economic and social matters of concern to the member governments and their non-self-governing territories in the Caribbean.

With the emergence of a number of newly independent countries in the Caribbean, the Commission was transformed into the Caribbean Organization in September 1961. Of the original members, only France remained in the new Organization. The United States participates as an observer, but the Commonwealth of Puerto Rico and the Virgin Islands of the United States are members. The Caribbean Organization, a consultative and advisory body, concerns itself with social, cultural, agricultural, and economic matters of common interest to its members.

The United States has an active part in the South Pacific Commission. It is composed of governments of countries having territories in the region, and came into being in July 1948. Its purpose is to assist those governments in promoting the economic and social advancement of non-self-governing territories of the South Pacific region. It is an advisory and consultative body. Agriculture occupies an important place in the work of the Commission.

There are other regional bodies in the world that deal to some degree with agricultural problems within the context of broader terms of reference, but the ones I described are of most immediate interest to the United States and are examples of the kinds of approaches governments make to problems of coordination and to the development of common action on matters of regional concern.

THE FINAL GROUP of international intergovernmental organizations with which this chapter is concerned are those that deal with scientific, technical, and other matters related in part to agriculture.

The International Maritime Consultative Organization (IMCO) came into existence in March of 1958. Its headquarters are in London. Its purposes are to encourage the highest standards of maritime safety and efficiency of navigation and to provide for intergovernmental cooperation aimed at removal of discriminatory action and unnecessary restrictions on international shipping, and to provide for intergovernmental exchange of information. Since large quantities of agricultural products move between countries on ships, its work has a direct bearing on agricultural trade.

The International Atomic Energy Agency (IAEA), with headquarters in Vienna, came into existence in July 1957. It deals with basic problems in the use of atomic energy for peaceful purposes, including agricultural aspects. In this latter area, IAEA and the Food and Agriculture Organization cooperate, since FAO has a responsibility for atomic energy as an agricultural research tool and in other agricultural applications.

The International Civil Aviation Organization, with headquarters in Montreal, came into being in April 1947, although a provisional organization functioned from December 1944. It works to improve all aspects of civil aviation and to insure its safe and orderly growth throughout the world. Thus it contributes to the development of agricultural as well as other civil uses of aircraft.

The International Labor Organiza-

tion was established in April 1919 as an autonomous body associated with the League of Nations. Following the dissolution of the League, its constitution was amended to its present form in October 1946. ILO headquarters are in Geneva. It is a tripartite organization; that is, delegations from member countries to meetings of its governing body include representatives of government, management, and labor. It is concerned with many aspects of labor, including agricultural labor and labor in industries that process agricultural products or otherwise serve agriculture.

The World Meteorological Organization (WMO) was formed in March 1950, with headquarters in Geneva. It is a successor to the International Meteorological Organization, which, from 1878, had been coordinating weather-reporting activities of its members. WMO's objectives are to coordinate, standardize, and improve world meteorological services and to encourage efficient exchange of information among countries. It furthers the application of meteorology to aviation, shipping, agriculture, and other fields.

The World Health Organization (WHO), like WMO, has its headquarters in Geneva. An interim commission began work in July 1946, and WHO formally came into existence in September 1948. It is concerned with all aspects of human health. Many of its programs, such as that for malaria control and eradication, are of particular benefit to those who live in rural areas. Also, in cooperation with FAO, WHO is concerned with human protein requirements, with diseases—the zoonoses—that affect both animals and man, with hazards to human health arising from the use of pesticides, and with standards for food products.

The United Nations Educational, Scientific, and Cultural Organization was formed in November 1946 to contribute to peace and security by promoting collaboration among its member nations through education, science, and culture. Sound basic education and training in the sciences, as well as strong overall scientific research programs, are essential to provide the climate in which agricultural training and research can develop effectively and in which a modern agriculture can emerge and flourish. Thus, UNESCO's basic programs help to provide the foundation upon which agricultural improvement is built.

Also, in some areas, UNESCO cooperates with FAO on matters of direct concern to agriculture, such as the basic problems of arid zones, including alkaline soils, and ecological problems that affect agriculture.

The Pan American Health Organization (PAHO) began in 1902 with the first of a long series of conferences on sanitation and the formation of a permanent International Sanitary Bureau. In 1920, the name was changed to Pan American Sanitary Bureau, and in 1924 the organization was formalized under a convention. PAHO was formed in 1947, with the Bureau as its Secretariat. It is located in Washington. In addition to its own concern with the health needs of the Americas, it also serves as the regional office of WHO for the Western Hemisphere and, by agreement with OAS, it serves as a specialized organization of OAS.

Another regional body is the Inter-American Statistical Institute (IASI), which was created in 1940, with headquarters at the Pan American Union in Washington. Its parent organization was the nongovernmental International Statistical Institute, founded in 1885, in The Hague. In July 1950, the IASI agreed to become an integral part of the OAS system, and its Secretary General also serves as director of the Pan American Union's Department of Statistics. It is charged with promoting progress in statistical work in the Western Hemisphere.

Before leaving this general description—which is only a broad survey of the intergovernmental organizations that have emerged since 1900 and some of their functions—of international organizations dealing with agri-

culture, we should note the interrelationships among organizations in the United Nations family, since these relations are not generally understood.

Each of the organizations in this family is an independent body, with its own constitution, its own governing body, its own membership (which differs from organization to organization), and its own budget, which is fixed by representatives of governments in the respective governing bodies, and to which member governments contribute in accord with agreed scales of contributions.

Thus the United Nations in December 1963 comprised 113 member countries, and the General Assembly is its main organ and governing body. FAO comprised 106 member countries and 6 associate member countries, and the FAO Conference is its governing body. Most of the organizations that deal with specialized fields have entered into agreements with the United Nations whereby they also have functions as specialized agencies. (The International Atomic Energy Agency is an exception.)

The General Assembly or the United Nations Economic and Social Council may request a specialized agency to carry out a particular task, but the decision as to what it does rests with its governing body.

Each organization therefore is able to move forward in its own field, coordinating its actions with those of other organizations where this is desirable and feasible, but without being hampered by roadblocks that may prevent or slow down progress in another organization.

WE COME NOW to the final questions. Do these organizations contribute enough to the solution of the complex problems of a modern world to justify their continuation?

Without them, how could the present and ever-increasing needs for intercourse among nations be met?

These are essentially rhetorical questions. If real needs had not been felt, governments would not have undertaken the considerable effort and expense required to set up the international and regional intergovernmental organizations. Nor would scientists and other groups have taken the trouble to organize themselves into the many nongovernmental organizations through which they maintain contacts across national boundaries.

The many and diverse problems with which these organizations deal cannot be expected to disappear. Some will be solved, but as they are, others may appear.

As I said at the beginning, it is in the nature of human relationships to grow more complex. As man increases in number, as his level of knowledge rises (at a rate entirely unprecedented in man's history), and as contacts among peoples and nations increase, the need for consultations, for exchange of information and ideas, and for reaching agreement on common and cooperative courses of action certainly will increase.

All the organizations that now exist will not persist in the forms they had in 1964. Some will no doubt disappear entirely and be replaced by others.

But international organizations as such seem certain to continue. If it should be decided tomorrow, for example, that all the organizations in the United Nations family should be abolished forthwith, the governments of the nations would have to begin at once the task of developing new mechanisms for consultation on these many fronts. So the basic problem is not whether to have intergovernmental and nongovernmental international organizations but, rather, how to make such organizations serve their intended purposes effectively and efficiently.

It is not easy to achieve efficiency at the international conference table. Each country has its own problems, its own history and way of thought, its own interests to protect. When more than 100 countries meet to discuss problems of world agriculture in an

FAO Conference, it is hardly to be expected that they will agree on all.

A common mistake in evaluating the work of an international intergovernmental organization is to overlook both its form and its function and to regard it as a building and a staff. For example, the United Nations is an organization of governments whose territories spread over the entire world. The headquarters building in New York houses its Secretariat and provides meeting places for the representatives of its member governments—but it is the governments that constitute the organization.

It is so with FAO and with each of the other organizations. FAO has its headquarters building in Rome, where the central staff is housed and where the FAO Conference and many other intergovernmental meetings are held.

But the member governments are FAO.

Only when we recognize this basic fact can we evaluate the work of any intergovernmental body.

These bodies are set up by governments to serve governments. They provide the forums in which governments debate and decide issues, the stages upon which government representatives act out international plays.

Efficient, competent staffs can do much to facilitate debates, to guide participants toward decisions, and to organize international activities, but in the final analysis, governments take the decisions leading to common actions by countries or to the authorization of actions by the staffs on behalf of governments.

The province of an international wheat agreement is determined by the governments who sign it. A major difference on an agricultural trade matter cannot be resolved in the GATT until the views of opposing governments can be reconciled. Common action against a locust attack cannot be organized by FAO unless the governments in the affected region give their agreement and support. An international or regional maize or rice breeding program is ineffective without active government participation.

This is not the place for a detailed analysis of the degree to which each of the international organizations has achieved its objectives, whether they relate wholly or partly to agriculture.

Governments have been prepared to move faster and further in some areas than in others. It is easier to achieve common understanding and to promote cooperative action in some fields than in others. The whole concept of approaching common problems through international organizations is still quite new.

In intergovernmental organizations, experience had to be gained, both by those who staffed the secretariats and by those who represented their governments. It is still not easy to find men for posts in international organizations who are equipped in training and in experience.

So the international intergovernmental organizations have had to gain experience as they grew, to feel their way along uncharted trails before they could move forward with speed and precision.

Methods of work and areas of emphasis have been modified as they developed in order to meet changing needs, and to increase the effectiveness of international activities.

This period of growth and of learning how to conduct the affairs of nations efficiently and effectively through intergovernmental organizations is still with us—the learning process will no doubt require several decades.

The international nongovernmental organizations that serve agriculture have done much to facilitate the exchange of information and ideas and to promote international understanding of agriculture and agricultural science.

But they, too, are encountering problems in serving their members most effectively. For example, the international congress has been one of the useful types of activities sponsored by many of these groups. Yet, with easier travel; generally good economic conditions; great increases in the numbers of scientific, technical, and economic workers; and equally great increases in the outflow of new knowledge; the traditional congress for the presentation of papers has grown oversized and relatively less effective. So new methods of organizing such congresses are being thought out and tested.

IN CONCLUSION, we come back to the point, made at the beginning, that many international intergovernmental organizations have been formed during the 20th century. Through these organizations, governments tackle a wide variety of agricultural problems and problems that affect agriculture.

As relations among countries grow more complex, the role of intergovernmental organizations seems certain to increase in importance.

Since these organizations are the instruments of governments, it follows that it is a major concern of governments that the organizations direct their attention to the key problems of world agriculture and their other fields of endeavor and that they are made to function as efficient and effective instruments of policies shaped by the member governments for the overall benefit of member countries and their peoples.

RALPH W. PHILLIPS *is Director, International Organizations Staff, Office of the Assistant Secretary for International Affairs, the United States Department of Agriculture. He was formerly Deputy Director of Agriculture in the Food and Agriculture Organization of the United Nations, and in earlier positions he was in charge of animal genetics research in the Department of Agriculture, head of the Department of Animal Husbandry at Utah State University, and a member of the staffs at the Universities of Massachusetts and Missouri. He is the author of many papers on animal genetics, physiology of reproduction, and international agriculture, and was the founding editor of the* Journal of Animal Science.

FAO of the United Nations

by RALPH W. PHILLIPS and
   KENNETH A. HAINES

FAO, THE FOOD AND AGRICULTURE Organization of the United Nations, is the major international agricultural organization.

Food and agriculture, as used in the name, cover the broad fields of agriculture, fisheries, forestry, and nutrition and the economic, statistical, and institutional matters related to those fields.

Within those fields, it is the task of FAO to assist its member governments in the development of their programs and projects aimed at improving agricultural production, processing, and distribution.

FAO may be regarded as an international extension service, with the governments as the recipients of its services. In turn, the rural peoples and consumers generally benefit as information and the advantages of the improved services become available.

The comparison to an extension service does not mean that FAO is concerned only with the applications of knowledge. It is concerned also with the development of research.

It is concerned as well with the establishment and strengthening of the organizational structures for research, extension, training of leaders, and other government services to agriculture, as well as with the effective administration of these services.

Further, FAO is concerned with the economic and social structure wherein the results of research may be applied with maximum benefit to all rural populations and consumers.

However, FAO is not the doer of research, the conductor of extension services, the extender of credit, and so on. Its task is to assist countries in doing these things or in improving their internal structures for service to agriculture and their ways of rendering that service.

The task is large and diverse. Its diversity is mostly a reflection of the differing stages of development of the member countries. Because of widely differing stages of development, countries differ in the kinds of services they may need from an international organization.

A country that has already experienced the agricultural revolution of the past several decades and whose economic levels and individual incomes are generally high may be in a situation different from that of a country in which the average farm contains only a few acres, where much farmwork is still done by hand, and where the annual income is under 100 dollars per person.

In a complex world situation where developed countries are able to move ahead rapidly because of economic resources and trained personnel while less-developed countries move forward at only a slightly accelerated pace in their development programs, the gap between developed and less-developed countries tends to widen rather than to become narrower.

FAO has the task of serving all its members, from the least developed to the most highly developed country.

The less-developed countries are generally more interested in technical improvements in agriculture that may be put to use to help production keep pace with population increases and with economic problems relating to export crops upon which they depend for foreign exchange.

On the other hand, the developed

countries are generally more interested in the exchange of statistical and technical information, in problems relating to the disposal of agricultural surpluses and the use of such surpluses for economic development, in the overall problems of international trade, and in the degree to which an international organization may be used for channeling technical assistance to less-developed countries, as compared with bilateral channels.

These are only examples of differences in needs and approaches, but they illustrate why the program of FAO has so evolved that much of the regular program of the Organization consists of activities that are of benefit to all member countries, while the field programs are designed to meet the needs of the less-developed countries for technical assistance.

IT HAD ITS BEGINNINGS in a 44-nation Conference on Food and Agriculture at Hot Springs, Va., in May and early June of 1943.

That Conference, which was convened by President Franklin D. Roosevelt, set up an interim commission with headquarters in Washington.

The Commission functioned until the Organization was formally brought into existence at the first session of the FAO Conference in Quebec in October 1945.

At the beginning of the Quebec Conference on October 16, 1945, representatives of 34 nations signed the constitution. By the close of that Conference, 8 other governments had been admitted to membership, bringing the total to 42.

In adhering to the constitution, these nations indicated their determination to take separate and collective action to raise levels of nutrition and standards of living of their peoples, to secure improvements in the efficiency of production and distribution of food and other agricultural products, to better the conditions of rural populations, and by these means to contribute toward an expanding world economy.

Since the Quebec Conference, membership in FAO has grown from 42 to 106 member nations in 1963.

Provision has been made in the constitution for associate membership by territories that do not handle their own foreign affairs. There were six associate members in December 1963. They may participate in FAO activities but have no vote.

The scope of FAO's work is reflected rather fully in the internal structure of the Organization's headquarters staff.

FAO is headed by a Director General. He is elected by the FAO Conference and is assisted by a Deputy General and by five Assistant Director Generals, who head the Technical Department, the Department of Economic and Social Affairs, the Department of Public Relations and Legal Affairs, the Department of Administration and Finance, and the Program and Budgetary Service.

The Technical Department is made up of six divisions dealing with animal production and health, land and water development, plant production and protection, fisheries, forestry and forest products, and nutrition, and an Atomic Energy Branch, which deals with the use of atomic energy in agriculture.

The Department of Economic and Social Affairs contains four divisions, which deal with commodities, economic analysis, statistics, and with rural institutions and services.

The Department of Public Relations and Legal Affairs has two major services, which deal with public information and with publications. It also contains a large library; a Legislative Research Branch, which attempts to keep abreast of agricultural legislative developments around the world; and offices that deal with protocol and with the operation of conferences.

The Department of Administration and Finance contains two divisions that deal with personnel and management and with finance.

The Program and Budgetary Service is a part of the Office of the Director General. It contains three divisions.

The Program Formulation and Budget Division carries out the functions its name implies, in cooperation with other departments.

The Program Liaison Division maintains contacts with other international organizations, and with FAO's regional offices in Bangkok (for Asia and the Far East), in Accra (for Africa), in Cairo (for the Near East), in Santiago (for Latin America), in Geneva (for Europe), in Washington, D.C. (for North America), and with subregional offices in some of these FAO regions.

The third, the Division of Technical Assistance Co-ordination, coordinates activities financed under the Expanded Program of Technical Assistance and the United Nations Special Fund, as well as technical assistance under funds from other sources, including the Freedom From Hunger campaign. The work of the division includes the coordination of fellowship and training center activities.

Besides the five major organizational segments described, there is at FAO headquarters a group that deals with the World Food Program, a 3-year experimental effort to test the using of surplus foods in economic development. It is headed by an Executive Director, who is responsible to the Director General of FAO and the Secretary General of the United Nations.

THE FAO STAFF does not constitute the organization.

Rather, the staff is the Secretariat of an organization composed of governments, which manage FAO affairs through the FAO Conference and a series of subsidiary bodies.

The Conference holds regular sessions biennially. Special sessions may be convened to deal with emergency and special problems.

Each member government may be represented in each session of the Conference by one delegate and so has one vote. The delegate may be assisted by as many alternates, associates, and advisers as the member government wishes.

The functions of the Conference include acting on applications for membership in FAO, reviewing and approving the program of work and fixing the level of the budget for the coming biennium, setting the scale of contributions, making decisions on constitutional and administrative matters, reviewing the state of food and agriculture, discussing any special topics it may include in its agenda, appointing the Director General when that post is to become vacant, electing members of the 27-member-government Council, and appointing an independent chairman of the Council.

Other examples of the kinds of action taken by the Conference were the determination that the permanent headquarters of the Organization should be in Rome and the decision that FAO should participate in programs financed from sources other than the regular budget.

In addition to plenary sessions, in which major actions are taken, each Conference session normally breaks into three commissions, one dealing with government policies and problems in relation to food and agriculture, one with the activities and budget of the Organization, and one with constitutional and administrative matters.

THE FAO COUNCIL is composed of 27 member governments that are elected by the Conference. These members are elected for 3-year terms, and terms are so staggered that one-third of the memberships expire each year.

The Council is the second level of authority in the governing structure and is the policy-determining body between Conference sessions. It holds at least one full-scale session each year and brief sessions just before and after regular sessions of the Conference.

Much of the Council's work is based on preparatory work by committees, particularly the four standing committees—the Program Committee, Finance Committee, Committee on Constitutional and Legal Matters, and Committee on Commodity Problems.

Two ad hoc committees were set up by the Council and organs of other organizations to deal with special problems. One, the FAO/UNICEF Joint Policy Committee, is composed of 10 countries, 5 appointed by the FAO Council and 5 by the Executive Board of the United Nations Children's Fund. The other, the Intergovernmental Committee on the World Food Program, is composed of 24 countries, 12 appointed by the FAO Council and 12 by the United Nations Economic and Social Council.

The Committee on Commodity Problems performs much of its work through subcommittees or working groups—a consultative subcommittee on surplus disposal, a consultative subcommittee on the economic aspects of rice, a cocoa study group, a group on grains, a group on coconut and coconut products, and a group on citrus fruit.

THE ACTIVITIES of FAO are designed to provide its member countries with opportunities for intercountry consultation and with information, advice, and technical assistance. Various approaches or methods are used to achieve these ends. These methods are used either singly or in combination, depending on the nature of the problem or the task to be done.

International and regional forums are provided for the discussion of scientific, technical, and economic problems. Overall problems of food and agriculture are discussed in Conference and Council sessions and in regional conferences held biennially in most of the FAO regions.

In more limited subject-matter areas, periodic discussions take place; for example, in regional fishery and forestry committees and councils, the Committee on Commodity Problems and its subgroups, the International Rice Commission, and many meetings organized on an ad hoc basis to consider scientific, technical, and economic matters.

Such forums provide for the exchange of information and ideas in all of the fields covered by FAO and often lead to a coordinated action for the solution of common problems.

Considerable emphasis was placed on missions in FAO's early years. Missions were sent to Greece, Poland, Thailand, Nicaragua, and other countries to assist governments in the development of overall agricultural improvement programs or in some limited segment.

With the establishment of the Expanded Program of Technical Assistance and the United Nations Special Fund, resources became available to FAO for substantial assistance to governments on a project-by-project basis. The mission approach then fell into disuse. It is again being brought into use, however, particularly in assisting governments in planning development.

Much of FAO's direct assistance to governments is in the form of technical assistance under the Expanded Program of Technical Assistance (EPTA) and the United Nations Special Fund (UNSF).

Another major source of funds for work in certain fields has been the United Nations Children's Fund (UNICEF). These are the most important of the field programs we mentioned earlier.

Under EPTA- and UNICEF-supported projects, experts have been sent to countries for a few months to several years to advise and assist in many projects. As of July 1, 1963, FAO had 489 such experts in the field. Many fellowships have been provided for training outside the recipients' countries. Training and development centers, usually of a few months' duration, have been held in many fields.

In connection with these activities, limited amounts of technical equipment and literature have been supplied to facilitate the work of experts and for use in training centers. On the training side, experts serving in countries are also expected to impart training to national workers responsible for carrying on the projects upon which advice is being given.

Under UNSF, assistance is organized on a project-by-project basis, and each such project is substantially larger, on the average, than the units of assistance rendered under EPTA.

Once a project is approved and assigned to FAO as the executing agency, FAO employs the team of international workers required, obtains the supplies and equipment that are to come from outside the country, and works with the group supplied by the recipient government in carrying out the project. Late in 1963, more than 100 million dollars had been assigned to FAO by UNSF for the conduct of 128 projects.

Assistance to countries through the World Food Program for the use of surpluses in economic development also represents a type of technical assistance rendered through FAO, jointly with the United Nations.

As A PART of its regular program, FAO assists governments in planning agricultural development by sending out advisory teams in agreement with governments that request such help.

Also, as part of its regular program, FAO awards about 12 research fellowships each year. Recipients may be from developed or less-developed countries and are expected to carry out research on problems related to FAO's program of work. These are called André Mayer Fellowships, after the French physiologist who was active in FAO Conference and Council affairs in earlier years.

FAO prepares and publishes many documents that contain statistical, scientific, technical, and economic information for the use of member countries. These publications include yearbooks of production and trade statistics; technical and scientific publications in many phases of agriculture, economics, fisheries, forestry, and nutrition; reports of missions and experts serving on technical assistance projects; reports on training centers and technical and economic meetings; and reports on sessions of the FAO Conference and Council.

Documents are published in the three official languages—English, French, and Spanish.

Under its constitution, FAO has provision for the organization of continuing bodies, which are mechanisms for consultation among countries and for cooperative action in specific subject-matter areas where this is deemed desirable.

Regional committees and commissions on fisheries, forestry, and rice have already been mentioned. Others, for example, deal with foot-and-mouth disease, locust control, improvement of statistics, and pesticide residues. FAO also has developed an International Plant Protection Convention, which provides a general umbrella under which plant quarantine and related activities may be facilitated by regional groups and national services.

FAO has begun to develop, jointly with WHO, a new field of work aimed at the establishment of internationally recognized standards for food products, and for this purpose a Codex Alimentarius Commission has been created.

FAO staff members maintain contacts with agricultural leaders in various countries through visits, contacts during international and regional meetings, and correspondence. By these means, the flow of information and ideas in both directions between government officials and the staff is facilitated.

The various methods of work employed by FAO provide for a great deal of flexibility in carrying out its functions and responsibilities to member governments under its constitution.

FAO ACTIVITIES are financed from a number of sources.

The regular program is financed by contributions from all the member countries. Both the total amount and the proportion to be paid by each government are fixed by the FAO Conference.

Funds for the Expanded Program of Technical Assistance are contributed on a voluntary basis by countries that are members of any one of the organizations in the United Nations family.

Funds, in the currencies of the contributing countries, go into a central pool, the use of which is coordinated by a Technical Assistance Board, in which each participating organization has a seat.

The amount going to each organization for carrying out technical assistance is determined by the portion of requests received from governments and approved in the fields of the respective organizations.

Moneys for the United Nations Special Fund, like those for EPTA, are contributed on a voluntary basis by member countries of organizations in the United Nations family. The Managing Director of the Special Fund receives requests for projects from countries. Once a project is approved, funds for its operation are turned over to the organization that has been designated to execute the project. Thus FAO receives funds for the execution of agricultural projects.

The United Nations Children's Fund (UNICEF) also receives its funds from governments on a voluntary basis. For projects in which FAO and UNICEF are cooperating in rendering assistance to governments, UNICEF supplies funds to FAO for the employment of field personnel, for fellowships, and for the operation of training centers; UNICEF provides material assistance directly to governments.

Contributions to the World Food Program, whether in the form of funds, commodities, or services such as shipping, are also on a voluntary basis.

FAO also carries out a number of activities under fund-in-trust arrangements. Such funds come from various sources. A government of a less-developed country may wish assistance that it cannot obtain from established outside sources, and it may therefore provide FAO with funds to hire professional staff and to cover such other expenses as are necessary to carry out the work. By this device, a government can obtain professional

services that it could not secure under its own civil service regulations.

A private organization or a government may make a contribution to carry out some special project; for example, under the Freedom From Hunger campaign, wherein FAO undertakes to execute the project. In such cases, FAO manages the projects and, in addition to actual project costs, makes a suitable charge to cover the overhead costs.

Earlier in FAO history, technical assistance was rendered to nine countries under such a fund-in-trust arrangement with moneys transferred from the former United Nations Relief and Rehabilitation Administration (UNRRA). The work of the Codex Alimentarius Commission has been carried on with funds contributed from outside sources.

Thus FAO cooperates closely with several arms of the United Nations—EPTA, UNSF, and UNICEF—and with the United Nations itself on the World Food Program.

FAO and the United Nations also collaborate in other fields: Industrial development, a field wherein FAO has primary responsibility for small rural industries; water resources, wherein the United Nations maintains a Water Resources Development Center, while FAO is concerned with agricultural uses of water; land tenure, a field in which FAO has primary responsibility but the United Nations has an interest in the overall economic and social aspects.

In the United Nations regional economic commissions—ECE, ECAFE, ECA, and ECLA—the economic work related to agriculture is carried out together by FAO and the United Nations.

FAO also cooperates with other organizations, including WHO, IAEA, ILO, WMO, UNESCO, and the GATT.

FAO and the World Health Organization have mutual interests in the zoonoses (diseases that affect both man and animals), in protein deficiencies that affect human health, in pesticides that may be harmful to man, and in work on food standards under the jointly sponsored Codex Alimentarius Commission.

The International Atomic Energy Agency is concerned with the basic, overall problems of peaceful uses of atomic energy, while FAO is concerned with applications in agriculture, including use of isotopes in plant, animal, and soil research; preservation of foodstuffs by radiation; and protection of farm animals, crops, and rural families from possible ill effects of radiation. Hence, the two organizations coordinate their related activities.

The International Labor Organization is concerned with labor problems, including those of farm labor. ILO also has concerned itself with improvement of indigenous populations, such as the Andean Indians, who practice subsistence agriculture, and with the development of cooperatives. FAO and ILO have collaborated in all these fields.

The World Meteorological Organization engages in work on the development and improvement of meteorological services around the world and with the applications of these services in all fields of activity including agriculture. In view of the major importance of accurate weather forecasting to agriculture, FAO and WMO have mutual interests.

The United Nations Educational, Scientific, and Cultural Organization is concerned with basic scientific matters and with education, both of which touch on agriculture. FAO is concerned with specialized training of agricultural leaders and carries out a special program in Africa.

FAO is concerned also with the problems of soils in arid zones, particularly alkaline soils, and with problems of soil classification and mapping. In both areas of work, UNESCO has some interest in the applications of science to the solution of problems. Also, there is some collaboration in the fisheries field because of the interrelations between FAO's fisheries work and the activities of UNESCO's Office of Oceanography and the Intergovernmental Oceanographic Commission.

In relation to the General Agreement on Tariffs and Trade, FAO consults and compiles information on commodity problems in connection with the work of the FAO Council's Committee on Commodity Problems and its several subsidiary groups. The GATT, on the other hand, is concerned with actual negotiations aimed at reduction of tariffs and other barriers to international trade. Even so, the areas of work lead to definite overlappings of interest that require close consultation.

Mention should be made of another kind of interrelationship. In some cases, such as with cocoa and olive oil, consultations sponsored by FAO have contributed to the development of proposals for commodity agreements. When one of them develops to the stage of negotiating an international commodity agreement, however, the United Nations convenes the negotiating conference, and that conference may set up a council to administer an agreement.

One other example of interorganizational cooperation is that between FAO and the Inter-American Institute of Agricultural Sciences. FAO and the IAIAS have collaborated in various activities relating to animal production, agricultural extension, and agricultural education. A United Nations Special Fund project has been developed to strengthen the work of the Institute, and FAO is the executing agency for this project.

Other examples of interorganizational cooperation and collaboration could be cited, but these should be sufficient to show that, while FAO is the major international agricultural organization, it has a network of interrelations with other organizations in and outside the United Nations family.

POLITICAL, ECONOMIC, and social conditions in today's world are in a state of change. As the environment in which an international organization changes, the organization also must change.

FAO has undergone its share of changes as it has grown from small beginnings in 1945. To a considerable extent, the changes reflect the emergence of many newly independent nations and economic recovery after the Second World War.

Membership has grown from 42 members to 106 member countries and 6 associate members. Funds available annually to FAO have increased perhaps twelvefold—a precise figure is not possible, because some funds are not allocated on an annual basis.

THE BASIC objectives of FAO have not changed, but there have been substantial changes in emphasis and growing attention to technical assistance for less-developed countries.

During its first 5 years, activities were carried out almost entirely under the regular budget, and most activities were designed to benefit member countries as a whole. Some regular funds were used for sending missions to a few countries, and technical assistance was rendered to nine countries under a fund transferred from UNRRA. An International Emergency Food Council (later named "Committee") was set up for the voluntary rationing among countries of certain agricultural products and supplies that were then scarce. The idea of a "world food board" and of an "international commodity clearinghouse" was considered and discarded, although the discussions contributed to the establishment of the FAO Council, and keeping under review the state of food and agriculture was made one of its functions.

The period from 1951 to 1958 may be regarded as the second phase in FAO's development. The first 5 years of this phase were marked by rapid expansion, particularly in field activities. There was some expansion of field activities through projects supported by UNICEF. At the same time, there was a gradual increase in the regular program. Under both the regular and technical assistance programs, there was an increasing tendency to use regional approaches to problems and to encourage intergovernmental consultation through technical and economic meetings and development centers. The last 3 years of this phase were marked by some overall growth but in general represented a period of leveling off.

The upward spiral of FAO's field activities was renewed in 1959, following initiation of the United Nations Special Fund in October 1958. There also was a substantial increase in the regular budget for the 1960–1961 biennium and a considerably larger increase for 1962–1963. Too, there was a rapid increase in the UNICEF-supported aid to nutrition and related fields of work. The Freedom From Hunger campaign was developed, and various projects were undertaken under this banner with support from funds in trust. This upward swing in the overall level of activities has continued. In 1961 the World Food Program, for the use of food through international channels for economic development, was authorized for a 3-year experimental period.

As a result of these changes, a much larger portion of the total funds available to FAO may be channeled into activities for the benefit of the less-developed countries than in earlier years, and conversely, substantially less of the work is of direct benefit to the member countries as a whole.

THIS POINT is underlined by the fact that a little more than one-fifth of the member countries that may be regarded as developed contribute more than 87 percent of the regular budget, and these developed countries contribute an even larger share of the budgets for the various technical assistance activities.

The rapid upswing in field activities also has had a substantial impact on the regular program, since increasingly large proportions of the time of the headquarters staff have had to be devoted to the managing and servicing of field activities. Much of the regular budget is, in fact, being used in support of field programs, for which the financing from other sources covers only a portion of the costs.

IT CAN BE ARGUED that the developed countries benefit in the long run from improved economic and social conditions in the world as a whole and that therefore they benefit indirectly from the large portion of the Organization's activities that directly benefit the less-developed countries. That is true.

At the same time, there is an important question of balance, if the continued active interest of all member countries in the affairs of FAO is to be assured and FAO is to make a maximum contribution toward the objectives set out in the preamble of its constitution, wherein the nations accepting the constitution expressed their determination to promote the common welfare by furthering separate and collective action through FAO for the purposes of: Raising levels of nutrition and standards of living of the peoples under their respective jurisdictions; securing improvements in the efficiency of the production and distribution of all food and agricultural products; bettering the condition of rural populations; and thus contributing toward an expanding world economy.

In effect, the pendulum has swung from one extreme where in the beginning FAO had few resources for field activities to the other extreme where the bulk of its resources, including a substantial portion of the time of staff financed under the regular budget, are being used for this purpose. Perhaps, in due time, better balance will be achieved, and the pendulum will come to rest somewhere near the center.

This in no way depreciates FAO's important and useful role as a multi- lateral instrument for technical assistance. It does, however, emphasize the role of FAO as a world forum for intergovernmental consultation and collaboration on many fronts, a role that is certain to become more important as pressures on the land increase and as man must find ways leading to ever-increasing efficiency in agricultural production if the needs of existing and expanding populations are to be met.

In the broad context of world affairs, it should be recognized that the time has passed when ministries and departments of foreign affairs can carry the full load of foreign relations for their countries. The agricultural scientists, economists, and the policymakers are playing an increasingly important role in international affairs. This does not mean that foreign ministries have a lesser role. As problems on the foreign affairs front grow more complex, the size of the task increases. It has already increased to the point where support is needed on many fronts, including that of food and agriculture and their place in the overall economic, social, and political problems of the world.

FAO is one of the avenues through which the countries, with the active participation of their agricultural leaders, scientists, and economists, can make progress in the solution of these problems.

RALPH W. PHILLIPS *is Director, International Organizations Staff, Office of the Assistant Secretary for International Affairs.*

KENNETH A. HAINES *is Assistant Director, Foreign Research and Technical Programs Division, Agricultural Research Service. He joined the Department of Agriculture in 1933 as an entomologist in the former Bureau of Entomology and Plant Quarantine. In 1954 he undertook program appraisal work in the Office of Administrator of ARS. His work since 1959 has dealt primarily with international organizations and with technical assistance.*

The Inter-American System

by CHARLES R. DAVENPORT

THE ORGANIZATION of American States has evolved as the inter-American system and mechanism for the Alliance for Progress program for the development of the Western Hemisphere.

The system and the Alliance are the product of nearly a century and a half of cooperative development, from the dream of Simón Bolívar to the vision of Juscelino Kubitschek, former President of Brazil.

Simón Bolívar, the great Latin American liberator, convened the Congress of Panama in 1826 to organize an American league of states with the primary purpose of a mutual defense against Spain or possibly against other foreign powers.

Bolívar hoped that this league would lead to unification of the American countries into a single nation. All were invited, but several, including the United States, did not participate.

After considerable delay, two United States delegates were appointed, but one died before reaching Panama and the other did not leave until after the Congress adjourned.

The Congress produced a treaty concerned with common defense and related measures, which never became effective. Its real importance was that it marked the beginnings of the inter-American system.

Seven congresses followed with increasingly important results. They led to the First International Conference of American States in Washington in 1889–1890. It marked a second major step in the development of the inter-American system through the creation of the International Union of American Republics and a Commercial Bureau of American Republics.

Nine more conferences followed. The last in 1954 engendered the present inter-American system.

In this series, the Ninth International Conference of American States in Bogotá, Colombia, in 1948 represented the third major step in the development of this system. It produced the charter of the Organization of American States, which established the Organization of American States (OAS), largely as we know it today, with a new and permanent juridical structure.

Except for Canada and the newly independent countries of Jamaica and Trinidad and Tobago, all nations of the Western Hemisphere belong to the OAS. The Government of Cuba was excluded from participation in OAS activities in 1962, however.

OVERALL POLICY and policy guidance of OAS is provided by three groups: The Inter-American Conference, the meeting of consultation of Ministers of Foreign Affairs, and specialized conferences.

The Conference is the supreme organ of the OAS and normally meets every 5 years to decide general action and policy.

The meeting of consultation bridges the periods between conferences by serving when convened as the organ of consultation to consider urgent problems. It is also to provide a policy guidance for the Advisory Defense Committee as the charter calls for.

Special conferences meet periodically to consider technical matters or related problems of the semiautonomous specialized organizations or permanent agencies and special agencies and commissions.

Specialized organizations are the

Inter-American Institute of Agricultural Sciences (IAIAS) at San José, Costa Rica; the Pan American Health Organization (PAHO) with its executive organ, the Secretariat of the Pan American Sanitary Bureau, Washington; the Inter-American Commission of Women (IACW), Washington; the Inter-American Children's Institute (IACI), Montevideo, Uruguay; the Pan American Institute of Geography and History (PAIGH), Mexico City; and the Inter-American Indian Institute (IAII), Mexico City.

Special agencies and commissions, located in Washington, are the Inter-American Commission on Human Rights (IACHR); the Inter-American Defense Board (IADB); the Inter-American Nuclear Energy Commission (IANEC); the Inter-American Peace Committee (IAPC); the Inter-American Statistical Institute (IASI); and the Special Consultative Committee on Security (SCCS).

The Council of the Organization (COAS), the permanent representative body, is in Washington. It is the day-to-day operating arm of the OAS, works closely with the specialized organizations and special agencies and commissions, and provides policy guidance to the organs of the Council and the Pan American Union (PAU). It can also constitute itself as the provisional organ of consultation.

The organs of the Council are the Inter-American Economic and Social Council (IA–ECOSOC), Washington; the Inter-American Council of Jurists with its Inter-American Juridical Committee, Rio de Janeiro; and the Inter-American Cultural Council, with its Council for Cultural Action, Mexico City.

The Pan American Union is the permanent and central organ and general secretariat of the OAS. It has departments and offices concerned with public information, statistics, technical cooperation, secretariat services, public services, and financial, economic, social, and legal affairs.

The PAU, in addition to assisting member states, has sponsored technical assistance projects in Argentina, Brazil, Chile, Colombia, and Venezuela.

Special and specialized conferences within the framework of the OAS and its predecessors and related events have forged the latest development in the inter-American system and the OAS.

After correspondence with President Eisenhower and with other chiefs of state of the American Republics in 1958, President Kubitschek of Brazil proposed "Operación Pan Americana" for development.

The proposal was followed by the organization of the Inter-American Development Bank (IDB) in 1959, the Act of Bogotá in 1960, and the Alliance for Progress under the Charter of Punta del Este in 1961.

The IDB is a specialized regional institution to which all OAS members, except Cuba, belong. The Bank uses its ordinary capital resources, authorized at 1 billion dollars, for regular loan operations. It also administers, with some assistance from the United States Agency for International Development and the OAS, the Social Progress Trust Fund of 500 million dollars for special development projects not in regular loan operations.

The Act of Bogotá was adopted by all OAS members, Cuba excluded. The act provided for strengthening the OAS and recommended ways and means of accomplishing economic and social development.

President Kennedy first proposed the Alliance for Progress in his inaugural address of January 20, 1961. He put this proposal into more concrete form on March 13, 1961, when he called for a 10-year program for the Americas and requested a special meeting of the Inter-American Economic and Social Council to consider means of achieving the program.

A meeting of the Council at the ministerial level took place in Punta del Este August 5–17, 1961. There the Alliance for Progress was forged. It has been entered into by 20 of the 24 American countries.

Nonparticipating nations of the Western Hemisphere are Cuba, who abstained from joining, Canada, and the since independent states of Jamaica and Trinidad and Tobago.

The Alliance marked the fourth and boldest step in the inter-American cooperation.

ALLIANCE OBJECTIVES are contained in the several measures adopted at Punta del Este, which included a declaration to the peoples of America, the Charter of Punta del Este, and several appended resolutions.

In the declaration, the American Republics agreed to establish an Alliance for Progress: "A vast effort to bring a better life to all peoples of the Continent." The declaration recognized the principles of democracy and individual dignity and outlined 12 broad social and economic goals.

The United States, for its part, pledged to supply financial and technical cooperation, including a major part of the minimum of 20 billion dollars estimated as external needs over the next 10 years.

External needs of 2 billion dollars a year are expected to be met approximately as follows: 1.1 billion dollars in United States public funds and 900 million dollars in roughly equal amounts by United States private capital, private capital from Western Europe and Japan, and funds from international organizations.

Such international organizations include the World Bank, the International Finance Corporation, the International Development Association, and the United Nations Special Fund.

As the initial step, the United States pledged to make available more than 1 billion dollars for the 12 months beginning March 13, 1961.

The countries of Latin America agreed to devote a steadily increasing share of their own resources and to make the reforms necessary to achieve Alliance goals. Latin American countries themselves are expected to pro-

vide a minimum of 8 billion dollars a year. Their contribution is also to include the formulation of a national development program by each.

The charter established the Alliance for Progress within the concept of President Kubitschek's Operation Pan America. The charter consisted of a preamble and four titles—objectives, economic and social development, economic integration of Latin America, and basic export commodities.

GOALS to be achieved in the sixties were based on the declaration and listed as 12 objectives in title I.

Two were aimed at an economic growth: To attain income levels sufficient to assure self-sustaining development and to narrow the gap in relation to more industrialized nations, with target growth rates of not less than 2.5 percent per capita per year; and to achieve a more equitable distribution of income while assuring a higher proportion of the national product for investment.

Three objectives are related to economic development: To lessen dependence on primary exports and capital imports and to achieve export stability; to accelerate rational industrialization, with special attention to capital industries; and to increase productivity and to improve marketing of agricultural products. One basic objective is to encourage comprehensive agrarian reform programs to eliminate extremely large and extremely small holdings.

Other objectives are improved education and the elimination of adult illiteracy by 1970; increased life expectancy and improved public health; accelerated construction of low-cost housing and provision of public services; stabilized prices; Latin American economic integration; and cooperative programs to prevent harmful fluctuations in primary export earnings.

Title II, Economic and Social Development, prescribed guidelines for basic development requirements, national development programs, immediate and short-term measures, external assistance to support national development programs, and Alliance organization and procedures. The need is recognized for technical assistance from the Organization of American States, the Economic Commission for Latin America, the Inter-American Development Bank, and United Nations specialized agencies.

Title II provided also for a panel of nine experts attached to the Inter-American Economic and Social Council to give assistance to member countries as requested.

The assistance is in the form of help with country programs by an ad hoc committee appointed by the Secretary General of the OAS, composed of no more than three panel experts and an equal number of other experts. Committee comments, with country consent, are to be made available to guide external financing priorities and decisions. Finally, the Inter-American Economic and Social Council is required to make an annual report of progress and recommendations to OAS.

Title III, Economic Integration of Latin America, dealt with this goal in some detail and provided that countries still under colonial domination should be invited to participate in the Alliance as they achieve their independence.

Title IV, Basic Export Commodities, included national measures and international cooperation activities designed to expand trade in such commodities, increase foreign exchange from exports, reduce cyclical or seasonal price fluctuations, and improve the terms of trade of such commodities.

Sixteen resolutions appended to the charter enlarged on certain aspects of Alliance provisions or their execution.

Three resolutions dealt with special education, public health, and taxation programs. The establishment of Alliance task forces for programing was recommended. Four studies were called for.

Seven resolutions were concerned with Latin American primary exports, singling out coffee, meat, and wool.

Finally, guidelines were established for preparation of the annual Alliance progress and recommendations report by the Economic and Social Council in connection with annual meetings of the Council.

The charter also recognized a role for regional integration. This recognition specifically included the Latin American Free Trade Association (LAFTA) and the Central American Free Trade Area (CAFTA). The basic objective of both LAFTA and CAFTA is to accelerate economic development, though mechanics differ.

LAFTA members in early 1964 included Argentina, Brazil, Chile, Colombia, Ecuador, Mexico, Paraguay, Peru, and Uruguay. Bolivia and Venezuela have maintained an active interest. CAFTA members are Costa Rica, El Salvador, Guatemala, Honduras, and Nicaragua. Panama has participated in CAFTA meetings.

THE ALLIANCE CHALLENGE has been likened to that of the 1948 Marshall plan for Europe. That is true in part, but it is also an oversimplification. Alliance problems are more complex.

In the Marshall plan, capital was the primary need as a catalyst for the reconstruction and modernization of an already developed industrial society. The Alliance, however, concerns an underdeveloped complex of nations and calls for a successful assault upon a whole range of closely interrelated social and economic problems.

Basic economic and social problems of the Latin American countries are similar, but the order and intensity of the problems vary considerably from country to country.

Latin America has an area more than twice that of the United States. Its population, estimated at 207 million in 1960, is growing at the rate of almost 3 percent a year and is expected to reach 270 million by 1970.

Social problems are many. They range from average illiteracy rates of

40 percent to a land tenure system under which, it is estimated, less than 5 percent of the population owns more than 90 percent of land in farms, and under which much of the remaining land is plagued by fragmentation.

On the economic side also, problems are severe. National income averages about 250 dollars per capita a year. Inflation and fiscal insolvency are almost chronic. Balanced foreign trade is difficult because of a heavy dependence on primary commodity exports.

Agricultural production has been barely keeping pace with growth of population. Sizable numbers of people are receiving diets inadequate in terms of minimum nutritional standards.

Public health is a problem. The incidence of human and animal disease is high. The rudimentary elements, such as safe drinking water and preventive medicine, are lacking.

These are the difficulties that the American countries, under the Alliance, are committed to resolve in the present decade.

ALLIANCE PROGRESS is impressive in terms of its recent beginning and the nature of problems faced.

Task forces have been formed to assist panel committees and country groups in the evaluation and formulation of program proposals. The Inter-American Committee on Agricultural Development, formed by joint agreement between the OAS, FAO, the Economic Commission for Latin America, and the Inter-American Institute of Agricultural Sciences, has been operational since October 1961 and has participated in reviews of country development plans and fulfilled many advisory assignments.

The establishment of six special committees with nine members each was approved during the first annual meeting of the Inter-American Economic and Social Council in October 1962. The committees have to do with planning and project formulation; agricultural development plus agrarian reform; fiscal and financial policies and administration; industrial development and financing of the private sector; education and training; and health, better housing, and community development.

The Latin American countries have taken important internal actions. Leaders in government, business, and education throughout Latin America have supported Alliance objectives. At the same time, the people, from factory workers to campesinos, are coming to appreciate and support the principles of self-help and dedication that are inherent in the Alliance and which are based on the realization that external assistance alone cannot solve the problem.

EIGHT COUNTRIES have presented development plans to the panel of experts—Colombia, Chile, Bolivia, Ecuador, Venezuela, Mexico, Honduras, and Panama. The panel has evaluated and commented on plans submitted by Bolivia, Chile, Colombia, Mexico, and Venezuela. Evaluation by the panel has been formally accepted by Bolivia, Chile, Colombia, and Venezuela.

Tax reforms or related measures have been started in 13 countries—Argentina, Bolivia, Brazil, Chile, Colombia, Costa Rica, the Dominican Republic, Guatemala, El Salvador, Mexico, Panama, Peru, and Venezuela. Reforms are being considered in most other member countries.

Land reform has made progress or has been instituted in Bolivia, Chile, Colombia, Costa Rica, the Dominican Republic, Guatemala, Honduras, Mexico, Nicaragua, Venezuela, Panama, Paraguay, and Peru. Agricultural production has also increased along with land reform programs in Bolivia and Mexico, although both instituted their programs long before the Alliance got underway.

Considerable progress has been made under LAFTA and CAFTA, with internal trade liberalization generally ahead of schedule.

Overall political stability has generally been maintained comparatively well for the area in spite of problems in several countries.

External assistance made available from United States public funds has met the set goals. Other external assistance probably has lagged. Internal financing by the countries themselves has shown many increasing trends; tax reforms are expected to assist further. Project results are less apparent, however.

In spite of the progress made, the impact on the bulk of the population has been small. Little general improvement has been made in per capita income and its distribution, per capita agricultural production and food consumption, literacy, inflation and fiscal solvency, and the heavy dependence on primary exports.

The race with population and the immensity of problems faced make quick results difficult in those fields. It is in this critical area that progress is urgently needed for success of the Alliance, the development of human resources and improving the lot of the common man. Most of the task lies ahead.

THE UNITED STATES STAKE in the Alliance is a heavy one and involves a complex of financial, economic, and political factors.

Our cost of financial assistance to support the Alliance is large, particularly when added to our farflung economic and military assistance commitments to other parts of the world. The United States provided a total of 2,128.3 million dollars in public funds to the Alliance in the first 2-year period, from March 31, 1961, through February 28, 1963. This assistance was at a rate of almost three times the average annual rate to Latin America in the previous 10 years.

Such obligations and loan authorizations provided under several programs were as follows (in millions of dollars): Agency for International Development grants and loans, 841.0; Export-Import loans, 532.3; Social Progress Trust Fund loans, 336.9;

Food for Peace programs, 401.4; and Peace Corps, 16.7. The total was 431.0 million dollars for grants and 1,697.3 million for loans. Success of the Alliance should reduce the need for assistance on this large scale.

United States trade with Latin America is important. In 1963, our exports totaled 3,537 million dollars and imports totaled 4,021 million dollars. Of this, agricultural exports totaled 500 million dollars, or approximately 15 percent of the total to Latin America, and imports were estimated at 1,800 million dollars, or 45 percent.

Agricultural trade with Latin America was almost 10 percent of our world exports and about 45 percent of our world imports of agricultural products.

Our principal agricultural exports to Latin America were wheat and wheat products, dairy products, oils and oilseeds, vegetables and preparations, fruit and preparations, and tobacco.

The main imports were coffee, sugar, livestock and meat products, bananas, wool, and cocoa. Such imports of coffee, sugar, and bananas were greater than supplies of these commodities from all other sources.

Success in attaining Alliance goals as a requisite for the maintenance or increase of United States exports to Latin America therefore is of basic importance to the long-run economic well-being of the United States.

Most important of all, the Alliance is a positive program of cooperative development. As such, it pits the United States—and the other Alliance members—against dangerous political extremes.

The Alliance is an unparalleled effort based upon the principles of democracy and free enterprise to develop the Latin American nations through peaceful revolution within the framework of the inter-American system.

CHARLES R. DAVENPORT *became Chief of the Western Hemisphere Branch of the Regional Analysis Division, Economic Research Service, in 1961.*

OECD and OEEC

by WILLIAM G. FINN

THE ORGANIZATION for Economic Cooperation and Development began its official existence on September 30, 1961, when it took the place of the Organization for European Economic Cooperation (OEEC), which had been operating in a similar sphere for nearly 15 years.

The OEEC originally was established to assist in administering economic aid under the Marshall plan. Its aim was to foster maximum European cooperation toward recovery after the Second World War.

The success of those undertakings and a growing awareness of interdependence among the western-oriented nations caused many OEEC activities to be continued, even after European recovery was well on the way.

Furthermore, the fact that changed world relationships caused policies of one country to influence economic conditions in other countries emphasized the need for more effective arrangements to promote cooperation among likeminded nations.

The new organization, OECD, besides having a broader name, differs from its predecessor in two important respects: The aims and tasks were redefined and brought up to date; the United States and Canada became full participating members instead of associated countries.

With those changes, OECD had a

membership of Western countries second to none: Austria, Belgium, Canada, Denmark, France, the Federal Republic of Germany, Greece, Iceland, Ireland, Italy, Luxembourg, the Netherlands, Norway, Portugal, Spain, Sweden, Switzerland, Turkey, the United Kingdom, and the United States.

On July 26, 1963, the Council of the OECD extended to Japan an invitation to accede formally to the convention of the Organization and to arrange for unlimited participation in its activities. Japan accepted in 1964.

A special status was provided for Yugoslavia and Finland. In some instances, full participating membership is accorded with regard to certain activities and functions; in others, the relationship is that of observer.

The OECD convention states that its aim shall be to promote policies designed:

To achieve the highest sustainable economic growth and employment and a rising standard of living in member countries, while maintaining financial stability, and thus to contribute to the development of the world economy;

to contribute to sound economic expansion in member countries as well as in nonmember countries in the process of economic development; and

to contribute to the expansion of world trade on a multilateral, nondiscriminatory basis in accordance with international obligations.

ACTION TOWARD multilateral efforts to aid underdeveloped countries opened a new chapter in the history of Western cooperation.

The decisionmaking body of OECD, the Council, comprises representatives of all member countries. Under its direction, various governmental and secretariat bodies operate to perform the authorized functions. A staff of about 1,100 persons is headed by the Secretary General. Headquarters of OECD are in Paris.

In the 20-odd subject fields with which OECD is concerned, such as economic affairs, development assistance, trade, agriculture, and fisheries, specialized committees are constituted to deal with the matters defined. Every committee meets at least once a year.

The Committee for Agriculture may be convened at the ministerial level whenever subjects to be dealt with are of a nature to merit such consideration.

Then the respective Ministers of Agriculture and Secretaries of Agriculture of the member countries are invited. At other times, meetings of the Committee for Agriculture are held at the official level. A separate fisheries committee handles all of the matters pertaining to fisheries.

The directorate for agriculture has four functional divisions—agricultural policies, agricultural markets, technical action, and fisheries. It has a professional staff of 30 persons.

Throughout the life of OECD and OEEC, the agriculture and food staff has considered a number of complex problems—a reflection of the place food and agriculture occupy in a healthy and thriving economy.

IN APPRAISING the work done by the successive organizations and in suggesting possibilities, I have considered the activities in three periods.

The period from 1948 to 1955 was characterized by the launching of the Marshall plan, establishing and developing the OEEC structure and functions, and stimulating individual country actions toward recovery.

The success of those undertakings has been acclaimed. A less-known fact pertaining to European agriculture is that areawide production in that sector was restored much more rapidly after the Second World War than it was after the First World War. This no doubt reflected in part the more advanced state of scientific and technical knowledge relating to agriculture. But perhaps to a greater extent it reflected a fuller use of new and proved techniques for communicating practical information to farm people.

Initially there was a tendency for agricultural recovery efforts made in the different countries to be carried on independently. In its time, however, OEEC has done much to get members to seek harmony in their agricultural programs.

The member countries and the United States formally agreed in 1953 on the establishment of a European Productivity Agency (EPA), to be incorporated into the framework of OEEC. Provision was made for a separate budget and for flexible operating procedures. The aim was to induce a sufficient modernization of methods in business and agriculture so that trade and commerce throughout the Atlantic community would become freer, more competitive, and truly multilateral, rather than narrowly protectionist.

Types of EPA projects pertaining to agriculture that were carried out during this period included: Demonstrations of methods for the most effective training of agricultural advisers; facilitating speedier intercountry exchanges of information on the newest methods of agricultural production and marketing; improving the timeliness, comparability, and accuracy of agricultural statistics of each country; developing the use of improved grades and standards for perishable farm produce; developing the use of methods for safeguarding the purity and dependability of agricultural seed; developing the use of international standards for testing farm equipment; and encouraging intercountry exchanges on peaceful uses of nuclear energy in agriculture.

Under the aegis of EPA, hundreds of agricultural experts from countries in Europe made study visits to the United States, and many American professional workers carried out special assignments in Europe. The exchanges fostered greater understanding among officials and led to a better comprehension of mutual problems.

BY THE BEGINNING of the second period, 1955 to 1961, the capacity of agriculture to produce had been restored to prewar levels more or less everywhere in the OEEC area. In fact, the question of finding adequate markets had become a key problem for several leading farm commodities, despite persistent and intensive efforts that the OEEC had made to induce widespread liberalization of trade.

At that time, the structure of OEEC was modified by creating within its framework a Ministerial Committee for Agriculture and Food. Tasks to be performed were also modified.

It seemed only natural to members that OEEC's newly established directorate for agriculture should be charged to make comprehensive analyses of the policies for agriculture carried on in the countries of Europe and North America. Until that time, the attention of OEEC in this respect had been focused mainly on problems that had grown out of the various agricultural policies rather than on the actual substance of the policies or on the underlying factors that influenced them to be adopted.

As it turned out, significant aspects of this new undertaking were to be projected through several subsequent years of the Organization's activity. At each phase, close and continuing cooperation was required between OEEC staff and policymaking officials in every government.

Of even greater significance was the fact that this process likewise gave the opportunity for objective, purposeful, face-to-face exchanges of viewpoints among the country policymakers.

Five OEEC documents entitled, "Agricultural Policies in Europe and North America," report on this work. In the fifth report, issued in 1961, observations were made on policy developments since 1955. It was concluded that individual country policies tend to consist of varying combinations of aims, such as those that pertain to income and price support, orientation of production, trade in agricultural commodities, farm population, and structural improvements in farming.

One chapter of the 1961 report reviewed changes that governments had made regarding methods used for the implementation of agricultural policies. Some countries had begun to emphasize longer term solutions, such as rural development and improving structural conditions in agriculture, but many still were relying mainly on short-term solutions, such as price supports. The use of the government subsidies to foster agricultural exports had become increasingly prevalent.

In carrying on the agricultural policy work and assembling the large amount of factual information contained in the reports, OEEC was no doubt trying initially to establish its own capacity for understanding country-by-country differences of agricultural policy and for reconciling conflicts of policy. But because information of this kind had never before been put together in organized form, the work had great usefulness elsewhere.

The OEEC program of work for agriculture during this period did not actively deal with the limitations on trade resulting from various types of quantitative restrictions imposed by governments. One justification frequently offered for this weakness was the chronic problem of balance-of-payment deficits, because many currencies had for so long remained inconvertible. But, when it finally became feasible to establish the free convertibility of European currencies, as eventually it did, any further use of such measures assumed a different significance—they became direct national protectionism, maintained for its own sake.

When providing for the transition from OEEC operations to those of the Organization for Economic Cooperation and Development—which occurred in 1960–1961—many important questions had to be resolved. To facilitate this work, a preparatory committee was established.

Besides agreeing on the objectives and the structure to be recommended for this new Organization, it seemed equally necessary for the preparatory committee to decide on functions and institutions proposed for discontinuance. In this respect, it was found, for example, that most duties formerly charged to the EPA had already been accomplished and that orderly liquidation of that agency would be justified. It also was concluded that some of the determinations formally enacted by OEEC would not be appropriate in the context of OECD.

By thus terminating old and outdated links and directing attention toward future development, virtually every feature of the Organization's structure was improved.

AFTER OECD came into existence, its agriculture directorate fostered the continuation of mutually beneficial work in agricultural policy, agricultural markets, and technical action. Reports on the results of such work are circulated regularly to governments of the member countries.

The OECD Committee for Agriculture held three meetings at the Ministerial level by early 1964. The Secretary of Agriculture of the United States, Orville L. Freeman, participated in all of the meetings.

During the 1962 meeting, Secretary Freeman reminded OECD member nations of the opportunities that exist for using food aid to speed up and strengthen economic growth in underdeveloped countries. With regard to policies affecting international trade in agricultural commodities, he expressed concern over some of the regressive tendencies that were beginning to appear, particularly in policies adopted by the European Economic Community.

In consequence of the deliberations at the 1962 meeting, a comprehensive resolution pertaining to the Organization's work pertaining to agriculture was developed. This resolution was endorsed unanimously by the Ministerial Committee for Agriculture. It subsequently was given full approval by the OECD Council.

Its section relating specifically to trade reads:

"That Member countries and groupings of Member countries should adapt their agricultural policies in the light of international trade responsibilities as well as domestic considerations, and that solutions to domestic agricultural problems should not be adopted which would jeopardize the development of traditional markets of efficient producers.

"[The Council] recommends to the governments of Member countries to formulate, either by themselves or as groupings of countries, their agricultural policies in the light of international trade responsibilities as well as domestic considerations, adopting solutions to domestic agricultural problems which do not jeopardize trade in agricultural products."

It is not possible so soon to foresee what effect such a resolution, or indeed the work of OECD as a whole, may have on the opportunities for expanding world trade in agricultural commodities.

SOME BASES FOR OPTIMISM, however, do exist: The Organization has been conceived soundly and launched objectively; a healthy thread of free-enterprise agriculture extends uniformly through its membership; and the aggregate volume of international trade in agricultural commodities creditable to the OECD community is considerably larger than that of all other parts of the world.

WILLIAM G. FINN *was in the Foreign Service of the United States from 1949 to 1961 and for 5 years served as Director of the Food and Agriculture Division, United States Mission to the OEEC. He served in the Department of Agriculture for 20 years. He was Assistant Administrator, Agricultural Adjustment Administration; a member of the Administrator's staff, Production and Marketing Administration; and adviser to the Graduate School. He was a member of the staff of the University of Kentucky for 6 years.*

Regional Economic Groups

by PATRICK J. MURPHY

COUNTRIES join economic communities with two ideas and in three ways.

The slogans, "trade or fade" and "in unity there is strength," express their belief that joint action can solve problems in the common interest.

Their regional economic integration may take the form of a free trade area, customs union, and common market.

A free trade area comprises two or more customs territories in which tariffs are eliminated on products that originate in their territories. Each member maintains its own tariff schedules on imports from nonmembers.

A customs union is a free trade area with a common external tariff against imports from outside countries.

A common market is a customs union that allows the free movement of resources, capital, and labor among the members.

Many such attempts at economic unity have bogged down and have given rise to another lineup. Some groups in existence no doubt will undergo some changes before they attain the stability they need to meet the social and economic challenges of a more competitive world.

From fragmented colonial Africa, 29 independent states emerged. They have teamed up in many overlapping groupings based on a common language, traditional ties, complementary economies, or common goals.

They have signed hundreds of agreements, which new arrangements have quickly rendered ineffective. A stabilizing factor in these growing pains has been the orientation of a country or group toward its onetime mother or master.

Africa in 1964 was in another formative stage of continentwide economic regrouping, and five important economic communities were in varying stages of operation—the African and Malagasy Union (UAM), the East African Common Services Organization (EACSO), the Equatorial Customs Union (UDE), the West African Customs Union (WACU), and the Organization of African Unity.

THE AFRICAN and Malagasy Union was founded in 1961 with 12 members: Federal Republic of Cameroon, Central African Republic, Republic of Chad, Republic of Congo (Brazzaville), Republic of Dahomey, Gabon Republic, Republic of Ivory Coast, Malagasy Republic, Islamic Republic of Mauritania, Republic of Niger, Republic of Senegal, and Republic of Upper Volta.

They have been known as the Brazzaville Twelve, and all are associate members of the European Economic Community and have, or have applied for, memberships in the General Agreement on Tariffs and Trade.

They share a common heritage of French influence, political association, and currency. They have depended heavily on France for financial, technical, and military assistance.

The economic functions of UAM cover three major areas: Economic and social development; foreign commerce, including tariff problems, possibility of enlarging the free trade zone, and development of a common market; and fiscal and monetary affairs. A uniform customs code has been planned as a first step toward a common market.

The UAM under able and dynamic leadership has initiated constructive work in all the planned economic fields. Its headquarters site is Cotonou, Dahomey.

THE EAST AFRICAN Common Services Organization succeeded the East African High Commission.

Its members in 1964 were Kenya, Uganda, and Tanganyika. Zanzibar was a partial participant. The EACSO made the transition from colonial authority to independent leadership without undue change in its character.

Its functions are economic and include the administration of customs and excise duties, statistics, industrial coordination, communications, and mail services.

Goods and capital pass freely among the members, and they have a common currency. Commercial policy usually is coordinated. An EACSO mission began conversations with the European Economic Community on a trading arrangement and set a precedent as a negotiating agent for the three members.

EACSO has been termed a key to economic stability and development of eastern Africa.

THE EQUATORIAL Customs Union (UDE) was established in 1959 by the Central African Republic, Chad, Congo (Brazzaville), and Gabon.

Cameroon has become a member.

The countries are contiguous; have similar languages, cultures, and products; and form a single currency area. They are members of the Central Bank of the States of Equatorial Africa and Cameroon.

The UDE countries maintain a common external tariff on imports from third countries, except for a preferential arrangement with the EEC. Supplementary taxes applied to such imports vary little among the members. Goods, capital, and services move freely within the UDE.

Besides administering the customs union, the UDE engages in efforts to harmonize investments and technical projects, fiscal regulations, and economic structures.

It is among the most active of the Af-
rican regional groupings, and its union should be beneficial in developing the economies of the members.

THE WEST AFRICAN Customs Union of the franc-zone countries of Dahomey, Ivory Coast, Republic of Mali, Mauritania, Niger, Senegal, and Upper Volta came into being through the signing of a convention in 1959.

It is in effect a limited free trade area, and its intention is to keep together the markets of the West Africans under the same former colonial regime. Its trade and economic institutions remain closely oriented toward France, as in colonial days.

The convention stated the intention to become a complete customs union, but that has been modified somewhat.

Some taxes on imports vary considerably among the members and unilateral changes in tariff policy apparently have been made without notice or consultation among the member states.

No quota or licensing restrictions have been imposed on goods traded within the West African Customs Union nor are natural products subjected to duties or taxes in intraunion trade. Generally, there is coordination of common customs and duties on imports from third countries.

THE CHARTER of the Organization of African Unity was drawn up on May 23, 1963, at a conference of Independent African States in Addis Ababa.

It was signed by 30 African nations and was hailed as the most comprehensive cooperative effort ever made by African countries.

It was the first attempt of diverse peoples of different cultures, religions, stations, languages, and races, from the Mediterranean to the Mozambique Channel, from the Gulf of Aden to Walvis Bay, to join efforts to seek their common goals.

During the 4-day conference, delegates adopted resolutions in a number of social, cultural, and economic fields. The charter called for the complete decolonization of the continent.

One of the resolutions was to send delegations to speak in behalf of all African nations before the International Court of Justice, the United Nations Security Council, and other international bodies.

It declared the continent to be a nuclear-free zone and called for cessation of thermonuclear bomb testing and disarmament by the Great Powers, particularly the United States and the Soviet Union. It outlined cultural, educational, health, and nutritional programs.

As to economic cooperation, the principal resolutions proposed to establish free trade throughout all Africa; formulate a common external tariff; coordinate transportation and communications; establish a monetary, fiscal clearing, and payments facility; harmonize existing and future development plans; and negotiate in concert with international trade bodies.

The conference took note of grave problems in Africa—a shortage of water in some places, lack of transportation, conflicts between new governmental structures and tribal customs, low levels in education and labor productivity, shortage of technicians, the dominance of one-crop economies, and a scarcity of investment capital.

Much of the world shared the hopes of the leaders at Addis Ababa that their nations and peoples could coordinate their efforts from the paper stage of the charter to the practical realities of the modern world.

THE GOVERNMENTS of Argentina, Brazil, Chile, Mexico, Paraguay, Peru, and Uruguay on February 18, 1960, signed the Montevideo Treaty creating the Latin American Free Trade Association (LAFTA).

The treaty provided for the gradual elimination of restrictions on trade among the signatory nations, reductions on a selective-product basis, and negotiations to lower tariffs on the basis of "reciprocity of concessions" among the members.

To effect full tariff elimination on intra-area trade, two separate lists were set for negotiation.

The first was a national list, to be drawn up annually, of concessions (at least 8 percent) granted on a bilateral basis among individual members and renegotiated every 3 years.

The second, or common, list is to comprise items that each member has put on its national list the preceding 3 years. It will then be applied to all members on a 25-percent reduction basis the first 3 years, 50 percent the second 3 years, 75 percent after 9 years, and 100 percent after 12 years.

In effect, the bilateral concessions negotiated every year become multilateral concessions every 3 years, and the reduction of intra-area trade duties to zero will be complete after 12 years.

Concessions on products on the national list may be withdrawn at any time. Once an item has been added to the common list, however, the concession is considered irrevocable. The treaty of Montevideo has a number of clauses by which the members can withhold numerous items from negotiation and some clauses that may result in preferences within the free trade area and for third countries.

The members of LAFTA conducted negotiations on tariff reductions in 1961 and 1962. The United Nations Economic Commission for Latin America (ECLA) estimated that the total value of concessions granted exceeded the target level of 8 percent annually. The concessions were mainly on products that were traditionally traded among member countries before the Montevideo Treaty and not on competitive products.

Negotiations on the third round of bilateral concessions began in Montevideo on October 1, 1963, and lasted until the end of that year. The annual target level of an 8-percent reduction in tariffs was reportedly attained. The negotiations on the first common list were postponed until 1964.

Each LAFTA country will retain its own individual tariff schedule on imports from third countries.

Other objectives of the Montevideo Treaty include: The industrial development of the area on a regional basis, the maximum utilization of all area production factors, and the adoption of other measures leading to the progressive integration of the economies of the member countries.

The members look to the trade liberalization program of the Montevideo Treaty to encourage the establishment of new industries and bring about a more fruitful utilization of domestic resources.

The development of wider markets among the LAFTA countries is expected to attract new investment and to reduce the costs of existing enterprises through facilitating mass production and distribution.

THE GENERAL TREATY of Economic Integration was signed in 1960 by El Salvador, Guatemala, Honduras, and Nicaragua and became effective in June 1961. Costa Rica applied for membership shortly after the General Treaty was signed and became a full and equal member in 1963.

The treaty incorporates some earlier agreements and forms the basis of the Central American Common Market. The treaty called for completely free internal trade by 1966 and a common external tariff on imports from third countries.

Ninety-five percent of all goods originating in the four countries already moved freely in 1964.

Trade among the five countries, primarily in agricultural commodities, had increased more than 300 percent by 1962 over the 1955–1958 level. A common external tariff was instituted by the Agreement on Equalization of Import Charges. The agreement and its protocols have been incorporated in the General Treaty. Thus, within 2 years, the movement toward Central American integration evolved from a free trade area into a partial customs union.

A Central American Bank for Economic Integration was provided for in the General Treaty but was established by a separate charter. It has an authorized capital of 16 million dollars. Since 1960 it has issued more than 20 loans totaling approximately 6 million dollars. Its purpose is to provide capital for regional industrial development.

The Central American Clearing House was established in 1961. In 1962 it handled about 60 percent of the total intraregional transactions. A common currency has the Central American peso as the unit of account. The headquarters of the bank and clearing house are in Tegucigalpa, Honduras.

The United States has loaned or granted 8 million dollars to the bank to help finance regional projects.

The Agency for International Development has given assistance for economic and social development.

The Central American Common Market looks optimistically to the future and has undertaken procedures to meet full common market conditions. A regional agreement on equalization of tax incentives for industrial development was promulgated to provide uniform treatment for investors interested in the region.

Other cooperative efforts were instituted to integrate transportation, communication, financial, and customs facilities.

The Central Americans have stated an intention to welcome neighbor countries into association or membership, to follow policies that will attract private foreign investments, and to expand third-country trade opportunities.

UPON RATIFICATION of a convention signed in Stockholm, the European Free Trade Association went into effect on May 3, 1960.

The signatories are the so-called Outer Seven of Europe. (Members of the European Economic Community are the so-called Inner Six.) The members are Austria, Denmark, Norway, Portugal, Sweden, Switzerland, and the United Kingdom.

The convention provided for a free trade area among the members by abolishing tariffs and other trade barriers on industrial products between the member states in 10 years or less.

The convention limited the application of free trade to industrial products, although limited arrangements for agricultural products and fish were concluded in May 1963.

EFTA was originally designed as a counter to the European Economic Community. Each member country remains free to decide its own external tariff and commercial policy.

Britain took the leadership in the formation of EFTA. Within EFTA, Britain retains her tariff arrangements with the Commonwealth whereby she grants preferences to imports from Commonwealth countries in exchange for corresponding preferences for her own exports to them.

As long as national tariffs differ, exporters from third countries may send their goods to the member countries with the lowest tariff schedules for transshipment to high-tariff member countries. But rules written into the convention define the origin of goods traded in EFTA and make it difficult to ship products to a high-tariff country by sending them first to a low-tariff country.

The absence of a common external tariff (CXT) of the seven members against outside countries has restrained economic, social, and financial economic integration regionally.

No provisions were made for common facilities for customs procedures, trading laws, communications, transportation, or a uniform monetary unit.

The level of industrial tariffs on internal EFTA trade has been reduced 50 percent below that of July 1, 1960, when EFTA began operating. On July 31, 1961, Finland, which had a form of associate membership, agreed to an additional 10 percent cut in her tariffs on imports from members.

Under EFTA, the external trade of the member countries has generally kept pace with the world expansion, but the rate of increase in intra-area trade has doubled.

The ministerial council of EFTA met in Lisbon in 1963 and decided to establish a final timetable for dismantling tariffs on industrial products. They agreed that these tariffs should be eliminated by December 31, 1966. The next reduction of 10 percent was set for the end of 1963.

The council decided also to schedule a West European fisheries conference and to establish an economic development committee, which would attempt to lay the basis for free movement of investment capital within the area.

As stated by the convention, EFTA's objectives are to promote a sustained expansion of economic activity, full employment, increased productivity, financial stability, and higher living standards; secure fair competition in trade among member states; and to contribute to the harmonious development and expansion of world trade and to the progressive removal of barriers to it.

There are special convention provisions that will minimize the disruption of some national industries that are expected to occur as a result of complete removal of their previous high-tariff protection.

THE ASSOCIATION of Southeast Asia (ASA) was launched in April 1962, when the ministers of Malaya, the Philippines, and Thailand met in the Cameron highlands of Malaya and agreed to a limited association to attack common problems and to promote cultural and social exchange. By such association, the members planned to work toward self-sufficiency.

During 1963, Malaya merged with North Borneo, Sarawak, and Singapore to form Malaysia. ASA has taken only tentative steps, mostly in the form of discussions, toward the attainment of the association's original goals.

PATRICK J. MURPHY *joined the Trade Policy Division of the Foreign Agricultural Service as an international economist in 1963. Previously he was a program funds analyst in that agency.*

The European

Economic Community

by JOHN E. MONTEL

THE EUROPEAN ECONOMIC COMMUNITY brought France, Italy, Germany, Belgium, the Netherlands, and Luxembourg together in an outstanding manifestation of cooperation among nations.

It was born of war—wars that spelled the end of European dominance of world affairs; brought joint occupation of a major European country by four countries; required massive aid from the United States in the form of food, clothing, technical assistance, and funds for rehabilitating peaceful industries; left a sense of frustration throughout Europe; and engendered finally a new and unique spirit of cooperation in Western Europe.

THE ENCOURAGEMENT of that spirit was supplied initially not so much by Europeans themselves as by the United States through the Marshall plan, which offered to help a ravaged Europe by channeling assistance through an organization of European countries rather than to individual countries.

Thus the Marshall plan provided the impetus for 16 countries—Austria, Belgium, Denmark, France, Greece, Iceland, Ireland, Italy, Luxembourg, the Netherlands, Norway, Portugal, Sweden, Switzerland, Turkey, and the United Kingdom—to create an Organization for European Economic Cooperation in April of 1948. It was

the first effort at a cooperative or community effort to solve postwar economic and other difficulties.

OEEC helped to expand trade among its signatory nations and urged them to liberalize their exchange. OEEC in 1950 encouraged its member states to form the European Payments Union, which was an instrument in reestablishing multilateral convertibility of exchange and thus facilitated payments in transactions. Again, trade expanded. OEEC in 1961 became the Organization for European Cooperation and Development, of which the United States and Canada became members.

The germ of the customs union feature of the Common Market had existed in the Belgium-Luxembourg Economic Union. Yet the BLEU Treaty, which was signed on July 25, 1921, and became effective on May 1, 1922, provided for no supranational authority or organizational structure that could have required the sacrificing of part of the national sovereignty of the two countries. For its success, it depended on the cooperation of the two governments and on respect for the provisions of the treaty. It was instrumental in abolishing duties and other restrictions on trade between the two countries and provided for a single currency.

The success of BLEU encouraged talks during the early forties with the Netherlands, which had had a traditional trade relationship with Belgium and Luxembourg. Discussions among their governments-in-exile during the German occupation led to the signing of a convention on September 5, 1944, that created the Benelux Customs Union.

The examples of BLEU and BENELUX encouraged France and Italy, which have similar agricultures and manufactures, to begin discussions for the eventual formation of a Franco-Italian customs union, popularly referred to at the time as FRANCITA. Discussions culminated in the signing of the Treaty of Paris in 1949, but

FRANCITA was stillborn almost from the start. The industries of one country feared competition from the other. The labor unions of France had visions of mass immigrations of Italian workers. The parliaments of the two countries never ratified the treaty.

Numerous other attempts to write recipes for combining nations with one another or with already established groups of nations were abortive—for example, FRANCITA with BENELUX (FINEBEL) and the Scandinavian countries and the United Kingdom (UNISCAN) on the one hand with Greece and Turkey on the other.

Meanwhile, in an attempt to further political union, especially for mutual assistance and defense, the BENELUX countries and Great Britain and France had signed the Brussels Pact of March 17, 1948.

Almost immediately thereafter, other European countries (except the Federal Republic of Germany) and the United States and Canada, encouraged by the success of the OEEC in economic cooperation and impelled by the threat of war, began negotiations to form a North Atlantic Treaty Organization (NATO) for collective defense and the maintenance of peace. NATO enlarged the 1948 Brussels Pact and became a reality in 1949.

The refusal of the French Parliament to ratify the European Defense Community Treaty in 1954 led to the signing on October 23, 1954, of the Paris Accords, which amended NATO to include Germany as a member and officially terminated the Allied occupation of Germany. It also amended the Brussels Pact to include Germany and Italy, which thereafter became known as the West European Union (WEU). Its members later tried to expand their collaboration in economic, cultural, and social matters.

But even before the revision of the Brussels Pact, and in the wake of the failures I described, European leaders had become aware of the impracticability of denying Germany a part in the postwar development of Europe.

In the summer of 1950, therefore, the French Foreign Minister, Robert Schuman, invited Germany to join France in a common market for coal and steel, two vital industries in war. The basic aim was political, but it was also an invitation to participate in a valuable experiment in economic integration.

Germany accepted M. Schuman's bid, and an eminent French parliamentarian, Jean Monnet, drew up plans. Italy and BENELUX also wished to join, and the treaty establishing the European Coal and Steel Community was signed on April 18, 1951, by the six countries. It entered into force on July 25, 1952, and was the first full-strength precursor of the European Economic Community.

ECSC was the first expression of a European policy that favored a European federal government because, as distinct from the other two customs unions, it empowered a supranational executive organ, the High Authority, to govern its functioning and to make decisions that are binding on its members. Although the sacrifice of national sovereignty was particularly objectionable to the French and modifications had to be made to accommodate them, ECSC nevertheless survived.

The emergence of the ECSC under the tutelage of M. Monnet was a meaningful formative stage in the development of the EEC. It could almost be called a pilot project because it gave the six governments badly needed experience with a supranational governmental body and gave training to persons who later assumed important positions in EEC. The Common Assembly of ECSC later became the European Parliament. It lay the groundwork for the functioning of the Court of Justice as the first really supranational court.

The ECSC opened up Europe's steel market to all producers and so created a common market in steel. Its performance in coal, however, has left much to be desired, because of a technological crisis in the coal industry. (One aspect of that is that United States producers have been able to place a ton of coal in the German port of Hamburg at less than it costs Germans to mine it.)

The birth of ECSC, the concurrent outbreak of war in Korea, and the presence of Russian troops only 200 miles away from the French city of Strasbourg encouraged another step forward in European cooperation, the ill-starred European Defense Community. Paradoxically, this French proposal to pool the armies of the "Six" also contained a provision for a European supranational political authority. The treaty was signed on May 27, 1952, and was ratified by five of the six signatory nations. The French Chamber of Deputies, however, rejected it on the basis that it would have meant too great a sacrifice of French national sovereignty. Once again, the other five learned that nations forming a community must have all interests and goals in common.

The French veto of EDC stilled for a while any new attempts at cooperation, and Europe entered a period of reflection. The drive for development of a community spirit soon reasserted itself, however, and the Six of ECSC agreed to meet at Messina in June of 1955 to decide what measures could be taken for further integrating their economies.

BENELUX proposed at Messina that there be established ". . . a united Europe by the development of common institutions, the progressive fusion of national economies, by creating a common market. . . ." The proposal marked the conception of full economic union and laid the basis for a truly common market. A committee was asked to draft two treaties for the creation of a European Economic Community (EEC) and a European Atomic Energy Community (EUR-ATOM). Both were adopted on May 30, 1956, at a meeting in Venice. They were signed in Rome on March 25, 1957, and entered into force on Jan-

uary 1, 1958, the date that marks the beginning of EEC.

The core of the Rome Treaty that established the European Economic Community, popularly known as the Common Market, is the creation of a customs union through a gradual and scheduled elimination of tariff barriers between its signatory members and the gradual putting into force of a single customs tariff against all goods imported from nonmember countries.

It envisaged, however, not only an area where goods eventually will move freely, but also an area where labor can shift at will from one country to another and where no barriers stop movements of capital or enterprise. As a parallel to the customs union, the Rome Treaty envisaged also the development of a common agricultural policy. This, with its customs union, has become a major foreign trade preoccupation of United States agriculture because it could be used to encourage uneconomic increases in farm production and to restrict trade with nonmember countries.

THE BASIC OBJECTIVE of the Rome Treaty is in article 2. It states that the Community will aim at encouraging "harmonious development of economic activities, a continuous and balanced expansion, an increased stability, an accelerated rising of the standard of living and closer relations between its Member States." The treaty states that this objective shall be attained by the "establishment of a Common Market and by the progressive harmonization of the economic policies of the Member States."

A tremendous objective. The six member states knew that its achievement would not be a short-term matter, especially in the light of the numerous disheartening failures in which they all had participated. Article 8 of the treaty therefore provided for a 12-year transition period beginning January 1, 1958, and divided into three 4-year stages, each one of which comprised a plan for the accomplishment of a part of the over-all objective.

Article 3 of the treaty gave a detailed plan of action:

Elimination of duties and quantitative restrictions on trade between member states;

Establishment of a Common External Tariff (CXT) and a common trade policy with third countries and the elimination of barriers to the circulation of people, services, and capital among the member states;

Creation of a Common Agricultural Policy (CAP);

Creation of a Common Transportation Policy;

Establishment of an arrangement to insure undistorted competition in the Common Market;

Application of procedures to allow the coordination of economic policies of the member states and to correct disequilibriums in their balances of payments;

Harmonization of national laws when necessary for the functioning of the Common Market;

Creation of a European Social Fund for improving the conditions of workers and their standard of living;

Creation of a European Investment Bank for facilitating economic development with a new source of capital;

Association of the oversea territories and states for expanding their trade and for communally developing them socially and economically.

In keeping with its federal structure, the treaty established several organs or institutions of its "government" for carrying out the plan of action, with checks and balances similar to those in the Constitution of the United States.

THE COUNCIL of Ministers makes most of the Community's decisions and insures coordination of the general economic policies of the member states. Its decisions are binding on the member states, but it can act only upon proposals by the Commission. Each member state is represented on the Council by one of its cabinet members.

During the first and second stages, most Council decisions must be made by unanimous vote. From the beginning of the third stage on January 1, 1966, important policy matters can be decided by a qualified majority of 12 of 17 votes. Votes are weighted among member states as follows: Four each for France, Germany, and Italy; two each for Belgium and the Netherlands; and one for Luxembourg. This distribution of weighted votes requires any two of the three large member states that may want to force their viewpoint on a third to have the support at least of Belgium and the Netherlands.

THE EEC COMMISSION is responsible for insuring application of the provisions of the treaty and serves as its guardian. It makes recommendations or proposals to the Council and carries out its decisions.

For implementing the Council's decisions and certain tasks set forth in the treaty, it has the right to make its own decisions by simple majority.

The Commission has nine members who, unlike members of the Council, do not represent governments of member states. They act for the well-being of the Community in complete independence of their own governments. The nine members of the Commission are appointed by unanimous decision of the six governments for 4-year terms, which are renewable. No more than two commissioners may be nationals of the same country.

The president and vice president of the Commission are appointed by the member governments from among the nine members for 2-year terms, which are renewable.

THE EUROPEAN PARLIAMENT, the legislative branch of EEC, has functions like those of the Congress of the United States. The 142 members—36 each from France, Germany, and Italy; 14 each from Belgium and the Netherlands; and 6 from Luxembourg—are selected by their governments from the national parliaments of the six member states. The EEC treaty provides that the parliament propose machinery for direct election of its members throughout the Community.

The parliament exercises control over the Commission and, by a two-thirds vote of censure, can compel the Commission to resign in a body. It also gives its advisory opinion, or appraisal, of proposals made by the Commission to the Council through the use of its special committees, of which the committee on agriculture is one.

The Court of Justice, the judiciary branch, has seven judge-members, assisted by two court advocates, who are appointed unanimously for 6-year terms by the Council. The Court insures that Council and Commission actions are consonant with the provisions of the treaty. It annuls those that it finds not to be consistent. Its judgments are binding on private individuals, private companies, national governments, the Council, and the Commission. Its functions make it comparable to the Supreme Court of the United States.

THE IDEA of a European organization of agricultural markets was first broached by representatives of French and German agriculture at the Fourth General Assembly of the International Federation of Agricultural Producers in Saltsjöbaden, Sweden.

They signed a declaration on June 7, 1950, in favor of a common agricultural market between their two countries. Soon after, the Consultative Assembly of the Council of Europe, the decisionmaking institution of the OEEC, recommended that a conference be held to create specialized European agricultural institutions in which several countries would be able to participate.

The idea caught fire. Similar proposals were made by the ministers of agriculture of France and the Netherlands, but many divergent views on the form and objectives of such an organization were voiced. At several meetings and conferences, attempts were made to resolve the differences. The OEEC Ministerial Committee of Food and Agriculture, which was created on January 14, 1955, to organize agricultural markets within the framework of OEEC, also considered them. Not until the Messina Conference of the six ECSC countries in 1955, however, was the idea of a truly common market ultimately elaborated into the Rome Treaty.

The decision to include agriculture in the concept of a common market was made only after long hours of heated debate, in which the farm interests of all member states of OEEC strove to have their special problems given particular attention.

For instance, the European Confederation of Agriculture said: "The problems posed in the trade sector and for European cooperation, as well as for the functions of the OEEC, put into jeopardy the vital interests of agriculture, of its place in the national economies of countries of Europe, and of its place in all of Europe."

The Council of Europe voted in October of 1954 to include agriculture in a common market. That decision facilitated the drafting and approval of the Rome Treaty that created the EEC.

ARTICLE 38 of the treaty states that the Common Market includes agriculture and trade in agricultural products—products of the soil, of animal husbandry, and of fisheries and their byproducts from primary processing.

It states further that the functioning and development of the Common Market for agricultural products must accompany the establishment of a common agricultural policy.

Article 39 specified five objectives of the CAP to be attained by January 1, 1970: To increase agricultural productivity through technological progress by insuring rational development of agricultural production as well as optimum use of the factors of production, particularly labor; to insure an equitable standard of living for the farm population, particularly by raising the incomes of farmworkers; to stabilize markets; to guarantee supplies; and to insure reasonable prices.

In attaining the objectives, paragraph 2 of the same article states that due account shall be taken of "(a) the particular character of agricultural activities arising from the social structure of agriculture and from structural and natural disparities between the various agricultural regions; (b) the need to make the appropriate adjustments gradually; and (c) the fact that in member states agriculture constitutes a sector which is closely linked with the economy as a whole."

Article 43 of the Rome Treaty provided for the convening of a conference of member states immediately after its entry into force in order to establish guidelines for eventual proposals by the Commission for developing a Common Agricultural Policy.

The conference, which has become known as the Stresa Conference of July 3-12, 1958, was notably successful for having overridden national secular interests in agriculture in the drafting of these guidelines although it did not resolve the problems that stem from them.

The United States was particularly interested in the principle, recognized by the Six, that a balance must be found between the Community's agricultural production and agricultural imports from third countries, on the one hand, and market outlets in the Community and in third countries, on the other.

This principle is found in chapter III, paragraph 2 of the final resolution of the conference. It states that: "The implementation of the Treaty must lead naturally to a progressive development of trade within the Community; it will also have to take into account at the same time the necessity of maintaining trade and Treaty, political and economic ties with third countries. . . ."

The first proposals for developing a CAP were made by the Commission in December 1959 in the form of draft regulations for grain, poultry, eggs, fruit, vegetables, pork, wine, sugar, dairy products, and beef. They were revised in 1960.

The specific measures for arriving at a CAP in each commodity area are based on the following objectives, as stated in the treaty: Common marketing policies for all products, a common foreign trade policy to replace existing national trade policies, controls and regulatory devices by one system of variable import levies and minimum import prices, and a policy for the modernization and improvement of the structure of agriculture.

The Commission's proposed regulations were approved by the Council on January 14, 1962, only for the first six of the products, and they became effective on July 30, 1962.

In general, the regulations for imports of grains, pork, poultry, and eggs from countries outside the EEC (third countries) provide for a control over imports by means of variable levies, which, in fact, prevent price competition by lower cost producers outside the Community.

Regulations as to fruit and vegetables control imports primarily by tariffs and the application of quality standards and minimum import prices set in relation to market prices in EEC member states. Its specific control features are more complicated. The wine regulation controls imports by quotas.

The regulation on grain applies to all grain except rice and has special provisions for durum wheat. No hard wheat is produced in the EEC. It established a variable import levy on imports of grain coming from another member state and from third countries and plans for eventual abolishment of all other trade-restrictive measures, such as quotas, mixing regulations, skimming charges, fees, and special taxes, on grain. This had been largely done in 1964.

The complex tools for supporting and protecting EEC grain producers and for constructing a common grain policy are a target price and the intervention price, a threshold price, a variable levy, rules for export, import and export licenses, and safeguards.

THE TARGET PRICE, in a sense a reference or guide price, is the heart of the CAP grain price structure because all other grain prices are a function of it. It is the price that is fixed each year before planting time at the wholesale level in the center of the most deficit area in each country. Target prices have been set by each member state, but a single target price for the most deficit area in the Community is to be established by the end of the transition period, when a single, or common, market is formed.

THE INTERVENTION PRICE is the one at which actual support purchases will be made of grain offered to agencies of the governments of the member states. The intervention price, to be set at 5 to 10 percent below the target price, guarantees farmers a minimum price for their grain.

The relationship of the intervention price to the target price does not prevent regional differences in market prices. Grain that is accumulated by intervention agencies may be sold in domestic markets at the target price level or may be exported. Wheat and rye that are denaturized (dyed or otherwise treated to make it unfit for food) may be sold for feed in the domestic market at intervention prices.

THE THRESHOLD PRICE is really a minimum import price. It is the target price less freight and marketing costs from a specified port of entry to the principal deficit area. In addition to meeting a threshold price, third countries are handicapped by a lump sum, or preference payment, of at present 1.10 dollars per metric ton, and a price adjustment based on quality. A common quality standard to which the quality of imported grain is compared for calculating price adjustments has been established.

A LEVY may be charged by each member state on intra-Community trade until the end of the transition period and on imports from third countries.

On January 1, 1970, all member states must charge the same levy on third-country imports, and none will be charged on grain moving from one member state to another. The levy on intra-Community trade is equal to the difference between the threshold price in the importing country and the market price in the exporting country.

The levy on imports of grain from third countries is fixed daily in an amount equal to the difference between the threshold price and the lowest offer price on the world market, c.i.f. European ports.

The lowest world market offer price is chosen for a single, comparable quality. The levy on a given grain therefore applies to all qualities of that grain regardless of its origin. In defense of its system, the Commission has maintained that the levy system exposes the Community to unlimited competition from third-country grain suppliers as soon as the world market price reaches or exceeds the target price. The world market price for grains, however, has consistently remained far below average internal EEC prices.

Since the target price becomes the threshold price when it is adjusted for costs to the border, it is in reality a minimum import price, which may be set at a high level to avoid competition from third-country grain. Thus EEC grain could always have preference.

In general terms, then, United States grain shipped to Germany is charged a levy equal to the difference between the world market price and the German internal price, plus 1.10 dollars per metric ton to give preference to intra-EEC trade. French grain shipments to Germany, on the other hand, are charged a levy equal to the difference between French and German internal prices.

Export subsidies are permitted by

the regulations for sales to third countries and (under certain conditions) to member states. The treaty gives the Community the right to resort to other aids to exports "to the extent that they are used on the world market."

IMPORT AND EXPORT licenses for intra-Community and third-country trade may be issued by the member states themselves. Import licenses normally are granted freely, and are valid for only 3 months. Importers must pay the levy in effect on the day of importation, but they are permitted to prefix the levy against payment of a premium. It is in effect a control system that attempts to regulate imports of grain to conform to an annual grain-supply program.

SAFEGUARD MEASURES are also called "escape clauses" because they permit member states to circumvent the provisions against quantitative restrictions by taking steps believed necessary, including the total suspension of imports, if their markets become "subjected to, or threaten to become subjected to, serious disturbances."

Such steps are subject to review by the Commission, which can sustain, change, or annul them. If a member does not agree with the Commission decision on its safeguard action, it may appeal to the Council, which can overrule the Commission by a qualified majority of 12 out of 17 votes.

When imports from other member states are restricted by escape-clause action, imports from third countries are to be restricted in the same way.

Some escape-clause actions that could be taken are quantitative restrictions on imports; suspension of import licenses; and additional charges on imports of processed grain products when their offer price does not correspond to the world market price of the unprocessed grain plus processing costs.

The protection offered to poultry is much more complicated because the member states do not want to engage in support purchases and therefore did not establish target or intervention prices as in grains. They wanted to combine the protection of fixed tariffs with a mechanism that would compensate for differences in feed costs between importing and exporting countries. They also wanted protection against imports at below normal prices. The result is a complex variable levy on imports of poultry from third countries, which is composed of three elements plus a so-called gate-price levy.

The variable levy affords triple protection to member states. It eliminates the advantage of lower priced feed grains on the world market compared to higher priced ones in the importing member state. It charges a duty which is to be reduced to zero by 1970. And, thirdly, it charges a preference payment, 3 percent for 1963–1964, which will be increased annually to 7 percent by 1970.

One member state may charge a levy on another that eliminates differences in feed grain costs between them and that charges a duty equal to the one in effect between them in 1962 before the CAP was approved.

A minimum import price, called gate price, is intended to prevent disturbances on member states' markets that may result from poultry imports from third countries at "abnormal prices." The gate price is adjusted quarterly by the Commission.

Changes in it must be approved unanimously by the Council until the end of the second stage and thereafter by a majority vote. It is calculated on the basis of world feed grain prices and a feed grain conversion factor, which is to be "typical for exporting third countries."

If offer prices are below the gate price, the levy is to be increased by the difference between them. The gate price provisions do not apply to third countries that guarantee that their poultry will not be offered at prices below the gate price.

Poultry exports to member states and

to third countries may be subsidized.

The CAP regulations for eggs and pork in general are similar to the poultry regulation, except that the fixed or duty element of the intra-Community levy is calculated at 5 percent for eggs and according to a formula for pork.

The CAP regulations for fruit and vegetables apply as well to their processed products. They provide for import tariffs and for trade controls through the gradual imposition of quality standards on imports from member states and from third countries as well as by a minimum import price feature. Quality standards have been established for only a limited number of fresh products in which the United States has a major trade interest—primarily apples, pears, lemons, and oranges. The regulations prohibit imports of products that do not meet the quality standards.

In the event that markets of member states are disturbed or threaten to become disturbed by imports from third countries below a reference price, such imports may be suspended, or an import fee may be levied on them equal to the difference between the import price and the reference price. This also is largely a minimum import price provision. It is calculated on the basis of an average of the lowest farmers' auction market prices during a certain base period for a standard quality of the product.

The CAP regulation on wines contains no provisions regarding imports and exports other than the following import quotas:

Germany: 920 thousand hectoliters of table wines, of which 30 percent is quality wines. Wines for must are fixed at a quota of 460 thousand hectoliters. (One hectoliter equals about 25.6 gallons.) Italy: 300 thousand hectoliters. France: 300 thousand hectoliters. The regulation defines the wine regions of Germany, Italy, and Luxembourg and, in the case of France, respects its system of controlled origin-names ("appellation d'origine controlee"). Among its most significant features are the provision for an annual wine cadaster and an annual inventory of wine stocks on hand. The first cadaster was to be completed in December 1964.

UNIFYING the economies of the Six, as provided for by the treaty, implies many adjustments in many sectors.

Those of most concern to United States agriculture affect trade in agricultural products. They concern us because our agricultural exports to the Common Market are almost 35 percent of our dollar farm sales to the world and because their total value almost equals the United States balance-of-payment deficit.

The treaty states in article 12 that member states may not establish new duties on trade among themselves after January 1, 1958, and they may not increase existing ones. It is possible also to eliminate these duties in three 4-year stages during a 12-year transition period or less.

A progressive alinement or equalization of the national tariffs on third-country imports has been taking place concurrently, so that by the end of the transition period there will exist a single, or Common External Tariff, to be applied to such imports. The CXT in most cases is the arithmetical average of the tariffs of the six member states for a given product.

The method for scheduled reductions in their individual national tariffs on intra-Community trade is specified in article 14. On January 1, 1959, the duties in effect as of the base date, January 1, 1957, were cut by 10 percent. Eighteen months from that date another 10 percent cut was scheduled, followed by a third cut at the end of the fourth year of the treaty on December 31, 1961. This was to have completed the scheduled reduction of 30 percent for stage 1.

The Council of Ministers decided, however, to accelerate the timetable for the first stage, and an additional cut on industrial products of 10 percent was made on December 31, 1960, thus eliminating the barriers to trade in such products among the Six on that date by a total of 40 percent.

The second stage provided for additional cuts on July 1, 1963, December 31, 1964, and December 31, 1965. In a further attempt to speed up the elimination of tariffs on trade with EEC, the Council decided on another reduction on industrial products. It took effect July 1, 1962. They also abolished quota restrictions on industrial goods that could have waited until 1970.

According to the schedule, the first 10-percent cut in stage 2 was to occur on July 1, 1963, but the EEC made the cut on July 1, 1962.

The treaty states that adjustments in the internal tariffs of the Six that remain for stage 3 shall be scheduled by decision of the Council acting on a proposal by the Commission. By December 31, 1969, the end of that stage, all tariffs on trade between member states will have been abolished.

The Rome Treaty also provided that member states' tariffs on imports from third countries would be replaced with a Common External Tariff by the end of the transition period. The schedule of alinements of national tariffs toward a CXT provided for a 30-percent adjustment on January 1, 1962, of the base rates that existed on January 1, 1957, and another 30-percent adjustment on January 1, 1966.

In an effort to hasten the movement toward full economic union, the members decided to accelerate adjustments of their national tariffs toward a CXT. On January 1, 1959, when the first reduction in internal tariffs took place, it was decided to extend the reduction to third countries, except if such a reduction would result in a lower tariff than the CXT.

On that date, therefore, the high tariff moved down by 10 percent of the base duty to 18 percent. Two years later, a year ahead of schedule, the first scheduled step of 30 percent toward tariff alinement on the CXT for industrial products was taken. But as part of its accelerated effort, the EEC offered the contracting parties of the General Agreement on Tariffs and Trade (GATT) to make this 30-percent adjustment on the basis of the CXT of 15 percent reduced by 20 percent—that is, to 12 percent. The high tariff thus moved down by 30 percent of the difference between 12 and 20 percent to 17.6 percent. Concurrently, the low tariff moved up by 30 percent of the difference between 10 and 12 percent to 10.6 percent.

The second alinement of 30 percent took place 30 months ahead of schedule. At that time, even in cases where the proffered 20-percent cut in the CXT by 60 percent of the difference between 12 and 20 percent was not negotiated in GATT, the high tariff was reduced to 15.2 percent, and the low tariff was increased by the same amount to 11.2 percent in a continued alinement toward the reduced CXT.

The next step presumably would wipe out the remaining 40 percent of the adjustment of national tariffs toward the 12-percent CXT, provided the reduction will have been negotiated in GATT. However, the method for making this final move was not laid down in the Rome Treaty.

AN IMPORTANT POLICY decision before the Community was to determine target price levels for farm products by 1970 and the steps needed to arrive at them.

Called harmonization of prices, the process eventually must be applied to all farm products. But harmonization of grain prices is the most significant, because their prices determine or influence the prices of most other farm products, and also because grain is widely produced in the EEC. Operation of the CAP variable levy system for poultry, pork, and eggs depends largely on a calculation of the amount and cost of grains that are utilized for their production.

The EEC estimated that about 45 percent of the Community's total agricultural area is planted to grain. The largest single source of farm income is from grain, including the value of that converted to livestock and poultry. The ultimate form of a CAP and of a farm income policy then depends on the influence that a common grain price level will have on agricultural production in general.

The highest target price (on the 1963–1964 average) for wheat among the Six is 3.24 dollars a bushel in Germany. The lowest is 2.70 dollars a bushel in France.

The declared EEC grain policy is that target prices for feed grain and wheat eventually will be set close enough in the price harmonization process so that feed grain may be substituted for wheat by the farmer when he seeds or by the livestock and poultry producers when they feed.

France has relatively the most important role in the framework of a Community grain policy because of her comparatively low grain prices, because she produces more than 45 percent of all EEC wheat and 40 percent of all EEC coarse grains, and because (depending on the magnitude of the price incentive) French farmers could put about 4 million acres of other land into grain. Increases in grain consumption by livestock and technological improvement in production are expected to result in further expansion of production.

The United States is concerned that political pressures in the governments of the Six, particularly in Germany, may result in setting the common grain prices substantially above present French and Dutch levels—that is, at an average of the present French and German prices and possibly even higher. That would further encourage uneconomic production of grain, even though soft wheat were in surplus.

The Community has a better opportunity to employ its excess of agricultural labor to produce livestock and livestock products than grain. Its officials know this, but strong political pressures by farm organizations have made it uncertain that they will be able to withstand the political expe-

diency of uneconomically high grain prices.

An ultimate high-price level for grain, which is protected by the variable levy system, would encourage substantial increases in grain production, particularly in France. In such an event, the United States and other efficient producers of grain would be excluded from the EEC market to the extent that production of wheat and feed grain increases in the Community. The stake of the United States in this market is substantial. It supplied about 30 percent of the Community's wheat imports and 45 percent of its feed grain imports in 1959–1960 and 1961–1962.

Another result of higher priced grain would be higher prices of livestock products to consumers and perhaps a consequent decline in sales of United States grain to the Community.

The high level of technology in American agriculture has made it one of the world's most efficient producers of many commodities. American farmers can compete favorably on the world's farm markets. But the fact that this efficiency makes it possible to land United States barley in Hamburg, Germany, at 1.40 dollars a bushel (about 1 dollar below the German price level) is to no avail as long as the variable levy eliminates such price competition.

Throughout the transition period— that is, until 1970—the variable levy system guarantees grain producers of each of the six member states priority access to their own country market for all grain they produce. By 1970, they all will be guaranteed absolute priority access to the entire Community market.

The lump-sum, or preference, payment of 1.10 dollars a metric ton on imported grain gives Community grain producers a small, additional margin of preference.

The net result of the functioning of the grain regulation therefore would be to continue third-country suppliers, such as the United States, in a more or less permanent position of residual supplier. The amount of wheat and coarse grain they will be able to sell to the Common Market will depend on its increases in grain production and the influence of the ultimate grain target price level on production.

What the United States needs, then, is some form of assurance from the EEC that its traditional grain markets will not arbitrarily be taken away by an economically unsound price policy.

Exports of United States poultry to Germany before the CAP regulations were subject to a moderate fixed duty charged as a percentage of the value of the shipment.

But they were subject also to exchange and quota restrictions at the same time. Before the CAP regulations, Germany gradually relaxed and then liberalized her quota restrictions on poultry imports. The regulations completely eliminated the latter, but they also introduced the new, enormously complicated protective features I have described and instituted a minimum import, or gate price, which was set by the Council at an arbitrarily high level.

Managed in this way, the system has prevented United States poultry from competing with EEC poultry, maintained consumer poultry prices at a high level, and retarded increases in poultry consumption. The net effect was an abrupt decline in sales of United States poultry to Germany. Our share of the German poultry import market declined from about 40 percent near the end of 1962 to about 10 percent at the end of February 1963, when the supplemental levy was raised to 30 pfennig a kilo, or 3.4 cents a pound.

The United States therefore formally asked the EEC Commission in June 1963 to enter into negotiations under terms of an agreement negotiated in the U.S.–EEC–GATT negotiations of 1961–1962. The Council of Ministers met twice thereafter, and on July 29, 1963, could agree only to direct the Commission to begin exploratory discussions with the United States with a view to determining solutions that would be acceptable.

The prospect of additional unproductive discussions after almost a year of talks prompted the United States to resort to compensatory withdrawals of concessions it had made in GATT in an attempt to redress the trade balance.

The United States also was a large supplier of poultry parts to Germany. Whereas the usual price relationships between whole slaughtered birds and poultry parts is 3 to 1, the levy and the gate price on the latter at first reflected a price relationship of 7.5 to 1, or an ad valorem duty protection of 75 percent.

Strong representations by the United States resulted in a reduction to 60 percent. The protection remained disproportionately high, however, and efforts were continued to correct this wrong relationship and make it reflect the true price relationship.

The EEC's pork regulation was first implemented only with respect to live hogs and carcass pork and established the import levy and gate price systems for all pork. The regulation dealing with pork parts, in which specialty meats are included, was approved in June 1963. Of all pork products, the United States is chiefly concerned with specialty meats, because its exports of frozen pork livers to Europe are a sizable trade item.

The regulation on pork parts provides that it will respect the guaranteed maximum duty of the GATT on pork livers. The United States has expected that the GATT binding will be respected and that the total charges, including any supplementary charge that is applied to imports from the United States to make up the difference between the offer price and the gate price, will be kept within the GATT maximum of 20 percent.

As to regulations on fruit and vegetables, concern has been felt over the minimum import price, called the reference price.

It provides for an additional charge or the suspension of imports when they are offered at prices below the reference price. Moreover, the regulations provide that quota restrictions on trade among the Six in these products will be eliminated gradually, but it does not set up a schedule for liberalization of trade with third countries.

A GATT agreement requires the elimination of quota restrictions imposed by member states against United States horticultural products, but France, Germany, Italy, and Belgium have maintained restrictions on many of them. Therefore, the United States thus far has taken action against France, Germany, and Italy under the terms of GATT to obtain compensation for the loss in trade.

Finally, the regulations speak of quality standards, not all of which had been established in 1964. Article 9 of the basic fruit and vegetable regulation provided for their liberalization according to a schedule for three quality classes not later than December 31, 1965. Since a condition of entry into the EEC fruit market is the meeting of quality standards, the United States has insisted that equivalent standards be applied to its products.

The only rice producers in the Community are Italy and (to a lesser extent) France. Both grow mostly round or medium-grain, soft varieties. Consumers in northern Europe prefer long-grain, hard varieties, which form the bulk of American exports to the Community. The United States is concerned that the levy system of 1964 may give priority access to Italian and French rice in those markets. The American trade would suffer thereby.

The suggestions for a final draft of the regulation regarding vegetable oils and oilseeds was approved by the Council in December 1963. The United States has a GATT binding that permits oilseeds to enter the EEC free of duty. The duty on crude vegetable oils is bound at 10 percent ad valorem. Since crushing adds only

about 10 percent to the value of the oilseeds, which are imported duty free, the 10 percent duty provides, in fact, a 100-percent protection for the processing costs.

A threatened butter surplus in the Community caused dairy producers to press for taxes on margarine and the products used in its manufacture in order to encourage consumption of butter. The tax of 14 pfennig a kilo (1.59 cents a pound) was approved by the Council in December 1963. The United States fears that such action would impair the commitments obtained in GATT negotiations.

Oil cake and meal entered the Community in 1963 on the basis of a duty-free GATT binding.

No regulation for tobacco had been proposed in 1963. The problem lay in a determination of duty levels on cigarettes and unmanufactured tobacco and in a shift from a fixed to an ad valorem duty in the progress toward a CXT.

Because practically no cotton is grown in the EEC, the member states plan no policy of protection against imports. American cotton sales to the EEC have continued to rise since the Rome Treaty was signed.

THE SIX Common Market countries have a highly advanced agriculture. Their total area is only 0.9 percent of the world's land surface but contains 2 percent of its agricultural area.

Six percent of the world's population and 2.7 percent of the world's population that depends wholly on the land for a livelihood live in the Six. EEC produces about 87 percent of its total food requirements.

The fact that France, the largest agricultural producer of the Six and the one with the greatest production potential, is at the threshold of an agricultural technological revolution like the one the United States has been experiencing heightens the significance of Common Market agriculture to United States agricultural trade.

There is an average of 2.5 acres of

exploitable agricultural land for every person in the world. The average is about 1.2 acres in the Community. A general trait of Community agriculture is its high concentration of farm population, intense cultivation, and a high average yield.

About 3.5 million farms supply the United States with its food and forage. The Community counts about 6.8 million farms larger than about 2.5 acres in size. United States crop and grass land covers 1,001 million acres, 5½ times larger than the Community's 194 million acres. But about 7 million persons in the United States work these lands, whereas the Community needs 15.1 million to work its lands.

This great population burden on the Community's land and the fragmentation of its farmland are the reasons why the Rome Treaty attached such great importance to the improvement of the agricultural structure and the best utilization of farm labor.

Farm mechanization in the EEC has burgeoned since the end of the Second World War. More than 200 thousand farm tractors have been added to the machinery pool each year since 1955. Germany, said to be the most highly mechanized member state, had slightly more than 37 tractors for each thousand acres in 1963. (The proportion in the United States was lower because its extensive range and grazing lands need fewer tractors.)

Since 1960, relatively more capital has been spent on other types of farm machinery, especially harvest machinery. Variations in this trend are due to fluctuations in the size of the farm labor pool, farm income, the size and intensity of production on farms, sales price and purchase terms of farm machinery, and other factors.

Expenditures per acre for farm machinery have been highest in Germany and lowest in Italy. Luxembourg, Belgium, France, and the Netherlands fall in between in that descending order. The increase in expenditures on farm mechanization (except in Italy) has been at a greater

relative rate than the increase in the gross value for farm sales. Concurrently, the numbers of farmworkers have declined.

Increases in applications of chemical fertilizers have kept pace with the general advance in agricultural technology. Compared to 1950–1951, in 1959–1960 (the latest year for which data are available) 73 percent more nitrogen, 61 percent more phosphate, and 57 percent more potassium fertilizers were added to the soil.

The rise in the use of fertilizer has been particularly marked in Italy and France, partly because of their comparatively low levels of use during the early postwar period. Belgium and Luxembourg, both with a history of high yields from intensely cultivated land, had the smallest increase, because applications there have been traditionally high.

The Commission has estimated an average increase in consumption of nitrogen of 37 percent in 1964 over 1958; of phosphate, 24 percent; and potassium, 28 percent. The average figures hide even more spectacular increases, however. France is expected to double her applications of nitrogen and almost double her applications of the other two elements. Italy is expected to increase consumption of potassium by 57 percent. Germany will increase use of nitrogen by 38 percent, phosphate 32 percent, and potassium 25 percent.

THE GROSS VALUE of farm production in the Community in 1963 was set at somewhat more than 18 billion dollars—60 percent in livestock and livestock products and 40 percent in crops. That is equal to slightly more than 92 dollars per acre of crop and grass land compared to 41 dollars in the United States, where large tracts of range and grass land account for the less intensive agriculture.

Each farm laborer contributes only about 1,192 dollars to the gross agricultural product of the Community, substantially less than the 5,857 dollars per farm laborer in the United States (on the basis of realized gross farm income).

The Commission has recognized that differences exist in the production potentials of the various regions. Furthermore, a slow growth rate of employment in some industrial areas tends to deprive farm labor of an alternate source of employment and so complicates the problem of surplus farm labor in EEC.

Growth of income in more highly developed areas has reached the point where the elasticity of demand for food products has diminished measurably. In lesser developed areas, where one can expect the elasticity to be greater, the rate of growth of income has been low. The rate of economic growth in the Community in general has been far more marked in industrial than in rural sections.

But industrial production and incomes in general have continued to grow since the birth of the Community and there has been a concurrent rise in demand for more and better food in the industrial areas where this has occurred. This is the most favorable factor in attempting to improve the structure of farming.

Italy and Germany are the EEC countries that will have to undergo the most far-reaching structural changes in their agriculture.

Italy in particular has a large number of small farmers. Their inefficiency and comparatively low incomes, particularly in southern Italy, Sicily, and Sardinia, leave them almost on the fringe of Italy's economic mainstream.

The German Government's policy of protection through heavy subsidies and high duties on imports of competitive, although badly needed, farm products keeps thousands of small, inefficient German farmers on the land.

They have great political strength because of their numbers. Nevertheless, it is estimated that more than 40 percent of them have left the land and that more than 300 thousand farms have disappeared since 1950. Some of the farms were absorbed by larger ones,

but many went out of production. Some German farm economists estimate that 400 thousand farms will have disappeared before 1970.

Now, as to the outlook.

I noted earlier that an important element in the determination of the CAP is the price of wheat and coarse grain.

The first step toward adjustment or harmonization of the grain prices failed to be taken in April 1963, as specified in the CAP grain regulations, chiefly because of political resistance in Germany to a reduction in prices.

(The regulations require that Council decisions on the grain price be unanimous during the second stage of the transition period. Thereafter, beginning on January 1, 1966, decisions can be made by a qualified majority; that is, by 12 of a total of 17 votes.)

In June 1963, the Council reached agreement on several adjustments in feed grain prices, some of which were related to changes in quality standards. Neither the German high prices nor the French low prices for wheat were affected, however. Those for barley, rye, and corn changed slightly.

In July 1963, Germany suggested that it would be willing to consider lower grain prices if German farmers would be compensated by some form of direct payment. Some observers took the proposal as foreshadowing a satisfactory decision as to an eventual target price level for grains significantly below the price of the German level. If so, it could have removed the chief obstacle in the path toward a CAP.

With an eye, no doubt, to political factors, the EEC Commission submitted a price proposal to the Council of Ministers in November 1963. This proposal would have established a common wheat target price for 1964–1965 season roughly midway between the French and German levels. That would result in a common wheat price of about 2.90 dollars a bushel.

With an awareness of the tendency

toward surplus production of soft wheat, the November proposal would have fixed the target prices for barley and corn, the main feed grains, at levels close enough to the wheat price to encourage their production in place of wheat. However, a decision on the November price proposal was indefinitely postponed by the EEC Council in March 1964.

If no progress is made during the second stage, the United States is concerned that the Commission may raise its sights to a price level above the midway point because of pressure politics in Germany and because of continuation of an upward trend in grain prices throughout the EEC.

The effect of an eventual price level on grain production is of great concern to the United States and to the Community because an increase in prices implies larger supplies and a restraint on consumption.

In expressing concern over the grain price issue, Sicco Mansholt, the Commission vice president in charge of agriculture, said in an address to the International Grain Trade Conference in Hamburg in 1962: "Our price and production policy must be aimed at avoiding any extension of the area under grain in the Community. This means that the optimum grain prices must not exceed a level at which French land reserves would be mobilized on a large scale."

Despite such assurances, the EEC Commission favors a common EEC grain price level which would, in the opinion of many experts, lead to reduced import needs.

There have been a number of projection studies concerning the EEC's future grain import requirements. The EEC Commission itself has estimated that with no increase in grain prices and no increase in acreage devoted to grain, Community net imports of grain by 1970 would be only maintained at the current average of 10 million metric tons. But it is feared that this grain price and acreage situation will not develop.

In a study prepared for the United States Department of Agriculture, Elmer W. Learn projected EEC grain net imports at only 5.8 million metric tons if the common grain price is set at the average of French and German prices.

A rise in incomes will tend to increase discrimination in quality, and an increase in the demand for harder, higher quality wheat, especially spring wheat, can be expected. Europe does not produce hard wheat, but the United States will have to compete more effectively with Canada for this market.

The chief European feed grain is barley, and its production can be expanded sharply through higher yields and increased acreage. Barley can be substituted for soft wheat, and some land in grass or fallow can be seeded to it.

But corn and sorghums, practically interchangeable in feed rations, are the main components of most mixed feeds in Europe. Although there are natural limitations on the production of corn and sorghum in Europe, import requirements for them could be curtailed by expanded barley supplies. This would be particularly injurious to the United States, which is by far the largest supplier of corn and sorghum to the Community.

Development of the European market for United States poultry has made available better and cheaper poultry to consumers. Per capita consumption of poultry meat is estimated to have risen from about 9.0 pounds in 1958 to about 12.8 pounds in 1962. The Commission expects that consumption will increase 116 percent by 1970.

The United States' share of the EEC poultry import market (principally Germany) rose to a high of about 40 percent by the end of 1962. But improved technology in the Community and the export of private American capital and skill to the EEC have been significant factors in the increase of European poultry production.

The Commission has estimated that

more than a million tons of grain are imported annually into the EEC in the form of eggs, poultry, and pork. Since EEC agriculture is a more efficient producer of livestock and poultry than of grain, Community farmers in the future may be able to supply more of its requirements of poultry.

Increasing hog production is no more of a technological problem to European farmers than increasing poultry production was, and it is generally accepted that the Community is practically self-sufficient in pork meat. However, import demand may continue for frozen pork and poultry livers in order to keep processing industries supplied with the raw material for sausages and patés.

An increase in the supply of domestic pork livers that may accompany a rise in hog production can only partially offset import requirements, and it is expected that the United States' share of this market may remain unchanged through the transition period.

Germany and the Netherlands particularly have tried to adapt American feedlot techniques to their conditions. In the Netherlands, the meat is even called the local equivalent of baby beef. The biggest obstacle to further development is the intensity of agriculture in Europe, the high cost of farmland, and the need for a rapid turnover in livestock for immediate needs for cash income. Furthermore, the large number of small farms and government subsidies favor the creation of dairy surpluses. These are the factors that, in turn, have traditionally favored development of the veal market. Nevertheless, the demand for beef has been increasing steadily, and the Commission expects that in 1970 it will be 50 percent greater than in 1958.

Although the United States as a net importer of beef may not be directly affected by that increase, a growing demand for beef and an increase in beef production in the EEC may give rise to more pressure on the United States by countries that traditionally have exported their beef to the EEC.

Production of beef and veal is related closely to the dairy situation because the source of beef is dual- or triple-purpose animals; that is, animals that are raised for milk and meat or milk, meat, and work.

EEC—notably the Netherlands, Belgium, and Luxembourg—has begun to have a problem of butter surplus, and the Commission has estimated an increase of only about 25 percent in 1970 (compared to 1958) in the consumption of butter. It has been estimated therefore that stocks of butter may be about 400 thousand metric tons by 1970. In sum, a determined effort to build up the number of beef cattle may worsen the surplus problem unless special measures are taken.

THE OUTLOOK FOR EDIBLE oils pressed from vegetable seeds is somewhat more complicated because of its interrelationship with butter, imported oils and oilseeds, domestic animal fats, and the livestock mixed-feed industry.

The Commission has estimated that the consumption of edible fats and oils, including butter, may increase by not more than about 17 percent during 1958–1970. But internal pressures have been mounting steadily to keep this increase for Community producers—those who grow rapeseed and olives and those who raise cows.

Moreover, the European Development Fund agreement that was initialed in 1963 with 18 African Associated Overseas Countries and became effective early in 1964 will provide for production subsidies at least for the 1964–1965 marketing year for peanuts and for peanut oil to help them compete in the European market.

Thus imports of soybean oil may encounter stiff competition for the expected small increase in consumption.

However, increases in the production of hogs, cattle, and poultry imply a substantial increase in demand for high-energy protein concentrates.

Sales of American soybean meal have increased markedly since 1960. Sales of soybeans also have increased, but to a lesser degree. This trend can be expected to continue—at least through the transitional period.

The consumption of deciduous fruit is expected to rise, but it is not likely that much of the increase will be supplied with imported fresh fruit, partly because of duties, continued national quotas, and even embargoes—restrictions that are effective trade protection devices.

But the most telling factors are the large areas in the Community that have been planted to new fruit, chiefly apples and pears, that soon will come into heavy bearing. A substantial increase in consumption of canned fruits is expected, and the United States may supply a significant share of it.

Imports of oranges and lemons may increase to supply part of the growing demand for them. Significant supplies of both originate in Mediterranean countries.

THE WILL to cooperate politically is basic to progress toward a Common Agricultural Policy, and the eventual emergence of the European Economic Community as a single political entity is pertinent to any discussion of the CAP. Political will is the lubricant for the CAP machinery, although it is conceivable that special regional interests can slow it down.

A lack of political harmony, such as that shown by France's veto on January 14, 1963, of the United Kingdom's entry into the EEC, created serious problems that considerably slowed progress toward a CAP.

For example, it was not until the following April that the member states could agree to another meeting of the Council of Ministers. Since then, France's approach to important agricultural questions has appeared to be designed in defense of her January 14 decision and in defense of other overriding political considerations.

Indeed, it would not be an exaggeration to say that the atmosphere of acrimony that resulted from France's action on that fateful day in a sense has carried over to the Council's deliberations in subsequent sessions in that the driving motivation of treaty objectives now seems to be only vaguely present.

That is why a working program for 1963 still had not been agreed upon by June of that year, a first step in harmonization of grain target prices had not been taken by early 1964, and the pending rice, beef, dairy products, and fats and oils regulations had not been approved by the Council until the end of 1963.

By the end of July 1963, the atmosphere had improved considerably, and action had been taken on several important matters. The levy system on pork meat and products was approved. The Treaty of Association with African States was signed. The atmosphere for negotiations of agricultural duties in the Kennedy Round of the Trade Expansion Act negotiations had cleared somewhat.

In my description of the short-lived EDC, I explained that a community of nations is formed to attain commonly accepted goals. In order that such a community survive, common agreement is needed that its survival by and of itself necessarily takes precedence over the attainment of goals. Lack of conviction on this point saps its strength, impairs its efficiency in resolving problems, and imperils its survival.

This was essentially the problem before the EEC in 1964, for the unilateral actions of one of its members have cast doubts on the existence of a unanimous will to survive. It is as much of a concern to the Six as it is to the United States, for as the EEC and its CAP go, so United States foreign agricultural trade policy must respond.

JOHN E. MONTEL *is agricultural attaché of the United States Mission to the European Economic Community in Brussels, Belgium. Previously he was agricultural attaché in Guatemala, Honduras, El Salvador, British Honduras, and Ecuador and assistant agricultural attaché in Venezuela, the Dominican Republic, and Haiti.*

General Agreement

on Tariffs and Trade

by A. RICHARD DeFELICE

THE GENERAL AGREEMENT on Tariffs and Trade (GATT) is an international multilateral trade agreement entered into by the United States and all its major trading partners.

There were 62 full-member countries in 1964. Several countries participate under special or temporary arrangements. They include almost all trading nations of the free world.

It is the most comprehensive agreement ever concluded to promote international cooperation in trade policies and reduce barriers to international trade. It is the principal instrument for such cooperation in the free world. The United States uses it as a major vehicle for developing its trade relations with other countries.

The United States entered the agreement under authority of the Trade Agreements Act, which was first enacted in 1934, when an intense economic depression gripped the world.

The domestic economic and international trade policies of countries after the First World War aggravated the situation. They tried to recover from destruction, chaos, and bitterness by setting up controls on foreign commercial relations. They raised tariffs and applied quotas to restrict imports. They made preferential trading arrangements, and encountered retaliation by countries that claimed the arrangements hurt them. The com-

plicated system of restrictive devices that developed endangered international trade and economic health of all nations.

The Congress enacted the Trade Agreements Act for the declared purpose of expanding foreign markets for American products and strengthening our economy. The President was given authority to enter into trade agreements with foreign governments for the reduction of tariffs and other trade restrictions on a reciprocal basis.

The United States accordingly negotiated agreements with other governments. In each agreement, the United States obtained reductions in duties applied against specified American goods in the market of the foreign country. In return, the United States made similar reductions in its duties on products of particular interest to the other country.

The agreement also provided rules and limitations on the use of other trade devices that could impair the value of the tariff concessions. It was necessary, for example, to provide that import quotas and discriminating internal taxes would not be used to nullify or impair what had been given as a tariff concession.

Thus the agreements contained specific commitments on the level of duties and general provisions as to such matters as quotas and internal taxes. As experience with the negotiation and operation of these bilateral trade agreements grew, succeeding agreements became broader in scope and more complex.

Up until the Second World War, the United States negotiated bilateral trade agreements with 29 countries. They helped stabilize relations and reduce the level of trade barriers.

Much remained to be done, however, to get effective agreement among trading nations to reduce obstacles to trade. Bilateral agreements seemed to have reached their maximum effectiveness for this purpose. Their limitations were recognized.

One was that they did not induce a

country to give up or modify an undesirable trade practice—for example, import quotas. Some countries felt the need to maintain an extensive quota system merely to be in a position to counter against another nation applying quotas against it. It was possible to obtain a country's agreement to remove a few specific products from the quota system, but no country was willing to commit itself to any great limitation on the use of quotas unless its main trading partners were likewise committed to similar undertakings.

Also, in bilateral agreements, countries tended to hold back tariff concessions lest other countries not party to the agreement would obtain benefits without giving any equivalent.

In those circumstances, the United States, near the end of the Second World War, initiated a series of meetings among the leading trading nations of the free world to develop a multilateral agreement to apply to international trade. A charter for an International Trade Organization (ITO) was completed in Havana in 1948.

The charter covered many details of economic affairs and international trade. It contained rules to govern the trade practices of member governments that directly affected their economic policies. The charter therefore was submitted for acceptance by governments at a later date.

Meanwhile, members of the conference agreed to begin negotiations to lower tariffs and other restrictions. The negotiations took place at Geneva in 1947 at the same time the ITO Charter was being considered.

The results of the negotiations were embodied in a multilateral trade agreement, the General Agreement on Tariffs and Trade, or the GATT. It was signed on October 30, 1947, and came into force on January 1, 1948. Twenty-three countries initially accepted it. What was initiated as an interim arrangement pending the adoption of the ITO Charter now remains an international agreement for the conduct of trade.

The contracting parties to the GATT on January 1, 1964, were: Australia, Austria, Belgium, Brazil, Union of Burma, Federal Republic of Cameroon, Canada, Central African Republic, Ceylon, Chad, Chile, Republic of Congo (Brazzaville), Cuba, Cyprus, Czechoslovakia, Dahomey, Denmark, Dominican Republic, Finland, France, Gabon, the Federal Republic of Germany, Republic of Ghana, Greece, Republic of Haiti, India, Indonesia, Israel, Italy, Republic of Ivory Coast, Jamaica, Japan, Kuwait, Luxembourg, Malagasy Republic, Malawi, Malaysia, Islamic Republic of Mauritania, Kingdom of the Netherlands, New Zealand, Nicaragua, Republic of Niger, Federation of Nigeria, Norway, Pakistan, Peru, Portugal, Republic of Senegal, Sierra Leone, Republic of South Africa, Southern Rhodesia, Spain, Sweden, Tanganyika, Trinidad and Tobago, Turkey, Uganda, the United Kingdom, the United States, Republic of Upper Volta, Uruguay, and Zambia.

Five countries acceded provisionally—Argentina, Switzerland, Republic of Tunisia, the United Arab Republic, and Yugoslavia.

Countries that participated in the work of the Contracting Parties under special arrangements were the Kingdom of Cambodia and Poland.

Countries to whose territories the GATT has been applied since 1948 and which, as independent states, maintained a de facto application of the GATT pending final decisions as to their future commercial policy were: Democratic and Popular Republic of Algeria, Kingdom of Burundi, Republic of the Congo (Léopoldville), Republic of Mali, the Republic of Rwanda, and Republic of Togo.

The Contracting Parties in November 1954 undertook an examination of the agreement in the light of the experience of the previous years. After more than 4 months of negotiations, they reaffirmed the basic objectives and obligations and revised certain of the trade rules to make them more effective and better adapted to meet future needs of the trading partners. (The term "contracting parties," when it is used herein without initial capitals, refers to member countries acting individually; when it is used with initial capitals—Contracting Parties—it refers to the member countries acting as a group.)

During the review, the organization provisions of the GATT were renegotiated for inclusion in a separate agreement to establish an Organization for Trade Cooperation (OTC), which would be a permanent organization whose principal function would be to administer the GATT. Several countries accepted the separate agreement, but it cannot become effective until it is accepted by more of the principal trading nations, including the United States.

THE GATT is a comprehensive and complicated agreement, but its technical provisions rest on three basic principles.

The first is nondiscrimination by each participating country in its trade with the others. In commercial policy, this is customarily referred to as "most-favored-nation treatment," or MFN treatment. Each contracting party in the GATT agrees to give all other contracting parties any trade advantage, favor, privilege, or immunity it grants to any other country, whether or not the other country is a member, subject to certain limited and expressed exceptions.

The second is that customs tariffs shall be the only means for affording protection to domestic industries. Import quotas are prohibited. Import quotas may be permissible or authorized for other purposes, to safeguard a country's balance of payments, for example, but their use for such must conform to defined conditions.

The third basic principle is to afford an international forum for discussing and settling mutual problems of international trade.

The fundamental principles are encompassed in a series of rules and provisions. The agreement is formally structured in 3 parts and 35 articles.

Part I deals with tariffs and preferences; part II, with nontariff barriers; and part III, with procedural and other matters.

The most-favored-nation obligation is imposed by article I. Certain exceptions are specified. The most important at the beginning applied to preferential arrangements between the United States and Cuba and the Philippines and between countries of the British Commonwealth existing in 1947. Preferential treatment then permitted is not to be increased in the future. Another exception permits countries applying any import restrictions for balance-of-payment reasons or for development of an underdeveloped economy to discriminate temporarily under specified conditions. This deviation was practiced in several countries.

New regional arrangements have brought into focus another and more lasting exception to the MFN principle. Article XXIV recognizes the integration of national economies into a customs union or free trade area as a means of furthering the objectives.

Under certain conditions, a customs union or a free trade area is exempt from the most-favored-nation obligation. These conditions are designed to assure that tariffs and other barriers to trade within the area are reduced and eliminated and that more restrictive barriers to trade would not be thereby created.

The purpose is to prevent the creation of preferential arrangements that would further restrict trade between the regional unit and the rest of the trading world.

SEVERAL TREATIES and conventions establishing the following regional arrangements have been examined by the Contracting Parties in accordance with the provisions of the GATT.

They are the European Economic Community (Belgium, Luxembourg, the Netherlands, the Federal Republic of Germany, France, and Italy) whose members are contracting parties to the GATT; European Free Trade Association (Austria, Denmark, Norway, Portugal, Sweden, Switzerland, the United Kingdom, and Finland, an associate member, all of whom are contracting parties to the GATT); and the Latin American Free Trade Association (Brazil, Chile, Peru, Uruguay—all members of the GATT—Argentina, Mexico, Paraguay, Colombia, and Ecuador).

Subsequently it was decided that some legal and practical issues called for further discussion and review.

Accordingly, procedures were established to provide for such further review by the Contracting Parties.

The tariff concessions agreed to at any conference to negotiate tariffs are listed in schedules, which are annexed to the agreement and become a part of it by the terms of article II.

Each contracting party has a separate schedule, in which the specific product identification and the rate of duty are set forth. A country is obligated not to charge a higher rate of duty than that specified in its schedule for that product. This obligation, however, does not prevent a country from imposing internal revenue taxes on imports at the same rates as those applied to a similar domestic product; any antidumping or countervailing duties; and fees or other charges for services, such as for documentation, that are reasonable for the services rendered.

AN IMPORTANT goal of the GATT is to reduce tariffs.

Because customs duties and other charges on imports often hinder trade, the Contracting Parties have made a major effort to reduce tariffs as a way to expand it.

Conferences are convened from time to time to negotiate about tariffs. The extent of participation is determined largely by the scope of a country's trading interests. The United States engages in the broadest negotiation.

Six major conferences have been convened by the Contracting Parties—in 1947 in Geneva; 1949, Annecy, France; 1951, Torquay, England; 1956, 1960–1961, 1964, Geneva.

The conferences have resulted in tariff reductions or commitments against tariff increases that affect more than 60 thousand items in world commerce.

It is estimated that tariffs have been lowered on products accounting for about half of world trade and that about 75 percent of American agricultural exports are to the GATT countries. More than half of these exports were subject to negotiated duties.

When the General Agreement on Tariffs and Trade was signed in 1947, it was agreed that the tariff concessions negotiated at that time would become effective on January 1, 1948, and remain in effect until the end of 1950.

At the end of that time, a contracting party could modify or withdraw any concession by negotiation and agreement with the country with which the concession was initially negotiated.

When modifying or withdrawing a concession, a country should seek to replace it with an equivalent concession, but if no agreement was reached on the substituted concession, the other country could withdraw substantially equivalent concessions.

There was the possibility therefore that extensive renegotiations under article XXVIII could result in a substantial reduction in the wide range of concessions previously negotiated. To forestall this possibility, the effective period for the schedule of concessions was extended from time to time by the Contracting Parties.

In its review of the GATT in 1954–1955, the Contracting Parties adopted a rule that effects an automatic extension of the firm period of the schedules for successive periods of 3 years. Adjustments in individual tariff rates may be negotiated during an open season of several months before the beginning of the new term.

Suitable opportunities are likewise

given for individual adjustment of tariff rates during the firm period when unforeseen developments make them necessary and the Contracting Parties approve.

Member countries concerned with renegotiations under this provision must seek agreement that will maintain the level of concessions covered by it. If they cannot agree, the country wishing to withdraw the concessions may do so. The other country or countries concerned may then withdraw from its schedule of tariffs substantially equivalent concessions negotiated with the country that modifies its concessions.

Article XIX contains an escape clause. It provides that if unforeseen circumstances and a concession lead to increases in imports that cause or threaten serious injury to domestic producers, a contracting party may withdraw or modify the concession long enough to prevent or remedy the injury. Other countries adversely affected may suspend equivalent tariff concessions or obligations unless the country invoking the escape clause makes compensatory concessions.

Part II covers trade barriers other than tariffs.

It has provisions for the treatment of internal taxes—foreign goods must be given equal treatment as domestic products—customs formalities and valuation, marks of origin, antidumping, countervailing duties, subsidies, state trading, quotas, complaints, and general exceptions to the basic rules.

A basic principle is a general prohibition on the use of quantitative restrictions or quotas on imports, which hamper trade because they establish an absolute barrier that cannot be overcome by prices or demand.

The widespread use of quotas between the wars reduced trade to the detriment of many countries, including the United States. The prohibition on the use of quotas, except in specific circumstances, prevents their use to nullify or impair tariff concessions negotiated in the GATT.

The main exception permits a country that has difficulties in balance of payments to impose import restrictions to safeguard its balance and monetary reserves. In special circumstances, the restrictions may be applied in a discriminatory fashion. The import restrictions must not exceed those necessary to accomplish the purpose of fulfilling the purpose authorized. Contracting parties applying these restrictions must progressively relax them as conditions improve and must eliminate them when they are no longer needed.

Various safeguards protect the interest of exporting countries whose trade is affected by these import restrictions. Unless specifically authorized, the permitted quantitative restrictions must be nondiscriminatory. Restrictions must avoid unnecessary damage to the commercial or economic interests of other contracting parties.

Provision also is made for the importation of minimum commercial quantities in order to maintain regular trade channels and to comply with patent and trademark requirements. The import restrictions of a contracting party are reviewed regularly.

A country that imposes new restrictions or intensifies old ones must consult with the Contracting Parties. Any country that considers that another is applying import restrictions inconsistent with the provisions of the GATT may bring the matter up before the Contracting Parties and seek redress for the damage to its trade.

During the exceptional postwar years, many countries invoked the balance-of-payment privilege to impose import restrictions. Consultations kept them under repeated review, discrimination was reduced, and the restrictions were relaxed or eliminated whenever conditions improved.

The widespread use of quantitative restrictions for balance-of-payment reasons could no longer be justified after 1959, when major trading countries took action regarding the convertibility of their currencies. Progress was made thereafter in dismantling the restrictions.

Faster progress was made in the industrial sector than in the agricultural sector. As a consequence, countries that no longer justified their action on balance-of-payment grounds continued to apply restrictions on imports of agricultural products, contrary to the provisions of the GATT.

Certain other exceptions to the general rule are stated in article XI. They include export restrictions imposed because of a short supply of food or other essential commodity; import and export restrictions imposed in connection with grading or marketing standards; and import restrictions on agricultural or fisheries products if the restrictions are necessary to the enforcement of domestic measures that restrict the domestic marketing or production of the like product or for the removal of temporary surpluses.

THE EFFECTIVENESS of the GATT in promoting trade among nations rests on its aims to reduce tariffs and eliminate quotas and other obstacles to trade.

Another major contribution has been its consultations.

The Contracting Parties generally meet in regular session once a year at their headquarters in Geneva. They have met twice a year to afford prompt consideration of trade problems.

A Council of Representatives was established in 1960 to handle routine details and certain urgent matters. The Council meets whenever business is to be transacted. At the regular sessions of the Contracting Parties, discussions center on trade problems and are aimed at reaching agreement on principles, trade policies, and practices of mutual benefit.

The meetings are the occasion also for settling any disputes that may arise. A formal basis for consultations and for considering the complaints has been established. Each member agrees that it will give sympathetic consideration and afford adequate opportunity for consultation to any representation made by another contracting party. If a satisfactory solution is not reached, the Contracting Parties may ask that the matter be brought up for general consideration.

The first step is for the complaining country to consult with the country concerned. If no satisfactory adjustment is approved in a reasonable time, a complaint may be lodged with the Contracting Parties. The Contracting Parties then must promptly investigate the matter and make recommendations or rule on the dispute. In exceptional circumstances, the ruling may authorize the complaining country to suspend the application to the offending country of such concessions or obligations under the agreement as are determined to be appropriate. In any such case, the contracting party against which the ruling is made may withdraw from the GATT.

The differences usually are adjusted through bilateral consultations. In instances when the complaints have been submitted to the Contracting Parties, panels of conciliation have been appointed to make an investigation and to submit a report with recommendations for decision to the Contracting Parties. A panel of conciliation is established for each complaint and comprises experts from countries that have no direct interest in the matter.

These procedures have been successful. This international forum for the frank discussion of mutual problems has proved to be an effective way to develop good will and cooperation among nations in resolving problems of trade relations. Although originally intended as a stopgap, the GATT is the only instrument that provides a set of rules for international trade and the machinery to carry them out.

A. RICHARD DeFELICE *is Assistant Administrator for International Trade, Foreign Agricultural Service. Before joining the Foreign Agricultural Service in 1954, he worked in the Office of the General Counsel of the Department of Agriculture.*

Preferential Trade Agreements

by ROBERT L. GASTINEAU

As LONG AS competition exists in international trade, political and economic conditions will prevail that seem to justify the seeking of competitive advantage through preferential trade.

Internationally accepted rules of trade policy recognize the existence of historic arrangements that give preference to one country over another. But traders know also that the rules, based on the most-favored-nation principle, carefully limit and define the establishment of new preferences. Trade liberalization through tariff reduction and a narrowing of preferential margins therefore has been a fashion of the postwar era. Equality of treatment is the goal. A high level of economic activity supports the trend.

THE POSTWAR CODE of conduct for trade in the free world is summarized in the General Agreement on Tariffs and Trade (GATT). Negotiated in 1947, the document reflects conditions that existed at that time. It also follows a pattern familiar in law; that is, the statement of a general rule is followed by exceptions.

First of all, postwar hopes for an expanding trade in a peaceful world of united nations are seen in the statement of GATT principles and ideals. Freer, multilateral, nondiscriminatory trade is the broad, general objective— an objective that is consistent with only those preferential trade arrangements that contribute to expanding trade.

Exceptions to the general rule grew out of a need to recognize the pressing problems caused by wartime dislocations and disruptions of commerce among industrialized nations. Closely related were political changes and an emerging call for a higher standard of living in a growing list of newly independent countries.

In both circumstances, balance-of-payment difficulties were an important influence in (and sometimes an excuse for) shaping patterns of trade that often were discriminatory in nature. Furthermore, many onetime colonies did not wish to surrender preferential trade ties with mother countries.

Finally, it was necessary to honor trade and tariff commitments made before the Second World War if governments were to join in efforts to effect an orderly expansion of trade.

Examples are the preferential trade agreements between the United States and Cuba and between the United States and the Philippines, the British Commonwealth system of tariff preferences, and similar arrangements in the French Union. All such previously existing arrangements had to be recognized. At the same time, it was agreed that existing margins of preference were not to be increased. As a matter of fact, substantial progress has been made since 1947 in reducing and eliminating these discriminatory practices.

As the name implies, preferential agreements provide for trade among two or more trading partners on terms more favorable than those extended generally. Such arrangements, formal and informal, vary widely. Some are enduring. Some are temporary. In all, however, is an element of discrimination, which the GATT seeks to eliminate or reduce as one means of progress toward its objective. Only to the extent that such arrangements do contribute to expanded trade are they considered to be acceptable.

Some forms of preferential trade agreements are mentioned in article I of the GATT. It is a statement of the most-favored-nation principle and a cornerstone of the agreement. It is a key provision, relating to nondiscriminatory trade, whereby "any advantage, favour, privilege, or immunity granted by any contracting party to any product originating in or destined for any other country shall be accorded immediately and unconditionally to the like product originating in or destined for the territories of all other contracting parties. . . ."

THE PREFERENTIAL tariff system of the British Commonwealth goes back far. With the exception of a period dating roughly from 1860 to 1920, when foodstuffs and raw materials were granted free entry into England, various forms of special treatment for products traded between the mother country and colonies were accepted as part of the colonial system.

As it exists today, the system stems largely from the so-called Ottawa Agreements, which were negotiated at the British Imperial Economic Conference at Ottawa in 1932.

Significant reductions in margins of preference have been made in subsequent bilateral agreements, however, as well as in several postwar rounds of tariff negotiations under the GATT program of encouraging nondiscriminatory trade.

Except for the European Economic Community (EEC) as a unit, the United Kingdom is the world's largest importer of agricultural products. Britain's agricultural and trade policy has aimed at supporting domestic agriculture first and Commonwealth agriculture second.

Consistent with that policy, tariffs have been imposed to protect many farm products imported from Commonwealth sources. The usual protective rate has been about 10 percent, but it has varied with the commodity. Several important commodities, such as wheat, corn, cotton, and wool, have been dutyfree. In general, however, the preferential tariff system of the Commonwealth had much less significance in 1964 than in 1932.

Like the GATT, the Ottawa Agreements reflect the conditions under which they were negotiated. They must be set against a backdrop of worldwide depression. They were part of a spreading protectionist spirit that reached a high water mark in the States with the Tariff Act of 1930.

Even though the conference recorded a conviction that world trade would be stimulated and increased by the agreements, they were essentially restrictive. It is generally agreed also that a considerable diversion of trade from outside sources to the Commonwealth resulted from them.

That the Commonwealth preferential tariff system has lost much of its significance over the years is seen in Britain's willingness to discuss a transfer of preferences from the Commonwealth to the EEC during negotiations in 1962 for British membership in the Community. I mentioned that the system has been modified considerably by progressive tariff reductions since 1932. I foresee more. But if Britain had accepted the common external tariff of the EEC, as reportedly she was prepared to do in the 1962 negotiations, the Commonwealth preferential system would have been phased out over an appropriate transition period. A French veto in January 1963 of Britain's application to join EEC left this question unanswered.

TERRITORIES of the French Union for which preferences were in force were listed in Annex B of the GATT as follows: France, French Equatorial Africa (Treaty Basin of the Congo and other territories), French West Africa, Cameroon under French Mandate, French Somali Coast and dependencies, French Establishments in India, French Establishments in Oceania, the French Establishments in the Condominium of the New Hebrides, Guadeloupe and dependencies, French Guiana, Indo-China, Madagascar and dependencies, Morocco (French zone),

Martinique, New Caledonia and dependencies, Réunion, Saint-Pierre and Miquelon, Togo under French Mandate, and Tunisia.

The list has been altered by political and geographic changes since the GATT was negotiated in 1947; nevertheless, preferential arrangements existed in 1964 among many of them.

A further complication in the changing relationships is the development of the EEC and its Association of Oversea Territories. Of 25 oversea territories originally associated in 1958 with the Community, 19 had gained their political independence during the first 5 years of the Community's development. While the area affected was still indefinite, in 1964, however, the idea of preferential treatment prevailed, although with reduced margins of protection.

A similar situation exists with Benelux and its territories, listed in Annex C of the GATT as including the Economic Union of Belgium and Luxembourg, Belgian Congo, Ruanda-Urundi, the Netherlands, New Guinea, Surinam, the Netherlands Antilles, and the Republic of Indonesia.

These areas also are being assimilated and replaced by the evolving European Common Market. As customs unions, Benelux and the EEC constitute a special form of preferential arrangement.

PREFERENTIAL TRADE agreements of the United States have been with Cuba and the Philippines. Like the other exceptions, both predate the GATT. Adherence by the United States to the most-favored-nation principle also predates the GATT.

Nondiscrimination in trade relations has been a general policy of the United States since the founding of the Republic. Deviations from this position have been few. Even the limited exceptions represented by the Cuban and Philippine agreements were losing their significance in 1964.

Guaranteed preferences have been accorded by the United States and Cuba on each other's goods since the Treaty of Commercial Reciprocity of 1902. This arrangement was continued by the 1934 Reciprocal Trade Agreement. The preamble to the latter agreement records the mutual desire, as a matter of continuing policy, to strengthen ". . . the traditional bonds of friendship and commerce between their respective countries by maintaining as a basis for their commercial relations the granting of reciprocal preferential treatment. . . ."

The foregoing agreements were suspended pursuant to the Exclusive Supplementary (to the GATT) Agreement of 1947, negotiated when both countries became parties to the GATT. According to its provisions, preferential treatment is set forth in part II of the GATT schedules of both.

Under the supplementary agreement and subsequent modifications, United States tariff duties were reduced on sugar, molasses, tobacco, and other products imported from Cuba. In turn, Cuban duties were reduced on wheat flour and fresh and canned vegetables, among others, and the duty on lard was guaranteed against increase. It was further agreed that Cuba should permit a low duty on a minimum tariff quota of 330 million pounds of milled rice. Provision also was made for a supplemental deficit quota at low-duty rates, if required.

Early in 1962 a general embargo was imposed by the United States on imports from Cuba and exports to Cuba. Regardless of developments in the ultimate disposal of preferential arrangements, it seems to me that little or no basis exists under the Castro government for preferential treatment based on "traditional bonds of friendship and commerce." The elimination of preferences, moreover, would be consistent with the GATT objective of furthering nondiscriminatory trade. Such action would also be consistent with the multilateral trade goals of the Trade Expansion Act of 1962.

On the other hand, for different reasons, steps were taken in 1946 and again in 1955 to phase out our preferential trade arrangements with the Philippines. The islands, which were ceded by Spain to the United States in 1898, gained almost complete autonomy in 1935 and became fully independent on July 4, 1946.

At that time, an agreement was negotiated with the Philippines, under authority of the Philippine Trade Act of 1946, that provided for a duty-free exchange of goods between the United States and the Philippines during the period to July 1954.

The agreement provided also for a gradual adjustment of rates from duty-free to full-duty status during the period 1954–1973. The duty-free period was extended in 1954 to December 31, 1955.

In September 1955, the 1946 agreement was revised further by altering somewhat the schedule of adjustments in rates from duty-free to full-duty status. The revised agreement provided, however, for an end to preferential treatment of trade, on both sides, by January 1, 1974.

Thus the United States is gradually eliminating its few remaining preferential trade ties. The major remaining exceptions to the most-favored-nation principle, as provided in the Trade Expansion Act of 1962, relate to trade with any country or area dominated or controlled by communism. They are not exceptions in the sense that preferential agreements governing commercial trade relations are here considered. Indeed, viewed in this light, the GATT itself is a preferential trade agreement of sorts.

THE REMAINING preferential arrangements mentioned in article I of the general agreement relate to certain neighboring areas in Latin America and in the Middle East.

They may seem to be historical, but they have some significance as furnishing a basis for preferences that could be put into force if the circumstances warranted.

An agreement between Chile, on the one hand, and Argentina, Bolivia, and Peru, on the other hand, remained in effect in 1963. Chile, Argentina, and Peru are, however, members of the Latin American Free Trade Association (LAFTA). And as the elimination of duties between members of LAFTA is negotiated, the limited exception to article I presumably will be superseded by wider application of GATT provisions relating to free trade areas.

Bolivia was not a member of LAFTA in 1963, and its preferential agreement with Chile was still in effect.

In the Middle East, the preferences I mentioned involved the Lebano-Syrian customs union, on the one hand, and Transjordan-Palestine, on the other. Since the GATT became effective, however, substantial political and geographic changes have overtaken this arrangement.

Aside from the GATT's recognition of certain preferential trade agreements as exceptions to the most-favored-nation principle in article I, other forms of preferential treatment are recognized later in the agreement.

Article XIV, for example, contains provisions for applying quantitative restrictions, imposed for balance-of-payment reasons, in a discriminatory (or preferential) fashion. Such arrangements are, however, considered to be of a temporary nature. They also are limited to those having equivalent effect to certain restrictions on payments and transfers for current international transactions under specified articles of agreement of the International Monetary Fund.

The foregoing exceptions were most significant during the immediate postwar period of widespread balance-of-payment difficulties. Discriminatory treatment of trade for this reason has largely disappeared, along with acute balance-of-payment problems, in most industrialized countries.

Exceptions to the rule of nondiscrimination, in the case of less-developed countries, are covered in article XVIII of the GATT. Criteria established for such contracting parties relate to the necessity ". . . to safeguard its external financial position and to ensure a level of reserves adequate for the implementation of its programme of economic development. . . ." Discrimination here may relate to categories of goods, such as luxury items, as well as to source.

The remaining forms of preferential trade are covered in article XXIV of the GATT. Aside from territorial application and frontier traffic, these are customs unions and free trade areas. One element common to all is that of preferential treatment of trade between member states of integrated areas.

Contracting parties to the general agreement recognize two important points in the development of customs unions and free trade areas: That it is desirable to extend freedom of trade through a closer integration of economies and that the purpose of integration should be to facilitate trade between the constituent territories and not to hinder the trade of others.

Accordingly, the provisions of GATT do not prevent the formation of a customs union or of a free trade area if two provisions are met:

First, with respect to a customs union, the duties and other regulations of commerce imposed at the institution of the customs union shall not on the whole be higher or more restrictive than the corresponding duties and other regulations of commerce applicable in the constituent territories prior to the formation of such union (substantially similar requirements exist with respect to free trade areas).

Second, a plan and schedule is included for the formation of the customs union or free trade area within a reasonable period.

ROBERT L. GASTINEAU, *Director, Trade Policy Division, Foreign Agricultural Service, began his career in the Department of Agriculture in the Colorado field office of the Crop Reporting Service in 1935. Since that time he has served as Secretary of the Crop Reporting Board in Washington and in several major assignments at home and abroad.*

Commodity Agreements

by JOHN C. SCHOLL

AN INTERNATIONAL commodity agreement is an undertaking by a group of countries to stabilize trade, supplies, and prices of a commodity for the benefit of participating countries.

A major effort to develop such agreements was made in the early thirties, when the production and consumption of raw materials were badly out of balance. Several were developed, with varying success, mostly between producing countries. Special attention was given coffee, rubber, sugar, tea, and wheat.

Since then, the growing complexity of trade has strengthened interest in them. Under the auspices of the General Agreement on Tariffs and Trade, a study of the feasibility of a world grain arrangement was initiated by a Cereals Group in 1963, and other groups began similar studies for meat and dairy products.

THE UNITED STATES favors international discussions and concerted efforts to find solutions to commodity problems. It participated in postwar agreements involving sugar and wheat and in 1962 took the initiative in developing an international coffee agreement.

Since 1962, the United States has indicated that it is prepared to consider international commodity agreements for a number of additional products—products not already covered by agreements—under appropriate conditions.

The conditions include a prior understanding as to the objectives and purposes of the agreement and firm arrangements for assuring the flow of trade.

THE THREE BASIC types of commodity agreements are the quota agreement, the buffer stock system, and the multilateral contract.

The quota agreement allocates export quotas to exporting countries and endeavors to maintain prices within an agreed price range by adjusting the quotas to changing market demands. The sugar and coffee agreements are basically of this type.

Countries accounting for the bulk of exports should be members of a quota agreement. Otherwise, it may be undermined by nonparticipating exporters who try to get the benefits of the agreement without sharing any of the burdens. Both the coffee and sugar agreements contain provisions under which member importing countries agree to limit imports from nonmember exporting countries. Under this system, exporting countries are generally obligated to take measures to adjust production to the needs of the market.

The buffer stock system endeavors to hold prices within a specified range through the operation of a buffer stock organization, which sells when prices reach the ceiling and buys when they decline to the floor. Its success depends largely on the resources and operating capacity of the buffer stock organization, which in some instances may make discretionary purchases or sales even though prices are within the price range.

The tin agreement is an example. It can adjust the price range and use export quotas in conjunction with the buffer stock system.

No formal international buffer stock agreements involving agricultural commodities were in effect in 1963.

The multilateral contract is essentially a contract between exporting countries and importing countries to sell or buy, if required, defined quantities or percentages of purchases of the commodity at prices no higher, on the one hand, or lower, on the other hand, than laid down in the agreement. The wheat agreements of 1949, 1953, and 1956 represent one example of this type of agreement, and the 1959 and 1962 agreements represent another.

Agreements often contain elements of more than one type. Export quotas, for example, have been introduced into the tin agreement to supplement the buffer stock operations.

One feature of the three types relates to prices.

The quota agreement is sometimes referred to as a hard agreement because it aims to establish prices by controlling the supplies entering the market.

The buffer stock is considered neither hard nor soft in that prices are not directly affected until they fall or rise to levels requiring the buffer stock organization to buy or sell.

The multilateral contract is considered softer than the other types, as prices are affected only by the agreement of importing and exporting countries to buy or sell within the price range of the agreement.

COMMODITY AGREEMENTS have followed guidelines set by the Havana Charter, developed in 1947–1948 by the United Nations Economic and Social Council in Havana.

The meeting, attended by delegations from more than 50 countries, was aimed at expanding world trade and employment.

Chapter VI of the charter established much of the framework for commodity agreements subsequently developed.

The Havana Charter set forth some objectives for international commodity agreements:

To prevent or alleviate serious economic difficulties that may arise when adjustments between production and consumption cannot be effected by normal market forces alone as rapidly as circumstances warrant;

To provide a framework for measures whose purpose is an economic adjustment designed to promote the expansion of consumption or a shift of resources and manpower out of overexpanded industries into new and productive occupations;

To prevent pronounced fluctuations in the price of a primary commodity so as to achieve stability and a reasonable return to producers;

To maintain and develop the natural resources of the world and protect them from unnecessary exhaustion;

To provide for the expansion of production of a primary commodity to the benefit of both consumers and producers; and

To assure the equitable distribution of a primary commodity in short supply.

The Havana Charter also suggested that agreements should come into force when a burdensome surplus of a primary commodity has developed or is expected to develop that would cause serious hardship to producers, among whom are small producers who account for a substantial portion of the total output.

It also states that a legitimate objective of commodity agreements should be to minimize unemployment.

Its other important provisions were that agreements should be designed so as to assure the availability of supplies adequate to meet demand and consumption; provide equality of voting between importing and exporting countries; result in supplies coming from the most economic sources; and require participating countries to undertake programs of internal economic adjustment necessary to assure progress toward solution of the commodity problem involved.

THE INTERNATIONAL COMMODITY agreements take time to negotiate.

The reason is the nature and under-standable differences in views between importing and exporting countries. It may sometimes be desirable or necessary to agree on interim arrangements to take care of a commodity problem until the agreement can be negotiated.

Importing countries generally have reservations about supporting agreements to raise prices of imported commodities. They may do so, however, if broad national interests of exporting countries would benefit from such agreements and if agreements endeavor to assure stable supplies at acceptable prices with adequate protection of importers' interests should prices approach unacceptable high levels.

Exporting countries do not always strongly support agreements, either. Low-cost producers often prefer to take their chances in markets free of restraints, whereas high-cost producers generally are better able to survive under protection afforded by commodity agreements.

Negotiation of prices is a major hurdle. Importers generally favor prices that exporters consider too low, and vice versa. Industrialized importing countries, however, do recognize the desirability of stabilizing prices of primary products that are essential in the economies of developing countries.

Differences develop among exporters themselves. High-cost producers prefer higher prices. Low-cost producers do not. High-cost producers want tighter quotas than low-cost competitors. Importing countries have fewer obligations under commodity agreements than exporters, but the ones they do have may be vital to the success of an agreement.

One has to balance favorable and unfavorable elements in considering an agreement.

Some favorable ones are that it gives opportunities for discussion and ways to gather statistical and economic material. Countries can do more when they work together than when they work alone. A method of stabilizing prices of commodities important to the economic planning of producing countries is provided. A better balanced supply-demand relationship and more efficient marketing programs are possible for producing countries. Supply-management programs should provide a better balanced and more diversified agricultural economy.

On the unfavorable side: Commodity agreements introduce certain restraints and rigidities in trade and tend to freeze existing production and trade patterns, rather than permit marketing forces to operate freely. They take time. They are difficult and costly to negotiate and operate. They may give nonmembers, particularly smaller producers, an advantage. They may force compromises among producers and consumers, high-cost and low-cost producers, and others that could cause serious conflicts with internal policies and programs of members.

SEVERAL GROUPS have been established to study problems of trade.

One, for example, the International Coffee Study Group, was established in 1958, with headquarters in Washington. It helped to develop the present International Coffee Agreement.

Many study groups are under the auspices of the Food and Agriculture Organization, which has established standards for them.

In essence, the criteria specify that the commodity must be faced with difficulties that can be studied usefully in international consultation. A reasonable number of FAO countries should benefit from the work of the group and should participate. The commodity must rank high in the trade and foreign exchange earnings or expenditures of the countries. Efforts of the study group should be directed to the promotion of short-term stability and longer term equilibrium of the commodity and improve economic information. The group should try to improve the marketing structure by establishing international grades and standards and assessing production and consumption trends and national poli-

cies and programs. It should establish that existing operating and administrative methods and facilities are inadequate to solve the problem.

The United States has participated in the work of the FAO Cocoa Study Group since its formation in 1956. The group developed a draft for a cocoa agreement that was presented to a United Nations Negotiating Conference in 1963. This draft was the outgrowth of several years of discussions and studies of the world cocoa situation and reviews and revisions of several draft proposals by the study group and its executive committee. The decision to call a negotiating conference was made at the meeting of the study group in Trinidad in March of 1963. This conference was held in Geneva in the fall of 1963 but failed to negotiate an agreement largely because of the wide differences between producing and consuming countries over prices.

Extraordinarily high prices led to large increases in cocoa production in western Africa during the late fifties and early sixties. The low prices that followed encouraged producers to seek an agreement. But prices increased somewhat during the middle and latter parts of 1963.

The Draft Cocoa Agreement submitted to the Negotiating Conference, like the coffee agreement, included a supply-management provision and a commitment by importing countries to work toward the elimination of import duties, which prevent a faster rate of increase in consumption than would otherwise occur.

This is in line with the United States policy of urging the freest possible trade in tropical products.

The draft also provided that importing countries limit imports from non-member exporters. It contained special provisions for handling excess stocks accumulating during the lifetime of the agreement. In this way it contained one of the elements of the buffer stock system. One provision was designed to hold prices within an agreed range, and special treatment was provided for small producers and producers of flavor cocoa.

OTHER INTERNATIONAL conferences study commodity problems.

The International Cotton Advisory Committee (ICAC) is an example.

The United States convened an international cotton conference in 1939 to try to get a sounder relationship between world supplies and demand for cotton. An advisory committee was formed to meet periodically in Washington. After the war, talks resumed, and all exporting and importing members of the United Nations and the FAO were invited to join.

The 40 members in 1963 account for about 96 percent of the cotton production, 93 percent of consumption, and 81 percent of the imports of cotton, excluding those of mainland China.

The functions of the ICAC are to observe developments affecting cotton, collect and disseminate statistics relating to cotton, and suggest suitable measures for maintaining and developing a sound world cotton economy.

ICAC for many years has published data on cotton and supplementary data on textiles and manmade fibers. It has placed considerable emphasis on world supply and demand. It has given attention to research on the production of cotton, physical standards and scientific tests for measuring quality, extra long and short staples, prospective trends in consumption, and government regulations.

The ICAC at various times has considered whether a need exists for an international cotton agreement and what its terms might be.

Several types of agreements have been considered—whether a multilateral contract, international trade quotas, a buffer stock system, or various combinations of arrangements.

A number of arrangements take on some aspects of agreements, even though falling short of being formal commodity agreements.

The Textile Arrangement, which deals with the problems of international trade in cotton textiles, is an example.

Beginning about 1956, international trade in cotton textiles began to expand significantly. Since the late fifties, changes in trading patterns worried importing and exporting countries. The domestic textile industries of the United States and other countries were threatened by an expanding volume of imports at low prices. Encouraged by large and lucrative orders, countries relatively new to the production and export of textiles enlarged their production without taking a longer view at the problems they posed for traditional exporters.

The United States in 1961 proposed multilateral consideration of the varied and complex problems under the auspices of the General Agreement on Tariffs and Trade. The negotiations led to a Short-Term Cotton Textile Arrangement, effective for the year beginning October 1, 1961.

A Long-Term Cotton Textile Arrangement became effective October 1, 1962. It provides for the expansion of exports, especially by the relaxation of restrictions in some major markets so as to avoid disruptive effects in importing and exporting countries. Importing countries can request limitations on textiles that are being imported in such volume as to have serious effects on the domestic industry.

In view of the rapid growth and high level of cotton textile imports into the United States since 1955, the United States Government has requested restraint on a number of categories of textile products from several exporting countries. Similar action has been taken by Canada, West Germany, and Norway. Other western European countries have dealt with their textile import problems outside the arrangement.

SUGAR, a highly regulated commodity, has been subject to international agreements of one kind or another for a long time.

The Chadbourne Agreement was developed after the First World War. A typical producers' cartel, it limited production and exports. It failed when nonmember and new producing countries expanded production.

A new agreement negotiated in 1937 included most major producers and a few importers. It provided export quotas and limited stocks in exporting countries to a specified percentage of their exports. It had no specific provisions as to prices. It became inoperative with the outbreak of war.

After the war, a 5-year agreement was negotiated and became effective in 1954. It tried to hold prices within an agreed range by adjusting quotas. Another agreement in 1958 also was a quota arrangement to run through 1963.

The Sugar Council, the operating arm of the 1958 agreement, established an executive committee of representatives of seven importing and seven exporting countries. The United States has 245 of the thousand Council votes assigned importing countries. Exporting countries also have a thousand votes.

The general aims of the 1958 agreement, like the 1953 agreement, were to assure supplies to importing countries and markets for sugar to exporting countries at equitable and stable prices; facilitate steady increases in the consumption of sugar and corresponding increases in the supply of sugar; assist in maintaining purchasing power in world markets of producing countries, especially countries that depend largely on the production or export of sugar by providing adequate returns to producers and making it possible to maintain fair labor conditions and wages; and to further international cooperation in connection with world sugar problems.

The agreement aimed to keep prices within an agreed range by adjusting export quotas. It established basic export quotas for 3 years and provided for a conference in 1961 to negotiate quotas for the final 2 years of the agreement. The 1961 conference failed

to agree on quotas—mostly because agreement could not be reached for a Cuban quota—and thus the quota (and price) provision of the agreement became inoperative January 1, 1962.

The price provision provided that if prices fell below 3.25 cents a pound, the quotas in effect would be automatically reduced 2.5 percent and the Council would meet in 7 days to decide about further reductions.

If no decision was reached, a further additional reduction of 2.5 percent would be made. In no event were reductions below 90 percent of basic quotas to be made as long as the price was above 3.15 cents. If the price fell lower than that, reductions could be made to 80 percent of the basic quota.

As prices increased from those levels, quotas also were to be increased. When prices advanced to 3.75 cents, the Council would meet in 7 days to consider increasing quotas. If the Council took no action, quotas in effect were to be increased 2.5 percent. If the price exceeded 4 cents, all quotas were to be removed until the price fell below 3.9 cents. Quotas were then to be reduced again as prices declined.

Under the postwar sugar agreements, importing countries have had no import quotas but have agreed to limit imports from nonmember exporters as a group. The agreements have endeavored to cover only about a third of the world sugar exports, because two-thirds move under preferential arrangements, such as United States imports under assigned foreign country quotas and imports by the United Kingdom at negotiated prices under the Commonwealth Sugar Agreement. This sugar trade is excluded from quota provisions of the sugar agreement.

The postwar sugar agreements have been fairly successful, although the quota-adjusting machinery proved inadequate to prevent sharp increases in prices during the Korea and Suez periods. Nor did it prevent a break through the minimum in January of 1962.

Because the 1958 agreement was to expire December 31, 1963, the Sugar Council met in London in April 1963 to decide whether to request a United Nations Negotiating Conference later in 1963 to negotiate a new agreement.

An international sugar conference under the auspices of the United Nations was held in London in July 1963. A new protocol was drafted to extend the 1958 agreement through 1965 under the same terms as those prevailing in 1963. Thus the organizational and administrative machinery of the 1958 agreement, including the statistical services, was maintained.

THE FIRST International Wheat Agreement was prompted by a serious decline in wheat prices, the accumulation of stocks in exporting countries, and the adoption of certain protectionist measures in importing countries. It was developed in 1933 but ended in 1935.

Postwar wheat conferences were held in 1945, 1946, 1947, and 1948. An agreement was developed in 1948 but never became operative. Another wheat conference in January 1949 in Washington developed an agreement substantially the same as the 1948 plan. It was ratified by 38 countries and became effective August 1, 1949, for 4 years. Successive agreements of 3 years each were negotiated and became effective in 1953, 1956, 1959, and 1962. The United States has been a member of each.

Price ranges (in dollars per bushel) in each of the four postwar agreements were: 1949 agreement, minimum 1.50, declining to 1.20, and maximum 1.80; 1953 agreement, 1.55 to 2.05; 1956 agreement, 1.50 to 2.00; 1959 agreement, 1.50 to 1.90; 1962 agreement, 1.625 to 2.025.

The basic minimum and maximum prices in these agreements have been in terms of No. 1 Manitoba Northern Wheat, in bulk in store, Fort William/ Port Arthur, Canada.

Formulas are provided to determine equivalents of the basic minimum and maximum prices for other points of origin and for all classes, grades, and qualities of wheat in world trade other than No. 1, Manitoba Northern, the basic wheat.

Postwar wheat agreements have been multilateral contracts. In the 1949, 1953, and 1956 agreements, the obligation of importing countries was to buy the guaranteed quantities only if and when prices were at the minimum. The obligation of exporting countries was to furnish, if requested, their guaranteed quantities only if and when prices were at the maximum. Under this system, there is no interference with the market as long as prices fluctuate within the price range.

Under the 1959 and 1962 agreements, importers are obligated to buy a specified percentage of total commercial purchases from member exporters. They also are obligated to pay the price range for any purchases from member exporters in addition to their committed percentage. Exporters are obligated to furnish, if requested by importers, a historical annual average quantity if prices go to the maximum, before prices may go higher. The general objectives of the 1962 agreement are like those of the sugar agreement.

Under the 1962 agreement, the minimum percentages of total commercial purchases that individual importing countries pledge to purchase from member exporting countries are published in annex A of the agreement. Importers are relieved of this obligation when prices reach the maximum.

The weighted average of all importing countries' percentage obligations equals 81 percent of their historical total commercial imports. The quantities that exporters must furnish before prices exceed the maximum are computed on the basis of moving averages of commercial purchases during a recent series of years.

At the end of 1963, the exporters' primary obligation under the wheat agreements had not come into force since 1953, as prevailing world prices were below the maximum in the agreement.

The 1962 agreement is administered by the Wheat Council, whose headquarters are in London. In the Council, the United States has 290 of the thousand votes assigned to exporters. The United States is represented on the executive committee, the advisory committee on price equivalent, and all major subcommittees or working parties. Most of the exporting and importing countries are members.

COFFEE has been the subject of numerous international studies.

Surpluses and low prices and scarcity and high prices have been the pattern since 1902, when accumulated world stocks, mostly Brazilian, caused prices to plummet.

Efforts to develop control programs date from the turn of the century. Since Brazil produced the bulk of the world coffee in the early part of the century, most of the efforts were concentrated there. They were primarily valorization schemes, under which coffee was purchased at a floor price and held off the market until prices increased. This was a kind of buffer stock plan. The efforts were partly successful in preventing collapses in coffee prices, except in 1930, when surpluses placed such a strain on the plan that it collapsed.

During the period of the Second World War, the Inter-American Coffee Agreement was developed between Latin American exporters and the United States. Exporters were assigned quotas for the United States and other importing countries. It worked well as a wartime measure.

Since then, large new plantings occurred following coffee shortages and high prices in the early fifties. Surpluses and low prices followed. As surpluses continued to mount, 1-year producer agreements were developed as holding operations, or efforts to bring about some degree of price stability and orderly marketings while working toward a long-term agreement.

The first of the annual producer agreements was developed for the 1957–1958 season among Brazil, Colombia, El Salvador, Guatemala, Mexico, Costa Rica, and Nicaragua. Brazil agreed to reserve a quantity of coffee equivalent to 20 percent of its exports. Other countries were to withhold the equivalent of 10 percent to prevent sharp price declines.

In June 1958, an International Coffee Study Group was formed, with headquarters in Washington. Through its efforts, an agreement was developed for the 1958–1959 crop. Fifteen Latin American countries participated. It, too, aimed to stabilize prices through a retention method—that is, the retaining of agreed quantities of coffee from export channels by the countries.

A new coffee agreement was developed for the 1959–1960 season. African producers formally participated for the first time. It was a quota agreement, but one provision permitted countries with exportable crops under 2 million bags to adjust quotas if their production reached a specified level.

The agreement was extended with minor modifications for the 1960–1961 year. There were 28 members. It was again extended for 1961–1962, and ultimately extended until it was replaced by a long-term agreement.

The series of producer agreements that began in 1957–1958, and included most major exporting countries by 1962–1963, provided a setting for the current agreement. The producer agreements, however, were only partly successful in bringing about orderly marketings and preventing drastic declines in prices. Export prices in 1962 and the early part of 1963 were at the lowest level since 1949, but prices advanced significantly later in 1963 and in 1964 as frosts and droughts in Brazil significantly reduced production in that country. The producer agreements generally did not maintain realistic quotas. In negotiating the current agreement, it was recognized that the development and implementation of more realistic export quotas were necessary to achieve the objectives of the agreement.

The current International Coffee Agreement was negotiated at a United Nations Conference in July–August 1962. The first meeting of the Coffee Council was in London in 1963.

The agreement became operative at the beginning of the 1963–1964 coffee season on October 1, 1963. It is a quota agreement. Representatives from 58 countries took part in its development. It was the climax of several years of efforts to develop a long-term, producer-consumer agreement.

The United States had a major part in negotiating the agreement in line with one of the objectives developed at the Inter-American Economic and Social Council meeting in 1961.

World coffee exports amounted to about 2 billion dollars in 1963. The United States took half of it. Every 1-cent change in coffee export prices results in a corresponding change of about 65 million dollars a year in exchange earnings of exporting countries.

The agreement extends through September 30, 1967. For marketing purposes, the coffee year is considered to run from October 1 to September 30. Exporting and importing countries are members. There are no specific price ranges, but quotas may be adjusted when price changes warrant. Any country may withdraw on 90 days' notice.

The International Coffee Organization was established to administer the provisions of the agreement and to supervise its operation. The seat of the organization is in London. The organization functions through the International Coffee Council, its executive board, executive director, and staff. The executive director is the chief administrative officer. The United States has 400 of the thousand Council votes of importing countries. Exporters also have 1 thousand votes.

Exporting countries have basic export quotas, which may be periodically reviewed and adjusted by the Council when circumstances warrant. Export quotas were increased in early 1964 after a substantial increase in prices.

Exporting countries undertake to adjust production of coffee while the agreement remains in force to the amount needed for domestic consumption, exports, and reasonable stocks.

They also agree to place into force a policy for reducing stocks when they are on a high level.

Exporting members agree to refrain from engaging in direct and individual linked barter transactions involving the sale of coffee in traditional markets.

Importing members are obligated to restrict imports from nonmembers to a specified level if they account for more than 5 percent of world exports. They also agree to require certificates of origin from exporting members for all coffee imports to help implement the quota provisions. They and exporting members agree to provide such statistical information as the council may require.

No DOUBT increasing emphasis will be given in the future to alternative types of commodity arrangements and agreements as a way to attack problems of both short-term fluctuations and long-term instabilities in prices of primary products.

At the Punta del Este meeting in August 1961, the United States declared its intention "to find a rapid and lasting solution to the grave problems created by the excessive price fluctuations in the basic exports of Latin American countries on which their prosperity so heavily depends."

In any consideration of future arrangements and agreements, major emphasis will be given to the problem of market access. In this day and age, nations have the responsibility of going as far as possible in opening markets to each other. Much has been learned from experience. This approach will be given intensive study for a number of our agricultural commodities in the future.

JOHN C. SCHOLL *was named Director of the Sugar and Tropical Products Division, Foreign Agricultural Service, in 1962.*

Foreign Assistance Programs

by D. A. FITZGERALD

SINCE THE END of the Second World War—and during it—programs of assistance have been a major component of United States relations with the rest of the world. We called them lend-lease during the war and foreign aid since then.

The help the United States gave its Allies during the war reflected a conviction that the integrity of its democratic institutions and the freedom of its people were at stake. The assistance for relief and rehabilitation just after the war largely reflected traditional American humanitarian concern for the hungry and the suffering.

The substantial and continuing assistance programs since then, however, represent a break with the traditional American peacetime policy of avoiding foreign entanglements. But today's world has broken sharply with the past. In the main, considerations of what was believed to be in the vital national interest, in the context of this new and infinitely complex world, have dictated the scope and content of postwar United States foreign aid.

Most, but not all, Americans have supported this program in principle, although opinions have differed on its magnitude, distribution, character, and immediate purpose.

From July 1, 1945—roughly the end of the war—to June 30, 1963, gross United States foreign assistance, according to official statistics, amounted to 104 billion dollars. That is a large sum in absolute terms, but it represents only a small part of this country's total gross national product. During the immediate postwar years, that percentage ran slightly over 2; in the 5 years that ended June 30, 1963, it was slightly more than 1 percent.

Our assistance usually is divided into two major categories. One is called military assistance. The other is economic assistance.

For the 18 years to June 30, 1963, the portion called military assistance amounted to a little more than 32 billion dollars—30 percent of the total.

Economic assistance amounted to nearly 72 billion dollars, or about 70 percent. Of the latter, however, nearly 40 percent has been provided through loans so that grant economic assistance during this period amounted to 45 billion dollars—still a large amount but less than half the gross total of 104 billion dollars. Because gross foreign assistance sometimes is confused with grant economic assistance, the magnitude of the latter may be exaggerated.

Gross foreign assistance during 18 postwar years had a moderate upward trend, although there were sharp yearly variations. The low period for economic assistance was 1952–1956, when military assistance was largest.

Postwar United States foreign assistance may be divided into four periods.

DURING THE FIRST—the immediate postwar period (fiscal years 1946–1948)—United States economic assistance consisted of a variety of short-term programs designed to deal with immediate problems. Longer term problems of international economic growth and financial stability would be dealt with by new institutions whose establishment had been strongly supported by the United States—the International Bank for Reconstruction and Development and the International Monetary Fund.

Economic assistance, aside from a capital loan of 3.75 billion dollars to Great Britain in 1947, was concentrated largely on relief and rehabilitation. Contributions to the United Nations Relief and Rehabilitation Administration were 2.8 billion dollars. Appropriations to the Department of Defense for Government and Relief in Occupied Areas, primarily Germany and Japan, accounted for another 2.5 billion dollars. The Export-Import Bank made loans of nearly 2 billion dollars, primarily to Europe, and a billion dollars' worth of surplus property was sold on credit.

During this period, United States economic assistance totaled 14 billion dollars, of which Europe received 10 billion dollars.

Economic assistance to the Far East—an area extending from Burma to Korea—amounted to 2 billion dollars, of which Japan received one-half. In the Near East and southern Asia—an area extending from Greece to India—the former was the only substantial recipient.

Assistance to Latin America was modest—the continuation of the small technical assistance program started during the war, a few surplus property credits, and less than 200 million dollars of Export-Import Bank loans.

Assistance to Africa was negligible.

Regional activities accounted for about 1 billion dollars, of which the largest single item was a contribution of more than 600 million dollars to the capital of the International Bank for Reconstruction and Development.

TWO YEARS before the start of the second period—the European recovery period (1949–1951)—it became clear that the ad hoc measures of the immediate postwar years would be inadequate to enable western Europe to overcome the effects of the war.

After substantial initial improvement, both industrial and agricultural production began to level off at 80 to 90 percent of that of the immediate prewar years, primarily because of a shortage of foreign exchange to purchase replacement parts, new equipment and raw materials and fuel. Rationing was widespread. Communist influence was mounting.

General George C. Marshall, who was then Secretary of State, on June 5, 1947, in a commencement address at Harvard University outlined the critical economic situation in Europe; stressed the adverse consequences of this situation for the United States and the world generally; emphasized that it was for the Europeans themselves to take the initiative in developing a program for dealing with the crisis; and indicated that the United States was prepared to support such a program to the extent that it was practicable to do so.

Western Europe responded affirmatively to the Secretary's initiative. The Soviet Union participated in the initial European discussions but almost immediately withdrew and caused Poland and Czechoslovakia to withdraw. Thereafter, the Russians described the Marshall plan as an instrument for world domination by American imperialism.

Total United States economic assistance during the 3-year European recovery period amounted to nearly 17.5 billion dollars, of which western Europe (including Greece and Turkey) received nearly 13 billion dollars, or 75 percent.

Economic assistance to the Far East amounted to 3 billion dollars, of which Japan received more than a billion; the Philippines, about one-half billion dollars under the rehabilitation program that the United States undertook for that country; and Korea and Taiwan, about 1 billion dollars each.

Economic assistance to the Near East and southern Asia (other than Greece and Turkey) during this period amounted to about 350 million dollars, of which India received more than one-half, primarily as a 190-million-dollar wheat loan in 1951.

United States assistance to Latin America amounted to nearly 600 million dollars, consisting primarily of

Export-Import Bank loans totaling 500 million dollars.

Direct assistance to Africa continued to be negligible.

THE THIRD PERIOD—the period of military support (1952–1956)—was dominated by defense considerations. Direct military assistance accounted for more than 50 percent of all United States foreign assistance.

In the first 5 years after the war, military assistance amounted to less than a billion dollars and was provided to Turkey, Greece, and China. The victory of the Allies, it had been assumed, had assured the peace of the world for the indefinite future.

The United States and the Allies (except the Soviet Union) rapidly dismantled their war machines. But a Communist-inspired civil war persisted in Greece, and the territorial integrity of Turkey was threatened. Civil war continued in China, which the Chinese Communists took over in 1949. A blockade of Berlin by the Soviet Union began in 1948 and lasted for almost a year before the successful Allied airlift forced its discontinuance. The Communists invaded South Korea in June 1950.

Prospects for a lasting peace faded, and emphasis began shifting from postwar economic rehabilitation and recovery to building up a defensive military strength.

Military assistance reached a peak of more than 4 billion dollars—nearly two-thirds of all foreign assistance—in the fiscal year 1953 and declined gradually thereafter. It ranged from 1.5 billion dollars to 2 billion from 1959 through 1963.

Half of all military assistance has been furnished to the European countries who were members of the North Atlantic Treaty Organization, including Greece and Turkey—most of it during the 5-year military support period.

Military assistance to the Far East also reached its peak during that period but continued at almost the same level. For the entire postwar period through 1963, military assistance to the Far East constituted 25 percent of all military assistance.

Military assistance to Latin America was first provided in 1952, although through 1963 it had been small and directed primarily to the support of military forces needed for the purpose of internal security.

Military assistance for the first time was extended to India in 1963, when Communist Chinese forces invaded that country.

From the inception of military assistance through June 30, 1963, the United States has provided, among other things, about 7,500 military planes, 16 thousand tanks, 1,100 maritime vessels, and 25 thousand missiles under the Military Assistance Program. It has also given technical training in the United States to more than 175 thousand members of the armed forces of the countries to which military assistance had been provided.

It has been asserted that the rapidly growing NATO countries should have borne a larger share of the cost of the free world's defense burden; that United States military assistance to some countries supported larger and more costly defense establishments than their military missions required; that military forces in some countries were incapable of being welded into an effective fighting force; that some countries were using or threatening to use military equipment the United States furnished them against other free world neighbors; that military assistance was being provided solely or largely for doubtful foreign policy reasons.

But United States military assistance has contributed significantly to the defensive strength of the free world and thus served vital United States interests. In western Europe, it was accompanied by and in part induced a doubling between 1951 and 1962 of the defense expenditures of our NATO Allies. In the Far East, it was of great importance in helping maintain the national integrity of South Korea, Taiwan, and South Vietnam.

Economic assistance during the 5-year military support period averaged about 2.5 billion dollars a year. Much of it was labeled defense support and was directed primarily to less-developed free world countries that also were supporting large defensive forces.

During the period, economic assistance to western Europe (other than for Spain and Yugoslavia) declined from its early dominant position to relative insignificance. The emphasis shifted to the Far East, where, because of war and threats of war, more than one-third of all United States economic assistance went.

Economic assistance to the Near East and southern Asia (particularly India and Pakistan) accounted for 13 percent of all United States bilateral assistance. Assistance to Latin America also increased—to 10 percent of the total, primarily because of expansion in the volume of loans made by the Export-Import Bank.

DURING THE FOURTH PERIOD—the 7 years after 1956—yearly economic assistance more than doubled, amounting in all to about 28 billion dollars. The relative importance of military assistance declined.

Economic assistance, which was only half again as large as military assistance in 1957, was three times as large in 1963. The geographic distribution of the assistance spread farther, and the geographic emphasis again shifted.

By the end of the period, the Near East and southern Asia were receiving more than one-third of all economic assistance, and Latin America was receiving 20 percent. Assistance to Africa increased from 1 percent in fiscal 1957 to 10 percent in 1963. The increase in Latin America reflected the emphasis given in the Alliance for Progress program initiated in 1961. The increase in Africa reflected the rapid pace of the independence movement from the midfifties on.

By 1963, 87 political units (that is, independent countries or dependent territories), 33 of them in Africa, were receiving some bilateral economic assistance from the United States.

Major changes also occurred in the relative importance of the various legislative authorities from which foreign economic assistance flowed. In the immediate postwar years, a series of legislative actions were taken. Beginning with the European Recovery Program and through the military support period, foreign assistance flowed largely from successive enactments on European Recovery and subsequently Mutual Security.

From 1957 onward, funds under the Mutual Security Act (and its successor, the Foreign Assistance Act) have constituted only about one-half of all United States bilateral economic assistance. The other half has been contributed in part by sharply expanded activities of the Export-Import Bank in making development loans, which averaged 600 million dollars a year from 1957 through 1963, and from economic assistance in the form of agricultural commodities provided under the authority of the Agricultural Trade Development and Assistance Act.

During the 7 years after 1957, assistance provided in the form of agricultural commodities had a market value of more than a billion dollars a year.

THE AGRICULTURAL TRADE Development and Assistance Act of 1954 became law on July 10, 1954. It has been extended by amendment several times, most recently to December 21, 1964.

Public Law 480, as the act generally is called, originally contained three titles.

The first authorized the sale of surplus agricultural commodities for the local currencies of foreign (buying) countries.

The second authorized grants of surplus agricultural commodities for famine relief and other emergencies.

The third continued the authority of the Agricultural Adjustment Act of 1949 for the Department of Agriculture to donate surplus agricultural commodities to nonprofit voluntary agencies for use in the assistance of needy persons overseas and authorized it to barter surplus agricultural commodities for strategic materials and materials, goods, or equipment required in connection with programs of economic and military assistance.

A fourth title, subsequently added, authorized the Department of Agriculture to sell surplus agricultural commodities with payment in dollars over a period not to exceed 20 years.

The legislation at the time it was enacted was conceived primarily as a means of alleviating the increasing agricultural surpluses in the hands of the Commodity Credit Corporation.

It was argued that exports of agricultural products could be increased substantially if they were sold for local currency and that the proceeds from such sales could be used generally in lieu of dollars to develop new markets for United States agricultural commodities; purchase strategic materials and secure military equipment, materials, and facilities; finance the purchases of goods and services for other friendly countries; and pay United States obligations abroad.

All such uses of the sales proceeds were authorized in the original act.

The act also authorized grants and loans of these local currency receipts to promote multilateral trade and economic development. Through June 30, 1963, about 6 billion dollars' worth of local currency sales proceeds have been earmarked for economic development, one-third in the form of grants and the rest in the form of loans.

Another development during this period was the increasing proportion of all economic assistance provided on some sort of a repayment rather than a grant basis. Ever since the beginning of the Foreign Assistance Program after the close of the war, some portion of all assistance has been on a loan basis.

More than half of the immediate

postwar assistance and about 15 percent of the assistance during the period of European recovery were in the form of loans.

The proportion of assistance in the form of loans began to increase again with the passage of Public Law 480 and was further accelerated by the establishment in fiscal 1958 of a development loan fund as a semiautonomous component of United States foreign assistance activities.

All in all, some 27 billion dollars, more than one-third of all United States bilateral economic assistance of the United States since the end of the war, have been on a loan basis, of which just under 25 percent is repayable in local currency and the balance in dollars. Interest payments, principal repayments, and prepayments on these loans probably exceeded 10 billion dollars by June 30, 1963.

The portion of the United States bilateral assistance provided in the form of loans has been highest in Latin America (nearly 75 percent) and lowest in the Far East (about 15 percent).

Loans in the other regions have ranged from 36 to 45 percent of all assistance. Somewhat less than half the loans made in the Near East and southern Asia are repayable in dollars; 92 percent of the loans to European countries are thus repayable.

Although the proportion of United States economic assistance provided as loans increased from about 5 percent in 1954 to about 55 percent in 1963, this should not be taken as indication of a dramatic improvement in the repayment capacity of the borrowers. Per capita income for many of the less-developed regions has averaged less than 125 dollars a year—as compared to about 2,500 dollars for the United States.

Moreover, incomes in most of the less-developed regions have been growing relatively slowly. The growth of population, level of literacy, experience of the leadership, traditions, and natural resources all have a bearing on the rate of economic and social progress.

Thus the reasonableness of repayment prospects—and, in some instances, even the desirability of repayment—must be suspect.

As I NOTED, United States economic assistance in 1957–1963 was directed primarily to the less-developed areas and increased about 75 percent during the period.

American assistance to those countries constituted about 55 percent to 50 percent of the help they got from all external sources. The other major sources were Western Europe and Japan, which contributed about 40 percent; international agencies, which contributed some 4 to 6 percent; and the Sino-Soviet countries, whose contribution increased from practically nothing at the beginning of the period to about 5 percent in 1963.

Net economic assistance to the less-developed countries from all sources totaled about 4 billion dollars in 1957 and amounted to about 7 billion dollars in 1963.

The number of sources and the variety of terms often are confusing to recipient countries and are not without problems of competition and duplication among the donors. Some useful progress has been made in coordinating assistance through the Development Assistance Committee of the Organization for Economic Cooperation and Development.

THE ACTUAL PROVISION of economic assistance has ranged from the assignment of an expert for a few weeks to the construction and initial operation of a large modern industrial facility; from the delivery of a United States Treasury check to arranging for the flow and financing of hundreds of commodities.

Three general types may be noted.

The first, nonproject assistance, the provision of commodities and services, is effective and economical in situations in which the receiving country can convert a large proportion of available goods into new additions to productive facilities and in which high priority is given to meeting the internal market demand growing out of inadequate domestic production.

By far the largest part of all United States bilateral economic assistance since the war has been nonproject assistance, although the proportion has been declining. Initial emphasis in nonproject assistance is on real resources and their transfer. Nonproject assistance typically excludes designated capital projects, although all the components—cement, structural steel, machinery, and equipment—could be obtained as nonproject assistance.

Expenditures for nonproject assistance under authority of the European Recovery Act and its successor acts totaled about 21 billion dollars through June 30, 1963. About 40 percent consisted of raw materials and semifinished products—nonferrous metals, steel products, chemicals, pulp and paper, lumber, cotton, tobacco. Some of the products went into capital facilities, but most of them were processed into capital goods or consumption goods. Another 13 percent of all nonproject expenditures has been for fuel, used mostly to turn the wheels of industry.

Food—23 percent—ranked next to raw materials in magnitude of nonproject assistance.

Expenditures for machinery and vehicles—capital goods—were third but have become more important.

Most nonproject assistance enters into the commercial trade of the receiving country. The mechanics are simple. An agreement is reached between the United States and the receiving country regarding the approximate kind and amount of the individual commodities to be imported and paid for by American aid.

The United States issues a series of authorizations to the country confirming the dollar funds it is earmarking to pay for each such commodity or group of commodities and setting forth any special conditions pertaining to the purchase.

The receiving country then authorizes its importers, through the issuance of import licenses or otherwise, to place orders with the suppliers. The supplier ships the commodities ordered to the buyer in the importing country, but sends the bill of lading and other required documentation to a designated United States bank with which the importer has established a letter of credit. The bank pays the supplier and is in turn reimbursed by the United States aid agency.

Transactions thus financed are subject to selective audit by the aid agency and to other regulations designated to protect United States funds from improper disbursement.

All assistance under Public Law 480 is nonproject, and comparable mechanics are used for all of these transactions.

Nonproject assistance almost invariably generates local currency with a value approximately equivalent to the dollar cost, since the commodities obtained thereunder generally move through commercial channels. The importer is required to pay to his government the local currency equivalent of the dollar cost. A small part of this local currency is reserved for use by the United States, but most is used by the country concerned, upon approval by the United States, for a wide range of internal purposes.

These local currencies, it should be noted, do not represent an additional resource available to the country—the commodities that generated them represented the additional resource— but rather a potential claim on the resources available within the country.

As such, they may be important in influencing the utilization of such resources. Depending on the priorities, the local currencies may be used to cause a larger proportion of the country's available resources to flow into defensive strength or economic development or social progress and into public education, transportation, irrigation, agricultural expansion, industrial growth, or electric power.

From the beginning of the European Recovery Program through June 30, 1963, local currencies generated or to be generated from United States economic assistance programs totaled the equivalent of some 24 billion dollars, of which about 22 billion has been or will be used by the countries in which they were generated.

The balance of 2 billion dollars has been used or is available for use by the United States in lieu of or in addition to dollar expenditures. To the extent that the United States uses them in lieu of dollar expenditures, this represents a reduction in net United States assistance.

The largest single use, 6 billion dollars, has been for support of military establishments. About 10 percent each has been used in agriculture, including drainage and irrigation, in industry, and also in transportation and communications.

THE SECOND GENERAL TYPE of assistance — project assistance — includes capital projects and technical assistance projects.

The capital project form typically is used for large and expensive physical facilities, such as major roads, steel mills, and powerplants.

Usually the United States assistance covers all the foreign exchange costs and sometimes all or part of the local currency cost of the project and is approved only after a complete analysis is made of its technical and economic soundness. Generally the use of American supervising engineers and construction contractors is required.

Most development loan funds and most Export-Import Bank funds financing long-term development (that is, loans for 5 years and longer) are made available as project financing.

Both, however, from time to time make funds available for nonproject purposes.

Throughout the postwar period, the proportion of all assistance provided in project form has been increasing. The proportion, less than 5 percent in 1949,

increased to nearly 20 percent in 1955 and to about 50 percent in 1963.

TECHNICAL ASSISTANCE projects are also known as point 4 projects, from the fourth point in President Truman's inaugural address of 1949.

Capital projects are concerned primarily with physical resources. Technical assistance projects are concerned primarily with human resources.

Technical assistance is designed to help overcome the single most important factor limiting the growth of less-developed countries—the lack of adequately trained manpower.

The provision of organized technical assistance by the United States started during the war. The Institute of Inter-American Affairs was established in 1942 to work with Latin American Republics on technical programs in education, health, and agriculture. The activities were expanded after the war, first by the Institute as an autonomous body and later as a part of the Technical Cooperation Administration, which was established in 1950 to administer the provisions of the Act for International Development, which the Congress enacted in response to President Truman's fourth point.

Some technical assistance was carried out in the European Recovery Program, but it was relatively minor. In most of the countries participating in the European Recovery Program, inadequately trained human resources were not the limiting factor in economic recovery and growth that it is in developing countries.

The Technical Cooperation Administration, including the Institute for Inter-American Affairs and the Mutual Security Agency, were consolidated into the Foreign Operations Administration in 1954.

TECHNICAL ASSISTANCE has a number of facets.

American (or other) experts are assigned to work and help countries to increase the technical competence of their nationals in almost all fields of specialization and to improve the local institutions operating in these fields.

Additional training in the United States (or in other countries) is provided for nationals of the countries. Some demonstration equipment and supplies are furnished for training.

In the Foreign Assistance Act passed the first year of the Kennedy administration, technical assistance (point 4) activities were provided for under development grants, which also could be used to finance capital facilities needed to expand national programs of education and training.

Nearly 4,500 American citizens employed by the Agency for International Development (AID) in 1962 were point 4 technicians and experts. Most of them were stationed overseas. The entire American staff of AID numbered fewer than 7,500. AID also employed about 5 thousand foreign nationals, primarily in custodial and clerical positions.

Besides the technicians hired directly by the foreign assistance agency were 1,500 Americans who worked overseas for private organizations and firms that had contracts with the Agency for International Development.

Some were employees of firms that were building capital facilities financed by foreign assistance. Others were professors in the 65 American universities that had 107 contracts with AID to help universities in 37 countries. Technical assistance through such contracts increased during 1953–1963.

During that decade, about 72 thousand foreign nationals have been given training outside their home countries under United States economic assistance programs. Of these, some 58 thousand received at least some training in the United States. The rest received training in other countries, primarily western Europe and Japan. Of those receiving at least some training in the United States, about 2,500 were sponsored and supervised by the universities that had contracts with AID.

Training ranges all the way from brief inspection tours of a few weeks to several years of academic study. About half the participants have taken formal courses of instruction in American educational institutions, frequently with some on-the-job training. The others had some on-the-job training in Government and industry or observation tours, plus special instruction courses or lectures.

Many of the participants had attended or graduated from institutes of higher learning in their home countries, but many had only a high school education. In the United States they studied or observed industry and mining, food and agriculture, education, labor, public administration, transportation, health, public safety, community development, and housing.

About a third of the participants came from the Far East, notably Japan. Participants from Latin American countries were about 25 percent of all arrivals in the United States. The Near East and Europe accounted for about 30 percent. The number of participants from Europe has been declining; the number from the Near East and southern Asia doubled during the decade. The number from Africa increased more than tenfold.

While technical assistance activities engaged most of the agency's employees and were responsible for a major part of its work, they absorbed only a small proportion of all foreign assistance costs. Less than 5 percent of all foreign assistance in the early fifties was attributable to point 4 activities; in 1961 it was about 7.5 percent. The proportion went up to nearly 15 percent in 1962–1963.

Like any new activity in an uncharted, expanding field, technical assistance has had its problems and failures, and there is room for improvement, but its aggregate contributions have been significant.

THE THIRD GENERAL TYPE of assistance consists in the provision of cash.

A country is tendered a check in dollars. In some instances, there are no specific provisions or limitations as to its subsequent use.

In others, a deposit in a special account of local currency having an equivalent value is required.

A third type of cash transaction involves agreement by the aid-receiving country to spend the dollars thus received in the United States (or alternatively not in certain countries). It may or may not require the deposit of an equivalent amount of local currency in the special account. It may or may not require detailed United States approval of expenditures from such special account.

While for some purposes the differences in the various types of cash transactions are significant, the central fact is that in this type of assistance the first link in the chain is a financial transfer and not, initially, a transfer of resources, as is the case with project and nonproject assistance.

Assistance in the form of cash has represented a minor but slowly increasing component of United States economic assistance. In 1962 it amounted to nearly 500 million dollars, nearly 20 percent of all economic assistance that year.

Assistance in the form of cash almost always has been undertaken as an emergency measure, usually to buttress a government or in return for some concession, such as rights to a military base.

The emergency may have been a shortage of local currency in the hands of the government with which to maintain normal government services. Assistance for this purpose has come to be known as budget support.

Generally, cash grants are made only for a short period until the emergency that required them had been ameliorated or longer term arrangements made.

FUNDS for foreign economic assistance undertaken by the United States can be provided only by the Congress directly by appropriations and indirectly by congressional authoriza-

tion to borrow from the Federal Treasury or to reuse specified interest receipts and principal repayments.

The preparation and submission by the executive branch of requests to the Congress for authority and funds, consideration of the requests by the Congress, and subsequent actions by the executive branch to allocate and obligate the funds actually made available usually we call programing.

For various reasons, including the custom of the Congress to appropriate funds for obligation only in a single year, this process is an annual one.

Each programing cycle begins about 15 months before the fiscal year itself and sometimes is not completed until several years after the end of such fiscal year. Thus at any given moment, different stages of several annual programs will be active.

The programing is complicated by the requirements of the various legislative authorities under which foreign aid may be provided.

The Congress has always kept a tight reign on direct authorizations and appropriations for foreign assistance.

During the immediate postwar and early recovery years, the authorizations and appropriations for various emergency assistance programs and proposals were separately authorized and appropriated.

Beginning with the passage of the Mutual Security Act in 1952, authorizations and appropriations for the basic foreign assistance program were consolidated, originally with separate subappropriations for military and economic assistance by geographic regions, although there was authority to transfer limited amounts of funds from one subappropriation to another.

Beginning in 1955, authorizations and appropriations were reorganized, and global appropriations were made for various categories of assistance (that is, military assistance, defense support, technical cooperation, and so on).

Beginning with 1958, further flexibility was afforded the executive branch by virtue of the establishment of a contingency fund within the general foreign assistance legislation. The fund could be used without regard to almost all the other requirements of the legislation or could be shifted to any one of the other appropriation accounts at the discretion of the President.

The Foreign Assistance Act of 1961, which succeeded the Mutual Security Act of the previous administration, continued global appropriations by functional activities, such as military assistance, development grants (previously technical assistance), supporting assistance (a combination of the previous defense support and special assistance), development loan fund, and some minor accounts.

IN CONTRAST TO mutual security (now foreign assistance) legislation, that under which the Export-Import Bank operates is much more general. The Bank, an independent agency established by an act of Congress in 1934 and administered by a board of directors, of which the Secretary of State is a member, is authorized to borrow funds from the Federal Treasury and obtains almost all of its funds from this source. Its aggregate lending authority was 7 billion dollars in 1964.

Funds of the Export-Import Bank generally are not programed in any formal sense and are made available to any applicant whose requests otherwise meet the requirements of the basic legislation and of the Export-Import Bank. From time to time, the Ex-Im Bank has made loans that meet the basic requirements of the basic legislation and also contribute directly to the accomplishment of some foreign policy objective.

Foreign assistance provided under the authority of the Agricultural Trade Development and Assistance Act is financed in the first instance by the Commodity Credit Corporation from funds it borrows from Treasury. Subsequently, the Congress appropriates funds to reimburse the Commodity Credit Corporation for any losses incurred in such activities.

Foreign assistance provided in the form of surplus commodities under the authority of Public Law 480 also is not formally programed. Occasionally, when the existing monetary ceiling (which has been raised periodically since the act was first passed in 1954) was being approached, some priorities had to be established, but generally the other criteria of the legislation—those requiring precautions to safeguard usual marketings of the United States and insure that sales under this act would not unduly disrupt world prices of agricultural commodities or normal patterns of commercial trade—were controlling.

Thus systematic programing has been undertaken primarily for foreign assistance authorized by the Foreign Assistance Act of 1961 and preceding legislation. At each stage in the process, however, assumptions were made as to the possible magnitude and character of foreign assistance available from the Export Bank and under Public Law 480 and allowed for in programing aid under the basic aid legislation.

Many considerations must be taken into account in developing programs of assistance. Even for the most underdeveloped country, foreign assistance constitutes only a small fraction—perhaps 5 percent or even less—of the annual national income of the country. It rarely exceeds 25 percent of the annual investment in the country and frequently is considerably less.

Thus effective management of a country's own resources is of crucial importance. This is not an easy task under the best of circumstances and often requires the making of decisions and the taking of actions which will be unpopular and therefore difficult for an unsophisticated and perhaps insecure government to take.

Effective mobilization of internal resources requires that the government obtain sufficient revenue adequately to carry forward the activities and investments that can be undertaken only by the government—provisions for law and order, education, health services, transportation, and communications.

It requires also that the government encourage, induce, or, if necessary, require constructive use of other resources. Moreover, such mobilization needs to be undertaken with reasonable regard to human equities and social justice: Are taxes assessed with reasonable regard to capacity to pay and are they collected with reasonable efficiency and impartiality? Is the governmental fiscal and monetary management such as to build up confidence in the integrity of the currency, thus (among other things) encouraging saving and investment?

Efficient utilization of resources requires at least the establishment and periodic revision of broad but measurable key targets or goals, some means of setting priorities and of allocating resources to them, and some means of measuring progress.

Here, too, the cold rationale of economic priorities must be tempered by the warmth of social justice. The benefits of economic growth should not inure to the privileged few but be broadly spread among all classes.

Country programing and programing of United States assistance are intimately related but are not identical. The programing of assistance in the interests of economic development is facilitated if a country has begun its own economic and social planning.

The absence of a country program may be due to a variety of causes, but almost invariably one major reason is the lack of trained personnel. The United States and most other countries that provide substantial assistance to less-developed countries are prepared to respond favorably to requests for technical assistance in this field.

In the absence of a country program (and a mere shopping list of the things a country would like to have is not a program), the United States has found it useful to develop at least a broad outline of one as a guide in programing its assistance.

UNITED STATES AGRICULTURE benefits from and contributes to United States foreign assistance programs.

American farmers, along with all other Americans, benefit from the increasing number of countries that have been able to maintain or achieve political and economic independence and standards of individual freedom and justice, which are compatible with, and frequently parallel to, those of the United States.

American farmers and other Americans benefit from the increased economic strength of the free world and particularly from the economic growth of countries that have been helped along the road by United States foreign assistance. This growth has expanded the market for exports, including agricultural goods.

United States farmers have benefited from exports of their products financed directly from foreign assistance funds. Since the end of the war, foreign assistance programs have financed the export of some 20 billion dollars' worth of United States agricultural commodities.

Agricultural exports constituted as much as 50 percent of all foreign assistance during the immediate postwar years, including the first year. These exports went largely to help feed the people of western Europe and Japan. As production recovered from war and as other more normal sources of food supply became available, food exports from the United States financed by foreign assistance funds declined, while exports of industrial raw materials, machinery, and equipment increased.

At least half of the assistance provided under Public Law 480 appears likely to have resulted in higher levels of consumption than would otherwise have been the case, and somewhat less than half was translated into increased capital investment and development.

In most countries that have received bilateral assistance from the United States, and certainly all the developing countries, the major proportion of its annual production is from agriculture, and an even larger proportion of the population lives on the land.

As a consequence, economic growth is possible only if there is growth in the agricultural sector; growth to help feed an expanding population; growth to help feed an even more rapidly expanding community of nonagricultural consumers; growth to help provide a market for the production of the rest of the economy.

THE CONTRIBUTION OF AGRICULTURE to this growth has been a major component of United States foreign assistance programs. Since the end of the war, hundreds of American agricultural technicians have worked overseas to help improve the productive efficiency of agriculture. They have been specialists in agricultural production, extension, research, marketing, and agricultural credit.

Similarly, all elements of the United States agricultural community—the Department of Agriculture, the land-grant colleges, the extension services, agricultural industries, the farmers themselves—have helped to provide training to thousands of agriculturalists from other countries.

The policy has been to concentrate assistance in agricultural enterprises whose output went largely, if not exclusively, to improving domestic consumption levels and to avoid direct support of enterprises in which world production was already in excess of world demand.

THERE IS A TENDENCY, I believe, to assume that the immediate purpose of all United States economic and technical assistance is to stimulate and help support economic and social development on the assumption that economic development in itself will result in the emergence of a community of free, peace-loving nations, democratically oriented, with interests and attitudes compatible with ours.

The assumption is not necessarily valid. History shows a number of instances in which economic growth is associated with strong international aggressiveness. What can surely be said, however, is that economic growth is a necessary precondition or concomitant to such emergence, and in its absence probabilities are enormously increased that there will be, sooner or later, a violent swing to the radical right or radical left that would be incompatible with our interests.

Also rather widespread is the assumption that foreign economic assistance and economic development are synonymous—that all economic assistance is provided for the purpose of stimulating (and should result in) an economic development.

In fact, the immediate purpose of economic assistance frequently has not been economic development per se.

In some instances, it has been made available for the immediate purpose of helping to support military establishments larger than the country could support with its own resources.

In others, the immediate purpose was to deal with what has come to be called short-term foreign political exigencies—providing budget support for a friendly faltering government or to meet a balance-of-payment crisis, or even as a concrete manifestation of our support for a friendly country which was being subjected to pressure from countries whose international policies and attitudes were considered inimicable to the United States.

Historians a generation from now will be able to make a much more accurate appraisal of the real contributions of the United States postwar foreign assistance. Nevertheless, it seems clear that such assistance has contributed mightily to the ultimate objective, United States security.

The ad hoc measures of the immediate postwar years dealt effectively with certain pressing problems of the day—the hunger and disease that followed in the wake of the war, the millions of refugees, the urgent need for food and raw materials. The overwhelming consensus is that the European Recovery Program was an outstanding success—witness the booming economies of western Europe.

The evidence for the military support period seems nearly as convincing. For example, it seemed certain that a number of countries, including Greece, South Korea, and Taiwan, could not possibly have maintained their national independence without United States military and economic assistance.

The evidence of the years during which United States foreign assistance has been directed largely to the less-developed countries is not yet in. Economic and social and political development being a slow process at best, even a decade of experience affords a wholly inadequate basis for final judgment, but even here the preliminary evidence, on the whole, is affirmative.

Economic growth in a substantial number of countries has been accelerated. A few of them have reached the point where their future growth can be based on their own resources plus recourse to normal sources of external capital—the international lending agencies and the international capital markets of the world.

Day-to-day administration of foreign assistance programs has been adequate at least and, in many instances, outstanding. There is, however, always room for improvement. Immediate objectives need to be more clearly defined, and, in my opinion, ultimate interests will be better promoted if foreign economic assistance is concentrated more on long-time economic development and less on short-time political exigencies.

D. A. FITZGERALD *joined the Brookings Institution in 1962 as a member of the senior staff to make a study of foreign aid. Previously he was Deputy Director for Operations, International Cooperation Administration. From 1946 to 1948 he served as Secretary General of the postwar International Emergency Food Council on loan from the Department of Agriculture, where he held various posts beginning in 1935.*

International Financial Services

by WARRICK E. ELROD, Jr.

SINCE THE END of the Second World War, a number of financial services have been expanded to help countries overcome difficulties in their balance of payments, encourage stability in international trade, and accelerate economic development.

The methods of aiding countries to achieve those goals have included the establishment of programs that permitted the United States to distribute surplus agricultural commodities in a way that, in effect, has provided development capital to developing countries. Also included are international and regional banking institutions that have provided loans for a wide variety of projects and programs whose interest rates and maturities have varied widely.

The capstone of the international financial system is the International Monetary Fund (IMF), to which 103 nations have subscribed more than 15 billion dollars, approximately one-quarter of which is in gold.

PUBLIC LAW 480 is of particular interest. Its title I authorizes the United States to sell surplus agricultural commodities against payment in local currencies. Its title IV permits the United States to provide long-term credit for dollar purchases of the surplus commodities to governments or the private trade. In addition, the

United States provides agricultural surpluses for famine relief and related programs (title II) and for nonprofit voluntary agencies and intergovernmental organizations as well as for barter contracts (title III). Titles II and III have little to do with financial servicing of the recipients; titles I and IV do, in effect, offer a type of financial service.

Forty-three percent of the local currency receipts under title I by 1964 had been lent for long terms to the recipient countries to help them finance their economic development as mutually agreed between the country and the United States.

An additional amount (33 percent) had been allocated to grants, common defense projects, and Cooley loans, which provide local capital for private United States firms or their affiliates for development in the countries.

The remainder (24 percent) of the currency receipts had been reserved for United States uses, mainly to defray various diplomatic and military expenses.

Since the beginning of Public Law 480 in 1954 through December 31, 1963, the equivalent of slightly more than 9.5 billion dollars in foreign currencies (at export market value) had been generated in 47 countries. More than 2 billion dollars had been generated in India and more than 1 billion dollars in Pakistan. In 1963, local currency uses totaled 1.22 billion dollars, of which 746 million dollars were allocated for economic development loans to foreign governments. Another 211 million dollars went for United States uses.

Title IV agreements reached a cumulative value of 176 million dollars (at export market value) between 1961 and December 31, 1963.

United States agricultural exports under all titles (I–IV) of Public Law 480 had accounted for 28 percent of total United States agricultural exports during the first 9 years of the operations under the law.

Of the total amount of local curren-cies available from title I agreements, more than 4 billion dollars as of 1964 were made available for loans in almost all fields of economic and social activity: Food and agriculture, industry and mining, transportation, health and sanitation, education, and community development. An additional 2 billion dollars were provided as grants to promote economic development and trade in the recipient countries.

THE EFFECT of United States agricultural commodity assistance in recipient countries may be deflationary, inflationary, or neutral, depending on the means of marshaling and expending the funds required in financing economic development and the time periods involved.

A title I sales program is likely to be the most beneficial to the economic development of the recipient country and to the payments position of the United States in countries that purchase surplus agricultural commodities and where United States Government expenditures are relatively small, earnings of convertible exchange are expected to be meager, and payment for agricultural commodities with local currency can be made without adverse effects on the domestic monetary system.

If United States Government expenditures in the recipient country are of such magnitude as to provide the recipient country with a net dollar gain after deferred payment for the commodities, it becomes advisable from the point of view of the country to enter into a sales agreement under title IV.

In countries where the United States Government has an exceptionally large military and economic assistance commitment, foreign currencies acquired through the sale of surplus agricultural commodities under title I can be utilized almost immediately in financing part of these operations. This utilization of foreign currency without the need to purchase with dollars is beneficial to the United States balance of payments.

Under a title IV program, the annual repayment of dollars may be so small as to be less beneficial to the United States balance of payments than foreign currency acquired through a title I program. A large downpayment and shorter repayment schedules may permit title IV agreements to give greater short-run benefit to the United States balance of payments, but such terms are not likely to be accepted by recipient countries, and title I most likely will continue to be of greater benefit to the United States when its needs for local currencies are substantial.

THE AGENCY FOR INTERNATIONAL DEVELOPMENT (AID) has responsibility for carrying out nonmilitary United States foreign assistance programs and for general direction of all assistance programs under the Foreign Assistance Act of 1961.

AID was created on November 4, 1961, as an agency within the Department of State. It combined the previous International Cooperation Administration and the Development Loan Fund.

The programs AID administers are in four major categories: Development grants and long-term dollar loans (including those financed through title I of Public Law 480); investment guarantees under which private investors are offered protection against loss from specified political actions by foreign governments and partial protection from all risks; investment surveys; and Public Law 480.

AID administers the loans and grants of local currency generated by title I of Public Law 480. AID also administers title II, and directs United States contributions to the Alliance for Progress and to other international organizations.

From 1945 through 1962, AID and its predecessor agencies had committed 33.57 billion dollars for economic assistance. Of this total, 4 percent—

1.44 billion dollars—was devoted to agriculture; that is, economic assistance that directly aided the agriculture of the recipient country.

THE INTERNATIONAL BANK for Reconstruction and Development—the World Bank—was founded, along with the International Monetary Fund, at the Economic Conference held at Bretton Woods in July 1944 and began operations in June 1946.

Its purpose is to assist in the reconstruction and development of the economies of its member countries by facilitating the investment of capital for productive purposes.

Within a few years after the Bank came into operation, the reconstruction part of its activities was completed, and the Bank now is concerned mostly with the capital needs of developing countries. The Bank had 102 members, with subscriptions totaling more than 21 billion dollars, in 1964.

The resources available for lending by the Bank are derived from paid-in capital subscriptions by members, funds borrowed by the Bank in private financial markets, repayment of loans, and other sources.

The Bank makes long-term loans for specific projects directly to member governments and to public or private entities in the member countries. In the cases of loans made other than to the government itself, a guarantee by the government is required. The Bank's interest rate at the end of 1963 was 5.5 percent.

At the end of 1963, the Bank had made 371 loans totaling 7.6 billion dollars in 70 countries or territories. At the beginning, the Bank's authorized capital was 10 billion dollars, but in 1959 it was increased to 21 billion dollars. The United States Government has furnished nearly 31 percent of that amount.

As of December 31, 1963, the Bank had made more than 40 loans, totaling about 220 million dollars, for agricultural purposes. The loans were used for general agricultural development, irrigation and land reclamation projects, construction of storage facilities, forestry projects, the purchase and improvement of livestock, and farm mechanization. In addition, there were 21 multipurpose loans, equaling 314.1 million dollars, of which some part has been used to develop agriculture.

THE INTERNATIONAL DEVELOPMENT ASSOCIATION (IDA) began operations in November 1960. As of December 31, 1963, there were 90 members, with subscriptions totaling just under 1 billion dollars in various currencies. It is an affiliate of the World Bank, but it is an independent legal entity with financial resources separate from those of the Bank. IDA makes credits available on terms less burdensome than conventional loans to a country's balance of payments.

As of June 30, 1963, IDA had made 47 development credits amounting to the equivalent of 490 million dollars. Of these, 12 were agricultural credits aggregating 117 million dollars. Because the initial resources of convertible funds available to IDA had been committed fully by 1964, additional resources totaling 750 million dollars in freely usable funds were obtained early in 1964 from 17 governments whose currencies are freely convertible.

THE INTERNATIONAL FINANCE CORPORATION (IFC), a lesser known affiliate of the World Bank, is an investment institution established by the member governments to assist in the economic development of the less-developed members.

Investments are made in "productive private enterprise." They are not guaranteed by governments, and the rates of interest are higher than those of the World Bank.

IFC provides financing through subscriptions to capital stock, through a combination of stock subscriptions and loans, or through loans with equity or other special features.

The IFC makes its investments in association with private investors but does not compete with private capital. Its participation has been limited to less than 50 percent of the capital cost of an enterprise, and investments usually have been moderate, averaging slightly more than 1.25 million dollars by 1964. The IFC aids development banks with equity investments, loans, and technical aid.

Its investments have been primarily in industrial enterprises; it does not invest in public utilities, real estate development, or in land reclamation.

The IFC membership at the end of 1963 was made up of 75 countries, which provided the 100 million dollars of authorized capital. Membership is open to all governments that are members of the World Bank.

THE INTER-AMERICAN DEVELOPMENT BANK grew out of the meeting in 1958 of the Committee of Twenty-one, composed of representatives of Latin America and the United States, one of whose task groups developed the idea of such a bank. The Punta del Este Conference, almost 3 years later, led to the establishment of the Bank.

Another task group developed the first proposals for a solution to the problem of serious imbalances in trade and payments. The proposals sought to offset volatile changes in export earnings from primary products that often adversely affect the terms of trade of the developing countries.

The proposals ultimately led to the IMF arrangement for compensatory financing of such losses in export receipts, an arrangement permitting a nation to draw a special tranche of 25 percent of its IMF quota.

The Inter-American Development Bank was established to finance Latin American economic development and to provide technical assistance in the preparation of development plans and projects. The agreement establishing the Bank entered into effect on December 30, 1959, and the first loan was approved on February 3, 1961.

All member countries of the Organization of American States are members of the Bank. The largest contributor to it, the United States, has provided 40 percent of capital resources.

Not only may the Bank lend to Latin American governments; it has authority also to make direct loans to private enterprise without requiring a guarantee from the government involved.

It is also responsible for promoting investments of public capital for the purpose of economic development and for encouraging private investment in developing projects.

The Bank's lending volume, including loans under the Social Progress Trust Fund, totaled 800,219,000 dollars on December 31, 1963. This volume represented approximately 40 percent of the total cost of the projects that the Bank was helping to finance. Loans for agricultural development constituted about 20 percent of the entire lending volume.

The loan operations of the Bank are conducted through three separate "windows."

One "window" is for ordinary capital resources. Under the terms of the agreement establishing the Bank, the subscribed ordinary capital resources amounted to 813 million dollars. Of this sum, slightly less than half was paid-in capital. The balance was callable capital. The callable capital in effect has constituted a guarantee for the securities that the Bank has issued.

In 1962, the Bank sold nearly 100 million dollars in bonds in financial markets in order to increase its ordinary capital resources. Total lending volume reached 328.4 million dollars at the end of 1963; 18 percent of it assisted agricultural ventures, such as citrus fruit processing, livestock improvement, and irrigation.

Loans from the fund for special operations, the second "window," have been extended on terms and conditions appropriate for dealing with special circumstances arising in specific countries or with respect to specific projects. In the operations of the fund, the financial liability of the Bank has

been limited to the resources and reserves of the fund, and its financial resources have been separate from ordinary capital resources. The fund's lending volume was 104.2 million dollars by the end of 1963. Agricultural development projects and technical assistance accounted for approximately 45 percent of the total.

The third "window" is the Social Progress Trust Fund. At the Bogotá Conference in 1960, the United States declared its intention to establish a special Inter-American Fund for Social Development and proposed that the Inter-American Development Bank administer the fund. In June 1961, 394 million dollars were assigned by the United States to the Social Progress Trust Fund, as part of a 500-million-dollar program under the Alliance for Progress.

As administrator of the trust fund, the Bank has granted loans for projects or programs in four fields: Land settlement and improved land use, housing for low-income groups, community water supply and sanitation facilities, and advanced education and training. The first category accounted for 18 percent of the trust fund's lending volume of 367.6 million dollars on December 31, 1963.

In the field of technical assistance, the role of the Bank has grown in importance, particularly through professional training in connection with development banks, agricultural credit, and land reform. The value of technical assistance in 1963 reached 14 million dollars.

THE INTERNATIONAL MONETARY FUND, like the World Bank, was the creation of the Bretton Woods Conference of 1944.

From an original membership of 32 countries, the Fund has grown until in 1964 its 103 members provided through their subscriptions more than 15 billion dollars of currency resources, upon which members may draw in amounts equal to 200 percent of their respective quotas. An additional drawing right, established in mid-1963, the so-called compensatory financing drawing, in effect increased this percentage to 225.

Members may draw upon the Fund's reserves to meet their foreign exchange obligations during periods of deficits in their balance of payments.

Use of the Fund's resources has been linked to reduced exchange restrictions and discrimination and to establishment of convertibility of currencies.

Each Fund member has undertaken to establish and maintain an agreed par value (in terms of the dollar and thus of gold) for its currency, to contain fluctuations in the exchange rate of its currency within three-fourths of 1 percent either side of the established par, and to consult the Fund on any change of as much as 10 percent in the initial par value.

The Fund has been also a major forum for the consideration of foreign exchange problems of its members. If a member has needed to draw upon the Fund, the Fund has considered the request in the light of the member's fiscal and monetary policies, and the consistency of its operations with Fund principles.

Drawings are made in tranches, a tranche being 25 percent of the respective member's quota. Drawings on successively higher tranches are subject to increasingly less easy approval and more stringent conditions. Only the so-called gold tranche and the special compensatory financing tranche are almost automatic. If successive drawings bring a member's total drawings near 100 percent of its quota, a member will likely be required to accept a stabilization program on which the member and the Fund agree.

A drawing is a foreign exchange transaction. The member who makes the drawing pays the Fund an amount of its own currency equivalent, at the par value agreed with the Fund, to the amount of currency it wishes to draw. The member is expected to "repurchase" its own currency from the Fund within 3 to 5 years, with a payment

of gold or dollars or some other currency acceptable to the Fund.

A member may use the currencies which it draws in a flexible way to relieve its payments difficulties. The Fund's assets are not, however, intended to be used to finance a large or continuing outflow of capital or for programs of economic development.

In serious foreign exchange crises, the Fund has represented the single largest source of quickly available credit. Members may establish standby arrangements, such arrangements permitting members to draw upon what are in effect lines of credit.

The Fund's operations were modest during the first 10 years of its existence, but following the Suez crisis of 1956, a rapid increase in the use of its resources occurred. In one year, beginning in December 1956, the Fund's transactions increased by the equivalent of 1 billion dollars. As a result of the demands upon the Fund, its resources were increased from 9.2 billion dollars in 1958 to 14.4 billion dollars at the end of 1960.

Early in 1963 the Fund created a facility designed to broaden its balance-of-payment support of member countries, particularly those exporting the primary products, which have experienced temporary declines in their export earnings arising out of circumstances beyond their control.

In the past, the Fund has financed deficits resulting from declines in export earnings, and member countries have made frequent drawings for such a purpose.

The compensatory financing facility, which normally does not exceed 25 percent of a member's quota, is available to members, provided that the Fund is satisfied that the earnings deficit is of a short-term character largely beyond the member country's control and also that the member country will cooperate with the Fund in an effort to find, where required, appropriate solutions to its balance-of-payment difficulties.

The provision of such financing

permits the drawing member to maintain its imports and continue its economic development. At the same time, the level of worldwide trade is maintained as the drawing country continues to import capital goods which it would likely have to forego or finance at the cost of increased external indebtedness if compensatory financing were not available.

In June 1963, Brazil made the first "compensatory financing" drawing upon the Fund for an amount of 60 million dollars. The United Arab Republic made a drawing of 16 million dollars in October 1963. Thus automatic compensatory drawing rights additional to normal Fund facilities have been made available as a further aid to developing countries. An idea first offered in 1958 has become reality.

ALL IN ALL, then, I think that recurring discussions in international financial circles concerning the reformation of the world's monetary structure to improve the mechanisms to achieve the three goals I mentioned at the beginning and decisions to analyze proposals for reformation taken at annual meetings of the International Monetary Fund and the International Bank for Reconstruction and Development should not obscure the commendable strides toward the coordination, expansion, and improvement of international financial services.

Those three goals are:

First, to help countries overcome difficulties in balance of payments.

Second, to encourage stability in international trade.

Third, to hasten economic development.

WARRICK E. ELROD, JR., *became Chief of the International Monetary Branch of the Economic Research Service in 1962. He formerly was an economist in the Division of International Finance of the Board of Governors of the Federal Reserve System and for 10 years before that a Foreign Service officer with duty in Europe and the Department of State.*

Public Programs To Share Food

by HARRY W. HENDERSON

A SOBERING DILEMMA of our time is hunger in some countries and a surplus of food in others. It will not be solved soon.

Shortages of proteins, fats, and calories in many countries trace to low levels of food production—a result, in turn, of insufficient land, unfavorable climate, inadequate agricultural inputs, and a lack of technical skills; to rapid rates of population growths which keep per capita food supplies low; and to a lack of money or goods to exchange for substantial quantities of commercially imported food.

Sharp contrasts between food-deficit and food-surplus countries are cause for concern. The strength of the free world depends on the political stability and economic vitality of each free world member. The less-developed countries have gained political independence or are in the process of gaining it. They feel that independence should bring rapidly improved health, education, housing, and diets. Above all, they desire to improve their substandard diets. Unless they are able to raise their nutritional levels substantially—through their own efforts or through assistance—political unrest and unsatisfactory rates of economic growth could well result.

The United States has adopted the policy that urgent needs of the less-developed countries for food must be met with prompt aid until they can produce their own supplies or buy them commercially.

The primary aim is to combat hunger. A byproduct is a strengthening of our economy by building future markets and furthering foreign policy.

OUR SHIPMENTS of food had an export value of 12.8 billion dollars in 1955–1963—equivalent to about 33 percent of total agricultural exports over the period. The food went to more than 130 countries and territories, whose population was 1.7 billion.

In 9 years of operations, we shipped mainly to less-developed countries about 2.9 billion bushels of wheat as wheat and flour—a volume equal to two and one-half average United States wheat harvests. We shipped 90 million bags of milled rice, equivalent to two crops. We shipped 930 million bushels of feed grains, 6.4 billion pounds of fats and oils, 4.8 billion pounds of nonfat dry milk, and a number of other commodities.

Our food-sharing operations go under the overall name of "Food for Peace." The bulk of the food shipped under this program during 1955–1963—10.7 billion dollars' worth—represents exports under Public Law 480, the Agricultural Trade Development and Assistance Act of 1954. About 2.1 billion dollars' worth was moved, mainly in earlier years of the program, under the Act for International Development and the Mutual Security Acts.

Each of the four titles of Public Law 480 authorizes a distinct type of operation.

One allows us to sell our surplus farm products to less-developed countries and accept payment in foreign currencies, instead of dollars. We have sold 6.7 billion dollars' worth of farm products at export value under this authority. The largest recipients have been India, Pakistan, Yugoslavia, Spain, Poland, Turkey, Brazil, Korea, and Indonesia.

Another title authorizes food aid for disaster relief—such as is needed after earthquakes, droughts, and floods—and in other assistance measures, such as use of food in economic development, refugee relief, and child feeding programs. These donations amounted to about 1 billion dollars in 1955–1963.

Donations of farm products may be made to American voluntary agencies and international organizations that carry on foreign relief activities among schools, people in various types of institutions, family groups, and refugees. About 1.4 billion dollars' worth of foods have been used to combat hunger under this title.

We have shipped 75 million dollars' worth of commodities under title IV, which authorizes long-term supply arrangements and credit up to 20 years to individuals, commercial firms, agricultural cooperatives, or other organizations of the United States operating abroad as well as to friendly foreign countries.

OUR FOOD generally performs its vital role unostentatiously.

United States food purchased by a country with its own currency or obtained through donations or barter or acquired under long-term supply and credit arrangements is handled within the country in much the same way as though it had been purchased with dollars. Once it is received by the importing country, it generally is sold by the government to the commercial food industry for distribution through normal trade channels.

The routine way in which our food is handled does not diminish in the slightest the importance of its role in adding to supplies already available.

The United States has contributed to the feeding of 40 million children in school lunch programs in some 90 countries, largely through the efforts of American voluntary agencies and the Agency for International Development.

Foreign countries also have established school lunch programs of their own. Among the benefits to the less-developed countries are greatly reduced pupil absenteeism, improved pupil health, and stepped-up rates of learning.

The United States functions somewhat like an international rescue squad in supplying food aid to countries hit by disasters.

In 1963, for example, we rushed food to Yugoslavia when thousands of people were left homeless by earthquakes. We sent Food for Peace commodities by airplane to Haiti, Martinique, and other Caribbean countries within hours after Hurricane Flora struck in September 1963.

We sent food to the Republic of the Congo when prolonged internal conflict resulted in malnutrition and high infant mortality. We sent feed grains to Costa Rica when volcanic eruptions destroyed grazing land.

OUR FOOD is promoting economic growth.

The United States is lending or granting back to needy foreign countries a substantial part of the local currencies generated when we sell them farm products under Public Law 480. The funds are used for irrigation, reclamation, and reforestation projects; improvement of railroads, highways, and bridges; and construction of power facilities, hospitals, and schools.

The food also promotes economic growth by helping to control inflation of food prices. Food prices usually rise when employment on development projects creates purchasing power, which in turn lifts the demand for food. As food prices rise in response to demand, workers insist that their wages be increased. That means that fewer public funds are available for development projects. The inflationary spiral is checked to some extent when United States food is imported in amounts large enough to keep pace with increased demand.

We add to United States farmers' incomes when we ship about 1.5 billion dollars' worth of products annually to needy foreign countries. Our Food for Peace exports are tending to strengthen farmers' incomes indirectly by reducing supply pressures on domestic prices. Food for Peace is stimulating business for railroads, seaports, shipping lines, and other enterprises related to agriculture and so is creating jobs for many American workers.

Food for Peace is helping to reduce some Government outlays. When we ship our food and fiber abroad, we cut storage costs. Also, we use some of the foreign currencies generated by Public Law 480 sales abroad to pay some of our oversea bills. In 1963, we used the equivalent of 250 million dollars in foreign currencies to pay bills for military activities, Embassy supplies and services, education exchange programs, and market development operations.

Food for Peace, in promoting economic growth, is creating new markets for our farm products. In several countries in which our food has been an important component of economic aid, our dollar sales have increased.

Spain, which once obtained large quantities of United States farm products under Public Law 480, in 1963 had become a market for 128 million dollars' worth of our farm products. Spain is now the largest cash buyer of United States soybean oil.

Israel, which also has been a big recipient of our Public Law 480 commodities, is becoming a cash purchaser. Greece and Taiwan have been increasing their cash purchases.

Food for Peace is helping us increase the sale of American farm products all over the world. More than 40 producers and trade groups have joined with the United States Government in carrying on jointly financed market development activities in some 50 countries. The Government's share of program costs is financed largely with foreign currencies received from farm product sales under Public Law 480. These funds are used by the Government and cooperating groups to exhibit United States farm products at international trade fairs and other events.

We are strengthening with our food the will and the capacity of free world peoples to stay free.

Communist propagandists have charged that Food for Peace is a "surplus disposal" program. This accusation fails to recognize that we have shared scarce supplies as well as surpluses. On several occasions, especially at the end of two major wars, we shared our food with the hungry even when we ourselves were getting close to the bottom of the food barrel and had to conserve food so as to make it available for relief use abroad.

We are giving uncommitted countries an opportunity to compare the relative efficiencies of free and regimented agricultures. We are showing predominantly agricultural countries that farmers living under a free democratic system can outproduce collectivized farmworkers fivefold.

THE QUESTION is asked, "Why don't we ship all of our surplus food to the hungry people overseas instead of limiting Food for Peace exports to about 1.5 billion dollars' worth a year?"

Part of the answer is that we are shipping as much as the importing countries are able to take—or want to take. The limitations are largely on the taking side, not the giving side.

Part of the answer is that Food for Peace exports, like all agricultural exports, must be handled in an orderly, responsible manner. Otherwise, there would be waste and undue disruption of markets in both the exporting and receiving countries.

Many underdeveloped countries lack the transportation, storage, and distribution facilities needed to reach hungry people with imported foods. Also nonexistent in many countries are organizations, such as our church groups and civic clubs, willing or able to handle large-scale distribution. It is said that in some less-developed countries it is easier to sell food than to give it away, because commercial distribution systems exist, and large-

scale noncommercial channels do not exist.

Age-old dietary habits are a limiting factor. In some countries people are not eager to use some of the foods the United States has in greatest abundance. People who have always eaten rice do not readily turn to corn or sorghum grain or even wheat. Often they must be taught how to prepare foods unfamiliar to them.

We must safeguard the commercial trade of the United States and of nations friendly to us. Nothing is gained by giving food to a nation that can afford to pay for it. We want to furnish supplies that are in addition to what would normally move through commercial trade channels. If Food for Peace merely replaces commercial sales that would otherwise be made, it is not fulfilling its proper function.

We must also be careful not to disturb other countries' agricultural economies unduly. Agriculture is the leading occupation in most of the less-developed countries—and their farmers, like ours, must market their crops at fair prices. If Food for Peace supplies cause any material weakening of agricultural prices, farmers protest to their governments. Even in countries where populations have too little to eat, political pressure helps to regulate the volume of food, donated or bought, that may be imported.

THE LESS-DEVELOPED countries want our food aid when it is necessary, but they want to stand on their own feet as much as possible. More than food, they want technical assistance that will enable them to produce more of their own food, and that has been offered them.

The United States has been gratified to see other free world countries join in the task of providing food aid. Canada and Australia, for example, are making food available to countries in southeastern Asia. France has given substantial assistance, including food assistance, to some countries in Africa. The United States feels that no one nation, no matter how powerful, by itself can win the war against hunger. The United States has strongly supported the World Food Program, administered jointly by the Food and Agriculture Organization and the United Nations, which makes it possible to supplement food aid with a multilateral approach as well as the bilateral efforts being carried on by the United States and other countries.

The World Food Program, relatively small in terms of total international efforts, calls for contributions of a hundred million dollars in the form of commodities, services, and cash over a 3-year period. The United States has pledged 50 million dollars under authority of title II of Public Law 480, of which 40 million dollars represents commodities. Some 60 other countries have pledged assistance. Though relatively small, the program gives all nations an opportunity to take part in the food aid effort.

The imbalance of food supplies will continue—perhaps even be accentuated by more rapid gains in technology and production rates in the industrialized nations than in the less-developed countries. As long as the sharp contrasts between the food-surplus and the food-deficit countries exist, food aid programs will be needed. This should not disturb us.

Food aid for needy countries will have cumulative effects. Improved diets for children and adolescents now will mean stronger bodies later on. The economic growth that food is promoting now will furnish the basis for further growth.

HARRY W. HENDERSON *in 1962 became Assistant Director, International Programs, Foreign Market Information Division, Foreign Agricultural Service. He joined the Department of Agriculture in 1934 as junior agricultural economist, Crop Reporting Board, and has served in the former Agricultural Marketing Service, War Food Administration, Production and Marketing Administration, and Agricultural Stabilization and Conservation Service.*

Sharing Our Knowledge

by CANNON C. HEARNE,
   WILLIAM E. HARVEY, and
   ANDREW J. NICHOLS

JAPAN, to encourage migration to the island of Hokkaido, decided in the 1870's to establish a new agricultural college at Sapporo.

Word had reached Japan about the success of the land-grant colleges in the United States, and an American, William Smith Clark, then president of the Massachusetts Agricultural College (now a part of the University of Massachusetts), was invited to become first president of the new college.

He declined the position but agreed to head a mission of three to help get the institution started. He was acting president of Sapporo Agricultural College for 8 months and established a liberal school of applied science.

At the school the Japanese have learned and used methods of agriculture and extension to the extent that Hokkaido now produces an excess of food for shipment to other parts of Japan after taking care of the needs of the island population, which has increased in 82 years from 50 thousand to 5 million.

From it have come two crops of importance to the United States. William Penn Brooks, the fourth of 15 Massachusetts professors to be assigned to Sapporo Agricultural College, brought soybeans and Japanese millet back with him upon his return in 1889.

Dr. Clark left with the students in the Sapporo Agricultural College (which has become a part of the University of Hokkaido) a slogan that is now a byword in Japan, for every child learns about William Smith Clark in the fifth grade. His admonition, "Boys Be Ambitious," has inspired every generation of students.

His work in Hokkaido is an example of international training by American technicians and scientists. He received his doctor's degree from the University of Gottingen in Germany—an illustration of the goal of many Americans to study abroad.

The influence of Dr. Clark and others from the United States has continued with growing appreciation on the part of the Japanese. In 4 recent years, 835 came to this country for training. Their expenses have been borne by the Japanese Government since 1962; previously, the Agency for International Development and predecessor agencies paid the costs.

THEIR WORK in the United States was part of a share-our-knowledge policy in which the United States and other countries have welcomed individuals for study and training from abroad in the belief that the knowledge gained through exchanges of people is vital to a country's economic and social development, which can be made only as fast and as far as the capabilities of leaders and rural people permit.

Training thus is a part of the programs of technical cooperation of many countries to help other peoples develop resources and improve their living.

One hundred eighteen American agricultural colleges in 1964 had agreements with foreign institutions or governments for international technical assistance, which included training. In 1962, the 12 member countries of the Development Assistance Committee of the Organization for Economic Cooperation and Development received for training and study 135 thousand students and trainees from developing countries. The equivalent of about 325

million dollars was expended for technicians and for grants to students from other countries.

Grants for 60 thousand more students and trainees were provided in 1962 by other countries. The Soviet Union and other Sino-Soviet-bloc countries provided for 12 thousand; Egypt, 2 thousand; and Israel, 1,621.

The Organization of American States has provided a large number of fellowships for study and training in other countries. Other international organizations also have available fellowships or other assistance for training in agrarian reform, forestry, home economics, agricultural development and planning, veterinary services, tropical agriculture and agricultural engineering, statistics, and general agriculture.

VOLUNTARY and nonprofit organizations, including religious groups, have encouraged international training in agriculture and home economics for a long time. Most of their work is carried on in other countries, but a number make it possible for foreign nationals to study in the United States through individual fellowships.

Awards are made through representatives of the agencies in the national's home country and are based on tests and interviews to determine ability and suitability.

Representatives of these nongovernment agencies have shared their experiences with Government officials who are in charge of the public training programs. The Department of Agriculture, Agricultural Missions, Inc., and the National Council of Churches of Christ in the United States have conducted 9-day courses for new agricultural missionaries and as a refresher training for experienced workers.

THE FIRST OFFICIAL step of the United States to promote the international exchange of persons for technical assistance was taken in Buenos Aires in 1936 at a meeting of the Buenos Aires Cultural Convention, which adopted a resolution that called for a multilateral exchange of students and teachers.

The Congress in 1938 created an Interdepartmental Committee on Scientific and Cultural Cooperation. The act authorized Federal departments to grant fellowships to citizens of the American Republics to study and train in countries of their choice.

The Department of Agriculture and the Department of State established cooperative agricultural stations or missions in a number of Latin American countries. The main aim was to increase the production of strategic and complementary crops of particular value in wartime. American technicians were located at the missions, but a lack of trained national technicians hampered the conduct of the programs, and technicians were sent to the United States for training.

The Department of Agriculture supervised their study programs, which provided for work in the agencies of the Department and in land-grant colleges. Generally the technicians were men who held key positions and had had professional training.

The training proved to be useful.

The enactment in 1948 and 1949 of the Public Laws 402, 472, and 535 expanded international training in the United States to people from other countries. Foreign agricultural leaders, officials, and technicians at once began to embrace the opportunity offered them. In 1951, 1,064 persons participated in programs of the Federal Government; the Department of Agriculture made arrangements for 416.

In engaging in this activity, the Department drew on the resources in the land-grant institutions, which had volunteered their services in a letter to President Truman.

The objectives of the training programs are to equip the participant to make a significant contribution to the agricultural and rural life programs in his home country; help him transmit improved ideas, skills, and knowledge to others; give him an understanding of the people, culture, attitudes, and values of the United States; and help Americans gain an understanding of the participant's country, people, culture, attitudes, and values.

The Department, the land-grant institutions, and other cooperators engage in the foreign training effort as a contribution to the foreign policy of the United States and as an activity related to American membership in international organizations.

The establishment of the arrangements in the Department and with the members of the Association of State Universities and Land-Grant Colleges came about through the Department's long history of cooperative work in teaching, research, and extension.

The association at its annual meeting in 1950 ratified several recommendations to the Department and to its members regarding cooperative arrangements for foreign nationals.

The recommendations were that the Department handle through a single office (with a corresponding office in each land-grant institution) all matters relating to the cooperative training of foreign visitors.

MINISTERS OF AGRICULTURE and other high agricultural officials travel continuously to the United States to learn how the American agricultural industry has put science to work. About 1,200 of these individuals come to the United States each year for training related to the cooperative programs in the various countries where the Agency for International Development has missions.

Other hundreds of visitors, professors, teachers, and representatives of industry come each year for consultation, observation, or training—2,980 from 117 different countries in 1963.

Programs were carried out between 1956 and 1964 for 13,453 participants sponsored by the Agency for International Development and its predecessor agencies, the Food and Agriculture Organization and other specialized agencies of the United Nations, and other United States and international departments and agencies.

In addition, assistance has been given to 7,498 individuals not sponsored by the United States Government. They have been heads of state, cabinet ministers, professors, scientists, and businessmen.

Through an agreement between the United States and the Soviet Union, 20 programs have been carried out for 123 Russian agricultural officials and technicians. The programs have emphasized the exchange of knowledge among individuals of comparable training and responsibilities in the United States and the Soviet Union.

DEVELOPING and carrying out training, consultation, observation, and study programs for visitors from other countries is a cooperative process.

It involves the visitor; the sponsoring agency of the United States or foreign government, institution, foundation, organization, or other nongovernmental agency; the agencies of the Department of Agriculture; the agricultural and home economics colleges and universities; agricultural businesses, industrial firms, and organizations; farm families; educational and cultural organizations; and others.

The Department of Agriculture has a professional training staff for foreign participants and visitors as a part of the International Agricultural Development Service.

Specialists with experience in agricultural teaching and training work with technical representatives of the Department and cooperating institutions to plan, conduct, and evaluate training, observation, consultation, and study programs in the many phases of agriculture, forestry, home economics, and related sciences.

This staff is in daily contact with specially appointed foreign training persons in each of the member institutions of the Association of State Universities and Land-Grant Colleges; hundreds of private institutions and firms; farm and other organizations;

cooperatives; other governmental departments and agencies; and farm and rural families.

Through this cooperative network, the entire agricultural knowledge and competence of the United States is available for training opportunities and experience.

The training includes academic enrollment, special courses, on-the-job experience, consultation, and visits. Emphasis is placed on achieving the objectives of the United States agency, the international organizations to which the United States belongs, and other sponsors for the training.

The essential elements for successful training for international visitors include factors of human relationships; the participant's grasp or perception of the training to be achieved; available facilities in the right place; competent teachers; active involvement of the participant; wise use of training materials, aids, and resources; and a close relationship of training to the needs of the participant and to his opportunity to use the training.

All of these are taken into consideration by the staff in the sponsoring agencies and in the Department and cooperating institutions. Objectives, clearly stated by the sponsor and understood by participant and trainers, guide training arrangements and conduct of the program.

Several features are included in the process.

Members of committees that plan the programs of foreign visitors have wide knowledge of the rural economy and educational institutions of the United States. Specialists and technicians from every part of the Department, other Government agencies, private groups, and commercial firms are asked to be members of the committees.

Outlines for available training in agriculture and related fields are prepared annually and are sent to possible sponsors. The outlines help the visitor plan his training, help officials select participants, and guide the sponsor and the participant in what can be expected in the United States.

Proposed programs are prepared for review. They provide opportunities for approval or suggested improvements by sponsors, participants, and training cooperators. Suggestions are obtained from overseas and from United States cooperators before the participant embarks on training that may prove inapplicable.

The preparation of final programs takes into consideration suggestions obtained through the use of proposed programs and are the official guides for the participant and trainers. Each segment of the training is related to each other segment to avoid repetition or gaps in subject matter. Changes in emphasis within program segments are possible, but major changes require approval of the sponsors.

Evaluation occurs during training and just before participants return to home countries. Time to confer with program specialists, program planning committee members, and the sponsor's technical advisers provides an opportunity to learn the participant's reaction to the training experience. Special evaluation interviews are conducted under the guidance of trained evaluation specialists.

Programs are adjusted to fit the needs and understanding of visitors. Farm families, commercial firms and businesses, organizations, and cooperatives furnish opportunities for training participants to see and take part in the operation of American agriculture. For example, programs carried out in 1963 involved the cooperation of 399 private firms and organizations, such as chemical and timber companies, farmer cooperatives, the trade associations, and farm organizations.

International sharing of knowledge has been going on since the beginning of history. The newest (and to many the most exciting) form of sharing is the Peace Corps. At the request of the governments of 40 host countries, one-fifth of the Peace Corps volunteers have been working in agricultural programs—in soil conservation, land reclamation, animal husbandry, irrigation, forestry, agronomy, horticulture, dairy husbandry, poultry, vocational agriculture, agricultural engineering, and home economics.

Other volunteers engage in scores of useful activities.

The Congress established the Peace Corps on September 22, 1961. Its objectives are to promote world peace and friendship by making available to interested countries Americans who will help the people of those countries meet their needs for trained manpower, to help promote a better understanding of the American people on the part of the people served, and to help promote a better understanding among Americans of other peoples.

Peace Corps volunteers come from the cities, villages, and farms of all States, Puerto Rico, the Virgin Islands, and Guam. The typical volunteer is unmarried and is about 25 years old, but many married couples serve together overseas. Some volunteers are as young as 18, the minimum age, and several are more than 60. Among them are students, men and women who leave their careers for a time, and retired persons.

Volunteers receive a living allowance while overseas to cover food, clothing, housing, medical care, and incidental expenses. Each accrues 75 dollars a month for a total separation allowance of 1,800 dollars. The Peace Corps term of service is about 24 months.

CANNON C. HEARNE, *Director, Foreign Training Division, International Agricultural Development Service, has been a farm manager, county agent, and professor of extension education.*

WILLIAM E. HARVEY *has worked since 1951 as program specialist and Assistant Director, Foreign Training Division. After graduation from Virginia Polytechnic Institute, he was a county agent for 10 years.*

ANDREW J. NICHOLS *is Regional Coordinator for Latin America, International Agricultural Development Service.*

Private Foundations and Organizations

by A. H. MOSEMAN and F. F. HILL

PRIVATE FOUNDATIONS, organizations, and church groups have been pioneers in technical and charitable endeavors in all parts of the world. They have fed the starving, rehabilitated impoverished people and communities, and rekindled many a hope.

They work with substantial flexibility when and where needs arise. Their liberty of choice and action is a keystone in a bridge between American agriculture and the rest of the world. Unlike government agencies, they are free to work with an individual or a nation. They may support research in great centers of learning; they can just as easily encourage the application of the findings of research in one farmer's field or in one far-off village. They can create and accept opportunity to help.

The private organizations generally are concerned with the creation of ideas and the giving of things.

The foundations, such as the Ford Foundation, the Rockefeller Foundation, and the W. K. Kellogg Foundation, tend to pay most attention to research and education, including the extension of knowledge. Private organizations, such as CARE, buttress long-term development by direct aid.

The functions sometimes overlap. Sometimes they depend on each other for mutual success.

Basic in their planning and work is the realization that methods and knowledge cannot be transferred intact to some regions from countries that have applied modern science and technology to their agricultural industries. Agricultural development therefore is slower and more difficult than industrial development. That is a lesson specialists in technical cooperation have had to learn.

To build a new steel mill abroad is much the same as building a new mill at home, but that does not hold true for the transfer of farming materials and practices. An improved American variety of wheat will not necessarily grow well in Colombia. A fertilizing technique that works and a midwestern farmer can afford may not work or be economic in Thailand. Application of basic principles has to be modified in each instance. We have to devise combinations of new agricultural practices for each new environment.

To compound the problem, we still are lacking in some important areas of knowledge. Much less research has been done, for example, on farming in the Tropics than in the Temperate Zones. For the application of existing knowledge and the creation of new knowledge, a structure of research stations should be built up in the less-developed countries. For that, large numbers of people must be trained to staff the institutions.

The size of the task can be gaged from American experience. It has been estimated that in 40 years in this country about 350 thousand agricultural students have been graduated—the equivalent of about 1 graduate for every 10 farms. The heavy investment in trained people and in research and education facilities has figured largely in the growth of American agriculture during this century.

The developing countries may not immediately need this level of trained manpower, but realistic goals must be set and reached.

Agricultural scientists have learned to modify a number of production-inhibiting factors at the same time. This simultaneous attention to problems of crop production has led to the development of research centers where teams of scientists trained in different disciplines work to combat the hazards that cut crop or livestock yields.

AN EXAMPLE of this type of multiscience laboratory is the International Rice Research Institute, Los Baños, the Philippines. The decision to set it up stemmed from a fundamental need: Although half the world depends on rice as a daily food, there is almost never enough of it.

The reasons why rice crops are not bigger were charted for several years by staff members of the Ford and Rockefeller Foundations. The surveys indicated that answers could be found for most of the many problems.

The two foundations decided in 1959 jointly to establish a research and training center in the rice bowl of southeastern Asia. The Government of the Philippines cooperated by supplying land for laboratories, housing, and experimental fields next to the College of Agriculture of the University of the Philippines.

Since then, the Ford Foundation has invested more than 7 million dollars in its buildings and equipment. The Rockefeller Foundation has provided operating expenses of around 500 thousand dollars annually, plus the services of eight members of its own staff.

Enduring relief of the chronic rice shortage in the Tropics and subtropics will not be gained until existing knowledge can be successfully adapted to new and unfamiliar conditions of climate, soil, and social organization.

The paths that must be explored include the breeding and selection of improved varieties of rice suited for growing in southeastern Asia, the control of diseases and pests, improved knowledge about the management of submerged soils, and a number of economic and engineering factors about which little is known.

Since many parts of the overall problem are linked, solutions have to be sought through a complete interdisciplinary approach. This is no novelty in the United States, especially in the research of the Department of Agriculture and at the land-grant colleges and universities, but it has not been applied widely to agricultural problems abroad. How to apply this method under differing conditions is one of the lessons the Rockefeller Foundation learned in earlier crop-improvement work in Latin America and India.

The presence of a number of specialists at a research center makes possible the development of effective inservice training programs for the nationals of one or more countries to accelerate the move toward self-sufficiency.

In planning the rice research project, the two foundations sought a location near a strong college of agriculture.

The 45 students from many Asian countries who trained in 1963 at the Los Baños center saw broader agricultural horizons through their association with the College of Agriculture. The college also benefits from the participation of the institute's skilled scientists in its teaching programs.

Interplay between an old and new institution may go even further. Thus the Ford and Rockefeller Foundations and Cornell University made plans to strengthen the College of Agriculture at Los Baños. A 5-year plan for overall development of the college was drawn up by the University of the Philippines. The two foundations, the World Bank, and the Agency for International Development collaborated.

As a first step, the Ford and Rockefeller Foundations and Cornell furnished the services of American professional staff, fellowships for college staff members in the United States, and materials and other support for research and development. Students of both institutions are permitted to complete part of their work and take their degree at Los Baños or Cornell.

This joint endeavor reflects the ability of private groups to respond promptly to a new opportunity.

Planning and development of the International Rice Research Institute and the subsequent support to the College of Agriculture at Los Baños are examples of one kind of volunteer technical assistance. But there are about 200 private agencies in America that give regular, substantial help toward agricultural development overseas. Their methods vary, and while this chapter cannot be inclusive, we can discuss a cross section of the larger and more representative groups.

THE ROCKEFELLER FOUNDATION began its development work in the agricultural sciences in 1924, when it gave its first fellowship for training nationals of other countries.

The aim has always been to help train people who, on return to their home countries, will give direction and leadership in research and education. To that end, the foundation usually makes awards only to persons who have a post or are guaranteed one in a research or educational institution in their respective countries.

This is one facet of development work in which private groups have an advantage over government organizations: The Rockefeller Foundation, for example, can select its trainees in the light of its own judgment and standards.

A total of 1,291 fellowships had been awarded up to 1964 in the agricultural sciences to persons from 62 countries. Current investment is at the rate of about 1.5 million dollars. In 1963, that sum supported 300 scientists, from 24 countries, at 39 institutions in the United States and abroad.

This program will continue to get strong support from the foundation because, in the long view, the advancing countries will progress only when their own specialists are able to apply scientific principles to the solution of indigenous problems.

The Rockefeller Foundation has become increasingly active in using its own staff to spur development abroad.

The present pattern dates from 1943, when a cooperative effort was set up with the Government of Mexico to boost production of basic food crops.

The beginning was modest. A few scientists were assigned to guide research on improvement of crop varieties and methods of farming. From that small beginning has grown an operating program in which 50 foundation specialists have been sent to Mexico, Colombia, Chile, India, the Philippines, and Nigeria.

In each country, the first aim is to seek the factors that hold back the production of major foods. In Mexico, the attack has been focused on the production of corn, wheat, potatoes, and beans, nutrition, and the diseases of animals and poultry.

Colombia's major food crops—corn, wheat, and potatoes—have been studied. The range of climate from tropic to temperate and a corresponding range of topography make Colombia an ideal place in which to study animal physiology.

Activities in Chile are especially concerned with improving wheat and forage crops.

The agricultural program in India, begun in 1956, was the first in which both education and research were linked from the beginning. Research on improvement of corn and sorghum was designed to encourage participation by the Central and State Governments and thus make the best use of India's research resources.

The Postgraduate School of the Indian Agricultural Research Institute, established in 1958, was designed to furnish a model for other agricultural colleges and universities that were being planned by the Government of India and the Indian states.

The operating program has achieved measurable results in a few years. Mexico, a wheat importer 20 years ago, was self-sufficient in 1964. Average wheat production has risen from 11.5 bushels an acre in 1943 to 33.0 bushels in 1963. Total production has climbed from 300 thousand tons to 2 million tons. Mexico has also become self-sufficient in corn. The Food and Agriculture Organization estimated that Mexican food production grew 7 percent annually in the decade ended in 1959.

The cooperative program in Colombia was set up in 1950. It is estimated that improved corn hybrids and varieties make up 95 percent of the acreage planted to corn in the Cauca Valley. Nearly all of the country's wheat comes from varieties developed since 1950. The animal industry of the country is forging ahead, thanks to better nutrition and management practices and through control of pests and diseases.

In Chile, the spring wheat acreage is planted almost entirely to the improved varieties, Orofén and Chifén, bred and selected in the cooperative program. The country has had to import up to half of its animal products, but domestic production should increase substantially through wider use of improved clovers and other forages. New experiment station facilities at Santiago and Temuco were ready for use in 1964.

Experience gained in Latin America and the materials developed there were of value in planning the cooperative program in India. After only 5 years of work, four adapted corn hybrids were produced in India. Some of them yielded up to 150 percent more than the common commercial varieties. The hybrids were suited to varied growing conditions, from those of the Gangetic Plain to the Deccan Plateau and in the hill country. Three more hybrids were released in 1963, including one suited to starch manufacture. New hybrid sorghums, using Kafir 60 as a base parent, were due for release and commercial planting in 1964.

The foundation's most important contribution to Indian agriculture probably has been through creation of the Postgraduate School. About 400 students were enrolled in 1964, of whom 180 were studying for doctor-

ates. The others were pursuing the degree of master of science. In its first 6 years to December 1963, the school granted 77 doctor's and 305 master's degrees.

Wherever in the world the foundation has an operating unit, a training program is set up. Students get inservice training by working on research projects guided by the foundation staff.

In the Mexican and Colombian cooperative schemes and increasingly in Chile and India, research leadership positions are being filled by trained, competent nationals, many of whom have received their training with foundation aid.

The foundation also makes grants for research and teaching. These vary in size from modest travel grants, to permit scientists to broaden their experience, and to the massive support that sometimes is needed for the hard core of institution building. Fundamental research also is supported.

A typical grant is the one made to the Institute of Genetics, Misima, Japan, for research into the genetics and evolution of cultivated rice. A few grants have been made in the United States and Europe, where outstanding scientists are working on the frontiers of knowledge.

At the North Carolina State College of Agriculture and Engineering, for example, an investigation of quantitative genetics has been supported to the extent of 125 thousand dollars, plus (since 1951) 11 thousand dollars for related genetic studies.

The University of Nebraska has received 80 thousand dollars for studies in corn genetics.

A grant of 13 thousand dollars was made to the Institute of Genetics, Catholic University, Milan, Italy, for research on the inheritance of special characteristics in corn.

These kinds of basic studies are supported to further progress in the practical aspects of research in crop improvement.

Although it mounts its own fellowship and scholarship programs, the foundation also has made grants for training by other agencies.

The University of Hawaii was given 100 thousand dollars to help students from Asia and Pacific Basin countries to attend its College of Agriculture.

A similar grant enabled students from several tropical countries to attend the College of Agriculture of the University of the Philippines.

Scientists from the Middle East who are working on wheat and barley improvement are given inservice training in Mexico through a grant of 150 thousand dollars to FAO. From 1960 to late 1963, some 24 trainees from 12 countries had been helped.

Many education and research centers have been aided by institutional development grants. The improvement and establishment of experiment stations in Chile, undertaken by the Ministry of Agriculture, has been supported to the extent of 400 thousand dollars. In Mexico, the research and education center at Chapingo has been further developed by an appropriation of 1.3 million dollars. Grants totaling 822 thousand dollars have been made to the Agrarian University in Peru, an institution that North Carolina State College has helped through a cooperative program underwritten by the Agency for International Development.

The cooperative program in India is trying to coordinate the support of Federal and State Governments, and so the maize and sorghum improvement schemes are built around the experiment stations of the new agricultural universities of the states.

To support those institutions and to hasten their growth, grants have been made in the amount of 65 thousand dollars to the West Bengal College of Agriculture; 135 thousand dollars to the Coimbatore Agricultural College and Research Institute; 240 thousand dollars to the Uttar Pradesh Agricultural University; and 320 thousand dollars to the Punjab Agricultural University.

Most of this money has been spent on developing the experiment stations. American land-grant colleges, through contracts supported by the Agency for International Development, have furnished guidance for the education and extension activities in the new agricultural universities.

To enlarge the Mexican center at Chapingo, the Rockefeller Foundation has joined forces with the Ford Foundation, the Agency for International Development, and the Inter-American Development Bank to assist the Government of Mexico in establishing a national institution that will furnish coordinated leadership in research, education, and extension.

The Rockefeller Foundation up to 1964 had invested 66 million dollars in agricultural development—25 million dollars for operating programs, 11.3 million dollars for scholarships and fellowships, and 29.7 million dollars for the grants-in-aid to research and education.

THE FORD FOUNDATION's work in agriculture abroad has been mostly in three categories: The creation and development of schools and colleges; research and planning to raise production and levels of nutrition; and pilot projects and education-demonstration programs at the village level, with accent on rural self-help.

Ford's work in India since 1952 has contained most of these elements. The foundation was asked to help build extension training into Indian agricultural colleges at the start of the government's first 5-year plan. The Allahabad Agricultural Institute already had begun extension work when a Ford grant in 1952 helped establish a fully fledged extension department to specialize in village work. Later grants were made to build similar departments at eight other colleges.

The Government of India has used them as models in its plan of attaching an extension department to every agricultural college. The need for practical training is great, since few Indian students have had farm experience.

To help meet immediate needs, Ford has contributed 12 million dollars to India's community development program. We think it is the most ambitious national program of rural development ever undertaken by any country. Its aim is to raise the living standards of the 375 million Indian villagers.

The country is divided into blocks of about 100 villages, each totaling about 65 thousand inhabitants. Each block is supervised by a development officer, with a yearly budget for loans and grants to aid local self-help projects. The officer is helped by specialists in agriculture, animal husbandry, public health, social education, cooperatives, small industries, and in village self-government.

The backbone of each block lies in 10 village-level workers, each of whom covers about 10 villages. Their task is to persuade the villagers, both individually and as communities, to undertake self-help projects and then to arrange the technical guidance that is needed. Each village-level worker is given 2 years of training, half of it in agriculture.

The foundation began its help in 1951 with a grant of 1.2 million dollars. This underwrote 15 pilot centers of 100 villages each to devise and test education and demonstration methods and 5 centers to train village-level workers.

Since then, about half the grants have gone to a nationwide network of training centers and other training work. Instruction ranges from the village level up to block development officers and their staffs.

Other large grants have been made for an evaluation of the program, strengthening of agricultural extension and information services, university scholarships for outstanding workers, and a national center for the study of community development.

These first two Indian programs are thus concerned with education at the professional level and education and extension at the subprofessional level on a massive scale.

The third program is a combination of extension and direct aid. The aim is to produce an immediate increase in food supplies.

The intensive agricultural district program grew out of a survey in 1959 by American specialists, led by Dr. Sherman E. Johnson, of the Department of Agriculture. This team was recruited by the foundation at India's request.

Its prognosis was that a national food crisis would occur by 1966 unless emergency measures were applied to almost every part of the agricultural complex. As a model for an intensive nationwide drive, the government began a program in 1961 to boost food production in seven districts by 50 percent in 5 years.

More have since been added, until each of India's 15 states now is represented. Each district is the size of several average American counties.

Farmers join the program voluntarily. It is designed to demonstrate the application of several essential measures—adequate and timely supplies of fertilizer, pesticides, improved seeds, farm tools, and other production aids; cooperative farm credit to buy these supplies; storage, drainage, and other public works; education and assistance in farm management; and individual farm planning.

In the crop season beginning late in 1962, about one-fourth of all farmers (about 260 thousand) in the first seven districts took part. Production plans were drawn up for more than 1.2 million acres. About 96 thousand additional farmers, with more than 500 thousand acres, began to take part in the districts.

In the first crop season (1961–1962), the yields showed a significant response to the use of better methods. In the Shahabad district, the demonstration plots gave yields of rice that were 84 percent higher than on the control plots, 100 to 150 percent more for wheat, 78 to 200 percent more for potatoes, and 106 percent more for grain.

The Ford Foundation has appropriated a substantial sum to assist the program over a 5-year period. The funds have been used mainly for four purposes: Transportation of personnel, soil testing, and seed-treatment equipment in the first seven districts; imports of chemical fertilizers and insecticides for sale to farmers; the services of foreign advisers; and the training of Indian specialists.

Grants also have been made for special work that supports the program. The Allahabad Agricultural Institute has created a center where better farm implements are being developed for commercial manufacture. The Uttar Pradesh Agricultural University has set up a training and research program in farm management to apply the lessons learned in the demonstration districts.

The Ford Foundation, in cooperation with Michigan State University, has helped establish two academies for village development, one in East Pakistan at Comilla and one in West Pakistan at Peshawar. These are meant to give Pakistani civil servants the knowledge and skills needed to carry out rural development projects.

Comilla Academy completed a pilot trial of agricultural cooperatives, and a grant was made to enable the expansion of the cooperative plan to include 240 villages. The main purpose of the cooperatives is to obtain modern farm equipment and lease it to smallholders.

In many countries a great need exists for training large numbers of agricultural students as fast as possible to a subprofessional level. Otherwise, the agricultural services of underdeveloped countries may have to be staffed by persons who have had a high school education or less, plus 1 or 2 years of specialized training.

To help meet this kind of demand, the Ford Foundation assisted the Government of Burma to plan and create the State Agricultural Institute at Pyinmana in 1954.

Grants were used mainly to provide advisers and specialists in the agricultural sciences, equipment and material, and fellowships to give advanced training abroad to prospective Burmese faculty members.

By 1962, the institute had a Burmese staff of a principal and 15 lecturers, all of whom had been given some training abroad. Eleven more posts were filled in 1962 and 1963. Seventy students have been admitted each year from about 500 qualified applicants. About 415 students had completed a 2-year junior college course in agriculture in 1962. About one-fourth of them were employed as teachers. Most of the rest took posts in the Agricultural and Rural Development Corporation, mainly in extension work.

PROBLEMS OF FARM planning and cooperative credit were treated in a Burmese pilot project. In common with the farmers throughout most of southeastern Asia, the Burmese smallholder is often hampered by lack of credit and capital.

As an experiment in farm planning, the Ford Foundation made grants to the Burmese Government and International Development Services to set up a 75-member project in the village of Mweyoegyi. Individual farm plans were prepared for each member. Crop-production loans were made.

It was the first time in Burma that the amount of credit given a farmer was related to his production costs and to his ability to repay. Traditionally, credit was based on a fixed figure per acre for a specific crop and usually was too small to meet the farmer's needs. The trial was extended to another village. At its conclusion, it had shown considerable promise of increasing production and of being applicable to other Asian countries.

The Ford Foundation and International Development Services demonstrated that though farmers could not afford to own farm equipment individually, they could profit by the cooperative use of five or six tractors for the timely preparation and cultivation of sun-baked soils that were too hard to be worked with animal power.

Two important results from both schemes were the growth of self-confidence among farmers and the realization by government officers that these farmers accomplished more by using good judgment than by trying to follow manuals of instruction.

Since its first grants were made in 1951, the foundation's agriculture program has emphasized the creation or strengthening of the kinds of institutions that underdeveloped countries need for their advancing agriculture.

THE INSTITUTE of Land Reclamation and Development in the United Arab Republic is an example of a new body that was created to meet particular needs. The needs arise from the decision to build the High Dam at Aswan, which in turn arose from a critical shortage of farmland.

About 2 million acres are to be brought under irrigation—the equivalent of almost two-thirds the cultivated acreage before the dam was started. A further 2 million acres in use in 1964 must be improved if production is to keep step with population.

The Ford Foundation made a grant to the University of Alexandria in 1960 to help establish an institute to provide a 2-year postgraduate course in the reclamation and development of land, including desert and salt lands. The course gives intensive training in the scientific, engineering, economic, and social aspects of reclamation and settlement. The entering class in 1963 comprised 60 students. Fellowships made possible the training of a staff to replace the advisers who gave instruction in the first years.

Besides these examples of the several levels on which the Ford Foundation operates its development work, the foundation provides consultants to furnish a variety of services.

They include assistance in national economic planning; developing long-term plans for agricultural colleges,

research, and also extension groups; strengthening governmental services concerned with agriculture; and appraising proposals for pilot and experimental projects.

The total of Ford Foundation grants for agricultural and village development abroad between 1952 and 1964 was 39.6 million dollars, or about 17.8 percent of the total spent in the Overseas Development Program.

GRANTS made under other parts of the program also had a connection with agriculture. For example, a grant to provide the services of an agricultural economist to assist in the development of a national economic plan would ordinarily be classified under the heading of economic planning, although his services presumably would affect the resources made available for agricultural development.

A regional breakdown of grants shows that 83.6 percent of the dollar total was invested in southern and southeastern Asia; 13.6 percent in Africa and the Middle East; and 1.3 percent in Latin America and the Caribbean. One and one-half percent was invested in interregional projects.

It should be kept in mind that the first grants in southern and southeastern Asia and the Middle East were made in 1952; the first in Africa south of the Sahara was made in 1958; and the first grants in Latin America and the Caribbean were made in 1959.

THE W. K. KELLOGG FOUNDATION established a Division of Agriculture in 1953. Its grants, which reached more than 8 million dollars in 1964, have been made within the United States and to some countries in Europe and Latin America. It concentrates on the application of knowledge, rather than its creation, and gives aid mainly to experimental or pioneering programs.

A good deal of the foundation's effort in Latin America has been toward the general improvement of nutritional levels.

The Institute of Nutrition of Central

America and Panama was formed in 1949, and since then Kellogg has supported many of its activities, such as analysis of indigenous foods, improvement of the native diet to overcome protein deficiency and goiter, and educational programs in the fundamentals of good nutrition.

The foundation also has aided the Institutes of Nutrition of Mexico and Ecuador and nutrition programs in the Medical School of the University of Valle, Colombia, and the School of Health of the University of São Paulo, Brazil.

The two Colleges of Agriculture of the University of Colombia, at Medellín and Palmira, have been helped to expand their general programs and to set up a Commission on Higher Education in Agriculture, which has charted the course for further development of agricultural institutions in Colombia.

A WIDESPREAD DISTRIBUTION through Latin America of teaching aids was made possible by a grant to the Inter-American Institute of Agricultural Sciences, Costa Rica.

The Kellogg fellowship program in Western Europe is designed to help develop the leadership needed for expanding the resident instruction, research, extension, and service programs. Some 460 fellows have been brought to the United States for advanced study.

An example of the kind of experimental activity that Kellogg supports is the International Institute for Land Reclamation and Improvement, which has headquarters in the Netherlands and serves as a worldwide information agency.

Another example of the Kellogg Foundation's preference for applied-knowledge programs is the support given the Federation of Smallholders' Associations of Jutland, Denmark, to improve their extension work.

In Norway, aid has been granted for the establishment of a Department of Rural Sociology, an Institute of Agricultural Engineering, and a program of field experiments and demonstrations throughout the country.

In the United Kingdom and Ireland, the accent has been on training programs for rural youth and the preparation of urban youth for farming careers.

THE THREE FOUNDATIONS we have discussed are fairly typical. They all share some interests, but each has an area or areas it has made especially its own.

Rockefeller's work in cooperative research for improvement of crops and livestock production is one such area.

Ford's multifront pilot projects are another.

Kellogg's bent toward extension work is yet a third.

Other approaches are possible, and some of them can indeed be undertaken most effectively by the private groups.

One such approach is that of the Council on Economic and Cultural Affairs, which concerns itself almost entirely with one geographic area, Asia.

THE COUNCIL on Economic and Cultural Affairs was set up in 1953 with the support of John D. Rockefeller 3d and the Rockefeller Brothers Fund. In November 1963 it was reincorporated as the Agricultural Development Council, Inc. In later years the council also has been aided by the Ford Foundation.

Its field program in Asia is directed toward providing visiting professors of agricultural economics, rural sociology, and extension education to the colleges of agriculture; granting fellowships for graduate study, mostly within the United States, to younger professors and research workers in Asian institutions; and offering grants for research in their home countries by Asian specialists.

The core of the CECA program is its own permanent staff, six of whom were assigned in 1963 to work in Asia, two in the Philippines, three in Indonesia, and one in Malaya. Each staff member spends one-half to two-thirds of his time in teaching, conducting research, and consulting on other research projects at the institution to which he is attached. The rest of his time is spent in liaison with specialists elsewhere in the country or region, giving such help as is possible and reporting to CECA on the overall program. The council also sent a visiting professor on a 2-year term in Thailand and India.

The council has granted more than 150 fellowships for postgraduate study. The fellows have come from Japan, Korea, Taiwan, the Philippines, Indonesia, Malaya, Thailand, Pakistan, Ceylon, and India. More than half of them were candidates for the doctor's degree. The council keeps in touch with its fellows on their return home. Often its research grants have been for projects begun by former fellows.

The council believes that its best investment is in people rather than institutions.

That belief allows an efficient use of a budget of 800 thousand dollars and reflects the opinion that massive aid over many years will be needed before Asian universities become well established. Such aid is beyond the council's resources, but it helps the professional development of people who will make an immediate, as well as long-term, contribution to the agricultural development of their countries.

CECA launched two new programs in 1963 with the support of the Ford Foundation.

One was a project to encourage research on agricultural development overseas through American universities. It sponsors seminars and workshops on agricultural development, at which American professors formulate new research projects and discuss the results of completed work. Linked with it is a program of research grants of modest size.

The second project brings together what is already known about agricultural development so as to make it available to workers around the world. The project includes the selection of useful books and articles and the commissioning of new articles written in semitechnical style. The cost of the two programs has been set at about 400 thousand dollars a year.

INTERNATIONAL DEVELOPMENT SERVICES, a private agency formed in 1953, concentrates its efforts on the recruitment of technical-assistance teams and the planning and management of programs sponsored by other agencies.

The agencies include private firms, foundations, the United States Government, foreign governments, the United Nations, and other international bodies.

IDS has a field staff of 36 agricultural and rural specialists. Large numbers of technicians and scientists are assigned by local governmental agencies as supporting employees and trainees. The IDS staff works closely with official agencies and sometimes with private agencies. The annual budget is about 800 thousand dollars, most of which comes from the Agency for International Development for contracted programs. The rest comes from public and private sources.

THE COOPERATIVE for American Relief Everywhere was set up in 1945 as a service through which Americans could send food and textile packages to postwar Europe.

By 1963, CARE had delivered 50 million packages, had distributed more than 3 billion pounds of farm surplus in 55 countries, and was launched on the largest annual food program of its history—the distribution of 1.25 billion pounds of commodities to 35 million recipients in 38 countries of Latin America, Africa, Asia, the Middle East, and Europe.

These massive distributions of food have helped fulfill the basic needs of several hundred million persons, but it is recognized that temporary relief provides no long-range solution to low farm production in underdeveloped countries.

CARE accompanies its food program with large shipments of tools and equipment, which it integrates into local self-help programs. CARE does a good deal of planning, but it does not actually administer the programs, and it does not provide technical help for them. CARE acts as the bridge between donor and recipient, and so has encouraged projects as diverse as land reclamation, food preservation, and the organization of cooperatives, which in 1963 alone involved 5.5 million dollars' worth of commodities and materials.

In Korea, for example, CARE has helped hundreds of refugee families to build dikes and reclaim wastelands. A typical project gave to a group of Korean farmers bullocks, unweaned calves, fertilizers, seeds, pigs, and chickens. Within 8 months, 50 more acres were being farmed, so that the farmers could meet their own food needs and sell produce worth 3,800 dollars.

In Ceylon, India, and Vietnam, CARE has provided improved tools. A major new project, in cooperation with an American seed company, allows Americans to send packages of seeds to any country.

A typical CARE scheme in animal husbandry operates in the Philippines, where pork production is being raised through special purchases of purebred swine. Revolving loan funds have been set up in several countries to enable farmers to buy livestock and improve their farms. CARE has given much aid to groups of young farmers, partly because they are more receptive to new methods and new tools.

In supervising the distribution of surplus foods from the United States, CARE tries to make these part of a self-help effort. Thus, a "food for wages" program has been planned in the Philippines. It is a nationwide reforestation and soil conservation program, in which 6,400 young people are to receive 3.5 million pounds of food.

In the Dominican Republic, CARE equipment is used to train forest rangers in firefighting. Well drilling

and irrigation machinery have been sent overseas. A Nile River scheme, for example, is expected to double or treble the crops on a tract of 900 acres.

In a number of countries, cooperative groups have been helped because it is thought these can solve many of the credit and marketing problems of marginal farmers.

The apparent paradox of private, direct-aid agencies is that they hope eventually to disappear. CARE's working philosophy is typical: It distributes surplus food in ways which are designed to give farmers a sense of responsibility for their own welfare and reduce their dependence on outside sources.

THE HEIFER PROJECT is another example of a private agency which has found an individual way of helping development abroad.

It began in 1937 to help refugees in Spain under guidance of the Church of the Brethren. In 1944, the project worked closely with the United Nations Relief and Rehabilitation Administration, the Marshall plan, and other groups to replace livestock killed during the war.

At first, dairy cattle were shipped to areas where milk was needed; now all kinds of livestock are sent. The rationale is that these gifts increase, because they reproduce themselves, and that the original recipients can then pass on to other farmers a portion of the gift.

The multiplication factor of these shipments is illustrated by an airlift of 64 thousand chickens to Turkey in 1956. By 1959 more than 2.3 million hatching eggs and 1.4 million chickens had been distributed to farmers throughout Turkey. A national poultry congress met in 1959, and a continuing organization and a poultry journal have been established.

In another project, 40 Brown Swiss bulls and 10 heifers were shipped to Iran in 1953. They were used to develop an artificial insemination project, which involved 89 thousand inseminations in 1958. The crossbred cows that resulted yielded an average of 1,188 liters of milk more per year than native cows. The difference was valued at nearly 104 dollars per cow. For the 20 thousand crossbreds then in production, that meant a net gain of 2 million dollars.

The Heifer Project, which today is a multidenominational effort supported also by several American farm organizations, has shipped livestock and poultry valued at 7 million dollars to 73 countries since 1944.

THE CHURCH WORLD SERVICE is typical of the many private agencies that grew into agricultural development out of postwar relief projects.

CWS is supported by 27 major United States Protestant and Eastern Orthodox churches and operates in 40 countries. It distributes surplus food, but puts its main emphasis on aids to increase farm production.

Its material resources division operates CROP, a program through which American farmers in 28 States donate money, produce, and farm materials.

In Japan, for example, clover seed given through CROP was used by Church World Service to bring into cultivation 50 thousand acres that were unsuited to rice. Nearly 100 thousand farmers, mostly Korean refugees, have been settled in a thriving livestock development.

In Korea, 3 thousand acres have been reclaimed from the Yellow Sea. Laborers' payment was made in surplus food. Comparable basic help is given throughout Asia.

In the Middle East, the Hebron nursery has provided seedlings of fruit, olive, and other trees for sale at cost. In 1963 it supplied 75 thousand olive and fruit trees and 2 million forest seedlings. The gift of a large incubator led to the establishment of a poultry industry. Ancient reservoirs built by the Romans have been restored to allow cultivation of parts of the Arabian deserts.

An ambitious project for reforestation in Algeria contains elements of both short- and long-term aid. American surplus food has been used in part payment of 45 thousand workers employed in a 2-week rotation of 15 thousand men. The aim is to plant 50 million trees to improve water control and prevent erosion.

Similar schemes of demonstration, training, and cooperation have been started in several Latin American countries.

THE WORK of the eight organizations we have discussed is only a part of a great total effort. A full catalog of the work of private agencies in agricultural development abroad would be huge and would not be especially meaningful.

The problems of agriculture in underdeveloped regions are so great and so varied that they cannot be solved by any one organization, or by any one program, no matter how massive.

Because we are dealing with human beings, the problems tend to be as diverse as people. In this fact lies the essential role of the private agency— its ability to tailor its resources precisely to that part of the challenge that it tries to meet—to help impoverished communities, to rekindle hopes.

A. H. MOSEMAN, *Director for Agricultural Sciences of the Rockefeller Foundation since 1960, joined the foundation in 1956. He served in the Department of Agriculture from 1936 to 1956 as an agronomist and Assistant Chief and Chief of the former Bureau of Plant Industry, Soils, and Agricultural Engineering, and Director, Crops Research Division, the Agricultural Research Service.*

F. F. HILL *was appointed vice president of the Ford Foundation in 1955. Previously he was a statistician in the Federal land bank in Springfield, Mass.; professor of agricultural economics and provost at Cornell University; and Director, Center for Advanced Studies in the Behavioral Sciences, Palo Alto, Calif.*

Problems of Soil and Water

by C. A. BOWER and JESSE LUNIN

A CRITICAL NEED exists for research on soil and water in the Tropics and subtropics.

Although the basic growth requirements of plants related to soil and water are essentially the same throughout the world and few soil and water problems are unique to specific regions, problems of water shortage, degradation of quality of water, and salinity tend to be associated with arid climate. Problems of soil acidity and the fixation and leaching of nutrients are associated mainly with a humid climate. The maintenance of soil organic matter and nitrogen is most difficult in hot climates.

THE SUITABILITY of soils for cultivation depends strongly on the readiness with which they absorb and conduct water and air (permeability) and the ease with which they can be tilled (tilth). Supplying the water plants need, controlling drainage and salinity, and preventing erosion by water all require good soil permeability. Poor tilth adversely affects plant growth and makes necessary the use of more power in cultivation.

Because different kinds of minerals predominate in the soils, problems of poor permeability and tilth are most prevalent in dry temperate zones and least prevalent in humid zones.

Permeability and tilth tend to be

535

more favorable in sandy soils than in clayey soils but are determined mainly by the arrangement of soil particles.

High-clay soils, for example, may have excellent permeability and tilth if the particles are aggregated so as to form numerous large pores.

Conversely, the sandy soils may have poor permeability and tilth if their particles are dispersed so as to form small pores.

Soil scientists refer to the arrangement of soil particles as soil structure. Permeable soils that have good tilth have good structure.

A great deal remains to be learned about developing and maintaining good structure and about the nature of the surfaces of soil particles, the interaction of surfaces with water, the forces acting between particles, and the role of various materials in binding particles together.

Applied research has centered about the actions of organic matter, root growth, wetting and drying, and tillage operations in promoting a desirable structure.

Research on these actions must continue, but what is really needed to solve the problem of soil structure is the development of a cheap chemical compound that will bind particles into stable aggregates and be highly resistant to decomposition in the soil. Chemists have developed a number of such compounds, but their cost has prohibited their use except in special problems.

LONG AND INTENSIVE cultivation has depleted soil organic matter and nitrogen—the basic components of soil fertility—in many soils of the world. These components will decline in newly developed areas unless management practices that maintain them at their initial levels are adopted.

Soil organic matter helps maintain good soil structure, increases the capacity of soils to retain certain mineral nutrients, and contributes to the supply of nitrogen, phosphorus, and some of the minor elements.

We lack adequate information concerning the factors that affect the degree to which soil organic matter and nitrogen accumulate and are lost from the soil under various conditions of climate and environment, especially in humid tropical regions where the rates at which organic matter forms and decomposes may be high.

Because of the way in which it originates, soil organic matter has a complex and variable composition. Information is meager on the organic compounds present and the mode of their reaction with other soil constituents, such as clay.

Soil nitrogen is associated with soil organic matter because most of the nitrogen in the soil occurs in organic form. Nitrogen is added to the soil in the form of plant residues, by the fixation of atmospheric nitrogen, and to a limited degree in rainfall. It is lost through crop removal, erosion, leaching, and volatilization. That is the nitrogen cycle. Like organic matter, the rate of its accretion and depletion depends on soil type, the climate, and cropping system.

Research workers are attempting to evaluate more accurately the factors that affect the gains and losses of soil organic matter and nitrogen in order to explain some of the conditions observed in tropical regions. The conversion of nitrate and ammonium forms of nitrogen to gaseous nitrogen and the loss of gaseous nitrogen to the atmosphere are of particular interest because substantial amounts of nitrogen fertilizer are lost in this way.

Studies also have been undertaken to determine the effect of management practices on organic matter and the nitrogen levels. The information could be used to develop agricultural systems that permit the increase of soil organic matter in depleted soils and the maintenance of adequate levels in new land brought into cultivation.

LOSSES of soil and water from farmlands are serious in many countries, especially in humid regions and places where heavy, brief rains occur. Soil erosion greatly lowers soil fertility, raises the sediment burden of streams and rivers, and contributes to the silting up of waterways and storage facilities. As the land is taken out of native vegetation, the amount of runoff, loss of soil, and the dangers of floods all increase. In arid regions, protective measures also must be taken against wind erosion.

Preventive and corrective measures must be developed to meet the needs of the world's many agricultural systems.

Research therefore has been directed toward studies of the basic nature of soil erosion by wind and water, the relative erodibility of different soil types, and the effect of soil management practices on soil and water losses. The aim is to get new or to modify old systems in order to reduce soil and water losses.

Technicians of the Department of Agriculture have developed a way to predict the degree of soil erosion under various agricultural systems. New management practices are being developed that will improve areas already severely eroded.

Research in arid regions is directed toward a more efficient use of available rainfall as well as toward a reduction of soil losses.

LIMING ACID SOILS in temperate regions has been a common practice.

Reports from tropical areas indicate that crops there often do not respond to liming as they do in temperate regions and that a better understanding is needed as to why liming may be beneficial or have no effect or be detrimental on different soils.

Soil acidity has many direct and indirect effects on plant growth. Some acid soils contain toxic concentrations of soluble iron, aluminum, or manganese. Liming alleviates those toxicities. A nutritional deficiency of calcium or magnesium, or both, often is associated with soil acidity. An appropriate liming material corrects this condition.

Soil acidity also may govern to some degree the availability of major elements (such as phosphorus and potassium), the solubility of certain essential minor elements, and the types of soil micro-organisms, including those that fix nitrogen. Liming also may improve the structure of some soils.

We also want to know more about the role of aluminum in soil acidity and the nutritional requirements of plants for calcium and magnesium. All have a bearing on the development of more satisfactory methods of evaluating the amounts of lime soils need.

Because many acid soils in the Tropics do not respond to liming by standards developed for temperate regions, tropical soils must be classified and mapped, and their chemical and mineralogical characteristics must be determined so that the relation between soil acidity and plant responses to liming can be predicted better.

CHLOROSIS, a condition in plants characterized by a deficiency of chlorophyll and a yellow color, is one potential problem on almost one-third of the soils in the world. It usually is caused by a deficiency of iron and is associated generally with soils that naturally contain lime.

Iron deficiency, however, sometimes occurs in acid soils and in soils whose acidity has been reduced by liming. The problem is of economic importance, because the districts affected include many otherwise highly fertile soils and because the possibility of chlorosis restricts the choice of crops to those that are chlorosis-resistant.

Scientists do not understand fully the factors that affect the availability of iron in soils and the uptake of iron by plants. Besides the low content of iron and the presence of lime, bicarbonates in soil or in irrigation water, waterlogging, and poor soil aeration frequently are contributory causes of chlorotic conditions in plants.

Iron deficiency may also be induced in plants by deficiencies of potassium, calcium, and magnesium and by high levels of manganese, copper, zinc, molybdenum, cobalt, nitrogen, and phosphorus. Chlorosis in plants may result from any one or a combination of these conditions.

Investigations of the various causative factors in the soil and in the plant have as their goal the development of diagnostic techniques and remedial measures, such as newer and more effective chelating agents designed to make iron more readily available in both sprays and fertilizer formulations.

Trace elements, which plants need in tiny amounts, can harm plants if they occur in concentrations not greatly exceeding the optimum amounts.

Physiological disturbances of plants may result from inadequate or excessive concentrations of boron, zinc, molybdenum, manganese, and copper. In some instances, plants may not be affected, but animals that eat them may suffer physiological disorders.

An increase in soil acidity causes an increase in the availability of zinc, copper, boron, and manganese. Sometimes liming acid soils will increase plant response to molybdenum.

In some countries, such as Australia and New Zealand, spectacular increases in crop production have been obtained by applications of only a few pounds of trace elements per acre.

The identification of areas where deficiencies of minor elements exist has become a great need. Research in some of the lesser developed countries indicates that potential deficiencies of trace elements may be widespread but are masked by low levels of fertility.

As crop yields in those areas increase, the deficiencies must be corrected. New diagnostic techniques and survey procedures are being developed to facilitate this, and new fertilizer formulations and chelating agents are being developed as corrective measures.

IN PLACES where it is hard to maintain an adequate level of plant nutrients in soils and where fertilizer is greatly needed but is costly and scarce, adequate information has to be provided to permit the most efficient utilization of available fertilizers. Therefore, the most economic rates and methods of application and ways to cut losses due to leaching and irreversible fixation in the soil must be determined.

The efficient use of applied nutrients depends on a correct evaluation of the needs of a given crop on a given soil. Soil-testing procedures have been developed, but they must be correlated with plant response under different soil and environmental conditions if they are to be most effective. This type of information is lacking in many underdeveloped areas.

Serious losses of native and applied nutrients result from excessive leaching of water through soils, especially in the more humid areas. Ways to reduce leaching losses by varying the time, rate, and method of fertilizer application and to determine the proper combination of soil and fertilizer material are being studied. New fertilizer materials are being developed that dissolve slowly and thereby reduce the amount of nutrient subject to leaching at any given time.

Irreversible fixation in forms not available to plants accounts for large losses of mineral nutrients applied to soils. The problem is widespread and is particularly serious in humid tropical soils. Phosphorous fertilizers are fixed as insoluble iron and aluminum phosphates in acid soils and as an insoluble tricalcium phosphate in alkaline soils.

Research workers seek to evaluate various phosphorous mechanisms of fixation. The findings are utilized to develop management practices that will help make the use of phosphorous fertilizer more efficient.

OF THE ESTIMATED 49 million cubic miles of water in the world, about 3.2 million cubic miles, or less than 7 percent, is fresh. With a world population of approximately 3 billion people, the amount of fresh water per person is more than 1,200 million gallons. Only a small fraction of the fresh water is available for man's use, however. About 28 percent occurs as polar ice and glaciers; about 70 percent is underground, mostly at depths that make extraction costly; and 1 percent is in lakes and rivers.

Because the water in lakes and rivers and underground must be recharged for continuous use, the world's total water resource—disregarding the possibility of desalinating sea water—is essentially the annual precipitation, which is small in relation to total fresh water, being approximately 25,500 cubic miles.

South America, which is the most humid continent, receives a mean annual precipitation of 53 inches.

North America, Europe, Asia, and Africa each has a mean annual precipitation of about 25 inches.

In Australia it is 18 inches.

The percentage of precipitation that runs off into rivers is of special significance from the standpoint of water available for irrigation and domestic and municipal uses. This percentage varies from 36 to 39 for North America, South America, Europe, and Asia but is only 23 and 11 for Africa and Australia, respectively.

Estimates of the percentage of annual runoff utilized for domestic, industrial, and agricultural purposes are not available by continents, but for the United States the value was 19 in 1950. It is estimated that the percentage will increase to 36 by 1975 and to nearly 60 by the year 2000.

While annual runoff in world rivers amounts to about 3 million gallons per person, local water shortages are becoming widespread because the distribution of precipitation is not uniform and the cost of transporting water great distances is high.

One means of alleviating water shortages for agriculture is by developing water conservation practices. Considerable amounts of water are lost through evaporation from soil and from water surfaces. Soil scientists constantly are seeking improved tillage and mulching methods for reducing evaporation from

soil. The application of plastic films and various chemicals to soil surfaces for evaporation suppression is also under investigation.

A significant advance in reducing evaporation from ponds and reservoirs is the discovery that the application of certain organic compounds to water surfaces in amounts sufficient to form a film one molecular layer thick reduces evaporation up to 30 percent.

Growing plants transpire enormous amounts of water—up to 800 pounds of water per pound of dry matter produced in Temperate Zones. The ratio of water used to dry matter produced may be even higher in tropical zones. It is not surprising, then, that scientists throughout the world are seeking ways to reduce transpiration without affecting growth adversely.

Research in Israel and Australia centers around the application of various chemicals to plant leaves to close partly the stomata, the small openings through which most water leaves the plant. Stomata are also the pathway by which carbon dioxide for photosynthesis enters the plant. A basic research problem is how to manipulate the opening and closing of stomata so as to reduce transpiration without causing a deficiency of carbon dioxide for photosynthesis and growth.

Not all plant growth is beneficial. Weeds and woody growth in stream channels waste water. Research is underway to find better ways to eliminate this undesirable plant growth.

Another water conservation measure under study consists of treating or covering the surface of soil-supporting non-beneficial vegetation with materials that increase runoff which may be collected for beneficial use elsewhere.

In Arizona, for example, it has been found that surface treatments involving spraying an asphalt emulsion on cleared shrub lands causes nearly complete runoff. In Utah, ground covers and storage bags of artificial rubber have proved practical for supplying water to rangeland livestock.

Reduction of seepage losses from

earthen conveyance channels and more efficient application of water to fields in irrigated areas result in marked savings of water.

Much research is in progress to develop low-cost materials and methods for sealing earthen conveyance channels, including lining them with clay and plastic film and treatment with organic compounds that tend to seal soil surfaces.

Much research has been conducted on more efficient methods for applying irrigation water, but the adoption of improved methods depends on costs and labor. Research on sprinkler irrigation, an effective way to conserve water, is largely concerned with more uniform distribution of water and automation to lessen labor costs.

It is becoming evident that, even with the adoption of stringent water conservation measures, there will be places in the world where shortages of water will occur. Interest is great therefore in the development of low-cost methods for desalinating brackish and sea water.

Intensive research on the subject is in progress at many places in the United States and in other countries. We know at least six processes for removing salt from water. The cost of some processes, such as distillation, is essentially independent of the salt content of the water, but the cost of other processes, such as electrodialysis, is strongly dependent on salt content. Thus the choice of a process may be different for brackish water than for sea water. Research centers on ways to increase efficiency and lower costs.

Except in special cases, the present cost of desalinated water is too great for use in producing food and fiber. This becomes especially evident when one considers that the present cost of irrigation water is largely for distribution. Industries and municipalities undoubtedly will become users of desalted water before agriculture because they can afford to pay a higher price. But nobody knows how cheap the cost of desalination may eventually become through research. Enormous nuclear-powered distillation plants producing electricity as a byproduct may yet make desalinated water practical for agriculture.

FROM THE STANDPOINT of meeting world agricultural needs, the problem of removing excess water from soil is perhaps as important as that of water shortages.

Excess water in soil interferes with plant growth, tillage, and harvesting and normally results from a water table that is near the soil surface.

In humid regions and in arid areas where irrigation is practiced, artificial drainage is often essential for high crop yields. Many countries have large areas of waterlogged but potentially good cropland that can be reclaimed by artificial drainage. Artificial drainage is accomplished by constructing ditches, installing tile lines at depths in the soil, or by pumping from wells.

The drainage requirements of soils often are expressed as the permissible depth of the water table beneath the soil surface. In humid regions where the ground water is essentially salt free, the permissible depth is largely determined by that required to obtain adequate soil aeration. On the other hand, the permissible depth in irrigated areas is largely dictated by that required to control soil salinity. Salts in the irrigation water and in the ground water usually increase the drainage requirement.

A minimum allowable water-table depth that will permit adequate leaching and that will prevent concentration of salts in the root zone by upward flow must be established. Thus information on the rate of upward flow in soils of various types as a function of depth to water table is necessary for determining the drainage requirements. Considerable research on this subject has been undertaken.

Great advances in drainage techniques have been made through increased knowledge of the principles governing the flow of water through soils and the application of mathematics to flow problems.

Soil permeability largely determines the required depth and spacing of drains. Good field methods have been developed for determining the permeability of soil beneath the water table, but scientists are still seeking adequate methods for measuring the permeability of soil above the water table.

Another remaining problem, one that complicates the overall evaluation of soil permeability for the installation of drains, is how to take into account differences in the permeability of different soil layers and also differences in vertical and horizontal permeability within layers.

Scientists have found that the flow of electricity in an electric conductor resembles the flow of water in soil. Voltage corresponds to the force causing water movement, electrical resistance corresponds to soil permeability, and amperage corresponds to rate of water flow. Thus electric models of drainage problems can be built and tested, and the results can be interpreted in terms of water flow instead of electric current. Additional research on the application of this technique to practical drainage problems is needed.

The installation of drainage systems, especially tile drains, is costly. Tile is made of fired clay or cement and installed by digging trenches to the desired depth. Conduits of plastics and other materials are also in use or under development.

In some areas, tiling machines dig the trench, lay the tile, and backfill more or less in one operation. In much of the world, though, most tile is laid by hand, sometimes with the aid of simple machines. Drainage would be greatly facilitated by the development of cheaper tiling materials that could be installed by simple machines. In-place casting of concrete has been tried in England.

Research has been started in the United States on the use of perforated plastic mole drain lines, which are installed behind a shoe drawn through the soil at the desired depth.

WHEN RAINFALL is too scant for crops, many countries depend on irrigation, an ancient practice on which several once-flourishing civilizations were based. Their decline has led some persons to question the permanence of irrigation agriculture.

From the standpoint of permanence, the main difference between irrigated and nonirrigated agriculture arises from salinity. Rain is essentially salt free, but water for irrigation may contain several hundred pounds or even several tons of dissolved salt per million gallons. Plants in irrigated fields absorb the water but leave nearly all the salt behind in the soil, where it accumulates and eventually prevents plant growth unless it is leached out.

The accumulation of salt has caused the abandonment of much formerly productive soil and has undoubtedly contributed to the failure of civilizations. We have learned enough about the cause, prevention, and cure of salinity, however, so we can say with some certainty that irrigation agriculture can be permanent.

Irrigation projects usually are on suitable land near rivers. Plants use most of the applied water and return it to the atmosphere through transpiration. Some is lost by evaporation, however, and some leaches through the soil and becomes drainage water. The water that drains from a project contains nearly all the salt initially in the water diverted to the project; when it returns to the river, the salinity of the river increases. Thus the increased use of water for irrigation means that the salt content of many streams in arid regions is growing.

Increases in the salt content of irrigation water make salinity control in soils more complex and difficult. To meet this problem, we have sought more information on soil, water, and crop management for salinity control and better ways to evaluate and use saline waters.

Growing salt-tolerant crops is one way to utilize saline irrigation waters. Plant scientists at the United States Salinity Laboratory are attempting to learn the mechanism of salt injury to plants and the physiological basis of salt tolerance. We hope such information will make possible the development of crop varieties having superior salt tolerance.

The possibility of using brackish waters for supplemental irrigation in humid coastal areas also is being investigated. Here the leaching action of winter rainfall prevents the accumulation of salt in the soil and permits the use of waters having salt concentrations higher than the ones recommended for arid regions.

Some irrigation waters contain a high proportion of sodium, which reacts with the soil and causes it to have poor permeability and tilth.

Procedures are needed for predicting whether soils will accumulate harmful amounts of sodium from irrigation waters. Attempts are being made to improve present procedures for waters containing high amounts of bicarbonate as well as sodium and to develop cheaper and more effective methods for reclaiming soils that have become unproductive by the accumulation of sodium. Such soils have been reclaimed by the application of gypsum or sulfur.

Experiments have indicated that some types of sodium-affected soil can be reclaimed by plowing to depths of 3 or 4 feet. Others can be reclaimed by leaching with otherwise useless saline drainage water progressively diluted with irrigation water of good quality.

C. A. BOWER *became Director of the United States Salinity Laboratory, Riverside, Calif., in 1960. Previously he was in charge of soil chemistry research at the Laboratory and assistant professor of soils at Iowa State University.*

JESSE LUNIN *is Research Investigations Leader in Water Management, Agricultural Research Service, Norfolk, Va.*

Research in Forestry

by ROBERT K. WINTERS

RESEARCH IN FORESTRY has spread from its beginnings in the 19th century in central Europe to the far corners of the world.

Research institutes are of two broad classes. Some are engaged primarily in research on timber growing: Reproducing the forest crop; improving it by application of principles of genetics; protecting it from fire, insects, and disease; thinning and making improvement cuttings; and integrating timber growing with wildlife propagation, the grazing of domestic livestock, and recreation. At some institutes, research in principles of watershed management related to forest and grass cover also is conducted.

Research at other stations is devoted primarily to the utilization of forest products—the technical properties of wood of various species, improved methods of using them in the manufacture of various finished products, ways of increasing the serviceability of wood, and economical ways of integrating the use of the forest for a combination of products requiring various qualities of wood in such a way that the maximum economic return is obtained with a minimum of actual waste of wood.

Research is conducted also at many universities, sometimes in cooperation with experiment stations.

Some research is done by private

concerns in their own laboratories or under contract to improve their processing methods.

Research to develop a diversity of highly modified products from wood has become increasingly important for several reasons.

The development of metal, glass, and other substitutes for wood has made necessary a more precise knowledge of the properties of woods in order to market them for specific purposes. An increase in the importance of paper, paperboard, plywood, plastics, and other highly specialized wood-based products has resulted in research to develop new and more effective processing methods and products. The large volume of low-quality wood that became available when the use of fuelwood declined has stimulated the development of various hardboards and particle boards.

In the developing countries, especially those that have a substantial amount of old-growth timber, research to discover how to utilize the existing stands of timber more effectively is needed. The country's economy usually needs the cash that can be derived from the timber and from the employment required in its harvesting, processing, and marketing. The virgin timber must be removed in order to establish a growing forest. These countries are beginning a cycle of forestry development at a time when the importance of highly processed products like improved plywoods, building board, corrugated boxboard, and high-quality papers is recognized.

For example, the commercial tea crop of East Pakistan, aggregating 35 million to 40 million pounds, once was shipped in birch plywood chests imported from Europe. Research on local species developed processes that made possible their use for this purpose and made a considerable saving in foreign exchange and contributed to an expanded industry.

Research in timber growing in any country ordinarily concerns itself with discovering the best means to propagate the most valuable of the native species.

At the outset, species identification, nomenclature, and identification keys are important. Next, silvical characteristics of the species—that is, ability to grow in shade, seeding habits, and rate of growth—have to be determined.

Silvicultural systems then can be devised to favor the reproduction and propagation of the preferred species. If they happen to be "light demanders," clear cutting is called for. Conversely, shade-enduring species can be reproduced under partially cut stands. Furthermore, practicable means must be developed to protect the forest from insects, diseases, and fire.

As the importance of forest cover in controlling erosion and establishing a satisfactory use of water came to be recognized, research to ascertain the effectiveness of various types of tree and grass vegetation was inaugurated. Similarly, research has been undertaken to determine the effects of shelterbelts on climate and on the soil moisture.

Genetics has received attention. Hybrids having desirable properties, including a much faster rate of growth and resistance to specific diseases, have been developed. Strains of pine are sought that give high yields of resin. The possibilities of genetics research in producing improved tree and wood products are great.

The first research on the utilization of wood emphasized the mechanical and chemical properties of individual species. Tests to determine specific gravity, strength, shock resistance, hardness, durability, fiber characteristics, and other properties were devised and have been applied to the more important commercial species.

As this basic information became available and as technology advanced in the twenties, emphasis shifted to the development of improved processes using wood in one form or another, especially those using low-quality trees, wastewood, or species generally discriminated against commercially.

Examples include the development of the semichemical and cold-soda process for manufacturing paper pulp from hardwoods, the use of waterproof glues in the manufacture of plywood, and the development of house sheathing from wood waste. Research is still directed to the determination of physical and chemical properties of little-known species.

Another general type of research concerns itself with the forestry phase of national planning. It has to do with inventories of forest resources, forecasts of future national requirements of forest products, and the potential forest industrial development in a region. In a broader sense, this economic research includes land use in general—the determination of what proportion and what categories of land had best be devoted to forest growing as against other kinds of use.

FORESTRY RESEARCH institutions are widely distributed but are most numerous in Europe. There are 34 timber-growing institutes and 24 timber-utilization institutes in Europe; 24 and 14 in the Asia-Pacific region; 33 and 10 in North America; 14 and 5 in the Soviet Union; 10 and 5 in Latin America; and 6 and 2 in Africa.

Colonial powers frequently had both a tropical forest-products research institute that tested wood from their colonies and one working on domestic species. For example, the Institute National du Bois in Paris tested the wood of species in France; the Centre Technique Forestier Tropical in Nogent-sur-Marne did the same for wood shipped from French possessions. The Netherlands and Belgium had similar institutes.

Little research on utilization was conducted in the former tropical colonies of those countries. Wood specimens were shipped to Europe for testing. Those colonial silviculturists, however, from the beginning carried out dendrological and silvical research and established timber-growing experiments in the colonies. As the volume of this experimental work increased, timber-growing research institutes were established.

With the passing of authority from colonial to national status, the operation of some of the institutes may be interrupted or discontinued because of a lack of trained research leaders.

In Africa, Latin America, and parts of southeastern Asia, information regarding good practices in timber growing and in utilization is meager. Tropical forestry research therefore is confronted with relatively more problems and has fewer trained researchers to solve them than has research in the north temperate region.

Primary among these problems is the large volume per acre of little-used species alongside commercial species in the virgin forest. Utilization research to find uses for more of the noncommercial volume is vital.

The development of silvicultural systems by which the virgin forest can be managed in such a way that ensuing natural regeneration will be concentrated largely in the more valuable species also is vital.

In parts of Africa and elsewhere, most of these valuable species tend to be "light demanders," and several procedures have been proposed to perpetuate them. Research has not yet demonstrated which of these is best under a given set of conditions or if any is likely to be wholly satisfactory. The country, meanwhile, is likely to be moving ahead on timber-cutting schemes in an effort to develop its industrial base and bring in revenue. Hence the urgency of forestry research in the Tropics.

Progress is likely to be slow, however. In countries with inadequate primary and secondary educational facilities, no professional forestry schools, no senior forestry research leadership, and little research equipment, sound and adequate research programs cannot be expected soon. Some decades will be required to provide research staffs of a size and quality that can supply solutions for the most urgent problems.

Bilateral and multilateral aid programs of the advanced nations have given help with leadership and equipment, but much more needs to be done, especially in the education and training in Europe, North America, and elsewhere of leaders from developing countries. Periodic world forestry congresses have stimulated interest in forestry research. A number of private foundations and public agencies have offered financial support.

Practically all developing countries wish to establish some pulp and paper manufacturing plants. The campaigns against illiteracy require books, and industrial development requires containers for manufactured products. Both of these products require the long, strong fibers obtained most economically from the wood of coniferous trees or (under some conditions) from bamboo to mix in appropriate proportions with the short fibers from nonconifer species or the grasses. Tropical forests, and those of some other parts of the Southern Hemisphere, lack coniferous species and may lack readily accessible supplies of bamboo. Under those conditions, book paper and container board cannot be produced without importing long-fibered pulp.

To attain maximum self-sufficiency, some countries where these conditions prevail have considered the introduction of exotic coniferous species. Research is needed to indicate for each local condition what species is likely to be most satisfactory, the seed source that will give best results in a locality, and the best method of establishing plantations and thinning them at successive ages to give maximum production for reasonable costs.

ARID REGIONS have a different set of problems. They generally have been brought to an almost treeless state through centuries of land abuse.

Modern engineering and irrigation projects are increasing the population in some; that in turn increases the need for accessible forest products for fuel, food, forage, houses, and so on.

Research is needed there to select exotic species that will survive drought, heat, and local insects and diseases and will provide wood of a quality and rate of growth that will promptly meet local needs. Forest nursery and planting techniques must be developed that will provide acceptable survival rates in establishing forest plantations.

Since the Second World War, forestry research has been greatly stimulated by international agencies. The International Union of Forestry Research Organizations has been influential in coordinating and stimulating research, especially in Europe and North America. Its scope has been increased by the addition of working groups in forest products, forestry history, and wildlife and recreation.

The Forestry and Forest Products Division of the Food and Agriculture Organization of the United Nations, which administers forestry projects of the United Nations Special Fund, has helped establish or expand a number of research institutes.

FAO launched the Latin American Forestry Research and Training Institute in Merida, Venezuela, in 1956. Similar institutes were authorized in 1961 in West Pakistan and Sudan, and in 1962 in Peru, Lebanon, and Burma.

Considerable stimulation and coordination also have been provided by the several regional forestry commissions of FAO. As one example, the Latin American Forestry Commission has had an effective Forestry Research Committee. Although Latin America has only a few established forestry institutes, the committee has done much to stimulate wide interest in strengthening research and to systematize and coordinate research.

As professional forestry schools are established in developing countries, faculty-conducted research is likely to pave the way for later establishment of research institutes.

The bilateral aid program of the United States Government—the Agency for International Development—has also stimulated forestry research in developing countries. The Pakistan Forest Research Laboratory at Chittagong, East Pakistan, was established in 1952 under this program. The Forest Products Laboratory of the United States Forest Service in 1963, in cooperation with AID, undertook research in the potential utilization of Latin American woods.

The Public Law 480 program, under which certain funds made available by the sale abroad of United States agricultural surpluses, also finances forestry research. Under this program, important research results published in languages other than English have been translated into English. Under it, research of value to the United States is also being done abroad by local scientists. In Brazil, Uruguay, and Colombia, for example, certain American coniferous species are grown to learn what local insects and diseases are harmful to them and what can be done to control them if they were accidentally to be introduced into the United States.

Improved travel and communication systems and increased emphasis on growing better wood for specific uses no doubt will give additional importance to world forestry research and make it more closely coordinated. International organizations will tend to spread improved techniques and research results more quickly around the world.

In the decades ahead we can expect that the forestry research of any nation will be cross-fertilized and enriched by the research experience of every other nation.

ROBERT K. WINTERS *became Director of Foreign Forestry Services, the Department of Agriculture, in 1961. His previous professional career was devoted almost exclusively to forestry research in the Department. He was a member of the faculty of the School of Natural Resources at the University of Michigan, and in 1952–1954 as forestry adviser in Pakistan, he assisted in developing the plans for the Pakistan Forest Products Research Laboratory.*

World Problems

in Entomology

by PAUL OMAN

A MAJOR NEED in agriculture is to develop appropriate and effective methods to prevent losses caused by insects in the production and storage of food.

We need to discover ways to use effectively the insects that benefit man and to control with the least expenditure of effort and resources those that are harmful. The methods should not harm people and their possessions. They have to be economically feasible.

Research in entomology is concerned with problems that exist today, but a major aim is to meet also the needs of the future. Agriculture is constantly changing. As it changes, new problems arise, particularly in places where new crop plants are being developed to diversify agriculture, as in the United States, and in developing countries where modern methods and different crops are replacing the primitive. Crop plants transferred to new environments encounter a new array of insect pests, and so impose a new set of problems in control.

We have made great progress. We no longer believe that insects can compete successfully with man for food and fiber, except in regions that lack modern agricultural methods. The question is not: "Can harmful insects be controlled?" It is: "How efficiently can it be done?"

Long experience with DDT and other long-lasting organic insecticides has made it clear that they will continue to have great value against certain insects but are not the cure-all that they once seemed to be. Many insects have demonstrated an ability to develop resistance to them. The residues of some long-lasting insecticides limit their usefulness on many food crops.

These circumstances and the fact that widespread use of certain organic insecticides sometimes disturbs natural balances that are favorable to man dictate that much of our attention in research be concerned with other methods, some of which can be combined with the careful use of chemicals. Thus a great deal of effort has been devoted to the study of the life processes of insects.

ONE PROMISING method, originated and developed by scientists in the Department of Agriculture, is the use of sterile insects, especially sterile males, to destroy a natural population by preventing reproduction.

A natural population of a species is overflooded with individuals reared and sterilized before they are released in the places occupied by the pest species. If enough sterile insects are present, the number of matings between fertile individuals will be greatly reduced. As the proportion of sterile to fertile individuals increases, their reproductive rate declines until no fertile eggs are produced.

Insects may be sterilized by exposing them to radioactive materials or treating them with certain chemicals. Gamma rays from a cobalt 60 irradiation unit are used customarily to achieve sterility with radioactive substances.

A number of chemical substances can sterilize insects. They have several advantages over radioactive materials, one of which is that they can be used to sterilize naturally occurring populations of pests and so make it unnecessary to rear, sterilize, and release large numbers of insects, as must be done when irradiation is used.

Regardless of which method may be chosen, a great deal of information must be available—a thorough knowledge of the life cycle and adult behavior, the natural population density, their reproductive capacity, and economical methods of producing enormous numbers of insects for sterilization. The species that is to be attacked must be studied, for its life processes and traits may differ from those of other species and methods of controlling may be different.

We need to know, first, if individual insects can be made sterile without greatly affecting their behavior and viability, particularly their ability to compete with fertile individuals for mates. If sterile individuals will not mate with normal members of the natural population, they have no effect on the reproductive ability.

We also need to know how many times normal females mate during their lifetime. Female screw-worm flies, for example, mate only once, so that in the presence of a preponderance of sterile males, the chances are that a normal female will mate only with a sterile male. Thus, when we know the approximate percentage of sterile and normal flies in a given area, we can calculate the probability of matings between fertile individuals.

Females of other species may mate repeatedly during their lifetime, and the chances of a productive mating thus are increased. Then the proportion of sterile to normal insects may need to be much higher.

We need to know an insect's lifespan in order to schedule the release of sterile insects at appropriate times. We need to know how long normal females live and remain capable of reproduction. The fact that females of some species live longer than males may have some bearing on how often sterile males need to be released. The duration of the immature stages will also influence release schedules. The flight range of a species must be known to determine how far from known infestations releases of the sterile insects should be made.

Methods of rearing insect pests in large numbers is another problem. In order to overflood normal populations with sterile populations, millions of insects may be required.

TSETSE FLIES, vectors of trypanosomiasis in livestock and man, are a major obstacle to the economic development of vast areas of Africa. Trypanosomiasis of domestic animals prevents maintenance of draft animals required to till the soil and transport agricultural materials and commodities.

Although human trypanosomiasis—sleeping sickness—has been brought under relatively good control as a result of intensive efforts during the past few decades, any relaxation of vigilance could result in a recurrence.

Within the tsetse fly belt, an area considerably larger than the United States including Alaska, are 22 different species of tsetse flies (*Glossina*). One or another can live in any type of vegetation from the dense rain forests to dry thorn scrub. These pests and the several species of trypanosomes that occur there are responsible for conditions that make productive cattle raising impossible in more than 4 million square miles of Africa, because stock maintained there will die sooner or later of trypanosomiasis.

Drugs can protect people and domestic livestock from trypanosomiasis, but it is not economically feasible to use drugs on a large scale to protect livestock. Reservoirs of trypanosomes that exist in wild animals can be eliminated by destroying game. It is economically feasible to do so, but the method generally is not considered acceptable because large numbers of animals must be destroyed.

Tsetse flies may be eliminated by starvation through the destruction of game animals or by changing the habitat in which they live. From the standpoint of African game animals, these two methods have the same end result, for game animals are customarily driven out of regions where clearing of brush, the common method of alter-

ing habitats, is undertaken. Both methods thus have objectionable features.

Intensive studies of tsetse flies thus far (1964) have failed to produce acceptable and practical methods for controlling them. The Department of Agriculture in cooperation with the Agency for International Development and the Agricultural Research Council of Central Africa in 1963 began investigations on the feasibility of using the sterility method to control or eradicate tsetse flies. The objectives are to determine whether chemosterilants found to be effective on other insects will sterilize both sexes of at least one of the important tsetse fly species without modifying essential behavior and whether methods can be devised to produce large numbers of tsetse flies for field release after they are sterilized.

LOCUSTS are widespread, and the problems they raise are complex and many sided. The numerous species are able to appear overnight, strip fields, damage whole regions, and vanish to cause similar havoc miles away.

Locusts are the intensely migratory and swarming forms of otherwise stay-at-home species of grasshoppers.

Scientists studying outbreaks of the Old World desert locust (*Schistocerca gregaria*) in Africa estimated that 500 square miles of swarms, made up of 10 billion to 50 billion individuals, invaded Kenya in January 1954. A single swarm may have as many as 10 billion locusts, often with more than 100 million concentrated within a square mile.

The number in Somaliland in August 1957 was estimated at 16 billion. Computed at one-third of a million locusts to the ton, their weight would be 50 thousand tons. Since growing or migrating locusts eat about their own weight in green food each day, the figures give an idea of the damage locusts may do to agriculture.

Outbreaks of locusts begin with subtle changes in the physiology and appearance of individuals of the solitary form of the species. These changes can occur because of crowding when the hopper is developing.

Hatchlings produced by crowded parents differ in size, weight, and color from those produced by the solitary phase of the same species. Their subsequent growth rates, number of molts, and the number of eggs the females produce are all predetermined and vary according to the degree of crowding experienced by the previous maternal generation.

The hatchlings of crowded parents can survive longer without food and water; they are preadapted to the type of environment in which they are most likely to be found.

The Anti-Locust Research Centre in London, an internationally supported research organization, has made many contributions to our knowledge of the life processes and behavior of locusts. Mapping the origin of breeding and movement of the main locust species of Africa and Asia has made it possible to determine the outbreak districts from which plagues of the African migratory locust and the red locust (*Nomadacris septemfasciata*) originate. A close, continuing watch in the districts enables authorities to act quickly to suppress an outbreak before it can develop into a plague.

But the sources of outbreaks of the desert locust and some others are not so clear. Outbreaks of the desert locust apparently may occur at any of many places in the immense desert expanses from Morocco and the Republic of Senegal, in western Africa, to India. Incipient swarms may occur at various times in many areas.

Large swarms may develop from many small swarms and scattered individuals that join as they move from one favorable spot to another. It is necessary, therefore, to detect and destroy swarms before they get beyond control.

Locusts recognize no political boundaries. International cooperation therefore is essential. Countries need to be as much concerned over a swarm that is leaving its territory as one that is entering and recognize that the country from which a swarm arrives is not necessarily the country in which it originated.

LESS OBVIOUS than the damage to crops by the locusts, fruit flies, stalk borers, and similar pests is the loss of crops because of the activities of insects that transmit plant diseases. Most viruses that cause plant disease are transmitted by insects or related arthropods.

These arthropod-borne viruses are among the most important, the most complex, and the most widely distributed agents of plant diseases.

Because the chief vectors of the viruses are aphids, leafhoppers, mealybugs, and the like, with sucking mouthparts, the relationship of the insects to the incidence of disease in plants may be difficult to establish and often is overlooked. Yet such troublesome diseases as rice stunt, beet curly top, maize streak, phony peach, tomato big bud, and many others would not be agricultural problems if it were not for insects.

While losses due to some of the diseases can be lessened by growing varieties of plants that tolerate the viruses, controlling the spread of such diseases to agricultural crops is essentially an entomological problem.

OUTBREAKS of plant diseases caused by arthropod-borne viruses depend on the occurrence in one place of the disease-causing organism, plants that are susceptible to it, and efficient vectors. That an insect can transmit a virus is not sufficient in itself; the insect must move from one host plant to another if it is to transmit a disease.

All insect vectors of plant virus diseases apparently feed on a variety of plants. Among the many factors that lead insects to move from plant to plant are their preferences for certain plants, the range in which the plants grow and their condition, and the insect's life history. Also important are climate and physiological and behavioral factors of the species.

The importance of arthropod-borne plant viruses in world agriculture is not easy to assess because we still know so little about them. Relatively little attention has been given this problem in Eurasia (except Japan) and much of Africa, but it is likely that more careful investigations there will disclose a considerable number of diseases of virus origin.

To SOLVE the known and as yet unknown agricultural problems arising from arthropod-borne plant viruses, we need a much better understanding of the complex process of virus survival and transmission and the reasons why some viruses increase in their arthropod hosts and others do not.

Virus-vector interactions and relationships are still little understood, and studies of the histology and ultrastructure of organs of arthropod vectors are needed to determine if viruses cause changes in their insect hosts. Studies of vector species in relation to the type or types of viruses they transmit will also be helpful.

The problem of control of vectors is sometimes complicated by the behavior of the pests. The beet leafhopper and the aster leafhopper move great distances each year in their dispersal or migratory flights. These insects, like the migratory locusts, can damage crops in regions far away from those in which they breed.

CROP LOSSES due to insect attack may be reduced or avoided by properties of the plants themselves. Resistance of plants to insects may be of three types.

Some varieties may be unacceptable for egg laying, food, or shelter for insects because they may contain some chemical or have a color or texture or appearance that repels insects.

Plants may also have substances or characteristics that are antagonistic to an insect and affect adversely its essential life processes. This type of resistance is termed "antibiosis."

A third type of resistance—tolerance—permits the development of insect populations while plants survive without any great reduction in yield.

Naturally occurring crop plants that resist insects may be discovered more or less accidentally during severe infestations of pests.

By testing the offspring of plants that survive and comparing them with varieties known to be susceptible, we can get general information about the extent and sometimes the nature of the resistance. A full understanding of the nature of plant resistance to insects, however, requires more studies.

The production of new crop varieties, through hybridization and subsequent selection for specific desirable characteristics, customarily requires at least 6 years, usually many more, depending on the time required to mature the plants.

A thorough knowledge of the biology and behavior of an insect in relation to its host plant is fundamental to all attempts at improving or developing resistance to insect attack in crop plants. Work of this sort requires active cooperation by entomologists and plant breeders.

Several varieties of wheat resistant to the hessian fly (*Phytophaga destructor*) have been developed. In different parts of the United States where resistant wheats are widely grown, populations of hessian fly have been reduced drastically, even though some susceptible varieties of wheat were also grown and the climate was favorable.

THE IDEA that research on methods of rearing insect pests may help to control them may seem farfetched, yet such is the case.

For many experimental purposes, entomologists need healthy insects of known age and uniform stock. Without such uniform test material, their results may be erratic and lack meaning. The sterility method of insect control may require the rearing of enormous numbers of a species, usually on an artificial diet. Beneficial insects, such as honey bees, silkworms, and some parasites, predators, and plant pollinators can be used effectively only if we know how to rear them.

Thus a great deal of attention has been directed to methods of rearing insects. A part of this problem is an understanding of the nutritional requirements of insects and the relation between diet and behavior.

The diet of an insect may affect profoundly certain of its life processes. In some species of predaceous lady beetles that hibernate as adults, the ovaries mature following hibernation only after the females feed on aphids.

Females of two species of wasps of the genus *Bracon*, both parasitic upon the Mediterranean flour moth (*Anagasta kühniella*), are sterile, and their ovaries become atrophied if they are fed only on a diet of honey. If they are permitted to feed on the body juices of the larvae of their host, which they normally do in Nature, they are fertile, and their ovaries develop normally. However, female wasps fed only on honey live as long, and some of them live twice as long, as those that feed on both honey and flour moth larvae.

In several species of wasps parasitic on the scale insect, *Aonidiella aurantii*, the sex ratio, reproduction, and size and survival of the females as compared with males vary greatly, depending on the food of the scale insect on which they live.

Among plant-feeding insects there is similar evidence of exacting nutritional requirements for growth, development, and reproduction. Some species of fruit flies—such as the cherry fruit fly (*Rhagoletis cingulata*) and the Mediterranean fruit fly—can produce a few eggs if fed only carbohydrates and water. Others, like the oriental fruit fly and the melon fly, require proteins to produce eggs.

The need for different kinds of nutrient materials—proteins, carbohydrates, minerals, and vitamins—varies among species and may change for the different stages of the same species.

Certain micro-organisms also must be present to assure the proper nutrition of some species of insects. These micro-organisms are called symbiotes or symbiotic organisms, because they live with insects in a mutually beneficial relationship. Elaborate and complex arrangements sometimes exist to pass these symbiotes from one generation of the insect to the next.

In order to understand the relationships between diets and physiological functions, a great deal more work needs to be done with different kinds of insects having a wide variety of food habits. Often it may be necessary to develop diets whose chemistry we know exactly.

Artificial diets have been developed for a variety of pests, but despite intensive study by many scientists, much is still to be learned about the precise nutritional requirements of most plant-feeding insects. Plants contain many substances insects do not use as nutrients. The composition of plants may vary with climate, nutrition, day length, and other factors. Plants that are acceptable as food for one developmental stage of an insect may be unsatisfactory for others.

Among many insects, the choice of food plant for the young is made by the adult female when she deposits her eggs. Thus the tobacco hornworm moth (*Protoparce sexta*) prefers tobacco for oviposition. The chemical stimulus in the plant that induces the female to lay eggs is quite distinct from the one that attracts her to the plant. The two acting in sequence result in the young hornworms hatching on their preferred host plant, tobacco.

From the standpoint of world agriculture, there may be no single preferred method of combating a given insect pest. Methods that are economically feasible in a highly mechanized agriculture may be impractical in places where farming is primitive.

In the selection and coordination of methods, therefore, one has to consider the level of economic and technical development of an agricultural community and also the potential benefits and practicability of short- and long-range control methods.

Until these problems are understood and answered, entomological research has not met all its responsibilities to world agriculture.

THE DAMAGE to agricultural crops is more than offset by the help insects give man in crop production.

A growing awareness of the importance of pollination by bees of fruit and vegetables, their role in the production of legume seed, and the value of cross-pollination in many other crops has led to research on the use of insects to pollinate crop plants.

The bee industry's chief contribution to the economy of the United States and probably to other agricultural countries as well is the pollination service it renders. Bee renting is a common practice in places where pollination problems are acute, but most growers pay nothing for the service.

Although honey bees customarily are used as pollinators, because they are "domesticated," most bumble bees and other kinds of wild bees are much more efficient as pollinators of several legumes, such as alfalfa and red clover.

Alfalfa must have bees to trip and cross-pollinate enough flowers to produce a commercial crop of seed. By using domestic bees judiciously, placing seed fields where wild bees abound, and encouraging increase in wild bees by providing suitable nesting areas, farmers can increase seed production.

To do these things, we need to know much more about the habits, ecological preferences, and biologies of useful wild bees. Another possibility is to develop strains of honey bees that are more efficient pollinators.

Still another possibility is to find other wild bees that are efficient pollinators and can be sufficiently "domesticated" to permit manipulation of populations as needed in crop production. More than 50 kinds of bees in Utah visit alfalfa, and perhaps the total number on alfalfa, the world over, may be several hundred.

Two of the useful species of wild bees that are in the United States were accidentally introduced from the Old World, one from Asia, the other from Africa. Several species in southeastern Europe and south-central Russia are known to be highly efficient pollinators of alfalfa. In northern Europe, alfalfa, known there as lucerne, is so frequently visited by a species of solitary bee, *Melitta leporina*, that the bee commonly is called lucerne bee.

We believe that in various countries there are many pollinators specifically adapted to tomatoes, cotton, and other crops. In Peru, a number of kinds of bees favor tomato, a plant unattractive to most bees in the United States.

A systematic search for insects that pollinate plants of importance to agriculture, followed by studies of their behavior and biology, will surely reveal possibilities for improved crop production. Then it will be relatively easy to transfer desirable species from one country to another.

INSECTS ARE USEFUL ALSO in the control of weeds.

Beetles of the genus *Chrysolina* and other insects have controlled St. Johnswort or Klamath weed (*Hypericum perforatum*) that at one time infested 2.3 million acres of rangeland in California. Partial success has been attained in several other parts of the Western States and in Australia.

The use of insects has been completely or partly successful against a number of other weeds, among them *Lantana* in Hawaii, Koster's curse (*Clidemia hirta*) in Fiji, and black sage (*Cordia macrostachya*) in Mauritius.

Studies have been started on a variety of weed-control problems. Among these are gorse (*Ulex europaeus*) in the Western States, Hawaii, Australia, and New Zealand; tansy ragwort (*Senecio jacobaea*) in the United States, Australia, and New Zealand; noogoora bur (*Xanthium strumarium*) in Australia; puncture vine (*Tribulus terrestris*), Scotch broom (*Cytisus scoparius*), and halogeton (*Halogeton glomeratus*) in the

Western States; and alligator weed (*Phylloxeroides alternanthera*) in parts of the Southeastern States.

Investigations that are required in connection with the manipulation of insect populations for control of weeds are concerned primarily with ecological requirements of the insect species and the relationship that exists between it and the weed host. Normally only insects that have a very narrow range of host plants are considered for use in this sort of work. Particular attention must be given to the factors that cause an insect species to be specific in its selection of host plants.

The objective of these studies is to select species of insects that will not harm plants other than the one to be controlled or at least will not harm useful plants. This determination is customarily made by conducting starvation tests, in which populations of the species to be tested are confined on a variety of plants, and their ability to survive and reproduce is assessed.

Because biological control is mostly of a negative nature—that is, it prevents the appearance of damaging numbers of pests, rather than eliminating them after they are present—its significance to agriculture is hard to assess. Only occasionally, such as when the use of insecticidal chemicals has destroyed the natural enemies of certain insects in a given area, do we see positive evidence of the importance of the thousands of species of insects that live at the expense of other insects. As long as this balancing effect between prey and predators or parasites remains undisturbed, we have no way of knowing exactly what retarding pressure one insect or group of insects may exert that prevents a population explosion by a pest species.

The biological control method has involved the movement of parasites and predators from one region to another in which they were to be used. Most strains of parasites are adapted to a relatively narrow range of conditions and may have rather exacting host requirements. Relatively few of the species or strains introduced into new geographic areas therefore become established; of them, still fewer effectively control their pest hosts. That may be due to factors of climate, a difference in timing between host and parasite, lack of suitable alternate hosts, or other complex factors. Yet we have evidence that adaptive races of many parasitic species occur in Nature and hope therefore that improved strains of parasites may be developed.

Very likely the principles of selective breeding that have been used to improve strains of domestic animals and varieties of plants can also be used to develop or improve strains of parasitic insects.

The requirements are determination of the modifications desired, an adequate source of the germ plasm that contains potential for maximum variability, and adequate selection and breeding procedures.

Once desirable strains have been developed, their purity in the field will need to be maintained.

The possibilities of pest resurgence, or secondary outbreaks, are always with us when we use chemicals that are toxic to a range of arthropod species. These problems cannot be ignored.

Selective pesticides, more or less specific to the pest species and relatively harmless to their natural enemies, would be a solution, if they can be developed.

Research on methods of using non-selective insecticides so as to minimize their effect on arthropods other than pests in the environment is likewise needed. The earlier we recognize a potential problem of this sort, the better our chances of dealing with it.

TAXONOMIC ENTOMOLOGY is the arranging or classifying of species of insects in an orderly manner according to their relationships. Until insect species are named, they cannot well be talked about or written about. Until they have been described, they cannot be identified. Identification of a species permits us to find whatever information has been accumulated about it. Once a species is classified, we have a basis for making deductions regarding its general biology or behavior. Work in insect taxonomy has been in progress for nearly 200 years. Some 700 thousand kinds of insects have been named so far.

Yet reliable estimates of the total number of insect species in the world indicate that less than half have been named so far. Of the thousands that have been named, only a relatively small percentage has been described in a satisfactory manner.

To complete this task of describing, naming, and classifying insects, we need more workers, more facilities, new techniques of study, and more efficient methods for organizing, storing, and retrieving the enormous amounts of information we do have.

Even though many agricultural organizations and museums throughout the world maintain insect collections and employ taxonomists, the demand for identifications far exceeds what can be supplied by personnel concerned with this task. For example, each year the insect identification unit of the United States Department of Agriculture makes some 85 thousand to 100 thousand identifications as a service to scientists, farmers, and others. This work may require the analysis of 500 thousand individual insects. Many of the requests for assistance come from foreign countries.

It is to be expected that as new methods and new crops are introduced into developing countries and as agriculture expands into new regions, new or little known insects will appear as crop pests. More and more attention therefore will have to be devoted to the methods and means of identifying insects.

PAUL OMAN *is an entomologist with the Entomology Research Division, Agricultural Research Service, United States Department of Agriculture. He has published numerous papers on insects.*

Cooperation in Crops

by JOHN H. MARTIN

NO CROP is perfect. Every cultivated crop is amenable to improvement by breeding and better cultural practices. All varieties of every crop have certain weaknesses or characteristics that often limit their usefulness. All crop varieties are subject to injury by several insects, diseases, and unfavorable weather and soil conditions.

Average world yields of most crops are only one-tenth to one-half of those attainable when all conditions are favorable. Future world food shortages must be met by better crop production.

Crop yields in many underdeveloped and autocratic countries are now far below the levels that could be obtained by the application of modern crop science. The rapid rise in advanced countries since 1950 in acre yields of some of the major crops demonstrates the possibilities of improvement.

The development of corn and sorghum hybrids adapted to local conditions has increased potential crop yields in the United States and some other countries by 20 to 30 percent. Better cultural practices, such as heavy application of fertilizer and supplemental irrigation, permit thicker planting. These practices and better control of disease, insects, and weeds raise the basic yield level. Then a 25-percent increase in yield resulting from hybrids means more bushels per acre than from mediocre basic yields.

Crop yields may well be doubled by the combined improvements.

Uniform quality may be unimportant for food crops that are processed and consumed on the home farm, but is essential for industrial, market, and export commodities. Subsistence farms often grow mixed, local varieties of crops. Nearby communities may be producing different mixed varieties. These crops can be standardized by collecting, purifying, and testing the local varieties. Pure seed of the better varieties of good quality can then be increased and distributed to growers.

In many countries of Asia and Africa, the collection and evaluation of local grain varieties on a national scale was not even attempted until after the Second World War. In many instances, the general production of the better varieties is scarcely started.

THE GREATEST opportunities in crop research are in breeding, disease control, and mineral nutrition.

The development of disease- and insect-resistant varieties is most urgent. Some diseases, like the rusts and smuts of the cereals, are prevalent wherever grain is grown. Certain soil-infesting fungi that cause plant diseases are damaging most crops throughout the world. The insidious nematodes occur widely. Destructive insects are always present. Pesticides often prevent crop losses from these pests, but the cheapest control comes from the breeding of resistant varieties.

Sometimes resistance to a particular pest or disease can be found in adapted cultivated varieties. Usually, however, the best source of resistance is in exotic varieties or related wild species that are unsuitable for domestic culture.

In such instances, 10 to 20 years of intensive breeding are needed to develop a resistant variety that also is satisfactory to the grower and the consumer.

But resistance to the most important disease does not protect the variety from other losses. Thus, to insure a healthy crop, breeders must incorpo-

rate resistance to all of the damaging prevalent diseases. That requires many more years of effort during the initial stages of the project.

Later, when breeders over the world have developed lines that are resistant to several diseases, the hereditary factors may be combined to produce varieties with multiple resistance. This can best be realized by the free interchange of materials and knowledge among the research workers over the world.

Breeding crops for resistance to insects and nematodes will follow a similar pattern and must eventually be combined with disease resistance.

VARIETIES DIFFER in their content of vitamins and proteins and of certain of the amino acids that are essential in human and animal nutrition. The nutritive quality of many food crops could be improved by selection and breeding for those characteristics.

Likewise, many grain, fiber, and oil crops could be improved by breeding for better industrial or processing qualities.

Some examples: New industrial uses have been established in corn by breeding hybrids with an endosperm that is waxy or that is high in amylose content. Fibers can be lengthened, strengthened, or improved in spinning qualities by breeding. Oilseed crops can be improved in oil content, oil composition or protein content, and protein quality.

Fertilizers are used only sparingly for growing the major food crops in underdeveloped countries. Often the leading varieties grown in those places are the ones that have become adapted to soils of low productivity through a process of natural or manual selection. Often their response to heavy applications of fertilizer is limited.

When it is desired to increase crop yields by the use of ample fertilizer, it may be necessary to choose or breed other varieties so as to realize the maximum benefits.

Rice, sorghum, and pearl millet are

among the crops that will require modification to fit higher productivity levels in certain countries.

Improved farming technology, particularly in shifting to mechanized operations, also may make it necessary to breed varieties that are suited to changing methods. The grain sorghum varieties that grow 12 to 15 feet tall in tropical Africa cannot be harvested with a combine. The tall weak-stalked rice varieties grown in much of southeastern Asia often lodge so that they must be harvested by hand.

Grain sorghum, cotton, castor beans, sesame, rice, soybeans, and snap beans are among the crops in which varieties have been bred to meet the requirements for efficient mechanical harvesting and handling in the United States.

BASIC RESEARCH is essential to an understanding of the behavior, adaptation, and hereditary characteristics of each crop.

Extensive scientific facts, accumulated by research workers over the world, have been helpful to workers who are attempting to solve practical problems. Much of the crop improvement in past centuries was accomplished with little scientific knowledge to serve as a guide.

But progress is greatly accelerated if the research worker has sufficient basic information to enable him to formulate practical plans and to predict the probable outcome. The plant breeder may develop quickly a new variety with a desired characteristic when he knows the hereditary behavior of those characters in crosses.

Basic research often points the way to practical improvements. The concept of hybrid corn is an example. G. H. Shull, of the Carnegie Institution of Washington, was studying the genetics of corn characters at Cold Spring Harbor in New York. He was not engaged in the breeding of better corn varieties. It was necessary to inbreed the corn in order to obtain uniform lines for investigation. Inbreeding re-

sulted in small plants with little vigor. When he intercrossed certain of the runty inbred lines, he obtained vigorous and productive hybrid plants.

From this observation, in 1909, he proposed the breeding of corn hybrids to obtain higher yields.

The success of hybrid corn engendered an interest in developing other hybrids. Hybrids of most other crops, however, cannot be produced by a simple operation, such as the detasseling of corn plants to eliminate pollen shedding in the seed-parent rows of the hybrid seed field.

Another corn geneticist, Dr. M. M. Rhoades, reported a cytoplasmic male-sterile character in some of his progenies. This led to a search by others for this character. It since was found in a number of crops. The removal of anthers—the pollen-bearing flower organs—is avoided in producing hybrid seed on cytoplasmic male-sterile plants, because the anthers bear no pollen. Hybrid seed is produced merely by interplanting a pollinator line with a male-sterile seed parent line.

Hybrid onions, hybrid sorghum, hybrid sugarbeets, and hybrid castor beans now are grown on a big scale. Hybrids of wheat and several other crops merely await further developments. Many countries are reaping the benefits from hybrid seed by applying the knowledge obtained by research workers in the United States.

MANY COUNTRIES have established experiment stations to test crops, varieties, and cultural methods. Most have several such stations, and the larger countries have field stations, where the answers to local or national crop problems are sought. The better equipped stations provide laboratory facilities for plant pathologists, chemists, engineers, and entomologists to supplement the research of the crop scientists.

In the United States, research on crops, crop protection, and crop utilization is being conducted by the 50 State agricultural experiment stations at nearly 300 branch stations and laboratories and at perhaps 100 additional experiment fields. The United States Department of Agriculture maintains cooperation at many of these locations and also conducts research with crops at a number of independent locations.

THE INTERNATIONAL CEREAL RUST NURSERIES exemplify the cooperation among research scientists of different nations. This project involves about 150 scientists, who test more than a thousand varieties of wheat, oats, and barley for resistance to rust and other diseases in 176 nurseries at 85 experiment stations in 40 countries.

International research on rust began in 1919, when uniform wheat nurseries were planted at several experiment stations in the United States and Canada. Cooperative research was started with Mexico after 1940 and with several countries in South America in 1950.

The planting of rust nurseries in foreign countries is voluntary, and the cooperation is informal. Correspondence, reports, instructions, and seed shipments are routed directly between the scientific leader in the United States and the scientists overseas.

Each participating country provides seed of any of their lines that appear to be resistant to rust. These then are tested in all cooperating countries.

Copies of the data from all countries are sent to all cooperators. The information from other countries enables a scientist to evaluate his material quickly. Several more years of testing might be required if the tests were limited to his own country. Because natural rust epidemics are erratic, no useful data are obtained in years in which abundant rust is lacking at a particular station.

The international rust nurseries are particularly valuable because varieties of grain can be tested for reaction to the prevalent world races of the fungus organism without the hazard of introducing exotic races into countries where they do not yet occur.

Good will among countries has been fostered by the international rust nursery program. Breeders formerly were reluctant to supply their selected lines to workers in other countries before their release to their own growers, because of the possibility of competitive exploitation. Now they recognize the advantages of an international exchange that permits any country to utilize varieties from any cooperating nation. Seed of several new wheat varieties from other countries has been increased and distributed in a cooperating country after tests in the rust nursery.

THE BASIC FEATURES of the uniform rust nurseries and of other uniform crop nurseries conducted in the United States have been helpful in improving agriculture in many countries.

The United States Department of Agriculture coordinates the uniform testing of many crops. Workers at any interested State experiment station may participate. Many of the State experiment stations conduct the tests on an informal basis without Federal subsidy for the project.

The national potato improvement program involves about 40 States. A free exchange of materials and information speeds up recommendations and releases of new varieties by shortening the testing period. Usually tests continue about 5 years before new materials are recommended or released when the testing is confined to a single State. When tests in surrounding States confirm the local results, sound conclusions may be drawn after 2 or 3 years of testing. Similar progress can be expected from international testing.

SCIENCE RECOGNIZES no political or racial boundaries. Communication among scientists in different countries has gone on for more than a century.

The United States Department of Agriculture has been collecting seed and plant materials from all over the world on an organized basis since about 1890. The world wheat collection maintained by the Crops Research Division numbers some 16 thousand lots. These and other crop collections are available for use in any country where they are needed.

The late Russian scientist, N. I. Vavilov, assembled large world seed collections between 1920 and 1940. Limited numbers of the crop varieties in this collection occasionally are supplied to other countries.

INTERNATIONAL scientific societies conduct meetings at intervals of about 3 years. They are concerned with a specific scientific field, such as botany, genetics, seeds, or horticulture. Plant scientists employed by the Federal or State Governments of the United States frequently travel to other countries to participate in these meetings. These contacts are mutually beneficial in promoting international relations as well as in diffusing knowledge.

It is obvious that research accomplishments often are greatly accelerated when undertaken by teams of scientists with different types of training. Free interchange of information and materials among nations is equally important.

In 1908 the first president of the American Society of Agronomy stated that wheat varieties had been tested for 100 years previously and that new varieties would be undergoing tests 100 years hence. Now, after 55 years more of productive research on wheat, many other achievements still appear to be 100 years in the future. One should not be discouraged by the long task ahead.

JOHN H. MARTIN retired on July 1, 1963, after working nearly 49 years as research agronomist in the Agricultural Research Service. His research in crops covered many States and several countries in Europe, Asia, and Africa. He is the joint author of two textbooks dealing with crops. He contributed chapters to eight previous Yearbooks of Agriculture.

Problems in

Human Nutrition

by HAZEL K. STIEBELING and
RUTH M. LEVERTON

MUCH OF OUR PRESENT insight into the functions of nutrients and our nutritional requirements has come from studies of food habits of people who differ in health and physique.

The studies reveal great differences in the amounts of food customarily eaten by persons in different parts of the world and in the proportions of the different kinds of food.

The kinds of food we can put in three broad groups: (1) Seeds of grasses and of leguminous plants; nuts; and the flesh of beast, fishes, and fowl. (2) Starchy roots, tubers, and the fruits; sugars; and the separated fats and oils. (3) Milk, eggs, and the succulent vegetables and fruits.

The groups differ widely in nutritional value, but several similarities exist within each group.

THE SEEDS and cereals, pulses (peas, beans, lentils), nuts, and meat provide much the same assortment of nutrients—proteins, B-vitamins, and minerals, especially iron and phosphorus—as well as calories.

The contribution the cereal products make to the mineral and vitamin content of diets depends largely on the extent to which these nutrients are retained or restored when food is processed. Generally, though, the cereal grains contain less protein, minerals, and vitamins in proportion to their energy value (calories) than the pulses, and the pulses contain less than most products of animal origin.

An example is the differences in protein concentration in several types of food—a man using 3,000 Calories and 70 grams of protein (about 2.5 ounces) per day would be getting 2.33 grams of protein per 100 Calories: Polished rice, 1.85; all-purpose wheat flour, 2.90; degerminated corn grits, 2.40; mature dry beans, 6.56; peanuts, 4.63; low-fat soybean grits, 12.19; milk (3.5 percent fat), 5.39; milk (0.1 percent fat), 10; eggs, 7.91; lean round beef (11 percent fat), 10.25; codfish, 23.84; salmon, 10.37.

Those differences reflect differences in the degree of dilution of the protein with carbohydrate or fat or both.

Not only do milk, eggs, meat, and fish contain more protein per 100 Calories than most of the pulses or cereals. They provide more of the amino acids that the human body must have but cannot make. Proteins of animal origin therefore are said to have high biological value.

Most pulses, however, may supplement cereals in much the same way that animal products can. A comparison of the amount of lysine—one of the amino acids in short supply in cereals—provided in relation to the amount of protein (expressed as milligrams per gram of nitrogen) exemplifies the point: Rice, 235; white wheat flour, 130; corn, 150; quinoa, 414; ragimillet, 190; mature dry beans, 464; lentils, 382; chickpeas, 431; peanuts, 223; soybeans, 395; cottonseed flour, 268; sesame seed, 160; sunflower seed, 200; eggs, 400; milk, 496; beef, 546; fish, 548.

STARCHY FOODS (other than the cereals in the first group), sugars, and fats serve chiefly as sources of food energy. With few exceptions, they are practically devoid of proteins, minerals, and vitamins. They dilute the nutritive value of the total diet when they are used in large amounts.

THE THIRD GROUP—milk, eggs, and the succulent vegetables, and fruit—is often called protective foods, because they contribute nutrients not supplied at all or supplied to only a limited extent by the other two groups. They are the chief contributors of vitamins A and C, riboflavin, and calcium. Milk and eggs also furnish high-quality protein.

To exert a protective influence against deficiency diseases, it is desirable to include as much as 500 Calories per person per day from an assortment of the foods in group 3.

Southeastern Asia, western and central Africa, and countries in the northern and western parts of South America get one-half to more than three-fourths of their calories from foods in group 1—cereals, pulses, and meat.

In addition, western and central Africa get 40 percent of their calories from group 2—the starchy roots and fruits, sugar, fats, and oils. Southeastern, western, and central Africa use only small amounts of the protective foods from group 3.

It follows, then, that deficiencies of vitamin A, ascorbic acid, and riboflavin are observed in some regions and among some populations in all these countries and that calorie-protein deficiencies are prevalent, especially among young children, in western and central Africa.

Vitamin A deficiency is widespread in these low-calorie countries, particularly in Indonesia, mainland China, India, and elsewhere in the Far East, in parts of Latin America; and in the semiarid zones of Africa. It is due to insufficient intakes of green and yellow vegetables, or too little fat to promote utilization of carotene from these foods, milk, butter, eggs, fish-liver oils, and carotene-containing vegetable oils, such as red palm oil. Severe deficiency results in skin disorders, night blindness, and blindness.

Nutritional anemias also are frequent in countries where green leafy vegetables are eaten in only small amounts and where diets are low in meat and eggs. This condition may result from dietary deficiencies of iron, folic acid, and other nutrients associated with intakes of too little good protein.

Calcium intake is limited and often inadequate in parts of the world where diets are low in milk and green leafy vegetables. When low levels of dietary calcium are associated with little exposure to sunlight, there may be high incidence of rickets in children and bony deformities in mothers. These conditions are found in parts of India and Burma, the Near East, and northern Africa.

Other common signs of malnutrition in developing countries are sore lips and sore tongues due to lack of vitamin B_2, or riboflavin. The deficiency results from a high concentration of starchy staple foods and too little meat, milk, eggs, and fresh leafy vegetables.

In any place where diets comprise large amounts of cereal products, the forms used should be lightly milled, whole grain, or enriched with the B-vitamins and minerals. Beriberi, due to the lack of thiamine, virtually disappeared from areas in Indonesia, Taiwan, and India when people began to use undermilled or parboiled rice. The Government of Nigeria, where production of rice has been expanding, has insisted on the use of parboiled and undermilled rice, but the increasing use of machine milling and consumption of highly polished rice in some parts of the Far East has spread beriberi.

A disease, called kwashiorkor in Africa and pluricarencial infantil in Latin America, is common among young children in many sections of Africa, Latin America, the Near East, India, and southeastern Asia. It is due to a deficiency of protein and calories. The growth of afflicted children may cease; mental and physical lethargy, swelling of the soft tissues, fatty deposits in the liver, diarrhea, and skin ulceration, changes in the composition of blood, and greatly decreased resistance to infections may follow.

In places where protein-calorie deficiency is common, the chief low-cost food that is used as a source of calories may be corn, rice, sorghum, tapioca root (manioc, mandioca, or poi), crude sugar, yams, yautias, bananas, potatoes, or millet. All are good food when used in moderation with other food. When they are used to excess, the diet lacks enough good-quality protein, as is supplied by milk, eggs, and meat. Beans or other legumes may furnish some extra protein, but the quality or amount often is too low to permit normal growth or good health.

A nutritional survey in Uganda, where plantains, a starchy staple, are particularly important in the diet, showed an incidence of kwashiorkor ranging from 6 to 11 percent in different groups of young children.

Surveys in southern Nigeria, where yams and cassava are the staple foods, showed an incidence of kwashiorkor among young children of about 5 percent—significantly more than the 2 percent in northern Nigeria, where millets are the staple foods.

A high incidence of kwashiorkor has occurred in the Feshi district of Congo (Léopoldville), where cassava provides more than 80 percent of the total intake of calories. In regions where kwashiorkor is severe, the death rate among children from weaning time to 5 years may be 10 to 30 times above the rate when protein is adequate.

The reported occurrence of protein-calorie malnutrition refers to cases with well-defined clinical signs. Less serious cases are much commoner. It has been said that most people in central Africa have suffered from the disease at some time in their childhood, often with permanent aftereffects. An increasing use of pulses, as in India and Pakistan, and of milk and other animal products, as in Japan and Taiwan, is helping to reduce the incidence of protein malnutrition.

Poor sanitation and inadequate medical care contribute greatly to the kwashiorkor problem, but the primary impairment of health results from protein deficiency coincident with less breast milk for babies.

School feeding programs cannot meet the need because the greatest damage is done in preschool years. Half of the children may die before reaching school age. Those who survive grow slowly and seldom fully recover from early stunting.

Because it is hard in many regions to raise the production of foods that are rich in animal protein, minerals, and vitamins, attention has been given to increasing the use of pulses and oilseed cake, which contain amino acids that can supplement those from cereals.

The development, testing, and promotion of protein-rich products for children has been successful in Latin America, Africa, and India.

The product first introduced in Guatemala by the Institute of Nutrition in Central America and Panama and called Incaparina (formula 9) consists of 38 percent cottonseed flour, 29 percent grain sorghum, 29 percent cornmeal, 3 percent torula yeast, 1 percent calcium carbonate, and 3,500 international units per pound of a stable form of vitamin A. The formula provides a combination of plant foods that yields protein of high biological value and also contains minerals and vitamins needed to supplement the customary diets.

An uncooked form of Incaparina is used as a cereal gruel and in tortillas, soup, and similar products. A precooked, more stable and soluble form, formula 9–A, is used as a beverage or atole. Various modifications have been tested for use in other areas where cultural and farm practices are different. Formula 9–T is an uncooked product in which the corn and sorghum are replaced by 58 percent wheat flour. Formula 9–R contains 58 percent rice flour instead of corn and sorghum.

Cottonseed flour is used in the basic formula because it contains more of certain essential amino acids than corn, sorghum, rice, and wheat flour and thus can supplement them. Soy flour or sesame flour also is used.

Sunflower seed offers promise in some regions. Peanut flour, which is not quite as satisfactory, has been introduced in Africa and India.

Other protein products that contain fish flour, skim milk powder, or crude casein have been introduced in Latin America and Africa. Promising new forms of fish and soy products have been developed in Japan.

MOST OF THE PROBLEMS we have discussed so far are the results of diets that are poor in quality.

Undernourishment also is a problem, for an estimated 400 million people are undernourished in the sense that calories, rather than proteins, minerals, and vitamins, are the first limiting factor of their diet.

Some of them are dying of starvation. Others can do less work. The mental and physical development of children is retarded. Chronic undernutrition, especially during the period of growth, probably accounts in part for the slight build and short stature of people in some countries.

Research with domestic animals has shown that gain in height is reduced when diets are deficient in calories. Any gain in height occurs at the expense of gain in width of skeleton and the normal development of soft tissues. For many people, a chronic state of undernourishment and malnourishment has been the usual state for generations. We are beginning to realize the so-called national characteristics of size and build may actually be the characteristics of people needing more food and better food.

Overall food supplies for the Near East, Africa, and Latin America are estimated to be about equal to requirements. Those for the Far East fall short of the requirements by about 10 percent. Those for Europe, North America, and Oceania are sufficient to meet their average needs and exceed them by about 20 percent.

The sufficiency of estimated food supplies to meet requirements for food should be interpreted with care.

For example, the apparent self-sufficiency of calorie supplies in the Near East as a region is due to the somewhat higher level of supplies in Turkey, the United Arab Republic, Syria, Lebanon, and Israel. These countries account for half of the population in the region. The supplies of other countries in the same region—Iran, Iraq, Saudi Arabia, and Jordan—amount only to about 2,200 Calories per person per day.

The same observation applies to the Far East where, for example, Japan and Taiwan are relatively much better fed than other countries in the region.

Variation in the food supplies of different social-economic classes of the population within one country is larger in the developing countries.

It is believed that regions containing more than half of the world's population have enough food supplies at the retail level (not the actual intake) to furnish an average of fewer than 2,250 Calories per person per day. That is not sufficient for a population to be well fed. From the distribution of food by economic groups within countries, it has been estimated that at least 20 percent of the population in the Far East and probably 10 to 15 percent of all of the people in the world are undernourished.

Life expectation is less in countries where food balance sheets show per capita Calorie values under 2,200 per day and where the ratio of weight to height at every age tends to be less than in countries where food supplies are abundant. But in these situations, diets are generally inferior not only in calories but also in protein, minerals, vitamins, singly or in combination.

FOOD SUPPLIES furnishing an average of more than 2,750 Calories per person per day are available to less than one-third of the world's population. Some persons in these high-advantaged situations, including the few well-to-do in the poor countries, encounter nutrition problems also—the problems of too much food, of not choosing wisely

from abundance. They overeat in relation to the amount of muscular work which they do and run greater than average risks of coronary heart disease, cerebral strokes, diabetes, general atherosclerosis, hypertension, cancer, and liver and kidney ailments.

High-calorie regions, such as Western Europe, North America, and Oceania, tend to derive up to 1 thousand Calories or more a person a day from foods of group 2—those important chiefly for carbohydrates or fat and which, with few exceptions, are practically devoid of proteins, minerals, and vitamins. But, in contrast to western and central Africa, this high consumption of such foods is accompanied by a relatively high consumption—more than 500 Calories—of succulent vegetables and fruits, milk, eggs, and large quantities of muscle meats and fish. In consequence, deficiencies of protein, vitamins A and C, riboflavin, niacin, or calcium rarely occur.

Some nutritional diseases of man and animals appear to be rather independent of the kind and amount of food consumed or the economic prosperity of the population.

Environmental factors are involved, such as the iodine content of air, water, and food in relation to goiter, and the fluorine content of water in relation to the incidence of dental caries. Endemic goiter is a nutritional deficiency disease found in areas where the soil and drinking water are low in iodine.

QUESTIONS as to nutritional requirements for good growth, high work output, and longevity and factors affecting them are of great urgency.

What rate of growth is best? What is optimal body composition at different stages of the life cycle to promote good health and longevity? How much physical work is necessary to maintain muscle tone and to enable one to eat enough to meet protein, mineral, and vitamin needs as well as those for calories? What are the dependable food sources of these nutrients?

Research on the composition of food is essential in appraising customary diets and in planning the production of food for improved nutrition. The importance of regional studies of the nutritive values of local foods is highlighted by such findings as the difference in lysine content of proteins within classes of food.

There now are available compilations of the nutritive values of foods commonly used in Latin America and the Far East as well as for countries in Europe and North America. Most of these tables should be expanded to include a larger number of essential nutrients and the effects of commercial and household processing on the values of foods as they are eaten.

The task of learning the values of native foods as customarily prepared is a large one in all the developing countries. Such research has been undertaken in India, the Philippines, Japan, and some countries of Latin America and Africa.

We know that ascorbic acid prevents scurvy; thiamine, beriberi; niacin, pellagra; and vitamin D, rickets. But even where considerable advances have been made, there still is incomplete understanding. It is known, for example, that shortages of vitamin A can lead to xerophthalmia and blindness, but it is not known why this occurs in some places where there is an ample dietary supply of carotene, the precursor of vitamin A.

Studies have been started to determine whether the low content of fat, characteristic of such diets, is a factor, and if so, how much fat and of what kinds are needed to correct the trouble.

Anemias that result from simple iron deficiency have long been recognized, but in the United Arab Republic where dietary iron is ample, a zinc deficiency has been identified as a causative factor in anemias.

Clinical surveys of the health of population groups are used to point out specific troubles in specific areas and in specific individuals. While useful for the detection of frank disease, the purely clinical approach is unreliable for the evaluation of mild degrees of deficiency.

But clinical signs that are examined in conjunction with food intake and laboratory findings are meaningful in diagnosis of nutritional disorders that are less severe than those that result in obvious diseases such as beriberi or pellagra. Laboratory techniques are available for measuring the concentration of nutrients or their metabolic products in body fluids and for evaluating enzyme systems that depend on specific nutrients for optimal activity. The interpretation of the findings, however, requires more study.

We need more information of the kind we can derive from chemical and biological assays of the nutritive value of foods as consumed and information derived from controlled metabolic studies of the relationship between different levels of nutrient intake and nutritional well-being of the population groups.

Research is needed and some has been undertaken to determine the relative importance of nutrition and other factors in the cause or prevention of diseases still of uncertain etiology. Among such diseases are atherosclerosis, diabetes, sprue, bladderstone, and celiac disease.

Coronary heart disease is associated with obesity as well as with elevated serum cholesterol levels and hypertension. Obesity can be treated with diet. Elevated cholesterol levels can sometimes be brought under control by lower intakes of fat, together with some shift from highly saturated dietary fats to polyunsaturated oils. But other dietary factors are known also to be involved, such as the amounts and kinds of protein and of carbohydrate and the balance among several different vitamins and minerals.

Furthermore, research must clarify the relative importance of diet, physical activity, and heredity in preventing or controlling this disease. This is a problem of great importance, and much attention is being given it.

Study also must be made of the interrelationships between nutrition and susceptibility to illness and mortality from tuberculosis, measles, and other specific infections.

If people the world over are to benefit from research and understanding of the principles of nutrition, the results must be interpreted to answer the practical problems faced by family food managers, consumers, teachers, physicians, and public leaders and Government agencies that formulate national and international food programs. Many different combinations of foods can meet the nutritional requirements of normal, healthy persons.

Research also is needed to lead to better understanding of why food choices are made and how food habits can be modified. Dependent on such knowledge is success of programs of nutrition education and food distribution, as well as all efforts to influence people to use new or different foods.

Thus, further scientific research is needed to define the zones of intake of essential nutrients that will free people from obvious ill health and will undergird the highest possible level of physical and mental vigor throughout the life cycle and through successive generations.

Research must then translate the information into food practices and dietary patterns which are practical in view of economic, cultural, and agricultural potentialities of populations living in different parts of the world.

HAZEL K. STIEBELING *was Deputy Administrator, Agricultural Research Service, when she retired in 1963. She joined the Department in 1930 and was named in 1942 to supervise the Department's research program in human nutrition and home economics.*

RUTH M. LEVERTON, *Assistant Administrator, Agricultural Research Service, joined the Department of Agriculture in 1957. She has special responsibility for the program in Nutrition and Consumer-Use Research, including human nutrition.*

Problems in Animal Husbandry

by RALPH E. HODGSON and NED D. BAYLEY

WE ALL AGREE on the need to improve the diets of people in many countries.

We agree also that sources of animal protein must be expanded in order to accomplish that. While some of this protein food may come from local sources of fish, the larger part must come from farm livestock and poultry.

The problem then is to increase the producing ability of livestock and poultry—of which many countries have large numbers—by creating conditions of feeding and management that permit satisfactory performance and by controlling and eliminating diseases and parasites that cause staggering losses of animals and that contribute to low production.

Through long investigation and experience, we have found that greatest returns from animal production, whether it is milk, beef, swine, sheep and wool, eggs, or poultry meat, come when high animal performance is attained.

WE HAVE FOUND that 10 conditions are needed to achieve successful livestock and poultry enterprises.

The individual farmers should have the interest and ability and potential resources to engage in the enterprise with the prospect of success.

The enterprise should be adapted to the locality, the land, and the climate.

In establishing livestock or poultry enterprises, adequate information should be available to the individual.

Access to a market for the product produced should be assured. The existence of such markets and their availability to the producer have been critical to the incentives for improving the care and breeding of animals.

The livestock and poultry should be adapted to the existing environment. The ability of indigenous animals to reproduce and to produce efficiently and economically should be thoroughly tested and their abilities utilized.

Exogenous types with particularly adapted qualities should be introduced when conditions indicate.

Breeding programs, national, regional, and within herd, should be developed to improve steadily the producing ability of animals. Record-of-performance programs should be developed and applied to measure productivity, to guide management practices, and to identify superior breeding stock. Breeding service by artificial insemination should be developed and employed to use superior germ plasm to improve performance.

An adequate year-round feed supply, based on local farm-produced forage and grain supplemented with concentrate mixes to avoid nutritional deficiencies, is needed.

An effective program of disease and parasite control and eradication should include an adequate, qualified veterinary service. A livestock industry cannot flourish and meet a country's needs for animal foods under conditions of unabated diseases that terminate in death of animals or produce continuous ill health and low production.

An appropriate sanitary service should be available to supervise the production, processing, and marketing of animal products. The development and maintenance of good markets require that the foods be wholesome and produced in clean conditions.

A strong research and development effort is needed to improve husbandry and disease control practices.

An active extension program is required to take the latest research findings from the laboratory to the farmer and aid him in applying this new knowledge to his production problems.

IN REGIONS where livestock enterprises have prospered, research is directed toward making further improvement in an already efficient industry.

For example, research on nutrition and breeding have resulted in a broiler industry that can produce birds of 3.5 pounds for market in 65 days, compared to the 91 days needed before the research findings were applied.

Research investigators have turned their attention to increasing feed efficiency further by studying the inter-relationships of minerals, proteins, and other nutrients.

Geneticists also have undertaken to increase feed efficiency by selecting for that trait directly; selection previously emphasized increased rate of growth of the animals or an increase in production of milk, eggs, and wool per animal.

Except for broiler chickens, little progress has been made on improving the efficiency with which animals convert feed to animal products. This problem must be attacked if the livestock industry is to advance as it should. Success in the broiler industry indicates the potential gains to be made with other farm animals.

Studies with all classes of livestock have been started on fat metabolism, deposition of fat in the body, and the secretion of fat in milk. Efforts to produce lean, meat-type hogs through breeding have been successful.

Nutritionists and physiologists are probing the basic phenomena that make hogs different in their use of body fat and its composition. They are looking for means of controlling fat content of the meat by altering rations or by other practices. In beef cattle, dairy cattle, sheep, and poultry, similar problems are being studied.

Animal geneticists are asking themselves if the highly developed breeds and strains of livestock can be improved further. They are studying the possibility that plateaus in breeding may prevent or slow further progress. They are looking for new breeding methods that may be used to remove the plateaus or raise them higher.

To learn the basic principles underlying these problems, researchers have turned to pilot experiments with small laboratory animals, such as mice, and flour beetles and fruit flies. The scientists have been delving deep into the inheritance of biochemical and physiological processes that affect economic factors in the production of meat, eggs, milk, wool, and fur.

Physiologists have put renewed effort into studies on the ability of livestock to withstand stress—hot and cold climates, sudden changes in temperatures, natural resistance to diseases and parasites, and even the stress of high levels of performance.

Losses connected with reproduction remain a serious barrier to greater efficiency. In the United States, the reproductive losses in beef and dairy cattle, sheep, swine, and poultry are estimated to be 1.3 billion dollars each year. Many of these losses are hidden.

Techniques of artificial insemination and procedures in storing semen have been successful with cattle but have been less successful with swine, sheep, and poultry. The preservation of ova and sperm and tissue culture methods of growing animal embryos are research fields of great potential value and deserve greatly increased effort.

With dairy cattle, about 25 percent of the cows are replaced each year, 20 percent of which left herds because of reproductive problems. Reasons for replacement were sterility, calving difficulties, and embryonic mortality.

In poultry, it is common to experience that only 75 percent of the eggs set actually hatch.

Actual lamb production is only 95 lambs per 100 ewes, whereas the potential production is around 170 lambs.

It takes 13 million sows to produce the annual pig crop; under ideal conditions it should take only 9 million.

It is generally true that the reproductive insufficiency in livestock and poultry is even more of a problem in developing countries. Thus, research to improve the reproductive rate of farm animals is a fertile field of inquiry.

PROGRESS has been made in the control and eradication of animal diseases in many countries, but losses from infectious and metabolic disorders remain serious. Specialists have estimated that as much as one-tenth of the animal population in the United States is lost each year from diseases. Losses from all causes due to disease have been estimated to amount to at least 2 billion annually.

In cattle, mastitis is a major, serious, unsolved problem, particularly in the dairy industry. Among other costly diseases that call for more research are vibriosis, anaplasmosis, leptospirosis, leukosis, and chronic respiratory ailments of poultry.

Of all the diseases of domestic animals, those of swine have been most neglected. Hog cholera, atrophic rhinitis, enteritis, and erysipelas are plagues still. Swine flu, virus pneumonia, and pleuropneumonia-like infections demand study.

Control of parasites has always been recognized as critical to successful animal husbandry in the Tropics and subtropics. Its importance has been underestimated in the temperate regions, however, except in regard to a few of the more aggressive species.

Successful research on insect control has made a great contribution to the efficiency—or, indeed, the existence—of livestock production.

Research also is being continued to determine the levels of residues in animal tissues left by insecticidal treatments, how long they persist, and how they may be lessened or avoided.

Advances in areas where the livestock industry is highly developed involve further improvement by way of greater knowledge of the principles of animal biology, but the problems in developing countries require concentration on developing and applying the discoveries already made.

Worldwide, foot-and-mouth disease is probably the most prevalent infectious disease of animals. North America and Australia are the only large livestock areas that are free from it. It occurs in all parts of Africa, in most of Asia, and in most of South America.

Rinderpest, which destroys more cattle than any other disease, continues to be widespread in many districts of Africa and Asia. Contagious pleuropneumonia of cattle is still a problem in parts of Africa, Asia, and Australia.

African horse sickness and swine fever are destructive in Africa and have invaded some of the Mediterranean countries of Europe. Anthrax, a deadly killer that the United States is not always able to keep out, exists throughout the world; little is done in many regions to control it.

These and other diseases threaten the developing countries. Their uncontrolled existence in one country threatens livestock industries in all.

LIVESTOCK PRODUCTION cannot be improved if feed supplies are inadequate or unbalanced, as they are apt to be in developing countries because of low crop yields and unregulated numbers of animals.

Soil scientists, agronomists, entomologists, animal husbandmen, and biologists are among the scientists who have undertaken studies that pertain to supplies and use of feed: Analyses of plants to identify the nutrients in them; local sources of protein; the use of fish, seed, and vegetable byproducts for livestock feed; the nature of feed deficiencies; the need for new crops; the possibilities of using low-cost supplements, such as urea; the addition of relatively cheap synthetic vitamins to feeds; and more.

The mineral requirements of livestock have been studied for many years, and supplementation to overcome local deficiencies has been successfully practiced in some countries, but deficiencies are being discovered in some developing countries. The need there is to identify these and define the type and amount of supplementation. To do that in places that lack good laboratories, simple methods suitable for making field analyses need to be developed.

THE CREATION of progressive livestock industries in developing countries depends on a progressive total agricultural industry that makes the most of the resources available to it to produce crops and animal products in quantity, quality, and variety. Of the resources that go into such enterprises, the human resource—the man and his managerial ability—is by far the most important. He must be supported by a constant flow of new information on production, processing, and marketing.

This information comes to him from several sources—from his own experience, from dealers in agricultural equipment, and from research stations and educational institutions. All this is available to farmers in some countries but not in many developing countries, where a gulf separates the laboratory and the farm.

Therefore one of the first requirements in developing an advanced livestock industry should be the training of technicians who can develop the knowledge the livestock and poultry raisers need and who can help them put the information to work.

RALPH E. HODGSON *became Director, Animal Husbandry Research Division, Agricultural Research Service, in 1957. Previously he was Chief, Dairy Cattle Research Branch, and Assistant Chief, Bureau of Dairy Industry. Dr. Hodgson joined the Bureau of Dairy Industry as an assistant dairy husbandman in 1930.*

NED D. BAYLEY *became Assistant Director, Animal Husbandry Research Division, Agricultural Research Service, in 1961. Previously, he was Investigations Leader in Dairy Cattle Breeding and Management, Dairy Cattle Research Branch, in 1956–1961.*

Research Projects

in Other Lands

by HENRY W. MARSTON

SWEDISH, Dutch, and English scientists have undertaken research to improve methods of processing American cotton.

Technicians in Israel, France, and Italy have begun studies of new uses for American wheat.

Research workers in Uruguay, Poland, Pakistan, and India have embarked on surveys for natural enemies of insects that destroy crops in the United States.

They and many others are part of a program, started in 1958, in which the Department of Agriculture has entered into 519 research agreements in 27 countries.

The research is paid for with foreign currencies generated from the sale of American agricultural commodities under the terms of Public Law 480. The funds cannot be converted into dollars for use in this country.

The agreements are based on the understanding that the results may be expected to benefit United States agricultural processors and producers as well as those of the participating countries, but not to increase the competition our agricultural products may encounter in international markets.

The projects may originate in a foreign country or in the Department of Agriculture.

The technical aspects of the agreements are supervised by the agency of the Department that is responsible for the particular type of research to be undertaken. The screening of potentially useful crop plants, for example, is supervised by the Crops Research Division; the Forest Service oversees research in the biological control of forest insects.

The Foreign Research and Technical Programs Division of the Agricultural Research Service administers the program.

The agreements cover basic and applied research, but major emphasis is on the more fundamental studies. Many of the foreign scientists engaged in the program have made notable contributions to basic information.

Environmental conditions that could be duplicated in the United States only at great expense are taken into account in reaching an agreement on research to be undertaken.

The types of agreements underway in 1964 were in the fields of utilization, farm production, forestry, human nutrition, marketing, and economics.

ONE HUNDRED AND SEVENTY-ONE agreements in 17 countries called for studies to develop new uses for agricultural products or to make the products more attractive to consumers.

The biochemistry of the transmission of flavor constituents from the feed of dairy cattle to their milk is studied in Finland. Knowledge of the chemical changes and biological processes by which undesirable flavor constituents of feed find their way into milk will be valuable in controlling off-flavors of milk.

Studies on the processing of soybean oil to improve its acceptability and to increase the use of our product abroad have been started in several countries. In Spain, the aim is to develop an ion-exchange procedure for removing pro-oxygen from the oil to improve its flavor and stability, a procedure that would permit processing without the necessity of any objectionable additions to the oil.

Sterols have been suspected of being

responsible for off-flavors and odors in soybean oil. Research in Poland was designed to determine their role in producing the undesirable effects.

Investigators in Japan were given the task of studying the desirability of the partial hydrogenation of soybean oil to produce a stable oil with improved properties for use in Japanese foods.

The development of new and improved uses of wheat should increase the sale of this American commodity in other countries.

A study in Israel seeks to ascertain whether new industrial starches can be developed by introducing fluorine into wheat starch and starch products.

The effect of various phosphorous compounds on the solubility of proteins in baking flours is investigated in France.

An attempt is being made in Italy to determine how cereal grains may be used in a fermentation process to produce vitamin B_{13}.

The competitive position of cotton may be improved if new processes are discovered to make cotton fabrics more acceptable or if present processing methods can be improved. The mechanism of the burning of cotton cellulose is under study in England. A full understanding of the mechanism may lead to methods for developing flame-resistant treatments for cotton fabrics.

The effect on cotton fabrics of chemical treatments like dyeing and waterproofing is studied in Sweden.

Research in the Netherlands on the physical and chemical modification of cotton fabrics may make them more useful for specific purposes.

EIGHTY-TWO agreements for research in forestry have been signed in 16 countries.

Of concern to the United States is the possibility of developing better procedures for propagating forest trees to speed up the development of seedlings for reforestation.

Scientists in Chile have undertaken investigations of the use of artificial light to stimulate growth responses in pine cuttings.

An attempt is being made in Israel to develop a technique for propagating pine trees from bundles of pine needles. It would eliminate the need to collect seeds, germinate them, and transplant seedlings in nurseries. Such a technique would help us reproduce rapidly offspring of the best parent trees.

An interesting approach to the protection of forest trees from the damaging effects of insects has been initiated in Finland. An attempt is being made to discover the substances in trees that make them attractive to pests. Such a discovery would permit the establishment of baited traps in accessible stations where the insects could be destroyed.

Surveys in India, Pakistan, and in Spain have been made to locate natural enemies of forest insects of economic importance. The identified natural enemies are screened to determine whether they may be safely introduced into the United States to aid in the biological control of forest pests. Particular attention is given to finding parasites or predators of the gypsy moth, the balsam woolly aphid, and boring insects that attack poplars.

The losses caused by forest fires in the United States have prompted research in Spain to obtain new scientific knowledge of selected mechanisms of combustion and fire propagation that can be applied to the development of new or more effective techniques for the prevention and control of fires.

RESEARCH AGREEMENTS on various aspects of farm production problems number 200 in 20 countries.

Among them are projects dealing with the protection of farm animals and crops of the United States from exotic diseases or pests that may be introduced accidentally. Study of these production hazards in their native habitat offers a means of building up knowledge of their nature and means of transmission to be used in combating them should they reach America.

African swine fever, a devastating disease, has spread from Africa to Europe and thus poses a threat to the swine industry in the United States. A project was undertaken in Spain to develop a rapid, accurate method for diagnosing the disease so that it may be differentiated from hog cholera, which it closely resembles.

Surveys have started in India, Pakistan, Poland, and Uruguay to find parasites, predators, or pathogens of damaging insects now present in the United States. If parasites can be introduced safely into the United States, they should assist in reducing the amount of chemicals now used to protect crop plants from insect damage.

An attempt is being made in the United Arab Republic to induce sterility in male Mediterranean fruit flies. If it can be done efficiently, the release of sterile males will reduce the population of these injurious insects.

The search for economic plants or their wild relatives that are resistant to diseases and insects offers the possibility of introducing new germ plasm into the breeding efforts of American plant breeders. A number of projects have moved forward in this field—including sources of rust and nematode resistance of plants in Poland and Spain; resistance to disease of barley, oats, and related species in Colombia and Israel; and resistance to wheat rusts in the United Arab Republic.

To aid in developing control measures for the fire ant, a serious pest in the Southeast, a research project in Uruguay studies the life history and habits of the fire ant under different climatic conditions to ascertain which native plants attract the ants and the chemical compounds in them that make them attractive. A search is made for parasites, predators, and diseases of the ant that may be helpful in their control.

The enzymatic mechanism whereby carbon dioxide is fixed by the green leaves of a plant is studied by a research institution in India. The transformation of carbon dioxide produces intermediate compounds, which lead to the ultimate formation of starch.

Another Indian institution is investigating the physiology of the reproductive organs of seed plants. If proper conditions of nutrition, light, temperature, and humidity can be developed for inducing growth of unfertilized ovules, plant breeders will have a new, useful technique.

A project in Brazil collects and evaluates tropical and subtropical legumes that might improve pastures in the Southern States.

Screening native plants of other countries to find new oil, fiber, and feed crops for American farmers is done in Colombia, Israel, Pakistan, Spain, Turkey, Uruguay, and Yugoslavia. Samples of collected materials are sent to the Department of Agriculture for chemical analyses and other means of evaluation.

MORE THAN 30 marketing projects in 13 countries were designed to find better ways to maintain the quality of farm products by protecting them from deteriorating influences in marketing channels and to develop objective tests for measuring quality, which are necessary to make marketing procedures more accurate.

The purpose of a study in England was to determine how temperature and the concentration of carbon dioxide and oxygen affect apple respiration in a controlled environment. Information therefrom will assist in developing better storage conditions for apples.

The constituents of rice that influence quality and the development of objective methods for measuring market quality of rice have been studied in Spain. The purpose was to find methods that would minimize individual differences in evaluating the quality of the product being marketed.

The protection of agricultural commodities in storage frequently requires the use of fungicides and insecticides. The useful life of these chemicals and their effects on quality of the product should be known.

Research in Finland has sought to determine the stability of some insecticides and fungicides applied to crops after harvest during the marketing, processing, and preservation stages and their effect on food quality.

The effect of feed fumigated with ethylene dibromide on animals is being studied in Israel.

Mites in grain, cheese, cured meats, spices, and other stored products are difficult to control under most storage conditions. Polish scientists have been engaged to investigate the effect of certain nutritional, environmental, and physical factors on the biology, physiology, and susceptibility to acaricides of mites in stored products.

Information to assist in meeting economic problems of importance to American agriculture is being sought through nine research agreements in four countries.

The comparative advantage of forestry and agriculture under specific types of subarctic environments, such as soil, topography, and climate, with varying cost-price relationships for farm services and products, is studied in Finland. The analysis has potential usefulness in Alaska.

A study in Colombia deals with the rice market structure, costs and margins, and the possibility of improving marketing efficiency. The information developed will be of assistance to the United States in evaluating our trade.

An investigation at one institution in Israel, on the development and biological evaluation of protein-rich mixtures of foods from vegetable sources, has yielded promising results. Since proteins from plant sources are less costly than those of animal origin, the information developed will be of value in supplying the needs for one of the most common inadequacies of diets.

HENRY W. MARSTON *became Assistant Director, Foreign Research and Technical Programs Division, the Agricultural Research Service, in 1959. Previously he was on the staff of the Research Administrator, Agricultural Research Service.*

Expanding the Uses of Farm Products

by GEORGE W. IRVING, JR., and
SAMUEL B. DETWILER, JR.

THE NEW OR IMPROVED food and industrial products that research in chemistry and allied sciences have given us are part of the world's riches. The prospects are even greater.

The research is being done more in the United States than elsewhere, undoubtedly because of our plentiful supply of agricultural materials, but other countries are awakening to its need and value.

A well-planned program of utilization research today comprises a calculated blend of fundamental and applied research. One leads into the other. All of it has contributed values to the producers, processors, and consumers of farm products.

In the United States, the utilization research is conducted by the Federal Government, State agricultural experiment stations, colleges and universities, private institutions, and industrial processors of farm products. As concerns problems of national or regional importance, the major stimulus is provided by the Department of Agriculture, primarily through four regional research laboratories, which began operations in 1941, when surplus crops were becoming an increasingly important problem in the agricultural economy.

From the first gleam of an idea, the chemist proceeds methodically to test-tube studies and to large laboratory-scale evaluations before he is ready to collaborate with the engineer in pilot-plant studies. Thereafter, industrial evaluation may be necessary before industry is willing to risk capital in a processing plant. Meanwhile, as the development progresses, attention is given to its economic feasibility. No matter how attractive it is from a technical standpoint, a process cannot succeed if it can be carried out more cheaply with nonagricultural raw materials. Finally, the element of progress in world technology has an unpredictable part. As in any competitive enterprise, last year's achievement in agricultural research may be offset by this year's developments in nonagricultural industries.

WE CITE a few examples of accomplishment to illustrate the types of problems that have to be faced and the ways they were solved.

The Department of Agriculture began a cooperative program with the Armed Forces, pharmaceutical manufacturers, and British scientists in 1941 to develop large-scale production methods for making penicillin. Department scientists made two contributions—a new submerged culture method and a high-yielding mold strain—that made large-volume production of penicillin possible and are considered the foundation of the antibiotics industry.

New and improved processes for dehydrated mashed potatoes have made a market for 12 million bushels of potatoes a year. Potato flakes, a new form of dehydrated mashed potatoes, are produced in at least 10 commercial plants. An improved process for making potato granules—simpler and easier to control than the one in commercial use in 1964—is continuous and involves no recycling. Commercial-scale evaluation was pending in 1964. The retail value of dehydrated mashed potatoes was estimated at 60 million dollars in 1964.

The stability, whole-grain nutritive value, and its adaptability to diverse food customs make bulgur (parboiled wheat) a product that may very well broaden markets for wheat. Research on the processing of wheat into bulgur developed a new, continuous process that operates at atmospheric pressure. Economical in heat and labor requirements and employing conventional, readily available equipment, the process can be set up for any desired scale of production. More than a dozen companies produce bulgur by this process, primarily for export to food deficient countries. In 1964, plant capacity was about 600 million pounds a year.

Scientists in the Department and the oilseed industry perfected linseed oil emulsion paints, a new type of product that is superior in many properties to synthetic resin paints. More than 50 paint manufacturers are making the paints, which they expect will regain lost markets for linseed oil.

The production of oranges in Florida had reached an annual total of 4.5 billion pounds, with prospects of further increases in production but little outlook for increased markets. Department scientists, in cooperation with the Florida Citrus Commission, developed the first basic process for making a frozen-orange-juice concentrate. Success was immediate. The production of about 80 million gallons of concentrate in 1959, representing more than 60 percent of the Florida crop, had a delivered value of nearly 200 million dollars. The cumulative value in 1946–1958 exceeded 1.5 billion dollars at the manufacturers' level. The development, covered by a public service patent, is utilized by all major manufacturers of citrus juice products and has done much to stabilize the income of citrus growers.

Fundamental research by the Department provided a basis for the development of new and improved wash-wear, wrinkle-resistant cotton fabric finishes, which in a recent year accounted for the utilization of about a million bales of cotton. Several different chemicals are being used commercially to impart wrinkle resistance to cotton fabrics, but none of them gives a completely satisfactory product. A new wash-wear treatment, using a chemical known as APO, has good commercial potential.

Foam-mat drying, a process invented by Department engineers, has been applied in the commercial production of tomato powder for military use and for export. More than 50 foods have been successfully dried by this procedure. Its potential economic importance in preserving liquid and pureed foods (fruit juices, juice concentrates, tomato paste, soups, and sauces) is good. Products prepared by foam-mat drying are convenient to use, stable without refrigeration, and economical of weight and space.

Department scientists devised a new method for making wool shrink resistant, which was undergoing commercial evaluation in 1964. Employing the new technique of interfacial polymerization, the treatment results in the formation of an invisible polymeric film firmly attached to the surface of the wool fibers. The reaction occurs rapidly, requires no curing, and does not harshen or weaken the fibers. Wool fabrics treated by this new method retain their original texture and color. The treatment is compatible with processes, developed by Department scientists, for permanent creasing of wool. Wool garments made from fabrics given this new polymeric treatment are shrink resistant, muss resistant, and largely unaffected by laundering and drycleaning. Many kinds of wool materials, including yarn and blankets, as well as fine woven fabrics, can be made shrink resistant by the process.

Methods have been devised for transforming corn sugar, through fermentative procedures, into new gumlike polymers having properties that open up new applications for corn products. One of several polymers produced is a gum called phosphomannan, which is readily soluble in water. Extensive evaluation by more than 30 firms has

revealed potential uses in foods, pharmaceuticals, cosmetics, paper, oil-well drilling, and other applications as a thickening, stabilizing, dispersing, and suspending agent.

Vinyl stearate, a chemical prepared from a major component of animal fats, was in commercial production and use in 1964 as a result of research in the Department. Broad uses for polymers of vinyl stearate are being developed in water-base paints, lubricating oil additives, fibers, permanently flexible plastics, waxes (especially of the aerosol spray type), textile and paper coatings, and adhesives. Some of the uses have been commercialized. The total value of the development may exceed 2 million dollars.

In a related development, fats modified by a special epoxidation process possess unique stabilizing properties as plasticizers for vinyl plastics. Epoxidized fats are in use to the extent of 75 million pounds annually—worth approximately 20 million dollars—in garden hose, raincoats, and similar applications.

About 600 million pounds of fats were used in 1960 in poultry feeds and other processed feeds. Cooperative investigations with industrial and other groups showed that practically all grades of animal fats and tallow can be used in feeds, and methods were developed to stabilize the fats and other nutrients of the feeds. The fats have good nutritive value, minimize dustiness, and improve the color of the feeds. In a few years, this new outlet has begun to offset the declining market for animal fats in soapmaking, caused by the inroads of synthetic detergents; the price for animal fats has been stabilized; and continuing expansion is expected for the use of animal fats in mixed feeds. The cumulative value of fats used in feeds was estimated at 165 million dollars in 1964.

The Department's program of chemical screening of uncultivated plants has led to the discovery of seeds containing oils of unusual composition. Of a total of 1,037 seed samples analyzed, representing 655 plant species, 151 were shown to contain unusual types of oil. Four classes of these new oils, with properties different from those now produced domestically, offer promise for industrial applications that are not competitive with present domestic oils.

One particularly promising oilseed crop is *Crambe abyssinica*, which contains more than 50 percent of erucic acid, a potentially important industrial chemical that in 1964 was largely imported. Erucic acid from *Crambe* oil has good possibilities for conversion into new chemicals for production of resins, plastics, fibers, and coatings. Since it apparently can be grown in the principal wheat-growing areas of the Western States and the northern Corn Belt States, *Crambe* is a potential replacement for some of the surplus grains grown there.

The discovery by Department scientists that a chemical known as ethoxyquin can effectively preserve carotene (provitamin A), vitamin E, and the xanthophylls in dehydrated forages has resulted in the establishment of important new markets for dehydrated alfalfa. When this preservative is applied at a rate of about one-half pound per ton and at a cost of not more than a dollar, about three-fourths of the labile nutrients are retained over a storage period of 6 months, as compared to a one-fourth retention for untreated forage stored under the same conditions.

Thus, for example, alfalfa stabilized with ethoxyquin serves as an excellent source of the xanthophylls needed to produce the yellow-skinned poultry so highly desired by consumers in Japan and Europe. Previously, essentially no dehydrated forage was exported; 200 tons (produced on 40 thousand acres) were sold abroad in 1962. This is in addition to domestic uses of the ethoxyquin treatment, which include 90 percent of more than a million tons of dehydrated forage produced annually, and 10 million tons of poultry feed so treated to preserve vitamin E, which is mutually effective with ethoxyquin in preventing the occurrence of crazy chick disease. A large proportion of the alfalfa that is dehydrated is handled by some 50 firms licensed to use the development under a Department public service patent.

CONSIDERABLE agricultural utilization research is conducted in other countries, although rarely under that specific name. The extent of such research depends on the scientific manpower available, and the direction of emphasis depends on political and economic factors in each country.

Many of the less-developed countries have agricultural deficits, particularly in foodstuffs. Utilization research that is conducted there will tend to emphasize improvements in quality of processed foodstuffs, with particular attention to retention of nutritive value, and to the exploitation of native plants to provide new sources of edible protein, carbohydrates, and fats.

India is an example of an agricultural-deficit country that has a reservoir of scientific manpower. A number of research institutions in India, operating largely under government funds, are working to expand the supply of nutritious food products, particularly from native crops.

Other factors also work to influence the course of utilization research.

Some of it is directed toward the production of products that are imported so as to relieve the outflow of foreign exchange. Some of the processes under study have been examined in the United States and are considered to be technically feasible but uneconomic.

In India, where the labor costs for collection of raw materials and processing are relatively cheap, such processes may be feasible from the economic standpoint.

We can offer another generalization about utilization research in India. In new developments, much attention is given to setting up complete processes that can be offered to industrial concerns together with technical advice to put them into operation. In one instance, a government research institution took over a private manufacturing plant that was operating at a loss, installed a new process involving modern technological and management methods, proved that under these conditions the plant could make a profit, and returned it to its owners.

This situation is different from that in the United States, where the large processors of agricultural raw materials are well equipped to take up a new development in its intermediate stages, adapt it to their own needs, and conduct any necessary terminal evaluations before reducing it to industrial practice.

Despite a need for applied research on new processes and products in India, the scientific administrators realize that such research must be predicated on a great deal of fundamental work.

The situation in India has had parallels in such countries as Brazil, Uruguay, and Colombia, which have been deficit countries agriculturally but have scientific and technological resources to grapple with problems of food utilization. Economic and scientific assistance is helping speed the time when research can be applied to getting full value from crops.

WHEN A COUNTRY's agricultural production turns from a condition of deficits to sufficiency and finally to one of abundance, the changes may have a significant influence on its pattern of utilization research. The trend is away from new or improved food uses for farm crops and toward the development of new industrial products from the part of the output that is not needed for food.

In France, for example, systematic action has been taken to set up research programs to find industrial uses for surplus farm products. In other countries of the Common Market, all types of science are well established, and research institutions have been addressing themselves to agricultural utilization problems.

The United Kingdom traditionally has been a net importer of agricultural raw materials and has maintained strong research programs to derive products of maximum value from food and fiber. Several institutions are recognized internationally for their contributions to the chemistry of agricultural products.

Japan is in much the same category. Israel is another example of a net importer that has established strong programs of research on the utilization of agricultural raw materials.

Wars influence the course of utilization research. During the Second World War, the agricultural situation in the United States changed from one of surpluses to one of deficits, and the Department's utilization research program turned from an emphasis on industrial utilization to emphasis on improved food uses for crops. Much of the wartime research was in direct collaboration with the military services, in such fields as the development of better dehydrated foods.

A substantial supplement to the Department's domestic utilization research program was provided by the initiation in 1958 of a program of grants to foreign institutions, using foreign currencies derived from the sale of our agricultural surpluses under Public Law 480. As of January 1964, more than 160 grants had been made to institutions in 18 foreign countries for research on problems of mutual interest concerned with agricultural utilization research. The results have demonstrated how much we have in common with research workers abroad.

GEORGE W. IRVING, JR., *became Deputy Administrator of Agricultural Research Service in 1954. His duties as head of the Department's agricultural utilization research program were expanded in 1963 to include supervision of the nutrition and consumer-use research program.*

SAMUEL B. DETWILER, JR., *in 1958 became an assistant to the Administrator of the Agricultural Research Service, specializing in the development of grants to foreign institutions for utilization research.*

Problems in
Economics

by RAYMOND P. CHRISTENSEN

How to increase agricultural output and productivity and thereby help achieve national economic growth is a major agricultural economic problem in underdeveloped countries.

In the developed countries, where agricultural productivity already is high, a problem is how to manage rapidly expanding agricultural production capacity in such a way as to improve income of rural people and aid in an economic growth of underdeveloped countries.

In both, important questions concern ways to increase international trade in agricultural products on a mutually beneficial basis.

Agricultural production in developed countries has increased more than total population and has caused downward pressure on prices of farm products and on income of farmers.

During the fifties, for example, total population of the developed countries increased about 0.9 percent a year, but agricultural production per person increased 1.6 percent a year. Food consumption per person went up slightly with higher incomes but not enough to cause total demand for farm products to increase as rapidly as the total supply.

Expansion in agricultural output has resulted from the adoption of new technology and the use of more capital inputs—fertilizers, pesticides, petro-leum products, machines, and other materials from industrial sources. But widespread use of new technology by many farmers has caused total agricultural output to expand more rapidly than market outlets, and prices of farm products and incomes of farmers to decline in the aggregate.

How can farmers contribute to national economic growth and consumer welfare without being penalized for doing so? Gains in economic efficiency of farm production and marketing do not automatically result in higher incomes for farmers. Most developed countries have programs to support agricultural prices and incomes and a pattern of agricultural production better balanced with market outlets. But incomes of farm people still average only about two-thirds as high as those of nonfarm people.

Employment on farms decreased in all developed countries and by as much as 30 percent in several in the fifties. Many farm units, however, remained too small to provide adequate incomes. Farm people face difficult adjustments in shifting to nonfarm jobs. They usually do not have the specialized skills required by industry. Consequently many continue to operate small farms where they receive relatively low incomes.

Underdeveloped countries face difficult problems in achieving the large increase in production of food and other agricultural products required for national economic growth.

Many have had population growth rates of 2 or 3 percent a year. As incomes increase, 50 to 60 percent of the additional income is spent for food.

If, in addition, per capita incomes increase 3 percent a year, total food supplies must increase 4 or 5 percent each year in those countries to keep pace with growth in domestic food demand. Such increases are large compared with those achieved in most developed countries during the early stages of their economic development. Farm output in the United States, for example, has seldom increased more than 2 percent a year.

How to achieve large increases in agricultural output and productivity is a critical problem in underdeveloped countries. If supplies of food do not expand as much as demand for food, price inflation results and plans for industrial development are disrupted. Increased productivity in agriculture is needed to provide a basis for national economic growth.

Agricultural sectors of underdeveloped countries have abundant supplies of unskilled workers. Land and reproducible capital are scarce factors, but management and technical skills for adoption of improved technology are scarcest of all. This is true because more capital and labor applied to land now in cultivation by primitive methods will result in little, if any, increase in output.

Substantial increases in output can be expected if management and technical skills are used with a limited amount of capital to develop improved systems of farming that involve combinations of improved technology.

The efficient use of resources requires getting the most from a relatively fixed area of land, using available management and technical skills with a limited supply of capital allocated to agriculture, and using direct labor as effectively as possible.

How to make economic use of increasing numbers of agricultural workers is another major problem.

The population growth in many underdeveloped countries is 2.5 percent a year, and about 75 percent of the population is agricultural. Nonfarm employment would need to increase about 10 percent a year just to absorb the young people that join the labor force each year in the rural areas and cities. With economic growth, the agricultural population will decline relative to nonagricultural population, but the absolute number of rural people in most of these countries can be expected to increase for some time to come.

Agricultural population typically has increased during the early phases of the industrialization in the developed countries. In Japan, for example, the working population in agriculture, forestry, and fisheries increased during the first 20 years of industrialization, and remained relatively constant for about 15 years before beginning a gradual decline.

Productive work must be found in rural places, either in farm production or in improvement of rural resources, that will result in future expansion of farm production. Full advantage needs to be taken of opportunities for using plentiful labor supplies for improving the land, transportation facilities, and farm buildings.

Although many low-income countries have less arable land per person than the United States, Canada, and other developed countries, limited resources of land need not be a barrier to economic growth. Little correlation exists between income per person and land per person.

Many European countries, for example, have achieved high incomes although they have relatively little land. European countries have been net importers of food. They import only 15 percent of the food they consume, however—a proportion that has been declining with advancing agricultural technology. Most of the additional supplies of food and other farm products required for economic growth of developed countries has been grown at home.

Physical potentials for improving crop yields are large. Cereal yields per acre average less than half as high in underdeveloped countries as in the developed. Wide differences in yields per acre between neighboring farms in low-income countries indicate that doubling or tripling yields on many farms is possible. The high yields in developed countries are only of recent origin in the long sweep of agricultural history. For example, per acre yields of wheat in England and rice in Japan have gone up more in the 50 years just past than they did in the preceding 500 years.

INCREASES IN FOOD PRODUCTION in underdeveloped countries, even though accelerated, are not likely to be large enough to meet requirements for rapid economic growth. Their production of food since 1950 increased about 2.8 percent a year, only slightly more than the rate of population growth.

It should be possible to step up rates of increase in food production to 3 or 3.5 percent a year in a decade, but that still will be short of the annual increase of 4 to 5 percent required in many countries to meet rising demands due to growth in population and income.

Developed countries can foster economic growth of underdeveloped countries by helping them meet their rapidly expanding food requirements. Although food aid programs, such as those under Public Law 480, have helped many countries, advancing agricultural technology and productive capacity in the developed countries will make possible much larger food assistance programs in the future.

Underdeveloped countries will become better trading partners with the developed countries and import more products on a commercial basis when they achieve higher per capita incomes. Foreign trade is closely related to national income and purchasing power.

The underdeveloped countries have much smaller exports and imports on a per capita basis than do the developed countries, but they have as much foreign trade per dollar of income as do the developed countries. In 1959–1960, for example, the value of imports averaged 19 dollars for each 100 dollars of income for both the underdeveloped and the developed countries. Imports of agricultural products averaged 7 dollars per 100 dollars of income for the developed countries and 5 dollars per 100 dollars of income for the underdeveloped.

Underdeveloped countries are potential markets for much larger quantities of products from the United States and other developed countries. How rapidly markets expand in the low-income countries depends upon how rapidly these countries can achieve economic growth and increase their foreign exchange earnings.

ADVANCING AGRICULTURAL productive capacity in developed countries raises questions as to how foreign trade in agricultural products can be arranged on a mutually beneficial basis.

Underdeveloped countries depend heavily upon agricultural exports as sources of foreign exchange for financing imports of capital goods required for industrial as well as agricultural development. Agricultural exports account for half of total exports in the case of underdeveloped countries.

The total agricultural exports of developed countries, however, are about a third larger than those of underdeveloped countries. It is important that export supplies from developed countries do not depress prices of agricultural products in world markets and thereby reduce economic incentives to make full use of opportunities to increase agricultural output and productivity in underdeveloped countries. Underdeveloped countries need expanding markets at stable prices in order to earn the foreign exchange for financing imports of capital goods for economic growth.

Developed countries that have relied on agricultural imports to meet a substantial part of their food requirements in some instances may find it convenient to satisfy a larger part of their domestic requirements from expanding domestic production. If that is done through protectionist policies for domestic agriculture that reduce imports from low-cost producing countries, it interferes with the expansion of agricultural trade and the international specialization in agricultural production required for improving consumer welfare in all countries.

Developed countries that have been on an export basis but dispose of agricultural products at prices below domestic prices also could interfere with desirable trade expansion and efficient use of resources on an international basis. Freer trade, not increased impediments to trade, will contribute to economic growth.

In this connection, international trade agreements and other means of stabilizing world prices and promoting foreign trade in agricultural products merit much more study.

ECONOMIC RESEARCH on these many problems is being conducted by institutions and individuals throughout the world, although it was just getting underway in most developing countries in 1964.

Early economists were concerned with problems of food supply, population growth, land rents and taxation, and agricultural trade. But agricultural economics did not get established as a special field of study in the developed countries until the first two decades of this century.

The first studies were concerned with ways to improve the efficiency of farm production by applying new agricultural technology and by improving the organization and operation of farms, systems of farming, tenure, credit, marketing methods, prices and incomes for farmers, analyses of agricultural outlook, and so on.

The objectives of agricultural economic research changed during the fifties when pressure of increasing supplies depressed prices of farm products. Increased emphasis was placed on research designed to help farmers decide what adjustments they needed to make because of advancing technology and mechanization and changing foreign markets. More attention has been given to long-term projections of supply and demand for agricultural products, the development of rural areas, and foreign trade problems.

Needed now, especially in developing countries, is better economic information describing how agricultural production and marketing are organized and measuring economic conditions and changes.

Such information is a basis for deciding what are the obstacles to improving economic efficiency of agricultural production and marketing and increasing the economic welfare of rural and urban people. It also is a basis for preparing and implementing plans for national development.

Public programs that influence use of resources, production, consumption, savings, capital formation, and income distribution in agriculture and other economic sectors exercise much more control over economic growth in the underdeveloped countries than they do in the developed. Consequently, needs for economic information to provide a basis for national development plans are especially urgent.

Agricultural economists (and scientists) face great challenges in deciding how developing countries can increase agricultural output and productivity and increase contributions of agriculture to national economic growth.

It is known, for example, that knowledge, incentives, and means are required for agricultural development. Research is needed on their application in the developing countries. What levers can be used to move traditional farming towards more modern methods?

In the United States, the development and diffusion of knowledge about technology accounts for about half of the fivefold increase in agricultural production in the past century. The increased use of production inputs, chiefly capital goods, accounts for the other half. Obviously, expenditures for education and research have paid.

Economic incentives associated with family-operated farms have provided powerful stimuli to advances in agricultural output and productivity in Europe, North America, and Japan. But public programs that assure markets for farm products at stable prices have also been necessary to get farmers to make capital investments and try new methods. Also, farm people must be motivated to want higher incomes. It is essential that there be supplies of consumption goods of the kinds rural people want in larger quantities so that they can better satisfy their wants when they increase agricultural production.

In the less-developed countries, farm people cling to traditional farming methods because they feel sure these methods will provide enough food for survival. Many cannot afford to take risks and try new methods because they do not have resources to fall back on if the new methods fail.

ADOPTION OF new technology will require drastic changes and the learning of new skills and management techniques from outside teachers. Even the venturesome will require convincing evidence that substantial benefits will accrue from the change.

Even when benefits from improved farming methods are known and economic incentives have been provided through land and marketing reforms, the means for carrying out the new farming program may be lacking.

In addition to managerial and technical assistance for learning new ways of farming, farm people will need supplies of fertilizers, pesticides, better seeds, tools, and machines. Availability of supplies requires arrangements for importation or manufacture within the country. Many countries may have to give priorities to agricultural supply and processing industries if the food barrier is to be broken sufficiently to facilitate growth.

Because most farmers will not have either cash or credit to buy the necessary supplies, new credit institutions may be needed to supply credit on the basis of farm plans that promise increases in output and incomes. Local storage and marketing facilities will also be needed to handle the expanded production. Many countries therefore will require new marketing systems possibly through the establishment of publicly sponsored cooperatives.

Public work programs for underemployed workers can be organized to provide storage facilities, access roads, and other rural improvements needed to increase farm output and to transport the products to market.

In making plans for national economic growth, countries are faced with problems of how much emphasis to place on agriculture, manufacturing, mining, transportation, and other economic sectors in allocating scarce capital and managerial resources.

Agricultural and industrial development can be complementary as well as competitive. An expanding food supply at relatively low costs contributed to industrial growth in the United States and Europe. But industrial development in these countries helped increase output and productivity in agriculture by making available production-increasing supplies of fertilizer, pesticides, tools, and machines.

Movement of farm people to nonagricultural occupations was essential for expansion of manufacturing, construction, transportation, and service industries, but industrial growth created employment opportunities for rural people not needed in agriculture. It helped make farm mechanization possible and profitable and so contributed to increased productivity of land and labor in agriculture.

The emphasis on agricultural development compared with industrial development will need to vary country by country. Because capital is needed for industry and overhead services, as well as for agriculture, only limited capital from nonfarm sources will be available for the agricultural sector. The allocation between agriculture and other industries, however, should be planned to achieve balanced development, recognizing the importance of increased food output.

RAYMOND P. CHRISTENSEN *became Deputy Director, Development and Trade Analysis Division, Economic Research Service, in 1963. Previously he was Chief of the Economic Development Branch.*

Problems

in Marketing

by WINN F. FINNER

SIZABLE DIFFERENCES exist among countries in the magnitude of the marketing bill, but in all it is big.

Reductions in marketing costs may be reflected largely in lower prices to consumers, but the farmers also may achieve gains through increases in the prices they receive and through larger sales arising because of larger consumer purchases in response to lower retail prices.

The principal possibilities of lowering costs lie in finding ways to perform given marketing jobs more efficiently, in dispensing with certain services, or in changing some of the numerous external conditions that affect costs, such as tariffs, interest rates, and regulations pertaining to marketing firms.

The present costs of marketing may indicate where efficiency investigations can be directed most fruitfully. In the United States, for example, the costs of transportation, including local assembly, account for roughly one-sixth of the total marketing bill. Processing costs represent an additional one-third. Retailing is roughly of the same magnitude or a little higher. The balance goes to cover the costs of wholesaling, storage, and other functions.

Retail and wholesale operations are somewhat less subject to the application of engineering principles than processing is, but they often can be made more efficient through increases in the volume handled by individual establishments, particularly in cities.

A variety of other measures have been successful. In Puerto Rico, marketing specialists found that the retail costs could be lowered by the further expansion of chain retailing, including self-service, centralizing warehousing and docking facilities, outlawing of exclusive agents, and reducing other costs, such as those for advertising, through the consolidation of some of the existing stores.

Some governments have instituted price control in attempts to regulate retail prices, if not costs. Others, such as Mexico, have established mobile stores in an effort to improve the efficiency of retailing as well as food supplies in rural areas.

IMPROVING PROCESSING METHODS is a second way to lower costs of marketing.

Large gaps exist between methods that are known and used in some countries and the methods and facilities employed in some developing countries.

Careful appraisals of new technology must be made before one can determine which parts or kinds can lead to reductions in costs or to a more stable output, because low wage rates and high capital costs may negate the effectiveness of some machines and methods that are successful elsewhere.

A major consideration in improving processing operations concerns the number and size of processing plants. In some countries, markets are not large enough to support a sufficient number of large, efficient establishments to insure keen competition. In fact, the amount of pasteurized milk or canned vegetables or baked bread or other processed items that will be purchased may not be large enough to take the output of even one establishment large enough to employ most cost-reducing equipment and methods.

The choice then may be to continue with industries consisting of many small firms that have high costs and too small an output to export effectively or use much of the new technology; or to limit the number of firms in the industry; or to have government participation in order to consolidate most of the output in one or a few establishments.

A number of governments have elected to undertake or control marketing operations. Here, though, the economic consequences of the alternatives should be made clear.

The extent of the area from which raw materials should be drawn, the location of plants, the types of arrangement with farmers that will help insure sufficient supplies of products to be processed, the advisability of diversifying or specializing the products of a plant, the kinds of equipment to use, and the major markets to be served all require comparisons of costs and incomes if decisions are to be wise.

TRANSPORTATION LACKS often may hinder marketing.

In a number of countries, a significant proportion of all farms are a considerable distance from roads. In Thailand, for example, the average distance from farms to a road passable most of the year is more than 6 miles and from a navigable waterway about 18 miles.

In most Latin American countries, likewise, the absence of year-round roads and other transportation channels has seriously impeded agricultural development of some of the potentially better production areas. In many smaller countries that depend on ocean shipping to reach their markets, such as in much of the West Indies, the choice of crops to be grown is limited by the irregularity of shipping.

Poor transportation facilities raise costs of this service. They also raise other costs. Storage may need to be conducted in small establishments with resulting higher charges. The same is true of processing operations. Poor transportation also may lead to wide price differentials among different sections of a country.

Clearly, the physical construction of new facilities will be the major means of changing this situation.

A program of road expansion in Mexico since 1950, for example, has resulted in substantial increases in grain and fruit production in the regions the roads serve and has contributed generally to development.

Attention is needed in planning such construction, however, so as to serve best the future agricultural potential of the country.

Honduras, for example, requires that in the planning of new highways, the special problems of agriculture be given full consideration. Complicated appraisals may be necessary in order to determine the improvements in transportation that will yield the largest economic returns.

There likewise is a need to find ways to lessen the stultifying effect that high transportation costs can have on the development of new regions and industries. Such ways have been considered in some countries. In the meantime, benefits can be had by the wider use of such simple improvements as pneumatic tires on carts.

MAJOR IMPROVEMENTS can result from the better selection of markets in which products are sold.

A principal shortcoming of the agriculture of many countries is the existence of fairly rigid trading patterns and insufficient response to the changing profitability of alternative markets. In part, these rigidities may develop because of political relationships among governments or because of a community of interest, such as within the British Commonwealth.

They are attributable oftener to a failure to observe trends in prices in various markets or trends in production in competing areas.

The shift in the grain production in the United States from the Northeast to the Midwest and West has a counterpart in many other countries and many products. Some are longtime changes, such as the decline in the importance of the Caribbean area as a source of sugar. Others arise more rapidly.

Some prospective changes in markets are difficult to measure, or their permanence is beset with uncertainty. Nations such as Congo, India, and Nigeria, whose per capita incomes have been low, no doubt will change their habits of food consumption markedly as incomes increase. That will mean shifts to different foods and will open new possibilities for farmers. The timing may be difficult to determine, however.

The use of synthetic rubber illustrates another type of market change—a new type of product is partially replacing an older form. Synthetic rubber rose from about 37 percent of total world consumption in 1952 to almost 50 percent in 1962. This change may partly negate the efforts of some countries that produce natural rubber, such as Malaysia, to improve their incomes by planting higher yielding trees.

The more effective use of storage also may open new possibilities of spreading sales over a longer time.

Investigations by the Food and Agriculture Organization in Central America, for example, established a basis for the construction of storage to enable imports of grain during periods of seasonally low prices and to lessen the seasonal price differentials.

In other instances, prices received by farmers have been strengthened through the construction of cold storage facilities so that the use of a part of the crop could be delayed until prices rose.

Nevertheless, storage costs may be high, particularly if low temperatures need to be maintained or if volumes handled are small. These costs must be compared with the magnitude of price increases during storage or the other gains anticipated before one can determine the wisdom of storage operations and such related handling practices as drying and fumigation.

Another market alternative is the possibility of shifting between the sale of fresh products and processed products. The canning of part of a crop may make greater returns possible.

In Libya, for example, the considerable difficulty imposed on the exportation of fresh oranges because of the diversity of varieties and quality has led to an increase in the volume of fruit processed.

IN MANY COUNTRIES, a grading program for locally produced food products domestically consumed is sketchy or absent. Sometimes there is a solid justification for this.

Most buying and selling involves visual inspection, so that the buyer himself may determine quality. Also, most consumers have such low incomes that they are not prepared to pay for usual quality characteristics, such as color, size, and uniformity. Thus, grading programs and corollary quality-improvement efforts would not be justified by higher prices.

Attempts to expand sales of pasteurized milk in some countries have failed because most local consumers preferred the lower price and reportedly the flavor of boiled raw milk in comparison with pasteurized milk.

Likewise, efforts to establish a grading system for fresh meats have not always been successful because too few consumers are willing to pay higher prices for some portion of the supply.

Nevertheless, inadequate grading programs hamper agricultural development, particularly with respect to the production of products for export and for the small—but usually growing—proportion of the population prepared to pay for quality.

Sudan and a number of other African countries, for example, have benefited from improvements in the grading and standardizing of exported hides. But on the other hand, partly because of inadequate grading, farmers in other countries, such as Jamaica, have been unable to compete with imported supplies of fresh vegetables to meet the growing demand of tourists and of higher income groups within the local population.

Marketing research can help establish a grading system that will best reflect buyer preferences in the various markets in which sales are made.

Such elements as the number of grades, the important characteristics to be measured in determining grades, and ways of simplifying the grading system so that it is understandable and workable all need to be determined in light of their probable effects on total income from sales and on the costs of conducting grading and testing programs. Considerable progress also can be made in standardizing the weights and measures used in trading.

A MAJOR DIFFICULTY facing some developing nations is that of wide fluctuations in prices.

Marked changes in prices produce serious problems for producers, particularly for small farmers with narrow financial reserves. They likewise have effects on the governments' revenues. Stable prices even at moderately low levels are likely to encourage greater agricultural development than sharply fluctuating prices.

Efforts have been made to reduce the magnitude of price swings or to moderate their results. International commodity agreements are an example of the former. Stabilization boards or similar organizations are an example of the second.

Much remains to be determined regarding their effectiveness and the ways in which they can be employed most usefully. Questions have been raised, for example, regarding the feasibility of building up large stabilization reserves that may not be returned completely to producers.

Some countries, including Burma, the Soviet Union, Uganda, India, the Republic of Ghana, and Japan, in effect have levied a tax on agriculture through the retention of a portion of sales proceeds or through an export tax in order to obtain funds for other purposes.

In a number of poorer countries, agriculture is the main source of such funds, and historically, agriculture has provided much of the beginning capital for nations such as the United States, now much further developed. Nevertheless, the adverse effects of such reductions in prices received by farmers on agricultural output and improvement may offset the gains.

Careful evaluations are needed to determine the extent to which development capital can be obtained from this source.

Greater attention also needs to be directed to a determination of the conditions necessary for the successful conduct of such stabilization efforts and to the influences of changing market conditions on the effectiveness of various stabilization techniques.

Improvements also can be accomplished in pricing within domestic markets. A principal way to do that is to develop and disseminate accurate information regarding current market supplies and prices and prospective conditions, as indicated by plantings, growing conditions, and changes in other factors likely to influence prices and quantities.

GOVERNMENT has a major role in the marketing in many countries.

Exports of Ethiopian coffee, Australian eggs, Canadian wheat, and Argentine beef, for example, are handled by boards or similar bodies under some degree of government control.

In many other countries, certain domestic or export sales or both are transacted by public or quasi-public bodies, in some instances as a part of long-range plans and in others as a temporary expedient until private firms can take over these functions.

Particularly in the underdeveloped countries, the factors involved in determining the extent to which government conducts trading operations may differ considerably from those in the United States. Only a few individuals in a country may have experience to operate marketing facilities to serve export markets.

The inflow of foreign capital and managerial ability may be hampered by exchange controls and perhaps by political uncertainty, besides the business hazards involved. Again, private traders may command exorbitant interest payments, with the result that government may take a more active part.

The Food and Agriculture Organization, for example, has reported that interest rates paid by farmers to those extending credit and purchasing their output may range from 7 to 10 percent per month in Cambodia and from 25 to 400 percent a year among small farmers in the Philippines. The Nigerian Government established controls for the marketing of cocoa partly because of the view that private buyers paid unduly low prices relative to those at which they sold.

A major need that sometimes can be met by governmental action or sponsorship is to establish a continuity of markets so that at all times farmers will be assured of sales outlets.

In many instances, farmers now encounter difficulty in locating processors or other buyers for products not produced in large volume, for out-of-season production, or for production remotely located.

In other cases, operating markets do not offer price differentials for different grades or services needed by producers. Often the establishment of a continuing market has brought about additional output. A number of governments, such as those of Honduras, Ceylon, and Panama, have accomplished this through the establishment of government buying stations. In other instances, government departments have been assigned purchase functions or private dealers have been commissioned to conduct them.

Government also may insure the provision of other services specifically designed to assist small producers. It may arrange for the frequent purchase of small lots from farmers in order to lessen storage costs and the possibilities of spoilage before sale. Likewise, it may subsidize the extension of private transportation services to remote areas or on a more frequent schedule. It may meet certain costs of ocean shipping during periods when attempts are being made to develop new export markets, as the Canadian Government has done with respect to trade in the Caribbean.

Governmental trading activities frequently may be conducted under major handicaps pertaining to accounting, administrative, and employment procedures and because of failure to make timely adjustments in operating methods.

The fact that government may continue to perform certain functions after a number of private traders are prepared to undertake them may discourage innovation and retard improvements in efficiency. Lengthy delays may develop in resolving routine questions.

The fact is, however, that government conducts some of the commercial trading activity in most countries. In this situation, marketing investigations can provide a distinct service in assessing likely accomplishments, and they can determine the successes and weaknesses of governmental operations which are conducted, the ways in which they may be improved, and situations in which they should be expanded or terminated.

Investigations of this type have been valuable in revamping the activities of several African commodity boards. Research in Western Germany showed that the costs of marketing meat could be reduced about one-fourth if governmental restrictions were removed.

WINN F. FINNER *was appointed to the Staff Economist Group in September 1963. Previously he had been the Deputy Director of the Marketing Economics Division, Economic Research Service, having first joined the staff of that Division in 1947. He was on a special assignment with the Food and Agriculture Organization in 1961 to determine ways by which the agricultural marketing system in Jamaica could be improved. He joined the Department of Agriculture in 1937 after completing his graduate work at the University of Wisconsin.*

INDEX